NUFFIELD SCIENCE *in* PRACTICE

GNVQ
SCIENCE

ADVANCED

Heinemann

Contents

How this book is organised

This book will help you to cover the performance criteria and range for GNVQ Advanced Science and to see how scientific ideas are used in a wide variety of practical situations. The main units in the book are colour coded and they correspond to the GNVQ Advanced units making it easy to turn quickly to the right part of the book.

Scientific ideas and their uses

Each unit is organised into chapters which are in turn divided into short topics between two and six pages long. Some of these explain the basic science you need to know to meet the performance criteria and cover the range. Other topics are about people who use science in their work. Each topic starts with a short abstract (in bold type) which allows you to see at a glance what it covers.

The contents pages at the front of the book list the units and chapters in the book. The page at the start of each unit lists the topics in detail so that you can easily find the information you need.

Thoughts and actions

The *Thoughts and actions* at the end of each unit include a variety of activities which can help you to master the basic science, develop and practice core skills, or suggest starting points for practical assignments.

Reference section

The *Reference section* on pages 483–529 will help you when working on assignments, tackling problems, or making sense of theory. The section includes both guidance on skills and techniques together with explanations of technical terms and many tables of data.

Hazards and safety

Chapter 1C covers all that you have to know about health and safety for element 1.1. You should apply the lessons of that chapter whenever you do any practical investigations.

 The science information, case studies and reference section in this book all include descriptions of practical procedures. You should not attempt to carry out any of these procedures without first carrying out a risk assessment and checking your plans with a supervisor.

Other resources

There are two Advanced Assignment Packs in the Nuffield Science in Practice series. The packs include a wealth of ideas for vocational assignments covering the mandatory units and core skills. Pack 2 also includes a study guide which, along with this book, will help you to prepare for the end-of-unit tests.

Credits

Authors

Andrew Hunt, Nicholas Russell, David Sang

Writers

Robert Abrahamson, Ruth Bell, John Bilby, Peter Bond, David Brodie, Peter Capener, Del Clarke, Roger Eubank, Ann Fullick, Patrick Fullick, John Galloway, Peter Galloway, Valerie Galloway, John Hodgson, Suzie Horne, Chris Ingham, George Marchant, Lionel Milgrom, Lesley Newson, Janet Taylor, Colin Tudge, Mary Whitehouse

Consultants

Graham Harris, Darlaston Community College

Peter Harwood, St Chad's Roman Catholic School, Runcorn

Jane Morris, Acklam College, Middlesbrough

Cris Rainbow, Yeovil College

Chris Russell and Heather Sillitoe, Uplands Community College, Wadhurst

Project management committee

Lindsey Charles	Heinemann Educational
Andrew Hunt	Director
Nicholas Russell	Deputy director
Antony Tomei	Nuffield Foundation
Linda Westgarth	Administrator

The authors and publishers would like to thank the following people for their generous help with the case studies in this book:

page 4 Dr CR Monk, Bristol Royal Infirmary; John Flanaghan and Declan MacDonald, British Oxygen Company; *pages 26 and 36* John Piggins, Judith Morgan and Amanda Malavanie, Analytical and Environmental Services Ltd; Peter McHugh; *pages 30, 33, 39 and 40* Steve Patey, Andrew Smail, Stephen Byard, John Firth and Stuart McDougal, Sanofi Winthrop; *page 34* Dr Richard Toft, John Farndon and Anne Jones, The Leeds Laboratory of the National Rivers Authority's National Laboratory Service; *page 34* Dr Mike Guillain and Margaret Johnson, Wansbeck Hospital; *pages 47, 57, 58 and 60* Dr Meta Mitchell, Johnson Matthey Technology Centre; Dr Nigel Day; Dr & Dr Rabbits; *page 66* Roger Jones and DA Benaiges-Granville, British Standards Institute; *page 74* Peter Tazewell, Clarks International; *page 78* Janet Taylor, Engelhard Engineered Materials; *page 90* Dr Kate Hollinshead, Building Research Establishment; *page 94* Jim McDelmott, The Institute of Packaging; *page 98* Dr Sue Impey, Cranfield University; *page 116* R Haines, Dunlop Slazenger Ltd; *page 128* John Emsley; *page 134* John Hall, Norfolk Lavender; *page 146* Dr JL Turner, The Boots Company plc; *page 158* John Clough, Bob Madley and Ray Elliot, ZENECA Agrochemicals; *pages 161 and 340* Patrick McNeilly, ZENECA Fine Chemicals Manufacturing Organisation; *page 172* Brian McCartney, Richard Goulding and Bill Taylor, Durham Chemicals; *page 178* Nick Poulton, Rhône-Poulenc Chemicals; *page 188* Charlie Westhead, Neal's Yard; *page 222* Philip and Carol Hockley, Newton Farm; *page 252* Dr Majid Sadeghi and Richard Jones, Cranfield Impact Centre; *page 260* Nicola Gell, and the managers and trainees of Rolls Royce Aerospace Group; *page 264* Mike Lord, Loughborough University; *page 270* Paul Harbuz and John West, Nottingham City Hospital; *page 278* Peter Capener, Centre for Sustainable Energy; *page 298* Geoff Roberts, Liverpool; *page 300* John Flanaghan and Declan McDonald, British Oxygen Company; *page 318* Ron Rapley, Standard Fireworks Ltd; *page 334* Paul Howard, Ballard Power Systems; *page 336* Andy Arnold, Andrew Tomkin and Ian Doidge, University of Plymouth; *page 338* Keith Aubrey and Martin Tims, Esso UK plc; *page 342* Colin Andrews, Ged Adams and David Craig, Rhône-Poulenc Chemicals; *page 351* Mac Thorpe and Tony Woode, Brunner Mond Co Ltd; *page 360* Paul Coward, Fordingbridge; *page 367* Christine Newsome, Special Baby Unit, Southampton; *page 373* Vanda Henry, Fordingbridge Surgery; *page 380* Rob Griffiths, Littledown Centre; *page 386* Eamon Staunton, Fordingbridge Surgery; *page 392* Bernard Everard; *page 398* Sheila Watts; *page 400* Dieter Pevsner; Charles Pattison, Dr Jo Arrowsmith and Paul Bosworth, Middlesex Hospital; Dr David Lipkin, Royal Free Hospital; *page 418* David Shapiro, Nuffield Council on Bioethics; *page 424* Dr Roger Partridge, National Physical Laboratory; *page 438* Rachel Hunt, University of Bath; *page 444* Bob Press and Katie Hargreaves, The Natural History Museum; *page 448* Teresa White, Caroline Moore, Heidi Dale and Marion Tiller, Phase I Clinical Trials; *page 452* John Houston, Sefton Coast Management Scheme; *page 456* Janet Peart, John Innes Institute; *page 462* Giles Colborne, Institute of Physics Publishing, (their World Wide Web Server can be found at http://www.ioppublishing.co.uk ; *page 465* Ian Codd, Friends Provident.

Publications which were sources of information and ideas:

Nuffield Advanced Chemistry, revised and third editions, Longman 1984 and 1994.

SATIS and SATIS 16–19, Association of Science Education, 1988 and 1990.

Experimental chemistry, Peter Rendle, Michael Vokins and Peter Davis, Edward Arnold, 1972.

Modern chemical techniques, Ben Faust, Royal Society of Chemistry, 1992.

Analysis, Julian Tyson, Royal Society of Chemistry, 1988.

Salters Advanced Chemistry: Chemistry Storylines, Heinemann, 1994.

Chemistry calculation, J.A. Hunt and A. Sykes, Longman, 1985.

What you should know about the COSHH regulations, Scriptographic publications, 1989.

About fire safety at work, Scriptographic publications 1981.

What you should know about lab safety, Scriptographic Publications, 1983.

The University of Nottingham Safety Handbook General information and Safety Regulations, University of Nottingham, September 1993

UNIT 1

Analysis and laboratory safety

Chemical analysis

What do analysts do?

For tens of thousands of years our ancestors managed to survive despite being totally unaware of the fact that their environment was made up of chemicals. Why then do scientists, today, find it so useful to be able to make a detailed analysis of those chemicals?

▲ **Figure 1A1** *The scientist uses specialized equipment to investigate the effect of air pollution on the rate of photosynthesis in this young Scots pine sapling.*

Analysis for diagnosis

Urine contains wastes from body processes. If it contains glucose as well, it is a sign of diabetes. The presence of the hormone, human choriogonadotrophin, shows that the person is pregnant. If someone arrives with a drug overdose, a chemical analysis of blood tells the doctor which drug the patient has taken and how much.

Analysis to assess natural resources

Chemical analysis of soil samples is one of the clues used to detect ores. Once discovered, analysis of rock samples helps the mining company to decide whether or not it can mine the ore profitably.

Analysis to check the purity of products

It is only possible to manufacture, buy and sell chemicals if there are reliable ways to test the constituents of the products. Pharmaceutical companies, for example, routinely analyse samples of tablets to check that they contain the right amount of the drug.

Analysis to detect crime

For forensic scientists, chemical analysis can detect invisible clues that help detectives to solve crimes. Dyes, for example, have a chemical signature. Testing the dyes on a piece of fabric caught on a car bumper can reveal if it was involved in a hit and run accident.

Analysis to protect the environment

For scientists responsible for protecting the environment, analysis can reveal clues that all is not right. Routine testing of river mud downstream of a chemical plant can monitor levels of chemicals which could have come from the plant's effluent.

Analysis to test food

Food manufacturers test the raw materials they buy to make food. Samples of grain, for example, are tested for the presence of a wide range of chemicals which reveal the presence of anything from harmful moulds to pesticides to bird droppings.

Analytical strategies

Sometimes chemical analysis is a bit like the work of the detective in a crime story. The aim is to find out the identity of the mystery chemicals in a mixture.

Certain characteristics of chemicals are easy to pick up: their smell or lack of it; their colour; what they dissolve in. These help to narrow down the field and allow analysts to design a strategy for eliminating suspect chemicals one by one.

It is very rare for the analyst not to have some clues about what to look for. Finding all the chemicals in a clear odourless aqueous solution could be the work of a lifetime. But if the analyst is asked to find out if a solution contains certain ions, it can be done in a couple of hours by carrying out a series of chemical tests which force the mystery ion to reveal its presence.

Over the years, analysts have developed a range of chemical reactions to detect ions in solution. The trick is to find changes which produce a gas, or a colour change or an insoluble solid so that the analyst has a visible clue to what is happening. (Pages 8–13 give examples of tests based on acid–base, redox, precipitation and complex-forming reactions.)

These sorts of test-tube tests have limited use in identifying compounds with large and complex structures, especially the carbon compounds in living things (see page 19). Simple tests can, however, help to reveal some clues to the chemical nature of these compounds. At least such tests can suggest which chemical families they belong to. Discovering the precise structure of a complex molecule of a drug, dye or polymer requires more complex analytical techniques. (Pages 14–18 introduce some of the main families of carbon compounds, such as hydrocarbons, alcohols and organic acids with descriptions of some of their typical reactions.)

▲ **Figure 1A2** *The forensic scientist is taking a sample of dried blood from a shirt to analyse during investigations into a homicide.*

◀ **Figure 1A3**
Using chromatography equipment for analysis.

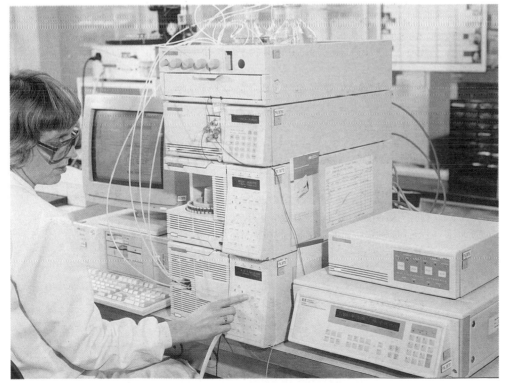

The gas that must be pure

Chemical analysis, even of the most basic kind, can be vital. A failure to detect contaminated raw materials or impure products can have tragic results if the chemicals are for use in medicine.

A hospital tragedy

In September 1966, a routine hysterectomy operation at Bristol General Hospital unexpectedly ended in tragedy. Shortly after the 39-year-old patient was anaesthetized the anaesthetist noticed that her lips had become slightly blue. This 'cyanosis', as it is known, is caused by insufficient oxygenation of the blood. It was soon clear that this woman would not be well enough for her operation. To everyone's horror, the same thing happened to the next patient on the list. She was taken off the anaesthetic gas at once and given oxygen to breathe. The surgeons cancelled the rest of that morning's operations.

A test revealed that the blood of both women contained methaemoglobin, a sign that they had been poisoned. It seemed likely that they had received the poison while they were being anaesthetized. The manufacturers of all the anaesthetic drugs used were immediately contacted and the drugs were taken away to be analysed. The second woman recovered but the first died. The post mortem showed that her lungs were solid and filled with water, a sign that they had been very badly damaged.

Tracking down the problem

The manufacturers of the nitrous oxide used in the operation wasted no time in discovering and informing the hospital that their gas was the source of the problem. The nitrous oxide was contaminated with other oxides of nitrogen.

It also didn't take long for the company to find out why their plant had produced contaminated gas. Nitrous oxide is produced by the thermal decomposition of ammonium nitrate.

$$NH_4NO_3(s) \longrightarrow N_2O(g) + 2H_2O(g)$$

The problem was caused by a bad batch of ammonium nitrate from another chemical company. Contaminants in the starting material had interfered with the reaction so that NO was formed as well as N_2O.

Monitoring raw materials

The manufacturing plant which produced the impure gas was closed down several years ago. All the nitrous oxide used in British hospitals is now produced by the British Oxygen Company (BOC) in Worsley near Manchester. They make the nitrous oxide by essentially the same method as in 1966. Production foremen, like Matthew Stockwin, are BOC's first line of defence against such a tragic mistake ever happening again.

'The nitrous oxide plant operates continuously, 24 hours a day and is controlled automatically so my job is really one of monitoring and checking. We buy in the ammonium nitrate from a fertilizer manufacturer up the road in Immingham. About once a day a tanker arrives with 24 tonnes of very concentrated ammonium nitrate solution, literally hot from the fertilizer plant. When it's in solution, ammonium nitrate is safe and easy to handle. As you probably know, in some states, ammonium nitrate will explode if not handled correctly.

▲ **Figure 1A4** *Matthew Stockwin, Production Foreman, carrying out an acceptance test on ammonium nitrate.*

'When the tanker arrives, the driver climbs on to the top, takes a sample from the inspection hatch and gives it to me. The first thing I notice is whether or not it smells right. It should have a faint smell of ammonia. I look at it to make sure it is clear, use electrodes to check its pH and test for the presence of chloride and then stick a thermometer into the sample. Such a concentrated solution of ammonium nitrate (90–92% by weight) will

▲ Figure 1A5   *Matthew carrying out an acceptance test on the finished product.*

only stay liquid above a certain temperature. When it leaves Immingham it is about 130 °C and it doesn't cool down much during the short trip to Worsley. I let the sample cool and take a note of the temperature when it solidifies. We expect it to solidify at about 108 °C. If I measure the temperature at solidification to be much different than that, then there is likely to be something wrong with the concentration or the purity of the shipment.

The quality of the ammonia nitrate is really the responsibility of the producer in Immingham, but we like to do these quick checks to be sure that the shipment is all right. They can point up quite a few problems. The aim is to check what we can, in the short amount of time available, before we transfer the liquid into the plant's storage tanks. If a bad batch does get in, we have to shut the plant down and clean it. If chloride ions are contaminating the ammonium nitrate, the problem is even more serious because they could damage the stainless steel pipework. Just in case something goes wrong, we have two complete nitrous oxide plants here operating side by side. Because we're the only manufacturer of nitrous oxide in Britain we have to be backed up or supplies of nitrous oxide will soon begin to get worryingly low. Each of our plants is capable of producing enough to meet the demand from all the hospitals in Britain.'

Checking the product

'I also monitor the cleaned and dried nitrous oxide gas as it flows out of the plant and into the storage tank. This is the first of a series of tests. If anything does begin to go wrong with the reaction, the sooner we know about it, the less chance there will be for the plant and storage vessels to be badly contaminated. The gas will be tested several more times before it leaves the site in its cylinders and is shipped out to hospitals.

'The plant has a number of electronic monitoring devices but our manager believes these should be backed up with chemical tests. We've set up a system that lets us do these tests quickly and reliably. Opening a valve causes a sample of the gas to flow through a series of glass tubes containing test solutions.'

Getting to know chemical behaviour

Chemists are able to detect, identify and make changes to chemicals because many years of investigation has brought an understanding of their behaviour. This behaviour is related to the structure of the atoms that make up the chemicals and how these atoms are bonded together. Except for the atoms of some noble gases (such as helium and neon), all atoms form bonds with other atoms.

Chemical compounds form when 'bonds' hold together the atoms of different elements. Under the right conditions, bonds can break and new ones form. This is known as a chemical reaction. It creates a different chemical structure and a different chemical compound.

▶ **Figure 1A6** *During a chemical reaction chemical bonds break then new bonds form. The atoms rearrange to make fresh products.*

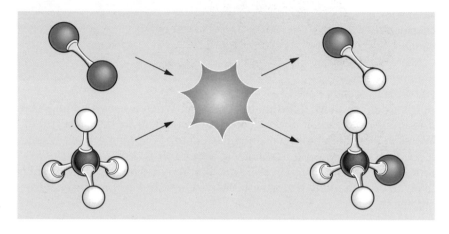

Understanding the behaviour of chemicals makes it possible to create a classification system for millions of different natural and synthetic chemicals. Classifying chemicals helps to predict how they will behave.

Classifying chemicals is seldom simple because most belong to several categories. Sulphuric acid, for example, is an inorganic compound, an acid, a dehydrating agent and an oxidizing agent. Glucose is an organic compound, a carbohydrate, a sugar and a reducing agent. This shows that classifications are not cut and dried so that all too often the chemicals do not fall neatly into groups.

▲ **Figure 1A7** *Atoms in a close-packed metal structure.*

The first step in sorting out chemicals is to divide them into elements and compounds.

Elements

In an **element** all the atoms are the same. Most elements, nearly 90 of them, are metals. In metal crystals, the atoms pack closely together in giant structures held together by strong **metallic bonds**.

There are only 22 **non-metal** elements. At room temperature, eleven are gases, one is a liquid and the rest are solids. In most non-metals the atoms cluster together in small groups called molecules. Examples are nitrogen, $N_2(g)$, bromine $Br_2(l)$ and phosphorus, $P_4(s)$. Note that the **state symbols** show whether the substance is a solid (s), liquid (l) or a gas (g).

▲ **Figure 1A8** *Molecules of oxygen, O=O. Strong, double covalent bonds hold together the atoms in molecules but the forces between molecules are weak so it is easy to melt or evaporate molecular substances.*

Compounds

In a **compound** there are two or more atoms of different elements joined together. Most elements, for example, combine with oxygen forming compounds called oxides. Metal oxides are ionic; they consist of positive metal ions combined with negative oxide ions which build up to form a giant crystalline structure.

$$2Mg \quad + \quad O_2 \quad \longrightarrow \quad 2Mg^{2+}O^{2-}$$

metal atoms	non-metal molecules	metal oxide ions

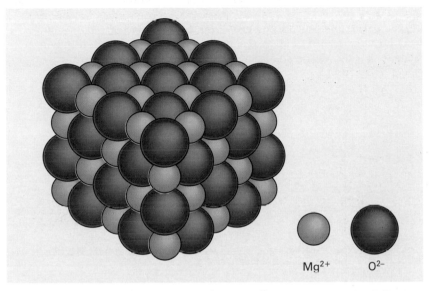

Mg²⁺   O²⁻

▲ **Figure 1A9**   *Ions in the magnesium oxide lattice. In an ionic crystal, positive metal ions strongly attract negative non-metal ions. This is ionic bonding.*

Non-metal elements also combine with oxygen to form oxides but the atoms link together in small groups. Non-metal oxides are molecular.

$$C \quad + \quad O_2 \quad \longrightarrow \quad CO_2$$

non-metal atoms	non-metal molecules	non-metal oxide molecules

As in the molecules of elements, the bonding in these molecular oxides is also **covalent bonding**. Note the double bonds between carbon and oxygen atoms (Figure 1A10).

◀ **Figure 1A10**   *Double bonding in carbon dioxide molecules. The double bonds holding the atoms in the molecule are strong. The forces between the molecules are very weak. So carbon dioxide is a gas at room temperature.*

Acid–base reactions

Acids and bases have always been important to analysts because they react to produce colour changes, gases and precipitates. With a knowledge of chemistry, analysts can interpret these clues to identify the materials they are testing.

Acids

The easiest way to recognize an **acid** is to test it with an indicator. Litmus and methyl orange turn red in acid, bromocresol green turns yellow while congo red turns violet.

Some mixtures of indicators make it possible to use the colour change to determine the pH of an acid solution. The **pH scale** is a number scale which shows the acidity or alkalinity of a solution in water (see Figure 1A11).

▶ **Figure 1A11** *The pH scale and the colours of full-range indicator.*

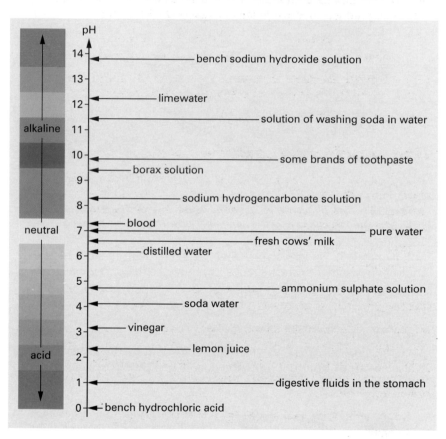

Pure acids may be solids (e.g. citric and tartaric acids), liquids (e.g. sulphuric, nitric and ethanoic acids) or gases (e.g. hydrogen chloride, which becomes hydrochloric acid when it dissolves in water). What all these acids have in common is that they produce hydrogen ions when they dissolve in water.

$$HCl(g) \longrightarrow H^+(aq) + Cl^-(aq)$$

hydrogen   hydrochloric

chloride   acid

Note that (aq) is the state symbol meaning aqueous (dissolved in water). Citric and ethanoic acids are examples of acids obtained from living things (see page 18). Sulphuric, nitric and hydrochloric acids are the three common mineral acids, so called because they come from mineral sources (see pages 342–5).

Bases and alkalis

The chemical opposite of an acid is a **base**. Common bases are the oxides and hydroxides of metals. Acids and bases neutralize each other to form **salts**.

$$CuO(s) \ + \ H_2SO_4(aq) \ \longrightarrow \ CuSO_4(aq) \ + \ H_2O(l)$$

base   acid   salt   water

Alkalis are bases which dissolve in water. The well-known laboratory alkalis are the hydroxides of sodium and potassium, calcium hydroxide (in lime water) and ammonia. Like acids, alkalis are easily spotted in solution because they too change the colour of indicators. Litmus turns blue in alkali, methyl orange turns yellow, bromocresol green turns blue while congo red turns red (see Reference section R28).

What alkalis have in common is that they dissolve in water to produce hydroxide ions. Sodium hydroxide (Na^+OH^-) and potassium hydroxide (K^+OH^-) contain hydroxide ions in the solid as well as in solution. Ammonia produces hydroxide ions by reacting with water.

$$NH_3(aq) \ + \ H_2O(aq) \ \longrightarrow \ NH_4^+(aq) \ + \ OH^-(aq)$$

ammonia   ammonium ion   hydroxide ion

During a **neutralization** reaction, the hydrogen ions from an acid combine with the hydroxide ions from an alkali to make water.

$$H^+(aq) \ + \ OH^-(aq) \ \longrightarrow \ H_2O(l)$$

Using acids to test for ions

Geologists use hydrochloric acid to detect limestone rocks which consist of calcium carbonate. They look for a 'fizz' when a drop of acid falls on the rock. The fizz is carbon dioxide produced by the reaction of the acid with calcium carbonate.

$$CO_3^{2-}(aq) + 2HCl(aq) \longrightarrow CO_2(g) + H_2O(l) + 2Cl^-(aq)$$

carbonate ion

Carbon dioxide is a colourless gas with no smell but analysts can easily identify it with limewater, which turns cloudy-white.

Sulphite ions, in compounds such as sodium sulphite, behave in a similar way to carbonate ions. Add hydrochloric acid and they give off sulphur dioxide. Sulphur dioxide is a pungent acid gas. Hold a piece of filter paper dipped in acid dichromate solution in the gas and it turns from orange to green.

$$SO_3^{2-}(aq) + 2HCl(aq) \longrightarrow SO_2(g) + H_2O(l) + 2Cl^-(aq)$$

sulphite ion

Using alkalis to test for ions

Sodium hydroxide solution is a useful reagent to test for metal ions. Adding the alkali to a solution of a metal salt often produces an insoluble solid. The colour of the solid helps to identify the metal (see Reference section Figure R18.2).

A salt forms when an acid neutralizes a base. In the formula of a salt, the hydrogen of an acid is replaced by metal ions. For example, magnesium sulphate, $MgSO_4$, is a salt of sulphuric acid, H_2SO_4.

Redox reactions

One chemical reaction everyone is familiar with is steel going rusty. Scratch the paintwork on a car and before long, the metal has a reddish brown coating of rust, so that it is easy to see that there has been a chemical change. Rusting is an example of a redox reaction accompanied by a colour change that is easy to see. Analysts use other reactions like this in their search for clues.

Colourful redox reactions also light up the night sky during firework displays (see pages 318–9). Some fireworks contain powdered magnesium which burns very brightly in oxygen.

$$\text{magnesium } + \text{ oxygen } \longrightarrow \text{ magnesium oxide}$$
$$2Mg(s) \quad + \quad O_2(g) \quad \longrightarrow \quad 2Mg^{2+}O^{2-}(s)$$

The magnesium atoms turn into magnesium ions by losing electrons. Oxygen molecules take the electrons from the magnesium turning into oxide ions.

$$2Mg \longrightarrow 2Mg^{2+} + 4e^-$$
$$O_2(g) + 4e^- \longrightarrow 2O^{2-}$$

This is one of the simplest examples of a redox reaction involving electron transfer from magnesium (which is oxidized) to oxygen (which is reduced). **Red**uction and **ox**idation always go together, hence the term **redox reaction**.

The term **oxidizing agent** (or oxidant) describes chemical reagents which can oxidize other atoms, molecules or ions by taking away electrons from them. Common oxidizing agents are oxygen, chlorine, potassium manganate(VII), potassium dichromate(VI) and hydrogen peroxide.

The term **reducing agent** (or reductant) describes chemical reagents which can reduce other atoms, molecules or ions by giving them electrons. Common reducing agents are hydrogen, zinc or iron in acid and sulphur dioxide.

Oxidation numbers

Chemists use oxidation numbers to keep track of the number of electrons gained or lost during a redox reaction. In Figure 1A12, movement *up* the diagram towards more positive numbers is oxidation. Movement *down* the diagram towards more negative numbers is reduction.

▶ **Figure 1A12** *Chlorine oxidizes magnesium. Oxidation Is Loss (OIL) of electrons – Reduction Is Gain (RIG) of electrons.*

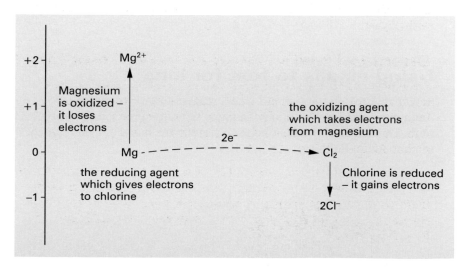

◀ **Figure 1A13** *Oxidation number rules.*

Oxidation number rules

1 The oxidation numbers of uncombined elements are zero
2 In simple ions the oxidation number of the element is the charge on the ion.
3 The sum of the oxidation numbers in a neutral compound is zero.
4 The sum of the oxidation numbers in a complex ion equals the charge on the ion.
5 Some elements have fixed oxidation numbers in all their compounds, for example:

Metals		**Non-metals**	
sodium	+1	hydrogen	−1 *(except in metal hydrides)*
potassium	+1	fluorine	−1
magnesium	+2	oxygen	−2 *(except in peroxides and compounds with fluorine)*
calcium	+2		
aluminium	+3	chlorine	−1 *(except in compounds with oxygen and fluorine)*

The oxidation numbers of elements are taken to be zero. In a simple ion the oxidation number equals the charge on the ion.

The names of inorganic compounds are based on oxidation numbers. In iron(**II**) chloride, for example, the Roman number **II** shows that iron is in oxidation state +2. In iron(**III**) chloride the oxidation number of iron is +3.

There are rules for working out the oxidation numbers of elements in molecules and in the more complicated ions (Figure 1A13).

In a molecule the sum of the oxidation numbers is zero. For example, in carbon dioxide, CO_2, each oxygen atom has an oxidation number −2. The oxidation number of carbon must be +4 if the total is to be zero. Similarly in sulphuric acid the oxidation of numbers of hydrogen and oxygen are as in Figure 1A14, so the oxidation number of sulphur must be +6.

In more complex ions the sum of the oxidation numbers is equal to the charge on the ion. In the manganate(VII) ion, MnO_4^-, there are four oxygen atoms each with oxidation number −2. The oxidation number of manganese must therefore be +7 so that the sum is −1. This shows that in the manganate(VII) ion, manganese uses seven electrons to combine with oxygen.

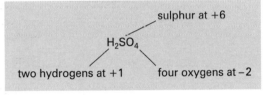

▲ **Figure 1A14** *Oxidation numbers in sulphuric acid.*

Chemical tests based on redox reactions

Some reagents change colour when they are oxidized or reduced and this makes them useful for detecting oxidizing and reducing agents. Potassium dichromate(VI), for example, is orange in acid solution. Add enough of a reducing agent and it turns green. (See Reference section Figure R18.5 for more details.)

Similarly, potassium iodide solution is colourless. Add an oxidizing agent and it turns brown as iodine forms. This test is even more sensitive if there is a little starch in the solution because starch forms a deep blue colour with even a trace of iodine. (See Reference section Figure R18.4 for more details.)

Precipitation reactions

Very often two reagents in solution react to form a new compound which is insoluble. The insoluble product separates out from the solution as a solid precipitate. This can be very handy in analysis because it makes it possible to see that there has been a reaction. Analysts can get more clues to help them to identify the chemicals by looking at the colour and general appearance of precipitates. So many simple chemical tests depend on the formation of precipitates.

A test for chloride, bromide and iodide ions

Silver nitrate and sodium chloride are both ionic and soluble in water. On mixing solutions of the compounds, two new combinations of ions are possible. One of the new combinations, silver chloride is insoluble and so it precipitates as a white solid.

▶ **Figure 1A15** *A precipitate forms on mixing solutions of soluble salts if a new combination of ions forms an insoluble compound.*

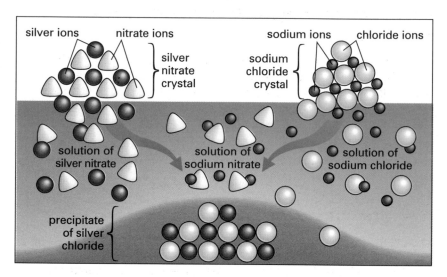

$$Ag^+(aq) + NO_3^-(aq) + Na^+(aq) + Cl^-(aq) \rightarrow AgCl(s) + Na^+(aq) + NO_3^-(aq)$$

silver nitrate solution   sodium chloride solution   silver chloride precipitate   sodium nitrate solution

Notice that some of the ions are not really affected by the reaction. They are in solution at the start and stay in solution at the end so it makes the equation clearer to leave them out.

$$Ag^+(aq) + Cl^-(aq) \longrightarrow AgCl(s)$$

The same test can be used to detect bromide and iodide ions. Silver bromide is a cream colour. Silver iodide is bright yellow.

A test for metal cations

A scheme for identifying metal ions is based on the hydroxides of metals (see Reference section Figure R18.2). Most hydroxides are insoluble in water so that a precipitate forms on adding dilute sodium hydroxide to a solution of the metal salt. The hydroxides of transition metals, such as copper and iron, are easy to spot from their colours. More tests are needed to identify the insoluble white hydroxides of metals such as aluminium, calcium and zinc.

Complex-forming reactions

Many gemstones owe their colours to the presence of small traces of metal ions: vanadium ions in sapphires, chromium ions in ruby and copper ions in turquoise. These ions may be colourless as simple ions but develop bright colours when other molecules or ions cluster round them making more complex structures.

The central ion of a coloured complex is often one of the metals in the middle block of the **Periodic Table**, the transition metals. The surrounding molecules or ions each have a lone pair of electrons which they use to bond to the metal ion. Hence the alternative name, co-ordination compounds.

Many chemical tests rely on reactions involving complexes. This is because the formation of new complexes may cause very noticeable colour changes or bring an insoluble precipitate into solution.

A test to distinguish chloride and bromide ions

When using silver nitrate to test for halide ions, it is easy to spot the bright yellow of silver iodide. Telling the difference between white silver chloride and creamy silver bromide is less easy. Adding ammonia to the precipitates helps because silver chloride redissolves in ammonia solution due to the formation of a complex ion. The other silver halides are even less soluble than silver chloride and do not redissolve.

$$AgCl(s) + 2NH_3(aq) \longrightarrow [Ag(NH_3)_2]^+(aq) + Cl^-(aq)$$
$$\text{diamminesilver(I) ion}$$

Distinguishing metal ions

The scheme for identifying metal ions (see Reference section Figure R18.2) uses ammonia solution to distinguish zinc ions from aluminium ions. Adding dilute ammonia to solutions of these ions precipitates the metal hydroxides but while zinc hydroxide redissolves in excess ammonia, aluminium hydroxide does not. The zinc ions redissolve because the metal ions form a complex with ammonia molecules.

$$Zn(OH)_2(s) + 4NH_3(aq) \longrightarrow [Zn(NH_3)_4]^{2+}(aq) + 2OH^-(aq)$$
$$\text{tetra-amminezinc(II) ion}$$

A spot test for iron(III) ions

Potassium thiocyanate, KSCN, solution produces a blood-red colour if mixed with a solution containing iron(III) ions. Iron(III) ions in solution have six water molecules round them; they are yellow. Thiocyanate ions, CNS^-, replace one of the water molecules round each iron ion forming the deeply coloured complex ion, $[Fe(CNS)(H_2O)_5]^{2+}$. The intense colour shows up even when the solution is very dilute so that the normal yellow colour of iron(III) is too faint to detect.

▲ **Figure 1A16** *Emeralds owe their colour to traces of chromium.*

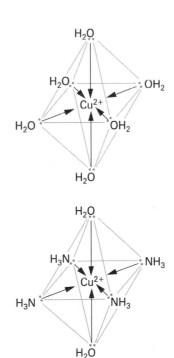

▶ **Figure 1A17** *Anhydrous copper(II) sulphate is white. Add water and it turns blue because water molecules form a coloured complex ion with copper(II) ions, $[Cu(H_2O)_6]^{2+}$. Add ammonia and the solution turns deep blue as ammonia molecules replace four of the water molecules to make a new complex ion, $[Cu(NH_3)_4(H_2O)_2]^{2+}$.*

Families of carbon compounds

There are more compounds of carbon than there are of all the other elements put together. The chemistry of carbon is so important that it forms a separate branch of the subject called organic chemistry. It helps to think of organic compounds as being made up of a carbon skeleton supporting more or less reactive groups of atoms.

Number of carbon atoms	Molecular formula	Name of alkane
1	CH_4	methane
2	C_2H_6	ethane
3	C_3H_8	propane
4	C_4H_{10}	butane
5	C_5H_{12}	pentane
6	C_6H_{14}	hexane

▲ Figure 1A18

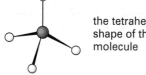 CH_4 — the molecular formula

 the displayed formula showing the chemical bonds

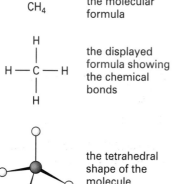 the tetrahedral shape of the molecule

the space filled by the molecule

▲ **Figure 1A19** *Four ways of representing a molecule of methane.*

It can be very hard to identify and classify important organic molecules in living things, in drugs, dyes and polymers because they have lots of different ways of reacting. To make sense of this complexity, it helps to think in terms of families of organic compounds and to learn the properties of the simpler reactive groups.

Carbon forms so many compounds because carbon atoms can join together in different ways building up chains, branched chains and rings. The carbon atoms form a skeleton to which other atoms can link themselves. In organic compounds, carbon is often bonded to hydrogen, oxygen, nitrogen and halogen atoms.

There are so many carbon compounds that it could be hopelessly confusing to study them separately. Fortunately it is possible to group the compounds into families and to learn about the families rather than about the individual compounds.

Alkanes

The alkanes are well-known because they are present in fuels such as natural gas and petrol. All the alkanes are compounds of just two elements: hydrogen and carbon. They are **hydrocarbons**. Alkanes do not mix with water but they do burn. In lots of air the carbon turns into carbon dioxide and the hydrogen combines with oxygen to produce water molecules.

Figure 1A18 shows six alkanes. Note that in each molecule every carbon atom forms four bonds with other atoms while hydrogen only forms one bond. In the ball-and-stick models shown in Figure 1A19, the 'sticks' represent strong covalent bonds holding the atoms together. Ball-and-stick models are better for showing the bonding between atoms but space-filling models give a better impression of their shape and size.

Butane and 2-methylpropane have the same molecular formula but different structures (Figure 1A20). They are examples of isomers.

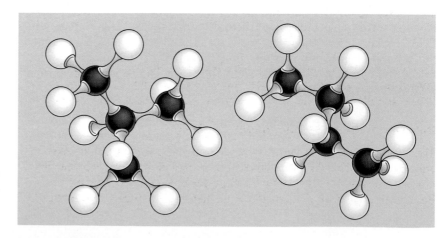

► **Figure 1A20** *Two molecules with the same molecular formula, C_4H_{10}.*

Alkenes

Hydrocarbons with double bonds

Alkenes make up another family of hydrocarbons. The special feature of alkenes is that they have a double bond between two carbon atoms.

The term **saturated** describes compounds such as the alkanes in which all the bonds are single bonds. Chemists call the alkenes **unsaturated** because of the double bond.

To name the simpler alkenes take the name of the corresponding alkane and change its ending to 'ene'. In but-1-ene the double bond connects the *first* and second carbon atoms in the chain. In but-2-ene the double bond connects the *second* and third atoms. Members of the International Union of Pure and Applied Chemistry (IUPAC) decide the rules for naming chemicals. The IUPAC rule is to number the chain from the end which gives as small a number as possible to label the position of the double bond.

ethene, C_2H_4

propene, C_3H_6

but-1-ene, C_4H_8

but-2-ene, C_4H_8

▲ **Figure 1A21** *Names, formulas and structures of four alkenes.*

Alkene reactions

Double bonds give alkenes their special properties and make them more reactive than alkanes. The two carbon atoms with a double bond between them make up a **functional group** which reacts in ways typical of alkene behaviour. In their important reactions, the alkenes use the double bond to add on more atoms.

Reaction with bromine

Bromine solution is a useful reagent for a test to detect double bonds in hydrocarbons. Shake a dilute solution of bromine with a few drops of the alkene and the orange bromine colour disappears.

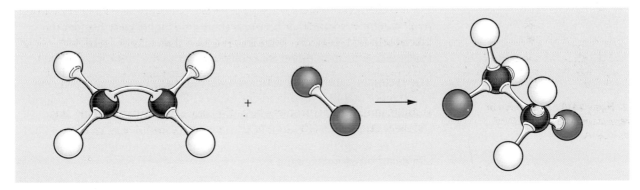

The reaction of bromine with an alkene is an example of an **addition reaction**. The molecules join together to form a single product. Bromine is orange but the product of the reaction is colourless so the colour fades.

▲ **Figure 1A22** *A model equation for the reaction of ethene with bromine.*

Reaction with potassium manganate(VII)

This reaction is another test for double bonds in hydrocarbons. Shake a very dilute, acidic solution of potassium manganate(VII) with a few drops of an alkene and the purple colour goes, leaving a colourless mixture. Potassium manganate(VII) oxidizes alkenes to a mixture of products.

Arenes

Hydrocarbons with benzene rings

Arenes are ring compounds based on the hydrocarbon benzene, C_6H_6. The benzene ring turns out to be remarkably stable so it can act as a firm foundation for building up a carbon skeleton. Linked to other functional groups, the benzene ring can form explosives, pigments, polymers, drugs and dyes.

Figure 1A23 shows three ways of modelling the structure of benzene. The first structure shows all the atoms and all the bonds. Note that as usual carbon atoms form four bonds with other atoms while hydrogen atoms form just one bond.

The second structure is a common shorthand which leaves out the symbols for the atoms and the bonds to hydrogen. 'Read' the structure by assuming that there is a carbon atom at each corner and that there are as many hydrogens as necessary for each carbon atom to form four bonds.

Chemists use the third structure to show that the six electrons of the three double bonds are not fixed between particular pairs of atoms – they are spread round the ring so that all six carbon–carbon bonds are the same. They have the same length and the same strength.

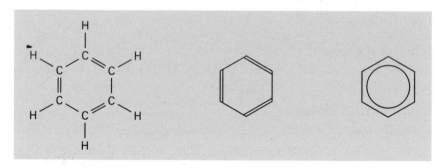

▲ **Figure 1A23**   *Alternative ways of showing the structure of benzene.*

At first sight it seems that benzene should be highly reactive like the alkenes. In fact, benzene is far less reactive than alkenes and does not easily take part in addition reactions.

The system of alternating double bonds makes the six-membered ring much more stable than one might expect. The reason for the increased stability is that the three double bonds are not isolated. In fact, the electron clouds in these double bonds overlap and merge to form a kind of 'double-doughnut-shaped' electron cloud that sandwiches the six-sided carbon-atom skeleton.

Alcohols

Compounds with —OH groups

Alcohols contain oxygen as well as carbon and hydrogen. The functional group is the —OH group. The first three members of the alcohol series are methanol, ethanol and propan-1-ol. To name them, take the name of the corresponding alkane and change the ending to –ol. So methan-e becomes methan-ol.

Unlike 'oily' hydrocarbons, simple alcohols such as ethanol can mix with water. The —OH group found in alcohols is like the —OH group in water. 'Like dissolves like' so these alcohols mix with water. Solutions of alcohols in water are neutral.

Alcohol reactions

Alcohols are more reactive than alkanes because C—O and O—H bonds are more reactive. The alcohols share similar properties because they all have this group in their molecules:

$$-\overset{|}{\underset{|}{C}}-O-H$$

Reaction with sodium

Alcohols react with sodium in a similar way to water. This is because alcohol molecules, like water molecules, include the —OH group. With water the products are sodium hydroxide and hydrogen; with ethanol the products are sodium ethoxide and hydrogen. Note that in the reaction, only the hydrogen atom joined to oxygen reacts. The hydrogen atoms linked to carbon are inert (unreactive), just as they are in the alkanes.

$$2\text{ H}-\overset{\overset{\displaystyle H}{|}}{\underset{\underset{\displaystyle H}{|}}{C}}-\overset{\overset{\displaystyle H}{|}}{\underset{\underset{\displaystyle H}{|}}{C}}-O-H + 2Na \longrightarrow 2\text{ H}-\overset{\overset{\displaystyle H}{|}}{\underset{\underset{\displaystyle H}{|}}{C}}-\overset{\overset{\displaystyle H}{|}}{\underset{\underset{\displaystyle H}{|}}{C}}-O^-Na^+ + H_2$$
sodium ethoxide

This is the equation for the reaction of ethanol with sodium showing the structures of the molecules.

The reaction is dangerously rapid with water, but much slower with alcohols. The safe way to get rid of waste sodium in the laboratory is to cut it into very small pieces and dissolve it in an alcohol such as propan-2-ol.

Oxidizing alcohols

Acidifying a solution of sodium dichromate(VI) produces a powerful oxidizing agent. The solution is orange. Add a few drops of an alcohol, warm the solution and it turns green. If the alcohol is ethanol the main product has a pungent, fruity smell.

Oxidizing an alcohol with the —OH group at the end of the chain (a primary alcohol) turns it first into an aldehyde (—CHO) and then a carboxylic acid (—CO$_2$H).

▶ **Figure 1A26** *Stages in the two stage oxidation of butan-1-ol.*

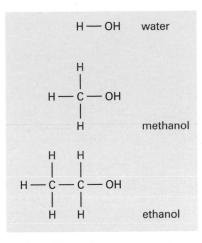

▲ **Figure 1A24** *The structures of water and two alcohols.*

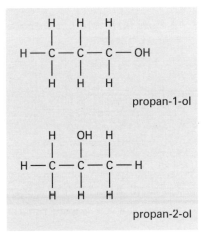

▲ **Figure 1A25** *Propan-1-ol (a primary alcohol) and propan-2-ol (a secondary alcohol) are isomers.*

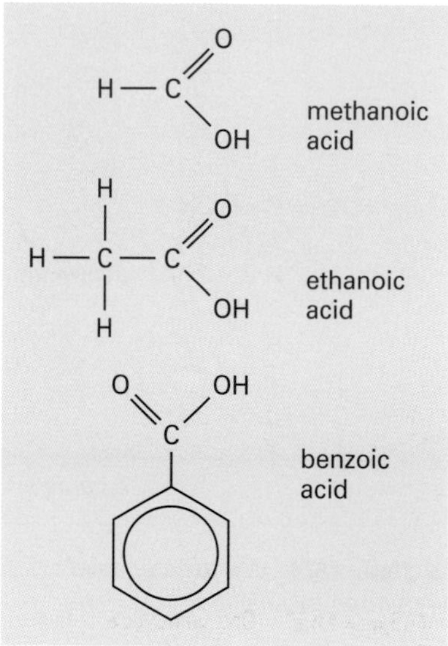

Organic acids and bases

Carboxylic acids

▲ **Figure 1A27** *Structures of three carboxylic acids.*

The rule for naming organic acids is to change the ending of the corresponding alk-ane to -anoic acid. Some older names are still used and they hint at the natural occurrence of the acids. Methanoic acid is otherwise known as formic acid because it was first isolated by distilling red ants, and *formica* is the Latin name for ant. Ethanoic acid appears on food labels as acetic acid from the Latin word for vinegar – *acetum*. Octadecanoic acid (with eighteen atoms in the molecule) is better known as stearic acid from the Greek word for tallow – *stear*.

Acids react with water forming hydrogen ions (see page 313). In a molecule of ethanoic acid there are four hydrogen atoms but only the hydrogen attached to oxygen is acidic. This equation shows ethanoic acid ionizing in water.

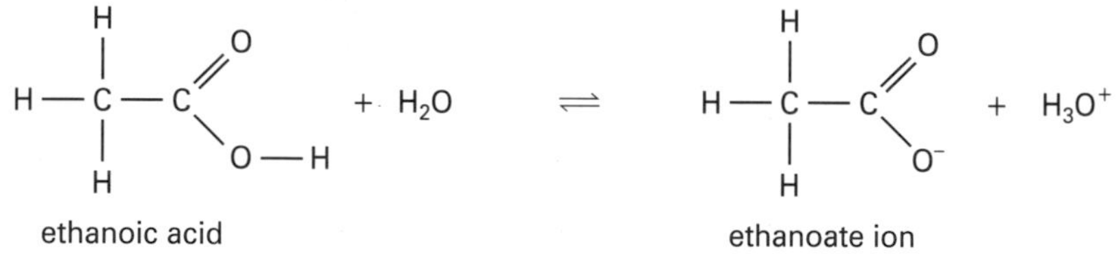

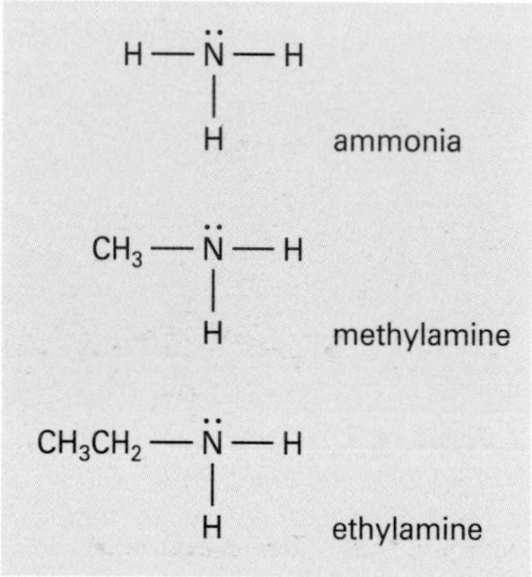

Amines – organic bases

Amines can be related to ammonia. A primary amine is an ammonia molecule with one of its hydrogen atoms replaced by a hydrocarbon side chain.

▲ **Figure 1A28** *The structures of ammonia and two amines.*

Like ammonia, amines are bases. They grab hold of hydrogen ions. A solution of an amine in water is alkaline because some of the amino groups take hydrogen ions from water making hydroxide ions which turn the solution alkaline. This equation shows the reaction of methylamine with water.

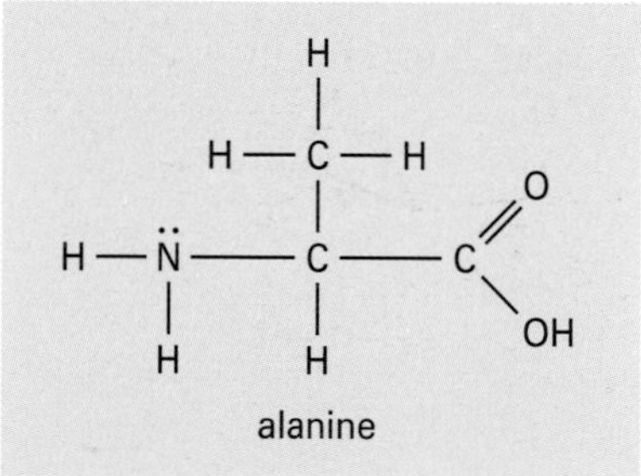

Amino acids – both base and acid

Amino acid molecules each have two functional groups: an amine group and an acid group.

▲ **Figure 1A29** *The structure of the amino acid, alanine.*

Glycine is a white, crystalline solid with a sweet taste. It dissolves in water forming a neutral solution. Effectively the basic amine group ($-NH_2$) and the acidic carboxylate group ($-CO_2H$) cancel each other out. In the crystals and in solution in water there is evidence that hydrogen ions are indeed transferred from one group to the other. Molecules of the amino acid glycine transfer hydrogen ions from the acid group to the amine group. This helps to explain why glycine is a solid and why it forms a neutral solution in water.

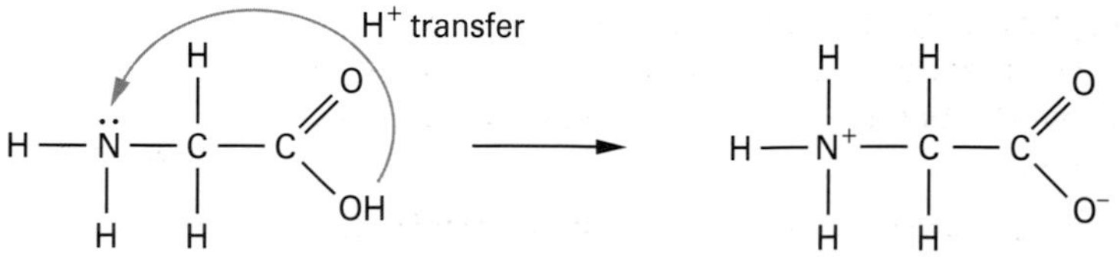

Natural products

Proteins

About 15% of the human body is protein. There are many types of protein molecule each doing a special job in the body. Skin, muscle and hair are fibrous proteins. Other fibrous proteins hold the body together by linking bone to bone and muscle to bone. The enzymes which catalyse all the body's chemistry are also proteins. The hormone insulin is a protein that controls the use of sugar in the body. Haemoglobin is also a protein which colours the blood red and enables it to carry oxygen around the body.

Proteins consist of long chains of amino acids. About 20 different amino acids link together to make natural proteins. Amino acids join by splitting off water between the acid group of one molecule and the amine group of the other molecule. This is an example of a **condensation** reaction.

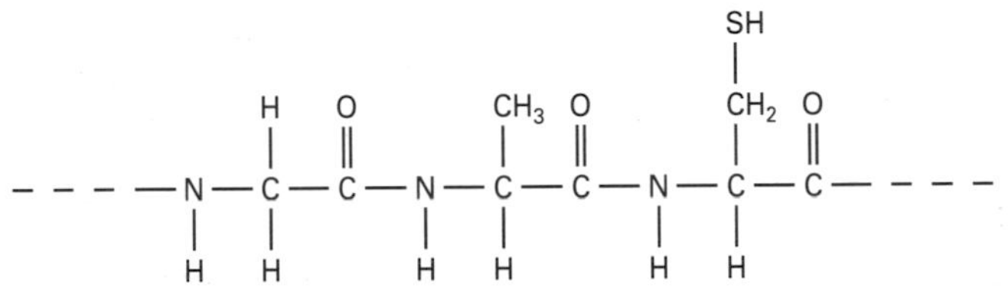

◀ **Figure 1A30** *The structure of a very short length of a protein chain.*

Carbohydrates

Starch, sugars and cellulose all belong to the family of carbohydrates which consist of the elements carbon, hydrogen and oxygen. Their name, carbo*hydrates*, arises from their formulae in which hydrogen and oxygen atoms are usually present in the same ratio as in water. The formula of glucose, for example, is $C_6H_{12}O_6$ which could be written as $C_6(H_2O)_6$. Neither way of writing the formula gives any idea of how the atoms are arranged in glucose molecules.

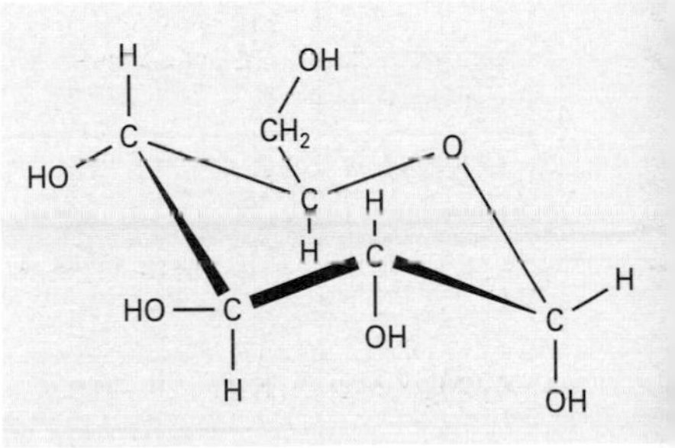

Glucose is a monosaccharide. Sucrose with two sugar units linked together (glucose and fructose) is a disaccharide.

Starch and cellulose are polysaccharides made up of very long chains of glucose units. The difference lies in the linkage between the glucose molecules. Plants make glucose by photosynthesis. Some of the glucose they store as a reserve of energy food; some of the glucose they use to build cellulose cell walls as they grow.

▲ **Figure 1A31** *The structure of a glucose molecule.*

▼ **Figure 1A32** *The structure of the cellulose in cotton.*

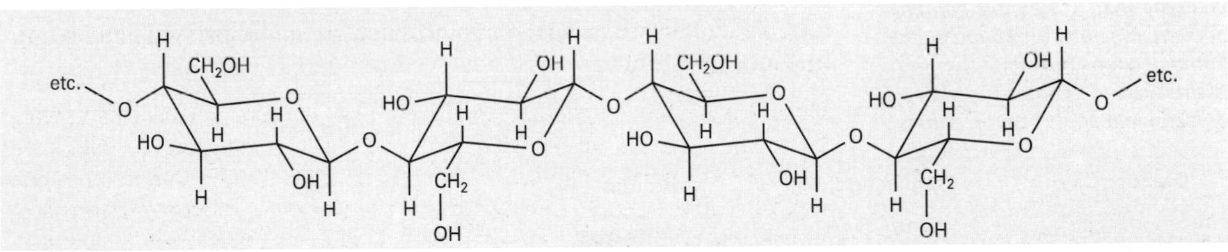

When people eat plants they digest the starch but not the cellulose. Digestion is a hydrolysis reaction catalysed by enzymes. Cows, and other animals that feed on grass, rely on bacteria in their intestines to help break down cellulose to glucose. Cows chew the cud to give the bacteria time to break down the long chain molecules.

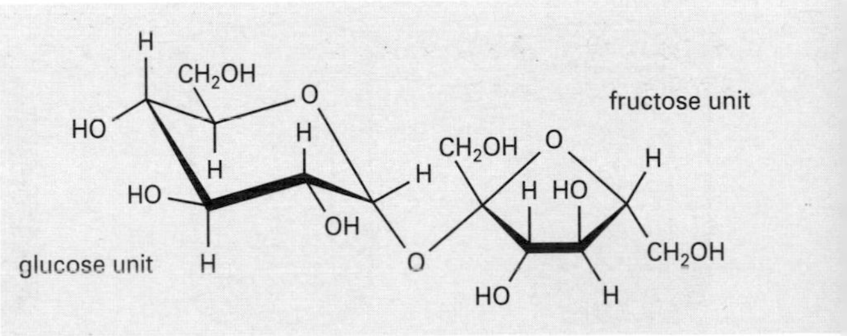

▶ **Figure 1A33** *The structure of sucrose (ordinary table sugar).*

Chemical amounts

Detecting and identifying chemicals in a mixture is known as 'qualitative analysis'. Analysts very often also have to carry out 'quantitative analysis'. They have to measure how much of a given chemical there is in a sample. Simply detecting alcohol on the breath of a motorist, for example, is not enough. To find out if the alcohol was affecting the motorist's driving it is necessary to have a quick and accurate way of measuring how much alcohol is there.

The same basic method of calculating amounts is used in titration (see Reference section R12), in the planning of chemical reactions to make new chemicals (see pages 132–3) and in calculating the yield from these chemical reactions (see page 21).

Amounts in moles

The key to this method is knowing the relative masses of atoms. The mass of a carbon atom, for example, is about twelve times that of the lightest atom, hydrogen. An atom of lead is over 200 times as massive as a hydrogen atom. To make the calculations accurate, chemists have devised a precise system of measuring the relative masses of atoms (see pages 42–3).

Scientists all over the world use a standard system of units known as the International System of Units (SI). The gram, metre and second are among the base units agreed for this system. The base unit of chemical amount is the 'mole'. According to their agreement, one mole of a substance is the amount of that substance which contains the same number of chemical entities as there are carbon atoms in exactly 12 grams of carbon-12. The 'chemical entities' in a mole can be atoms, molecules or ions.

The number of atoms in 12 grams of carbon-12 is huge but that number doesn't actually come up at all in the calculation of chemical amounts. Research chemists have measured the molar mass (the mass of one mole) for each of the elements and created tables like the one in Reference section R19 where all chemists can find the numbers to use in their calculations.

To find the molar mass of a compound is a simple matter of addition. The chemical formula of the compound gives the number of each sort of atom. Add up the number of grams per mole of each element. The formula for glucose is $C_6H_{12}O_6$ so, to calculate molar mass of glucose, first look up the molar masses of C (carbon-12), H (hydrogen-1) and O (oxygen-16). The molar mass of glucose is $(6 \times 12 \text{ g mol}^{-1}) + (12 \times 1 \text{ g mol}^{-1}) + (6 \times 16 \text{ g mol}^{-1})$ or 180 g mol^{-1}.

▼ **Figure 1A34** *Molar masses of some common substances.*

Element	Entity	Molar mass /$g\,mol^{-1}$
Hydrogen	H	1
	H^+	1
	H_2	2
Carbon	C	12
Oxygen	O	16
	O^{2-}	16
	O_2	32
Ozone	O_3	48
Water	H_2O	18
Carbon dioxide	CO_2	44

▼ **Figure 1A35** *One mole samples of elements and compounds. Each bottle contains the same number of the entities (atoms, molecules or formulae) shown on the labels.*

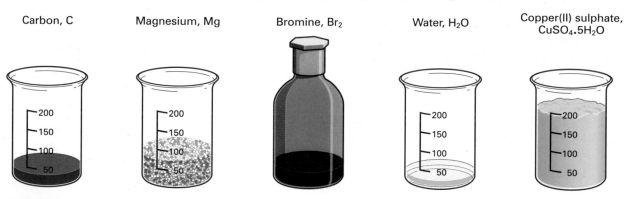

Carbon, C Magnesium, Mg Bromine, Br_2 Water, H_2O Copper(II) sulphate, $CuSO_4.5H_2O$

Formulas from analysis

Chemists use the knowledge of molar masses to find out the empirical formula of a new or unknown compound. For example, say a compound was found to be 52.2% carbon, 13.0% hydrogen and 34.8% oxygen. A 100 gram sample of the compound would, therefore, contain 52.2 grams of carbon, 13.0 grams of hydrogen and 34.8 grams of oxygen.

To find out the amounts of each element in 100 grams, divide each mass by the molar mass of each element:

$$\frac{52.2\,g\ carbon}{12\,g\,mol^{-1}} = 4.35\,mol \qquad \frac{13\,g\ hydrogen}{1\,g\,mol^{-1}} = 13\,mol \qquad \frac{34.8\,g\ oxygen}{16\,g\,mol^{-1}} = 2.18\,mol$$

Divide the amounts in moles by the smallest amount (2.18 mol), to see that the proportion of each element is then 2 mol of carbon, 6 mol of hydrogen and 1 mol of oxygen so the empirical formula is C_2H_6O.

Calculations from equations

A balanced equation shows the amounts in moles of each substance involved in a reaction. This allows chemists to use equations to work out the masses of reactants and products.

Calculating masses of reactants and products

Step 1 Write a balanced equation (see Reference section R11).
Step 2 In words, spell out what the equations shows about the amounts of the substances of interest.
Step 3 Convert from amounts in moles to masses in grams.
Step 4 Scale the masses to the quantities involved in the investigation.

Example

What mass of ethanol forms when 4.5 g glucose ferments?

Step 1 $C_6H_{12}O_6 \longrightarrow 2C_2H_5OH + 2CO_2$
Step 2 One mole of glucose ferments to two moles of ethanol. (Ignore the carbon dioxide here because it is not part of the problem.)
Step 3 The molar mass of glucose = 180 g mol^{-1}
        The molar mass of ethanol = 46 g mol^{-1}
        So 180 g glucose ferments to 2 × 46 g = 92 g ethanol
Step 4 Fermentation of 4.5 g glucose produces $\frac{4.5}{180} \times 92 = 2.3\,g$

Concentrations

Analysts often work with chemicals in solution. They measure concentrations by finding out the amount of substance in one litre (one cubic decimeter, 1 dm^3) of a solution.

$$concentration/mol\ dm^{-3} = \frac{amount\ of\ substance/mol}{volume\ of\ solution/dm^3}$$

Chemists often use square brackets as a shorthand for 'concentration in moles per litre', so in Figure 1A40 the concentration of the solution will be given by:

$$[NaCl] = 1.0\,mol\,dm^{-3}\ (or\ 1.0\,M)$$

The **empirical formula** of a compound shows the ratio of the numbers of atoms in the compound. In ethane the ratio of carbon to hydrogen atoms is 1:3, so its empirical formula is CH_3.

The **molecular formula** of a compound tells you the actual numbers of atoms in one molecule of a compound. In one ethane molecule there are two carbon atoms and six hydrogen atoms, so its molecular formula is C_2H_6.

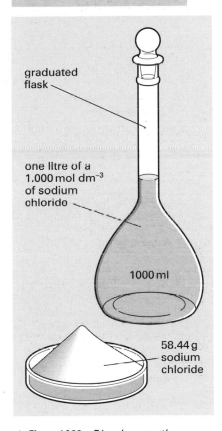

graduated flask

one litre of a 1.000 mol dm^{-3} of sodium chloride

1000 ml

58.44 g sodium chloride

▲ **Figure 1A36** *Dissolve exactly 58.44 g sodium chloride, NaCl, in water and make up to one litre of solution in a graduated flask to obtain a concentration of 1.000 mol dm^{-3}. Notice that the volume of the solution measures 1 dm^3. Accurate solutions are not made by weighing out the molar mass of solid and then adding 1 dm^3 water.*

Analytical methods

Stages in an analysis

Typically an analyst faced with a problem of quantitative analysis works carefully through a series of steps calling for judgement and skill.

Choosing an analytical method

This calls for experience and an understanding of the way that chemicals behave. Possible methods are described in this chapter.

Taking a representative sample

The analysis must be carried out on a sample which is representative of the bulk of the material under test.

Measuring out laboratory samples

Analysts must start by measuring accurately a known mass or volume of the material. Generally they carry through an analysis with two or more samples in parallel as a check on the reliability of the final result.

Dissolving the samples

Many analytical techniques call for a solution of the sample, so analysts have the problem of dissolving their samples. When working with minerals, biological specimens or polymers this can be a time-consuming and difficult task. The trick is to find a procedure to bring the samples into solution without losing any of the material or changing it in ways which could affect the measurements.

▶ **Figure 1B1** *Amanda (see page 36) making a preliminary visual examination of industrial effluent samples.*

Removing interfering chemicals

When working with a complex mixture, the analyst has the problem of isolating the chemical to be estimated while removing other chemicals which may interfere in some way with the measurements.

Measuring a property of the samples in solutions

In a quantitative procedure, analysts look for a property to measure which is proportional to the amount of the chemical to be determined. The property may be a mass or a volume or the extent to which the sample absorbs radiation.

Calculating a value from the measurements

This calls for an understanding of chemical theory allowing analysts to convert their measurements into chemical amounts.

Estimating the reliability of the results

Analysts have to state how much confidence they have in the accuracy of their results. Comparing the values obtained from two or three similar samples helps.

How reliable?

In professional analytical laboratories, whether in hospitals, water authorities or pharmaceutical companies, the results of analyses must be completely reliable. The National Measurement and Accreditation Service (NAMAS) sets the ground rules and regularly inspects laboratories.

Clearly the analyst must be competent, the technique used must be appropriate and the instruments reliable. The same test carried out in different laboratories should produce the same result.

It is now common practice to:

- identify the analyst on the print-outs of results
- run standards through the tests, alongside samples as controls, at regular intervals
- include extra control standards, which to the analyst look like genuine samples, among the samples for analysis.

▲ **Figure 1B2** *Two scientists using high-performance liquid chromatography to investigate the dispersion of a drug in the bloodstream.*

Volumetric analysis

Volumetric methods can be very accurate. An analyst can measure the volume of the liquid from a burette to the nearest $0.01\,cm^3$. If the total volume is about $25\,cm^3$, this represents an uncertainty of only 1 part in 2500. This precision makes volumetric methods a vital component of quantitative analysis.

Many analytical methods which use sophisticated instruments are now available but around 80% of the methods for estimating drugs described in the British Pharmacopoeia are based on volumetric analysis. Titrations are widely used because they are quick, convenient, accurate and easy to automate.

Titration procedure

Sarita works in a dairy where she determines the concentration of lactic acid in milk using a pipette to measure exactly $10\,cm^3$ of the milk into a flask. She then adds a drop or two of phenolphthalein indicator before running in a standard solution of $0.111\,mol\,dm^{-3}$ sodium hydroxide from a burette until she sees the indicator change colour at the end-point.

Her readings of the burette scale before and after the titration tell her the volume of alkali she added. From the volumes of the milk and the sodium hydroxide solution, together with the concentration of the alkali and the equation for the reaction, she can calculate a value for the concentration of lactic acid in milk, as explained in the Reference section, R12.

Preparing a standard solution

The accuracy of a titration can be no better than the accuracy of the standard solution in the burette. The direct method for preparing a standard solution is to weigh out a highly purified solid, dissolve it in water and then make up the solution to a precise volume in a graduated flask. The solid must be suitable for the titration, stable and not affected by exposure to the air. Suitable solids are hard to find; they are the **primary standards** on which volumetric analysis depends. Typical primary standards for acid–base titrations are anhydrous sodium carbonate and potassium hydrogenphthalate.

▼ **Figure 1B3** *The procedure for making up a standard solution.*

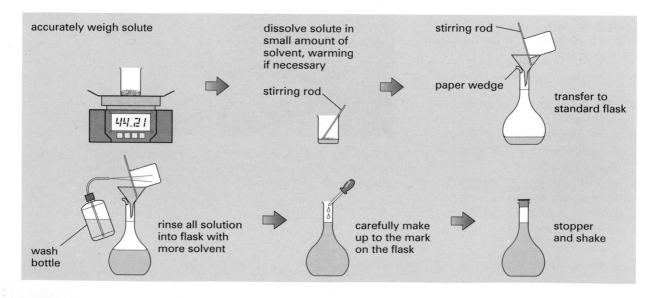

accurately weigh solute

dissolve solute in small amount of solvent, warming if necessary

stirring rod

stirring rod

paper wedge

transfer to standard flask

44.21

wash bottle

rinse all solution into flask with more solvent

carefully make up to the mark on the flask

stopper and shake

Acid–base titrations

A pH meter shows that there is a sudden change in the pH at the end-point of a titration. The analyst has to choose an indicator which will change colour sharply at the end-point. For a titration of a strong acid, such as hydrochloric acid, with a weak base such as ammonia, the sudden change spans the range pH 4 to pH 7 so a suitable indicator is bromocresol green which changes from colourless to pink in the pH range 3.8–5.4. For a titration of a weak acid with a strong base a possible indicator is phenolphthalein because it changes colour in the pH range 8.3–10.0 (see page 315 and Reference section, R28).

Redox titrations

Sometimes there is no need for an indicator in a titration because one of the reactants changes colour at the end-point. This is particularly so for redox titrations using potassium manganate(VII) which has an intense purple colour even when dilute. Potassium manganate(VII) turns colourless when used to estimate reducing agents such as iron(II) ions. Adding as little as 1 drop of excess $0.02\,\text{mol dm}^{-3}$ manganate solution at the end-point is enough to give a pink tint to the solution in the flask.

$$\underset{\text{deep purple}}{MnO_4^-(aq)} + 8H^+(aq) + 5e^- \longrightarrow \underset{\text{colourless}}{Mn^{2+}(aq)} + 4H_2O(l)$$

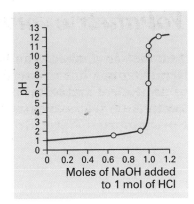

▲ **Figure 1B4** *The pH changes during a titration of a strong acid with a strong base.*

Example

An analyst crushed 'iron' tablets containing iron(II) sulphate, $FeSO_4$. She dissolved 0.240 g of the powder in water and added dilute sulphuric acid. On titrating with $0.005\,\text{mol dm}^{-3}$ $KMnO_4$ she had to add $25.3\,\text{cm}^3$ of the solution to give a pink colour at the end-point. What was the percentage of iron in the tablets?

Step 1   Write the equation for the reaction.
$$MnO_4^-(aq) + 8H^+(aq) + 5Fe^{2+}(aq)$$
$$\longrightarrow Mn^{2+}(aq) + 4H_2O(l) + 5Fe^{3+}(aq)$$

Step 2   Work out the amount of MnO_4^- added from the burette.
$$\text{The amount of } MnO_4^- = \frac{25.3}{1000}\,\text{dm}^3 \times 0.005\,\text{mol dm}^{-3}$$
$$= 1.265 \times 10^{-4}\,\text{mol}$$

Step 3   Calculate the amount of iron(II) in the titration flask.
The equation shows that $1\,\text{mol}\,MnO_4^-$ reacts with $5\,\text{mol}\,Fe^{2+}$
So the amount of iron(II) in the flask
$$= 5 \times 1.265 \times 10^{-4} = 6.325 \times 10^{-3}\,\text{mol}$$

Step 4   Calculate the mass of iron and hence the percentage in the tablets.
The molar mass of iron $= 55.8\,\text{g mol}^{-1}$
The mass of iron in the flask
$$= 55.8\,\text{g mol}^{-1} \times 6.325 \times 10^{-3}\,\text{mol} = 0.0353\,\text{g}$$
$$\text{The percentage by mass of iron in the tablets} = \frac{0.0353}{0.240} \times 100\%$$
$$= 14.7\%$$

Titration in practice

Judith is an analyst who is relieved that she has an autotitrator to speed up the many titrations she has to carry out each day. She is employed in the Inorganics Laboratory of Analytical and Environmental Services (AES) where scientists analyse samples taken from water treatment and sewage treatment plants owned by the Northumbrian Water Group.

Analysts at AES also carry out tests for other industries and advise on remedial action where necessary to avoid emissions of waste water and air which would otherwise harm the environment.

Judith became interested in rivers when studying A-level biology. Now she is one of the team of technicians who will, over the next three years, be trained to handle all analytical instruments in the laboratory. She attends a local college one day each week to take a vocational science course. If, at the end of two years, she is successful, she aims to continue part-time study and so obtain a degree in chemistry after a further four years.

Measuring the alkalinity of water

Judith uses an autotitrator for acid–base titrations when determining the alkalinity of drinking water or waste water. Water which is too acidic attacks the metal of the pipes; if it is too alkaline it deposits scale, blocking the pipes. The ideal pH is slightly alkaline, pH 7–8.

▶ **Figure 1B5** *Judith loading samples into the autotitrator.*

▼ **Figure 1B6** *Alkalinity of water: change in pH on addition of acid.*

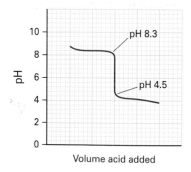

She loads up to fourteen $50\,cm^3$ water samples onto a turntable. The autotitrator then slowly adds sulphuric acid of a known concentration to the first sample. A meter connected to a pair of electrodes immersed in the mixture measures the conductivity as the acid runs in. Instruments convert the meter reading into an accurate pH value. The acid neutralizes the carbonate and hydrogencarbonate ions which make the sample alkaline. There is a sudden drop in voltage at the point when the acid has neutralized all the alkali. This corresponds to a fall in pH from 8.3 to exactly 4.5 (see Figure 1B6).

At this point the instrument automatically stops the titration and records the volume of acid added as well as initial and final pH readings for the sample.

Judith calibrates the machine by setting up a similar titration with a standard solution of sodium carbonate. This provides the data for a computer linked to the autoanalyser to translate the titration volume of acid into the concentration of sodium carbonate in milligrams per litre of water. The machine then provides Judith with a print-out.

Sample	1	2	3
Starting pH	7.683	5.193	7.660
Final pH	4.500	4.500	4.500
Volume of acid added /cm^3	11.615	0.1215	2.7716
mg equivalent of Na_2CO_3 per dm^3	232.3	2.429	55.43

▲ **Figure 1B7** *Typical results from the autotitrator – alkalinity of water.*

Measuring the chemical oxygen demand

Judith uses the autotitrator again to estimate the **chemical oxygen demand** (COD) of waste water. This is a measure of organic compounds polluting water. If high, the oxygen content of water is too low for fish and other living things to survive in the water. Judith gets her results in two hours. (Measuring the **biochemical oxygen demand** (BOD) is more accurate but it takes five days.)

Judith first 'digests' each sample to oxidize organic carbon to carbon dioxide. She mixes the sample with a known amount of acidified potassium dichromate(VI) and keeps the mixture at 150°C for two hours. During this redox reaction the carbon compounds reduce the dichromate(VI) to chromium(III).

She then loads the digested samples on the autotitrator, which titrates unreacted dichromate with iron(II) ammonium sulphate. The higher the COD, the less the amount of unchanged dichromate(VI) remaining and so the smaller the volume of iron(II) ammonium sulphate solution needed in the titration.

$$6Fe^{2+} + Cr_2O_7^{2-} + 14H^+ \longrightarrow 6Fe^{3+} + 2Cr^{3+} + 7H_2O$$

The machine detects the end-point either by recording a colour change, or more usually electrically, where a rapid drop in a meter reading denotes the end-point. The computer 'translates' the volume of added iron(II) ammonium sulphate into a COD value (in mg dm^{-3} of oxygen).

BOD and COD are both measures of the organic pollution of water.

BOD is determined by measuring the quantity of oxygen (in mg dm^{-3}) absorbed by water standing at 20°C for 5 days as microbes oxidize the carbon compounds.

COD is determined by measuring the amount of potassium dichromate(VI) needed to oxidize the carbon compounds in a litre of polluted water. The result is quoted in terms of the equivalent quantity of oxygen (in mg dm^{-3}) needed to bring about the same oxidation.

Typical COD values
Raw sewage:
about 400 mg O_2/dm^3
Drinking water:
about 10 mg O_2/dm^3

Chromatography

There are several types of chromatography and at first sight they seem very different. At the cheap and simple end, there is paper chromatography, which can be done with a piece of blotting paper and some solvent. At the expensive end is gas chromatography which involves high precision machinery and detectors. However, all chromatographic techniques work on similar principles.

Chromatography is a technique for separating the chemicals in a mixture. It can be used to:

- check the purity of a chemical preparation
- separate and identify the components of a mixture of chemicals
- identify the impurities in a chemical preparation
- purify a chemical product.

The classic demonstration of paper chromatography is the separation of the pigments obtained by solvent extraction from the leaves of green plants. A drop of the extract is allowed to dry at one end of a strip of paper and the paper is hung up so that the end dips into a solvent just below the spot of pigment.

The paper soaks up the solvent, which slowly travels upward saturating more and more of the paper. When the solvent reaches the spot of leaf extract, the pigment molecules dissolve and travel up the paper too. Molecules that don't dissolve in the moving solvent remain in the original spot.

Paper chromatography involves two liquids: one is water held in the pores of the cellulose fibres in paper, the other is the moving solvent. As the spots of pigment travel up the paper, they distribute themselves between the two liquids. Pigments which are more soluble in water tend to be stuck with the paper so they move more slowly. Pigments which are more soluble in the rising solvent move faster. After a time, the spots of different pigments separate and appear in different places on the paper.

Every type of chromatography involves a **stationary phase** and a **mobile phase.** In the case of the pigment separation on paper, water in the paper is the stationary phase and the solvent that moves up the paper is the mobile phase. The key to making chromatography work is choosing the right solids, liquids or gases to make up each phase. The chemicals in a mixture are separated by chromatography because they differ in the extent to which they mix with the mobile phase in preference to dissolving in a stationary liquid or being adsorbed by a stationary solid.

In chromatography with a liquid mobile phase, the stationary phase can be:

- water trapped in paper – known as **paper chromatography**
- a thin layer of adsorbent particles such as alumina or silica on a glass, plastic or metal plate – known as **thin-layer chromatography** or **TLC**
- adsorbent particles packed into a column – known as **column chromatography**.

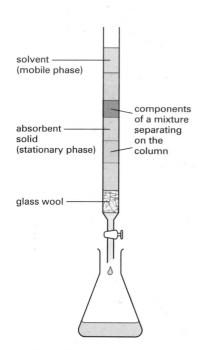

solvent (mobile phase)

absorbent solid (stationary phase)

components of a mixture separating on the column

glass wool

▲ **Figure 1B8** *Column chromatography. The solvent slowly runs down through the column. The substances in the mixture separate and emerge at different times from the base of the column depending on how strongly they are adsorbed by the powdered solid in the column. This technique, the earliest form of chromatography, was first used by the Russian botanist Tsvet in about 1900, to separate coloured plant pigments (hence chromatography; chroma = colour).*

Why use thin-layer chromatography?

Although TLC is 'low' technology, Andrew, in charge of a laboratory for a pharmaceutical company, regards it as useful before moving on to analysis by more complex techniques. TLC is quick, easy, cheap and only requires very small volumes of solution. A large number of samples can be run at once and technicians soon become skilled in its use.

Andrew explains that its chief use is in drug synthesis – it indicates that the right chemical reactions are taking place and that the right compound is being made. The technique is applied both in research laboratories and when checking the products of large-scale manufacture.

It is easy to interpret a TLC plate if the compounds in the sample are dyes or other coloured materials. Many colourless organic compounds absorb in the ultraviolet region of the spectrum so they show up on a plate impregnated with a fluorescent material. Under an UV lamp, the whole plate fluoresces except in the areas where the organic compounds absorb radiation – these show up as dark spots.

▼ **Figure 1B9** *Thin layer chromatography. As the solvent rises up the plate, compounds in the applied spots of solution travel different distances depending on:*
- *their attraction for the adsorbent*
- *their solubility in the solvent.*

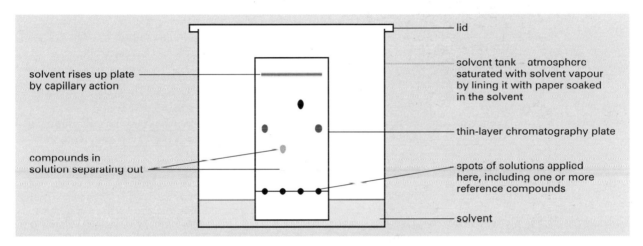

- lid
- solvent tank – atmosphere saturated with solvent vapour by lining it with paper soaked in the solvent
- solvent rises up plate by capillary action
- thin-layer chromatography plate
- compounds in solution separating out
- spots of solutions applied here, including one or more reference compounds
- solvent

Another way to find the position of organic compounds is to put the plate in a container with a few iodine crystals. Many carbon compounds show up as coloured spots when exposed to the vapour from iodine crystals.

On a TLC plate, mixtures of compounds are run against pure substances for reference, so that they can be identified. The intensity of colour, or the UV absorption, gives analysts a rough indication of the relative amounts of compounds in a mixture.

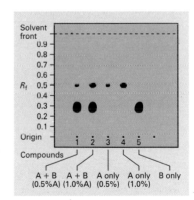

▲ **Figure 1B10** *TLC plate after development in a solvent showing absorption under UV light. Each compound has a distinctive R_f value. TLC is semi-quantitative.*

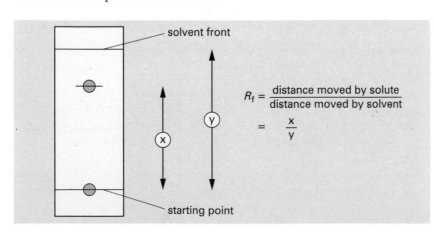

solvent front

$$R_f = \frac{\text{distance moved by solute}}{\text{distance moved by solvent}} = \frac{x}{y}$$

starting point

◄ **Figure 1B11** *R_f values measure how far different compounds move during paper chromatography or TLC.*

Monitoring pollution by gas–liquid chromatography

John is surrounded by instruments in his laboratory. He works for the National Rivers Authority (NRA) where he uses a number of specially designed GLC machines to identify pollutants in water.

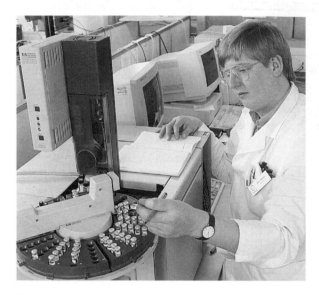

▲ **Figure 1B12** *John noting the details of a sample.*

John started work at the NRA laboratories after taking A-levels and has since studied for over five years on day release, first for a Higher National Certificate, then a degree in chemistry. Following experience in all areas of analysis, he now specializes in organic chemistry. He continues to update his knowledge and skills by attending courses run by the university and instrument manufacturers. The NRA also organizes 'in-house training' courses for small groups of scientists.

In GLC the mobile phase is a gas such as hydrogen or helium, and the stationary phase is a liquid coating the surface of a solid. The separation takes place inside a sealed tube (called a column) in which the pressure and temperature can be controlled.

The technique is only suitable for samples which vaporize without decomposing. In capillary column GLC the gas carries the mixture of vapours through a coiled Teflon capillary column about 30 metres long and with an internal diameter of about 0.25 mm. The liquid stationary phase is bonded to the wall of the column as a very thin film.

John injects a few microlitres of a solution of the sample. As the temperature of the column rises, a detector senses each component when it comes off the column, sending a signal to a recorder which displays a series of peaks. John notes the time for compounds to reach the detector. This is the **retention time**. He calibrates the GLC machine by injecting pure samples of known compounds. The retention times can then be used to identify the components of unknown mixtures. The peak heights give a measure of the proportions of the components, so GLC is a quantitative technique.

▶ **Figure 1B13** *The main features of gas–liquid chromatography.*

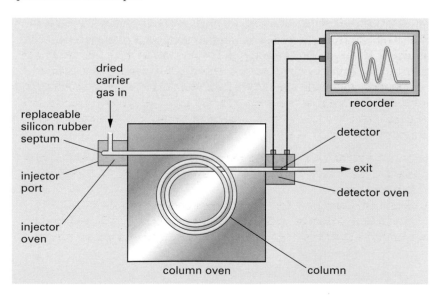

John needs a range of GLC chromatographs with different detector systems sensitive to particular organic compounds.

He uses a GLC instrument with a flame ionization detector to analyse hydrocarbons. The compounds from the column enter a very hot hydrogen/air flame where they ionize. The ions change the conductivity of the flame so that a current can flow between two electrodes, producing a signal. This is amplified and fed to the recorder. Results are very specific, like a fingerprint, and for diesel fuel it is possible to identify which firm is responsible for a pollution incident. This is partly because diesel 'weathers' over time as some of the more volatile components are lost so the pattern of peaks gradually changes and the print-out is characteristic of a particular batch of the fuel.

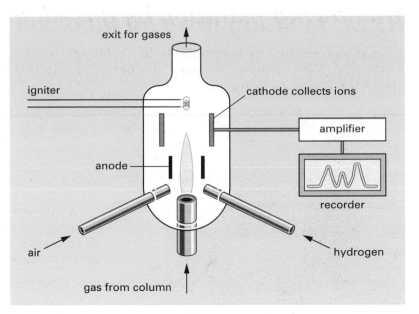

▲ **Figure 1B14** *A flame ionization detector.*

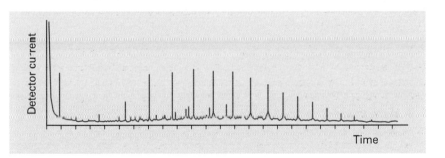

▲ **Figure 1B15** *A GLC print-out for a sample of diesel fuel.*

To detect chlorinated pesticides, John has an electron capture detector. The compounds from the column pass over a radioactive element (such as nickel-63) which emits electrons. The electrons ionize the carrier gas giving a steady background current between the electrodes. Organic compounds containing non-metals such as chlorine leave the column and 'capture' electrons without ionizing so that the background current falls. The variations in the current are fed to an amplifier which drives the recorder. John employs this system to:

- detect dieldrin and lindane in river water – though the use of these chemicals is banned in the UK, contamination arises from washing imported wools
- detect DDT and its metabolites in river sediments – thus GLC produces a 'snapshot' indicating past use of DDT in this country
- identify organic compounds containing nitrogen and phosphorus.

Absorb
A sponge absorbs water as it sucks up the liquid. The water soaks into the pores of the sponge. Paper is absorbent and soaks up the moving solvent during paper chromatography.

Adsorb
Solids adsorb very thin films of gases or liquids onto their surfaces. Glass adsorbs water vapour. Solids used in chromatography adsorb liquids.

HPLC to study drug metabolism

Stuart is a graduate in pharmacology and has been developing techniques using high-performance liquid chromatography (HPLC) for six years. His work concerns 'drug metabolism'. He aims to find out how the human body breaks down medicinal drugs so that they are removed from the body. Pharmaceutical companies need this information before they can apply to the licensing authorities for permission to release new drugs to the market.

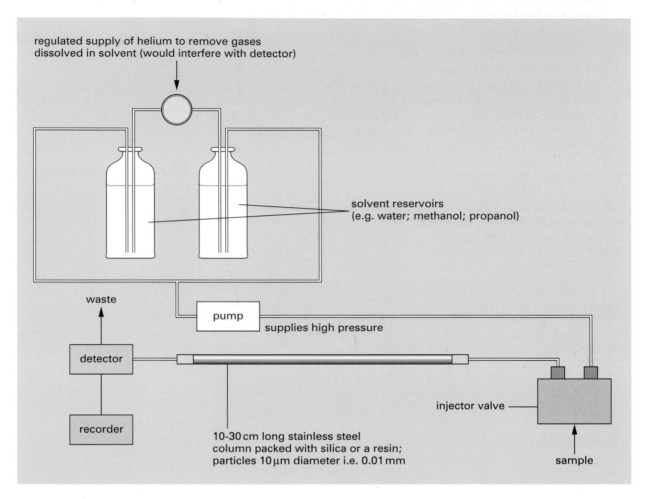

▲ **Figure 1B16** *The main features of HPLC.*

HPLC is a high tech version of column chromatography that is able to separate components of a mixture which are chemically very similar to one another. The mobile phase is a solvent or mixture of solvents of very high purity and the stationary phase consists of very small particles of a very regular size packed into a stainless steel column. High pressure is needed to force the liquid phase through the tightly packed column but the separation achieved can be far better than with other forms of liquid chromatography.

Early efforts to make column chromatography more efficient used very small particles of adsorbent to create a large surface area. However, this slowed the rate of solvent flow so that separations took many hours. With HPLC, analysts overcome the problem by developing instruments which apply very high pressures, several hundred times that of the atmosphere, to force the liquid mobile phase through a column. A high-pressure pump supplies the pressure to the solvent inside equipment.

There are three questions that Stuart hopes to answer.

- *How does metabolism change drugs before they are excreted?*
  Generally the body converts drugs into compounds which are much
  more water soluble and so more easily removed in urine and faeces.
  The products of metabolism have more —OH groups or ionizable
  groups so they mix more easily with polar water molecules.
- *How long does metabolism take to break down drugs?*
  If doctors use a drug for diagnosis, then the sooner the drug is
  removed from the body the better. If the drug is a painkiller,
  however, it has a longer lasting effect if it breaks down slowly.
- *Do any of the metabolites act as a drug themselves?*

Stuart labels drugs with radioactive carbon-14, which emits electrons
(beta particles). At intervals after administering the drug, the radioactive
compounds are extracted from urine and faeces. The breakdown
products are separated by HPLC and detected by a scintillation counter.
In the counter, electrons from carbon-14 collide with particles of a solid
such as calcium fluoride producing minute flashes of light. A
photomultiplier detects and amplifies the flashes so that they can be
recorded and measured. Breakdown products leave the column first,
any unchanged parent drug last.

The liver is the organ which does most to metabolize drugs. Stuart is
already thinking ahead to a time when drug metabolism is studied with
genetically modified micro-organisms carrying genes from liver cells.
Stuart will then need to change his techniques to detect metabolites
from such micro-organisms.

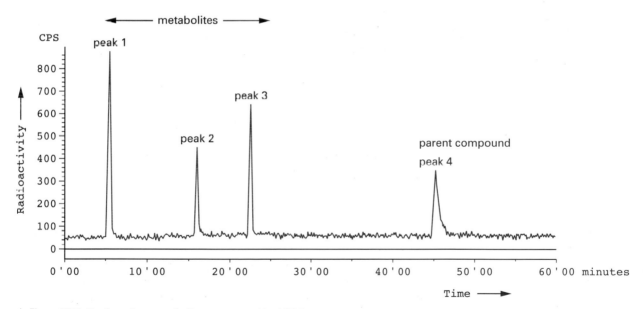

▲ **Figure 1B17** *Radioactive metabolites separated by HPLC.*

Electrophoresis in a hospital laboratory

Hospital laboratories analyse large numbers of diagnostic samples for doctors. This means that highly automated analytical instruments are essential. Techniques must be quick and reliable so that patients can be treated sooner and the effect of treatments monitored.

Margaret works in a hospital biochemistry laboratory. She is one of the Medical Laboratory Scientific Officers (MLSOs) responsible for carrying out analyses. Margaret originally graduated in zoology and has chosen to return to laboratory work after having a family.

Electrophoresis for diagnosis

Margaret uses electrophoresis to study proteins in blood serum. This is a technique for separating organic compounds which become electrically charged in aqueous solution at a particular pH value.

The compact work centre comes with staining compartments and its own microprocessor to control the conditions. Electrophoresis takes place on agarose gel strips immersed in a buffer to keep the pH constant (see pages 316–17). Margaret carefully applies up to ten samples to the centre of each strip of gel. One of the samples is a control.

She connects an 85 volt supply between the ends of the strips for 20 minutes. Charged protein molecules move through the gel towards the electrodes. Uncharged molecules barely move at all.

After 20 minutes, Margaret switches off the voltage. At this stage the colourless proteins are invisible so she immerses the gel strips in Acid Blue to stain them. Alternatively she can view the gel strip under UV light to see how far the proteins have moved.

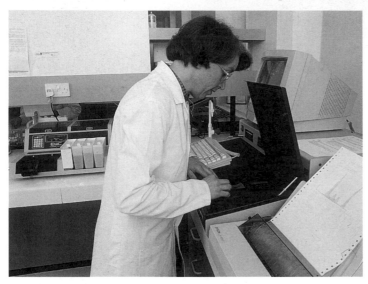

▲ **Figure 1B18** *Margaret working at a compact electrophoresis work centre with its own microprocessor to control the conditions of electrophoresis.*

▼ **Figure 1B19** *The main features of electrophoresis.*

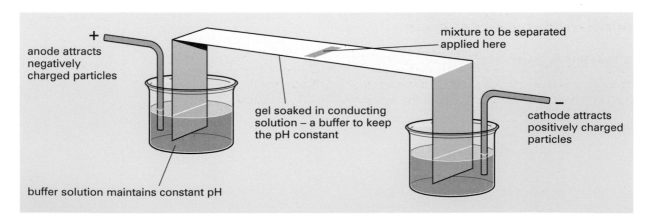

+
anode attracts
negatively
charged particles

mixture to be separated
applied here

gel soaked in conducting
solution – a buffer to keep
the pH constant

–
cathode attracts
positively charged
particles

buffer solution maintains constant pH

Myelomas

Margaret analyses serum samples to help doctors diagnose malignant tumours which interfere with blood cell production in bone marrow and cause anaemia. Electrophoresis of normal serum gives five groups of protein (see Figure 1B20). In myelomas, the staining for gamma globulin is very much darker than with normal serum. This is because the body produces large amounts of this protein as a result of disturbances in the immune system.

Diabetic control

If the blood sugar concentration in a diabetic remains high, glucose combines with haemoglobin by covalent bonding. Electrophoresis can detect the glucose–haemoglobin compound in blood, so the results help doctors trying to decide whether they are prescribing the correct doses of insulin and whether their patients are sticking to the recommended diet.

Other uses

Electrophoresis on a gel can detect other abnormalities in haemoglobin including sickle cell disease. The changes in two amino acid units in haemoglobin which cause the disease produce detectable changes in the pattern on an electrophoretic gel.

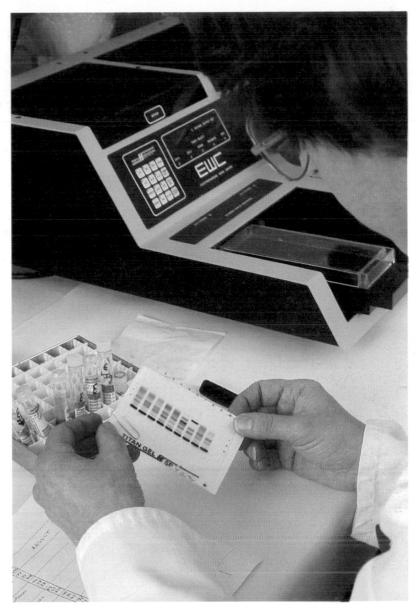

▲ **Figure 1B20** *The result of using electrophoresis to separate serum samples after staining with Acid Blue.*

Modifying electrolysis

Use of a polyacrylamide material in place of an agarose gel separates compounds according to size and charge. With this technique serum proteins separate into about fifty bands instead of five. This procedure has been used to monitor changes in the serum proteins of alcoholics.

Colorimetry and ultraviolet spectroscopy

Amanda, like Judith (see page 26), works in the Inorganics Laboratory of AES. She likes instrumentation and already has a BTEC Certificate. She is currently studying for a Higher National Certificate and hopes to follow an Open University degree course later. Amanda uses an autoanalyser with a colorimeter to test water samples for a variety of ions such as nitrate, nitrite, phosphate and cyanide ions. She makes sure that drinking water is not contaminated by high levels of nitrates.

Colorimetry

A colorimeter is an instrument for measuring the concentration of a coloured solution. The technique can also be used to analyse colourless substances if they react with a suitable dye.

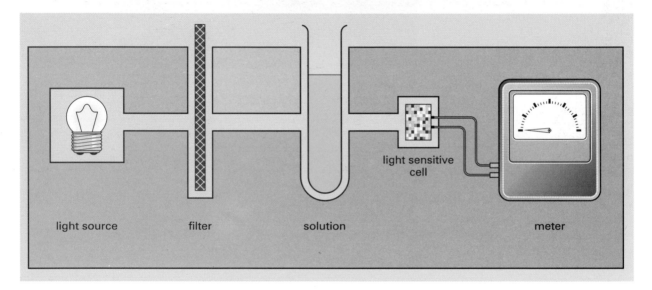

light sensitive cell

light source   filter   solution   meter

▲ **Figure 1B21** *The main parts of a simple colorimeter.*

Figure 1B21 shows the main components of a simple colorimeter. The light sensitive cell is often a silicon photodiode which gives an increase in current proportional to the intensity of the light falling on it. The operator selects a filter which lets through the band of wavelengths which are strongly absorbed by the solution to be analysed.

Instead of using a filter, Amanda can adjust the colorimeter in her autoanalyser to select the wavelength which her test solutions absorb most strongly. The absorption of light depends on the depth of solution (which is a constant for the instrument) and the concentration of the coloured compound in the solution.

Measuring the nitrite and nitrate ions in water

Nitrite ions are colourless but they produce a pink colour when they react with N-1-naphthyl ethylenediamine dihydrochloride. Amanda first has to calibrate the autoanalyser with a series of standard solutions of pink coloration produced with different known concentrations of nitrite. She feeds the standards one by one into the instrument, producing a calibration curve. The computer can then calculate the nitrite concentration in test samples using the calibration curve.

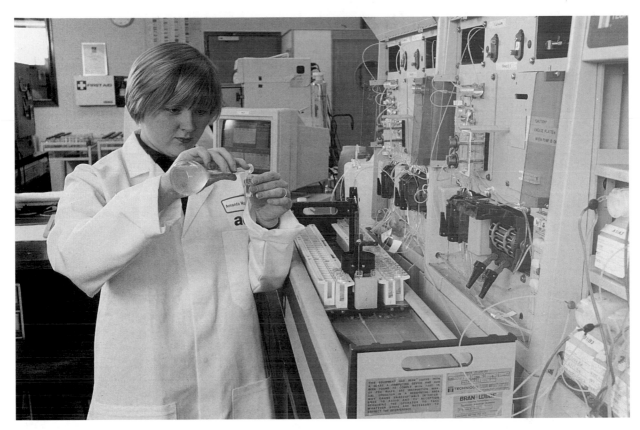

▲ **Figure 1B22** *Amanda with an autoanalyser and a colorimeter.*

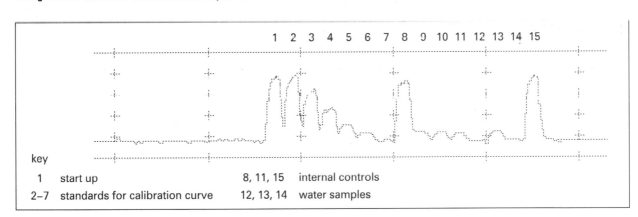

key

| 1 | start up | 8, 11, 15 | internal controls |
| 2–7 | standards for calibration curve | 12, 13, 14 | water samples |

▲ **Figure 1B23** *A print-out from the autoanalyser.*

Sample	$(NO_3^- + NO_2^-)$ /mg dm^{-3}	NO_2^- only /mg dm^{-3}
1	1.084	0.0014
2	2.584	0.0280
3	0.0530	0.0049

▲ **Figure 1B24** *Results for three water samples.*

Amanda first measures the nitrite concentration in one set of the water samples. Then she takes a second set of samples and treats them with alkaline hydrazine sulphate which reduces nitrate ions to nitrite ions. The readings for this second set give the total concentration of nitrite plus nitrate in each sample. The computer calculates the nitrate concentrations from the differences between the two series of values.

Ultraviolet spectroscopy

Spectroscopy originally referred to the analysis of substances using visible radiation. The term now includes the use of ultraviolet (UV) and infra-red (IR) radiation (see Figure 1B26). Technicians with vocational and academic A-levels can be trained to use spectrometers but postgraduate experience is needed to develop methods and interpret analytical results.

UV is particularly valuable for studying colourless organic compounds with unsaturated functional groups such as $C=O$ and $C=C$. The molecules absorb UV radiation at frequencies which excite shared electrons in double bonds. UV may also excite non-bonding electrons in compounds containing oxygen, nitrogen, sulphur or halogens. A UV spectrometer records the extent to which samples absorb UV radiation across a range of wavelengths.

UV spectrometers make it possible to extend the techniques of colorimetry to colourless compounds. In the pharmaceutical industry scientists use UV spectroscopy to analyse drugs such as paracetamol which absorb strongly in the UV region. The choice of solvent, the pH and the temperature can all affect UV absorption (see Figure 1B25) so the technicians must take measurements under carefully standardized conditions. They prepare calibration curves by measuring the UV absorption of solutions of pure compounds over a range of concentrations at specific wavelengths. Once they have standardized procedures they can use UV to check that medicines contain the correct amounts of drugs and that the products do not deteriorate in storage.

▼ **Figure 1B25** *The UV spectrum of paracetamol showing the effect of changing the pH. Absorbance, on the vertical axis, measures the proportion of the radiation absorbed, so there are peaks at wavelengths which the sample absorbs strongly.*

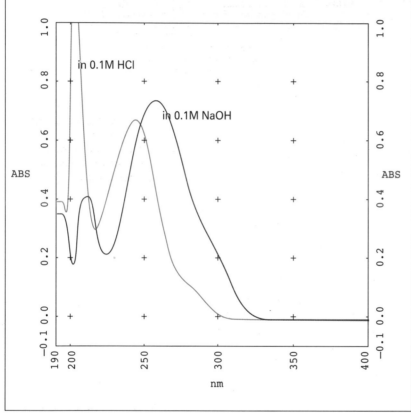

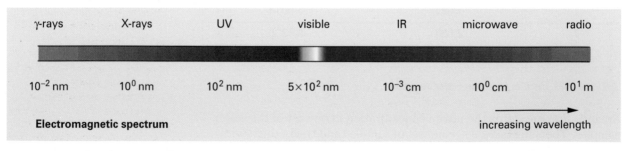

▲ **Figure 1B26** *The electromagnetic spectrum showing regions used for spectroscopy.*

Infra-red spectroscopy

Andrew is a senior postgraduate in a pharmaceutical company. His experience of all kinds of instrumentation enables him to select appropriate methods to solve a wide variety of analytical problems.

Most compounds absorb infra-red (IR) radiation. The wavelengths they absorb correspond to the natural frequencies at which vibrating bonds in the molecules stretch and bend. The bonds which absorb strongly as they vibrate are polar covalent bonds (see page 123) such as O—H, C—O and C=O.

Bonds vibrate in characteristic ways and absorb at specific wavelengths. This means that an analyst can look at the IR spectrum and spot particular functional groups (see Figure 1B28 and the Reference section, Figure R24.1).

In a molecule one bond affects the vibrations of others close to it. Even a comparatively simple molecule can vibrate in many ways. The aldehyde butanal, $CH_3CH_2CH_2CHO$, has over 30 ways of vibrating and although not every possible vibration produces an absorption peak, the spectrum is still complex.

Analysts now have access to computer databases, with IR spectra stored like 'fingerprints' for a large number of pure compounds. They can therefore identify specimens by matching the absorption spectrum of an unknown with one of the known spectra in a database.

Identifying functional groups with IR spectra helps to confirm information from other techniques such as nuclear magnetic resonance (NMR) and mass spectrometry. Spectra can also be used to follow the progress of synthetic reactions but interpretation is difficult because all the substances present produce spectra. Matching the IR spectrum of a product with that of a known pure sample can be used to check that the product is pure and free from traces of solvents or by-products.

▲ **Figure 1B27** *An infra-red spectrometer. The instrument compares the intensity of a beam of infra-red radiation passing through the sample with a reference beam from the same source.*

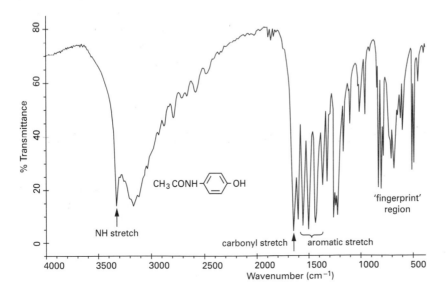

◀ **Figure 1B28** *The IR spectrum of paracetamol. The units along the bottom of an IR spectrum are wavenumbers (in cm⁻¹). IR wavenumbers typically range from 400 cm⁻¹ to 4500 cm⁻¹ and are easier numbers to work with than wavelengths in the IR region. The wavenumber is the number of wavelengths that will fit into one centimetre. Transmittance, on the vertical axis, measures the percentage of radiation which the sample lets through so there are troughs at the wavenumbers which the compound absorbs strongly.*

Nuclear magnetic resonance

Stephen is a senior scientist with a PhD degree in organic chemistry and spends a lot of his time operating an NMR machine. A technician can be trained to load and run samples on this instrument in a matter of days but preparing the samples in a suitable solvent and interpreting the results requires an extensive knowledge of organic chemistry.

Stephen has continued to learn with practice, and as new models of NMR emerge, he updates his own skills and knowledge – by contact with the instrument manufacturers, and by meeting with other NMR specialists at scientific meetings.

What is nuclear magnetic resonance?

The name of this complex instrument, usually abbreviated to NMR, describes the processes:

- **nuclear** – refers to the atomic nuclei of those atoms, such as hydrogen-1 (a proton) or carbon-13, which the instrument detects
- **magnetic** – refers to the behaviour of the nuclei of the atoms which act like small magnets in a strong magnetic field, lining up either in the same direction as the field or in the opposite direction
- **resonance** – refers to the absorption of radiowaves of the resonance frequency corresponding to the energy change as the nuclei flip from one alignment to another.

The procedure

Hydrogen NMR requires only 10–20 mg of material. Stephen dissolves the sample in a solvent with no hydrogen-1 atoms, such as $CDCl_3$. If the solvent were to contain hydrogen-1 atoms, it would have absorption peaks of its own. Nuclei of deuterium (D or hydrogen-2) do not behave like tiny magnets so they are not detected by NMR.

Also in the solution there is a reference material, such as tetramethyl silane, $Si(CH_3)_4$, which acts as the standard for subsequent measurements. Tetramethyl silane gives a single sharp peak well away from peaks in carbon compounds.

Stephen puts the mixture in a small tube and places it in a probe which can both transmit and receive radio waves. He supports the probe in a powerful magnetic field and switches on the oscillator to scan a range of radio frequencies (RF). The RF detector records the frequencies which the sample absorbs strongly.

▶ **Figure 1B29** *An NMR spectrometer.*

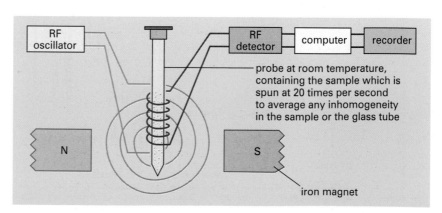

probe at room temperature, containing the sample which is spun at 20 times per second to average any inhomogeneity in the sample or the glass tube

iron magnet

What are the results?

The instrument displays an absorption 'peak' whenever the sample absorbs strongly so that there is a drop in the power of the signal from the detector. The peaks are displayed on a scale increasing from right to left. The hydrogen nuclei in the standard, tetramethyl silane, fix the zero on the scale (see Reference section, R25).

Each peak corresponds to hydrogen nuclei in a particular molecular environment. The area under the peak is proportional to the number of nuclei in each environment.

In ethanol, CH_3CH_2OH, for example, hydrogen nuclei occur in three environments, resonating at three different frequencies:

- three in the $-CH_3$
- two in the $-CH_2-$
- and one in $-OH$.

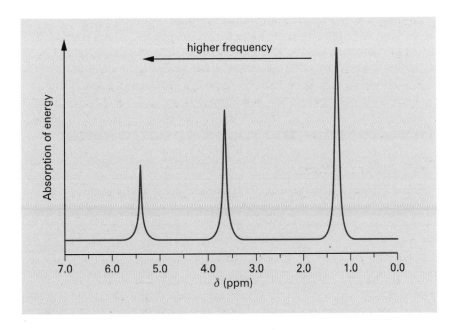

◀ **Figure 1B30** *The NMR spectrum of ethanol at low resolution.*

NMR in drug analysis

Stephen uses NMR to analyse drugs and determine their structure. An NMR spectrum, like an IR spectrum, can be used as a 'fingerprint' to check that the compound synthesized is the required drug. The NMR spectrum can also help to check for impurities, identify them and work out the scale of contamination.

NMR provides information about the molecular shape of a protein. With his NMR machine, Stephen can discover how proteins in tissues or tissue fluids bind with particular drugs. This helps him to understand how drugs function in the body.

Magnetic resonance imaging

Magnetic resonance imaging uses NMR to detect hydrogen nuclei in the human body, mainly those in water and lipids. A computer translates the information from a 3-D scan to produce images of soft tissues and organs. It is more powerful than X-ray techniques which are generally used to study bones.

Mass spectrometry

Mass spectrometry is a powerful technique for measuring atomic and molecular masses, determining molecular structures and identifying unknown compounds.

The procedure

A mass spectrometer contains a high vacuum so that it is possible to produce and study molecular fragments and ions which do not normally exist. The main steps to a mass spectrum involve:

- introducing the sample into the instrument and vaporizing it
- bombarding the sample with high-energy electrons which knock out electrons and produce positive ions – this step may also break up molecules into fragments
- accelerating the positive ions with an electric field
- deflecting the beam of ions with a magnetic field to focus ions with a particular ratio of mass to charge onto the detector
- feeding the signal from the detector to a computer which prints out a mass spectrum as the magnetic field steadily changes to detect a series of ions with different masses. The scale on the print-out is calibrated by running a spectrum of a reference compound with a known structure and molecular mass.

Results from the mass spectrometer

When analysing molecules, the peak of the ion with the highest mass is usually produced by ionizing the molecule without breaking it into smaller fragments. So the mass of this 'parent ion' is the relative molecular mass of the compound.

Fragmentation of the molecule by the bombarding electrons produces a variety of smaller ions. Mass spectrometry can distinguish compounds with the same molecular formula but different structural formulae because they have different fragmentation patterns.

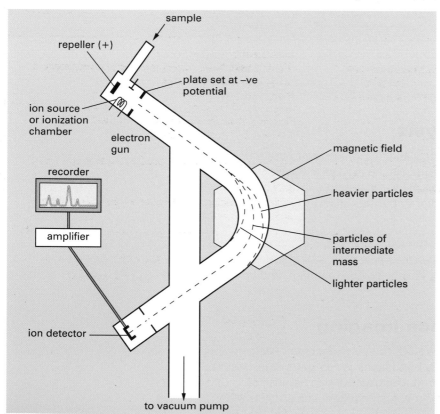

◄ **Figure 1B31** *A mass spectrometer.*

The computer is programmed to determine not just the relative molecular mass but also the structural formula. The computer has access to a database of mass spectra so that it can identify a compound by comparing its spectrum to spectra in the database until it finds a good match. The computer can also help to determine the structure of newly synthesized substances by identifying the fragments in the spectrum which the analyst can then fit together like the pieces of a jigsaw.

Coupling GLC and mass spectrometry

Coupling chromatography and mass spectrometry creates a powerful analytical technique. GLC and mass spectrometry both require gaseous samples. GLC first separates the components in a mixture then a mass spectrometer detects and identifies each component. The following diary of events illustrates the effectiveness of this procedure.

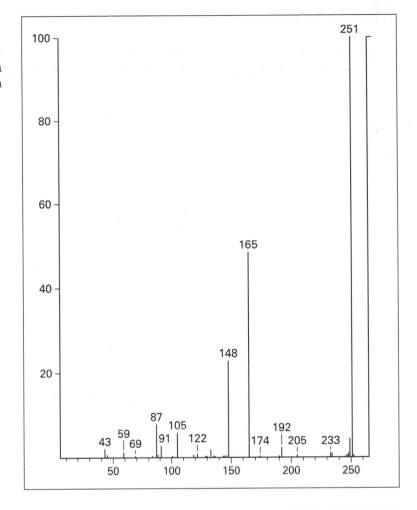

▶ **Figure 1B32** *The mass spectrum of an insecticide.*

■ 9.0 am 2nd June
Richard, managing the NRA laboratory, receives a report from a local fish farmer – many fish died overnight. This is an agricultural area – a pesticide or herbicide could be responsible.
■ 9.0 am 3rd June
Water analysis of the fish ponds, and river – up and downstream of the ponds. GLC coupled with mass spectrometry gives negative results except at the 'dead end' pond where pesticide is present. Perhaps the pesticide had been flushed away by the flow of water elsewhere.

■ 10.0 am 3rd June
Richard asks NRA samplers to collect specimens of moss from the river banks.
■ 12.0 noon 4th June
Analyses of moss samples collected from points A to C are positive for the pesticide lindane; samples upstream of C are negative.
■ 12.05 pm 4th June
Suggested explanation: pesticide was poured into river from bridge.
■ 7th June
Police investigations uncover a personal grudge against the fish farmer.

◀ **Figure 1B33** *Map of ponds affected by the fish kill.*

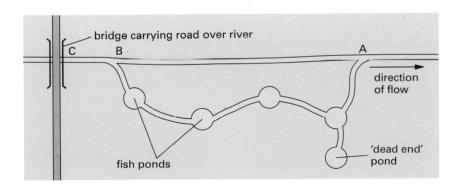

Health and safety

Things can go wrong

Accidents will happen; in our homes, on the roads and on the sports field, in fact they can happen anywhere. They can also occur at work. For most scientists, their workplace is a laboratory. Like other places of work, environment and behaviour in laboratories are subject to strict regulation, but even the best laid plans can sometimes go wrong.

A Near-Miss in the Lab

Kathy James is breathing a sigh of relief today. She knows she's lucky she still has her eyesight. 'Thank goodness I read the sign and put up the screen before I did the experiment,' she said. 'At least I did one thing right.'

Kathy, a lab assistant at Moordale Labs, was performing what she thought was a routine experiment yesterday, but somehow everything went wrong. 'There were many precautions Kathy should have followed before carrying out the experiment but didn't,' said Moordale's Health and Safety Officer, Jack Fergusson. 'It was just fortunate she took the one precautionary measure she did.'

Kathy had been trying to reproduce a chemical reaction that she'd first read about in a journal. She should have been especially alert to risks, since this reaction had never been carried out in her laboratory before. But because the reaction worked so easily according to the account in the journal, Kathy relaxed and felt she faced no hazards doing it herself. 'That was her first mistake,' Fergusson commented; 'there is always the potential for something that was successful once not to be successful another time.'

There were other reasons why she should have been alert to risks. For one thing she was using new equipment with which she was not familiar. Also she made some slight changes in the procedure, not knowing what impact these changes would have. 'I'm particularly embarrassed about this misjudgement,' Kathy said. 'I've always considered myself a responsible scientist, but here I was doing the one thing scientists shouldn't do. I was not thinking through the procedure in advance.'

'I did something else stupid by not thinking thoroughly. I was using six different components under high temperature, and one was an organic substance and another an oxidizer. Of course I knew that organics and oxidizers may be dangerous together, but somehow I just wasn't thinking straight.'

The last thing Kathy forgot was to wear eye protection. Even though there was a sign on the door that all workers in the lab had to wear eye protection, the experiment seemed so straightforward that Kathy did not bother putting them on. 'Discipline may have been getting a little too relaxed around here', said the Heath and Safety Officer. 'It takes an accident like this to wake everyone up.'

The one thing Kathy did do right was read and obey the Operating Procedures posted on the wall. These required a shatter-proof screen to be placed between the equipment and herself. When the chemicals exploded, shattered glass was sent flying everywhere, but the screen took the impact of the glass. Subsequent investigation showed to everyone's horror that some pieces of glass had been heading straight for Kathy's eyes.

John Fergusson had the final word: 'This whole incident just shows why we need several safety precautions in place. If some precautions fail or are not adhered to, there are still others in place to minimize the consequences. Kathy was almost a textbook case of what to do wrong. But she did one thing right and it saved her eyes.'

Humour in the Wrong Place

Students in the sixth form of Gruntley School are still in shock over the accident that occurred in the chemistry lab yesterday. Sixteen-year-old Ben Wanson was nearly suffocated in a freak accident, but was saved by the quick thinking of form teacher Mary Gleam.

Liz Marleson, another student in the class, was carrying a small, stoppered bottle of concentrated ammonia solution from her work bench to the fume cupboard where she was going to carry out a routine experiment. She was taking all the necessary precautions, walking calmly down an unobstructed aisle, holding the bottle carefully and paying attention to what she was doing.

To get to the fume cupboard she had to pass by the bench where Dave Tuller was telling his mates a joke he'd heard on the way to school. Liz passed just as Dave threw his arms wide at the punch line. His arm caught the bottle and sent it flying across the room where it landed on Ben Wanson's collar. He was innocently at work with his back to all the excitement.

Concentrated ammonia evaporates quickly, and that is what happened in this case, creating a cloud of ammonia gas which began to choke Ben.

The teacher was near by and alert. She promptly pulled Ben's jacket off and then rushed him out into fresh air. This did the trick and Ben, though shaken up, was all right.

'This just goes to show', said Mary Gleam, 'that no procedure can be considered entirely risk-proof. Unforeseen events can happen at any time. I'm like a lifeguard, just keeping an alert eye on what's going on around me. It wasn't lucky that I was there; it was my job to be there.'

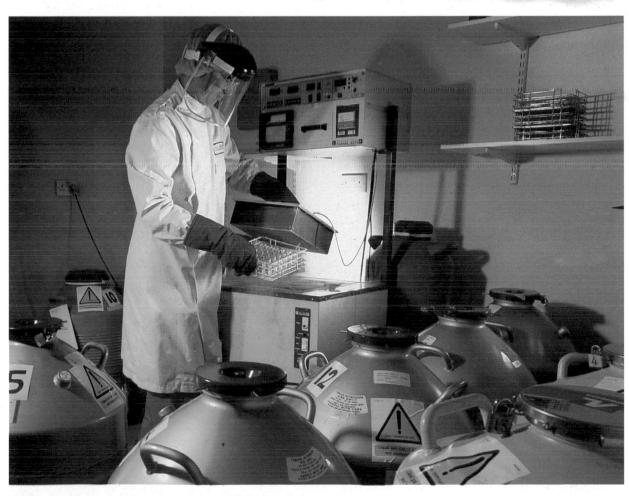

▲ **Figure 1C1** *A face shield and protective gloves are worn when handling tissues at very low temperatures or those stored in liquid nitrogen.*

Looking after yourself

Everyone working in a laboratory comes across all sorts of Health and Safety Regulations that govern how people should conduct themselves on the site. Before even walking into a lab people may be required to put on equipment like a white coat, plastic wrap-around glasses or special gloves to protect them from dangerous chemicals or substances that might infect them.

How to be healthy and safe in the laboratory

The principle behind Health and Safety Regulations is very simple

'Stop, Think and Do'.

In the lab there are specific guidelines for many of the operations performed there, such as mixing or heating certain chemicals in a well-ventilated enclosure called a fume cupboard or in a totally enclosed area known as a glove box because arms have to be inserted into long gloves to do the work. Everyone must be aware of other precautions having to do with electrical appliances and waste disposal, and must be familiar with instructions on what to do in case of fire or other accident.

With all this fuss about safety it might seem that labs must be very dangerous places. But they are only potentially dangerous; there is always the chance that something might go wrong. Health and Safety Regulations aim to reduce that chance as close as possible to zero. And, in fact, provided the workers obey the regulations, labs today can be some of the safest places to work in.

There may seem to be too many Health and Safety Regulations to understand and remember, but always keep in mind that these regulations are based on common sense. People in laboratories should take the time to think about what they are doing before they start work and pay attention to what they are doing while they work.

▼ **Figure 1C2** *Full protective clothing is worn in the clean room of a pharmaceutical factory – both to prevent any contamination of the drug being manufactured and to protect the workers.*

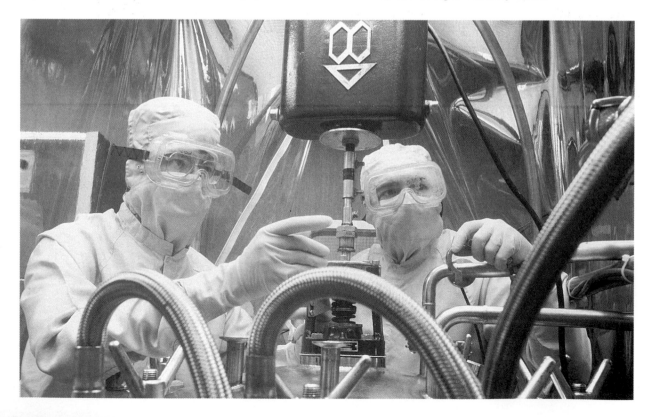

Who is in charge of Health and Safety?

Some people don't see the point of Health and Safety Regulations. They feel the regulations make laboratory work more complicated. They also fear that if they don't follow the regulations they are going to be in trouble with their employers.

Dr Meta Mitchell, in charge of Health and Safety at the Johnson Matthey Technology Centre near Reading, disagrees strongly with this attitude. 'Health and Safety Regulations', she says, 'are something you work with, not against. The regulations are not designed to make trouble for you or to make you feel guilty, but to protect you. I am not really a Health and Safety Officer, but a Health and Safety Adviser.'

'Some people feel that just because they've never had an accident so far they must be somehow invulnerable and never have to worry about safety or their health. This is their own business when at home, but at work the management is legally required to look after their heath and safety. The same applies at school.'

Dr Mitchell points out another very important benefit to following health and safety procedures: 'In order to follow the regulations you have to understand and control what you're doing, and doing this you are more likely to be successful. Or if you are not successful, at least you will understand why and can do something about it. If you follow good health and safety precautions you are at the same time following good scientific methods.'

A major part of Dr Mitchell's job entails walking around to see what is going on. Are the chemicals stored properly? Is there any mess lying around? Are people wearing the proper protective equipment? Are fire exits clear and fire extinguishers and the first aid box ready to hand? Are controlled areas properly controlled?

Communicating with the people working in the labs is crucial. Dr Mitchell has to inform staff about any new regulations that might apply to their work. But it is not enough simply to tell the people what the regulations are. She must also explain why they are there and what would happen if they were ignored. 'I can't treat people like babies and just tell them what to do,' Dr Mitchell explains. 'I have to help them understand the consequences of their actions. This isn't too hard; after all, they're scientists.'

People often come to Dr Mitchell for advice when setting up a new experiment. It is her job to know which substances are hazardous and which procedures risky and to know the proper precautions to take. She also meets with each new employee to explain the hazards and risks at the site and to outline the procedures appropriate to the work in the labs.

Dr Mitchell is responsible for compiling a Site Safety Manual, part of which is a set of Standard Operating Procedures (SOP) for processes and equipment. This covers all legislation applicable to the site and gives methods for implementation by describing the relevant site procedures, such as carrying out a risk assessment. The manual is available as a reference work for everyone on the site.

▲ **Figure 1C3** *Meta Mitchell (left) talking with laboratory staff during a regular site tour.*

▶ **Figure 1C4** *Three types of warning sign: caution (yellow), prohibition (red), mandatory (blue).*

What hazards will you find in a lab?

Anything that can cause harm if things go wrong is called a hazard. The chance (big or small) of harm actually being done is called a risk. An exposed electrical wire is a hazard. If there is no current running through it, there is no risk of electrocution or fire. As soon as the current is turned on, there is a risk. How serious it is will depend on how much wire is exposed, how much current passes through, how likely someone is to come into contact with the exposed wire, and so on.

Chemicals

There are several different hazards associated with chemicals. These hazards are identified by symbols that carry very specific meanings. The most important symbols are listed below.

 VERY TOXIC
A substance which if inhaled, ingested or taken in through the skin, may involve extremely serious acute or chronic health risks and even death.

 TOXIC
A substance which if inhaled, ingested or taken in through the skin, may involve serious acute or chronic health risks and even death.

NOTE: There are no specific symbols for carcinogen (may cause cancer), mutagen (cause heritable genetic damage) or teratogen (may cause harm to unborn child). Such substances are labelled 'toxic' or 'very toxic', with a risk phrase to describe the way they may cause harm.

 HARMFUL
A substance which if inhaled, ingested or taken in through the skin, may involve limited health risks.

 OXIDIZING
A substance which produces a reaction giving off great heat when in contact with other substances, particularly flammable substances.

 CORROSIVE
A substance which on contact with living tissues may destroy the tissues.

 IRRITANT
A non-corrosive substance which, through immediate, prolonged or repeated contact with the skin or eyes, may cause inflammation or lesions.

 EXTREMELY FLAMMABLE
A liquid having a flash point of less than $0\,^{\circ}C$ and a boiling point of less than or equal to $35\,^{\circ}C$.

HIGHLY FLAMMABLE
A substance which is:
- spontaneously flammable in air;
- a solid and may catch fire after brief contact with a flame and keep burning after removal of flame;
- gaseous and flammable in air at normal pressure;
- liable to emit highly flammable gases when in contact with water or damp air;
- a liquid with a flash point below $21\,^{\circ}C$.

 FLAMMABLE
A liquid with a flash point greater than $21\,^{\circ}C$ and less than or equal to $55\,^{\circ}C$.

 EXPLOSIVE
A substance which may explode under the effect of a flame or heat, or which is more sensitive to shocks or friction than dinitrobenzene.

 DANGEROUS FOR ENVIRONMENT
Materials which may harm the (mainly aquatic) environment.

WARNING! As soon as you become aware of any chemical contamination immediately wash the contamination off yourself and all surfaces. Whether there has been any contamination or not be sure to wash your hands before leaving the lab and before touching any part of your body.

▲ Figure 1C5 *Hazard warning symbols.*

Electrocution

Most people think they know how to put on a plug. But in 1989 the Electricity at Work Regulations stated that only 'competent people' could install a plug. The workers at one laboratory were furious to think they were not competent to put on a simple plug. There was lots of bad feeling.

The Health and Safety Department of the company conducted a survey of each plug on the site and found that 70% did not conform to standard requirements because of such faults as an incorrect fuse or wires of the wrong length. But even worse, 10% had potentially hazardous faults such as wrong connections, loose wires, silver paper instead of a fuse or wires stripped too far.

Electrical appliances always carry the potential hazard of electrocution. Follow these guidelines to reduce the hazards.

- Always check electrical appliances for damage, loose wires, exposed terminals.
- Guard against water or solvents spilling near any electrical item.
- Do not overload a socket; 3 kW is the maximum load.
- Keep cables and wires from trailing across the floor.
- Before replacing a blown fuse, inspect the appliance to discover why the fuse went in the first place.

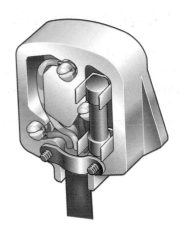

▲ **Figure 1C6** *A mains plug correctly wired.*

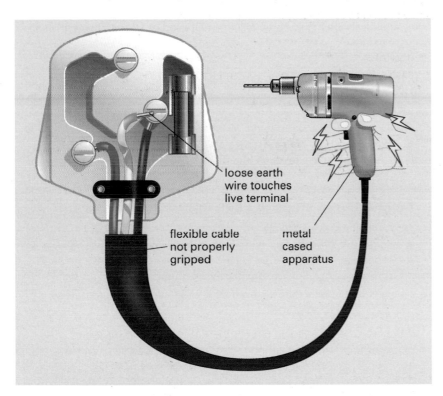

loose earth wire touches live terminal

flexible cable not properly gripped

metal cased apparatus

▲ **Figure 1C7** *Fuses do not protect from electric shock if a plug is incorrectly wired.*

Fire

The best way to fight fires is to prevent them from occurring in the first place. Most fires are caused by human error – poor judgement, ignorance, not following instructions – and therefore could be prevented if workers were a little more careful and alert.

Fire safety means being aware of and guarding against the following fire hazards found in labs.

Open flame	Burners, dryers or incinerators may be located too close to where people work or pass by or too close to combustible material; they may also be left insufficiently protected.
Spontaneous ignition	Under certain circumstances, if rubbish, oily rags or damp waste material is left piled up too long there may be a reaction which heats up the pile and then starts a fire.
Hot surfaces	Combustible materials may catch fire if they are placed too close to heat from furnaces, flues, pipes, soldering irons, and so on.
Mechanical sparks	Metal objects that happen to get caught in machinery can set off sparks.
Electrical equipment	Fires can occur when electrical appliances overheat or short out. (See page 49 for further discussion about electrical hazards.)
Static electricity	Most often found in areas of low humidity, static electricity can produce sparks.
Chemicals	Many chemicals are highly combustible and if used or stored improperly can ignite or explode.

▲ **Figure 1C8** *Fire hazards found in the laboratory.*

One hazard everyone must be aware of is mess, otherwise known as poor housekeeping. Scraps of paper or other material, spillages, shavings, dirt and oil in machinery can ignite if they come near flames. Obstructions can block passageways and exits and make it difficult to leave a burning area. The message is: **clean up as you work**. At the end of the day make sure your work area is clean and tidy.

Follow these steps in case you discover a fire:

- immediately raise the alarm
- assess the situation from a safe position
- determine:
  - the size of the fire and the likelihood of putting it out quickly
  - the substances that are burning and hence the appropriate extinguishing materials.

If the fire is small and you are competent to tackle it, make one quick attempt with one extinguisher, standing as close to an exit as you can, and then leave the room as quickly as possible.

Follow these steps in case you hear a fire alarm:

- if you are in the middle of an experiment, be sure to make the experiment safe by turning off the heat sources, extinguishing all flames, etc.
- close all doors and windows
- quickly and quietly vacate the building via the appropriate routes.

▲ **Figure 1C9** *Steps taken in case of fire.*

Kinds of fires

There are four kinds of fires, each requiring
a different extinguishing agent.

Ordinary combustibles

These are fires fuelled by wood, cloth, paper, rubbish,
rags, shavings or packing materials. There are four ways
to fight these fires:

- water and water-foam spray fire extinguishers
  (always coloured red)
- water from a hose or bucket
- blanket or sand used to smother the fire
- shovel to beat out the fire.

Electrical equipment

These are fires in appliances or wiring. If the electrical current is live,
disconnect the electrical supply and treat as for ordinary combustibles.
Otherwise use one of these extinguishers:

- CO_2 (carbon dioxide) extinguisher (black, or red with black colour
  code)
- halon extinguisher (green, or red with green colour code). Halon
  fumes may be dangerous and this type of extinguisher is being
  replaced by other types
- dry powder (blue, or red with blue colour code).

Flammable liquids and gases

These fires involve petrol, oil grease, paint, paint thinners, propane or
ether. There are two kinds of extinguishers to use on these fires:

- AFFF (foam) extinguishers (cream, or red with cream colour code)
- dry powder (blue, or red with blue colour code).

Combustible metals

Some metals, such as magnesium, titanium, zirconium, lithium and
sodium, can fuel a fire. For these fires a special kind of dry powder
extinguisher is necessary.

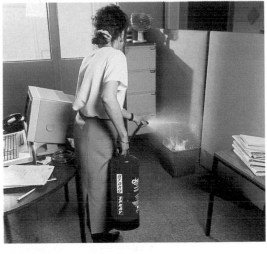

▲ **Figure 1C10** *Demonstrating the
use of a water spray to extinguish
a paper fire.*

Never use water to
extinguish an electrical fire.

◀ **Figure 1C11** *The colour code
for fire extinguishers.*

CARBON DIOXIDE (CO_2) GAS — FLAMMABLE LIQUIDS SAFE ON HIGH VOLTAGES

WATER CO_2 SODA ACID — WOOD, PAPER TEXTILES etc UNSAFE ALL VOLTAGES

DRY POWDER — FLAMMABLE LIQUIDS SAFE ON LOW VOLTAGES UP TO 1,000 VOLTS

FOAM — FLAMMABLE LIQUIDS UNSAFE ON ALL VOLTAGES

VAPOURISING LIQUIDS HALON — FLAMMABLE LIQUIDS HIGH VOLTAGES SAFE ON ALL VOLTAGES

Infection

In biology labs there is always a danger of contamination from infected tissues and fluids or from bacteria or viruses and therefore precautions must always be taken. In particular all specimens must be neutralized and protective equipment must be worn at all times.

To minimize the dangers of infection there must also be a high standard of hygiene and effective storage facilities. Any equipment used to handle potentially contagious material should always be decontaminated according to stated procedures. Specimens used for experiments must be stored well away from any areas where food or drink is stored, prepared or eaten.

HIV (human immunodeficiency virus) is perhaps the best-known (and most feared) hazard arising from handling human specimens in biology laboratories. Despite its tragic consequences, its discovery proved beneficial to the area of heath and safety in biology labs because it made everyone aware of the need for caution in handling any kind of potentially infectious agent. Nothing should be taken for granted; any sample from any patient might be contagious. New dangers could always appear.

Pathogens	Any agent causing a disease is called a pathogen. In a biology lab, pathogens are sometimes the very things you are working on, such as a flu virus. They are very carefully controlled and contained. Pathogens may also be (accidentally) present in a substance you are working on (e.g. hepatitis in blood) and will need to be eliminated.
Irritants	Powdered substances are common irritants, such as powdered detergent, which is used to dissolve protein in blood. The powder might get into the lungs and cause irritation there.
Carcinogens	Some substances used in a biology lab may be cancer-causing. Benzene, which is used in some staining procedures, is a carcinogen and must be treated with extreme caution.
Mutagens	Some substances used in a biology lab may cause mutations. Ethidium bromide is the most common mutagen. Note that many substances, such as ultraviolet light, are both carcinogens and mutagens.
Teratogens	Some substances used in a biology lab may cause genetic defects. Formamide, used in unfolding micro-molecules, is known to cause genetic defects, at least in mice.
Harmful to the environment	Some hazardous substances may be released into the air either in the laboratory itself or in the environment outside the building. The amount released by research or clinical lab work, however, is so minimal that it scarcely poses a threat to the environment. The amount released by industrial labs, however, may need to be controlled and monitored.

▲ **Figure 1C12** *Common hazards in biology labs.*

Glass

Glassware always needs special care in handling. Particularly dangerous is fitting flexible plastic or rubber tubing over glass tubing or a glass pipette into a safety filler or dispenser.

When the contents of glass containers are put under pressure care must be taken to ensure that the pressure does not build up to more stress than the glass can tolerate.

Sharp objects

Cutting blades pose the obvious hazard of wounding the person using the instrument. More serious are those wounds inflicted by a potentially contaminated blade. Steel mesh gloves are designed to prevent wounds from blades but, although they may protect against slashing wounds, they leave the wearer vulnerable to stab wounds. Like blades, syringes and needles can both wound and contaminate, and require extreme care.

Carelessly discarded sharps can accidentally cut or infect people. Therefore all blades, syringes and needles should not be thrown into a general waste bin, but be placed in specially provided receptacles (usually yellow) to be incinerated separately from all other waste.

Here are some examples of recent regulations.

Precautions when working with human blood

1 Blood must arrive at the lab in a tube with a secure screwed cap.
2 Laboratory technicians must wear a lab coat and gloves.
3 All work must be conducted in a class 2 safety cabinet, which both keeps bacteria from coming in and harming the specimen and keeps the air in the cabinet from getting out and harming the workers.
4 Before carrying out work on the specimen, the technician should inactivate any infections that may be present or potentially present in the blood. This is done by treating the blood with an agent (e.g. a detergent) that destroys the structure of protein. Since viruses are contained in the protein coat, they are also destroyed by this process. Any substances left are treated with bleach to deactivate other infectious agents such as bacteria.

▶ **Figure 1C13** *A technician taking tissue samples at an autopsy. This lab technician is wearing a protective gown and gloves to guard against contamination from tissues and fluids. Because of the danger from aerosol sprays, the technician also wears a face shield and a mask. Steel mesh gloves minimize the danger of cutting the hands when using sharp instruments.*

The legal framework

The world has become increasingly safety conscious over the years. There are now many national regulations designed to protect the people who work in potentially hazardous areas. Companies can be held responsible for any infringements of these regulations.

Here are some examples of recent regulations.

Control of Substances Hazardous to Health Regulations (COSHH), 1988

Regulation 2: Definitions of substances hazardous to health

COSHH regulations apply to:

- substances that are toxic, harmful, corrosive or irritant
- substances that have maximum exposure limits
- substances that cause cancer, mutations or birth defects
- micro-organisms that can transmit a disease
- any dust in substantial concentration
- substances that present comparable hazards to any of the above.

Substances hazardous to health are not just single chemical compounds, but mixtures of compounds or micro-organisms. The form of the substance matters: one that is relatively non-hazardous in lumps may be very hazardous when finely powdered because of the increased risk of breathing it in.

Regulation 7: Preventing and controlling exposures

Employers have a duty to prevent or adequately control any exposure of employees to substances hazardous to health. Employers must do their best to minimize exposure by carrying out such procedures as:

- substituting a new substance that is less hazardous
- changing the method of working
- modifying the process to avoid hazardous by-products or wastes.

Where it is not possible to prevent exposure, employers should first try to control the hazard by methods which do not require employees to wear protective clothing. This might involve enclosing the process, improving ventilation and regular cleaning. In essence, this regulation requires the employer to conduct risk assessments for all procedures (see page 56).

Personal Protective Equipment at Work Regulations, 1992

Personal protective equipment (PPE) includes clothing (such as aprons, gloves or safety helmets) and equipment (such as eye protectors or respirators). Open-toed shoes or sandals do not qualify as PPE. Long hair should be tied back. PPE should always be regarded as a last resort or as a back-up to other control measures. Alternatives not requiring PPE should always be considered first.

Regulation 10: Proper use of protective equipment

PPE should be used only after adequate training. Employees have a duty to use the PPE provided and to follow the instructions of the employers and guidance from the manufacturers. This means, for instance, that it is not enough just to wear gloves if they are called for, but to wear the proper kind of gloves (there are many varieties).

Regulation 11: Loss and defects

Employees must take reasonable care of the PPE provided and report any losses or defects to their employers as soon as possible.

Management of Health and Safety at Work Regulations, 1992

Regulation 7: Emergencies and danger areas

Employers must establish procedures to ensure employees know what to do in an emergency – in case of fire, for example. Employers must also establish procedures for coping with any special risks identified in a risk assessment.

The procedures must set out the roles of competent people with special responsibilities in an emergency. People are considered competent if they have sufficient training, experience or knowledge and other qualities to take responsibility in an emergency.

Emergency procedures should be written down and form part of the induction and training of new workers.

A danger area is a place of work where the level of risk requires special precautions. The hazard may occupy the whole area (for example, a toxic gas) or be in just one place (such as exposed, live electric conductors). Employees must be trained to cope with the hazard before entering a danger area.

Electricity at Work Regulations, 1989

Nearly a quarter of all reportable electrical accidents involve portable equipment. Most of the accidents cause electric shocks. Others result in fires.

Portable appliances include any electrical equipment which is connected to the mains by a cable with a plug and is likely to be moved while still connected to the supply. Extension leads, power packs, kettles and lamps fall under the regulations for portable appliances, as does office equipment including photocopiers.

Portable electrical equipment should be tested by a combination of:

- checks by the user
- visual inspection by a person appointed to do so
- inspection and tests (with a portable appliance tester) by a competent person.

Testing of portable equipment detects faults such as a broken earth wire or faulty insulation. At the same time the inspector should check that the correct fuse is in place and that the wires in the plug are connected to the right terminals.

▼ **Figure 1C14** *Testing a portable appliance to check that there is a proper earth connection and that the insulation is not faulty.*

What is a risk assessment?

Accidents can happen all the time but because of the potentially greater danger of an accident in a lab, scientists have to be much more careful about what they are doing.

A big breakthrough occurred in 1988 with the Control of Substances Hazardous to Health Act (COSHH, see page 54). This act laid down special procedures to follow before actually carrying out any lab work. Often known as a risk assessment, these procedures require you to follow certain guidelines.

1 **Look** around the site and thoroughly think through each step of the activity being carried out. Determine:
- what substances are present and in what quantities
- how each substance is used in the activity.

2 **Identify** any hazardous substances and the risks that might be involved in the work, in particular:
- the harm that might result from short-term or long-term exposure to a hazardous substance
- the way a person could be harmed by the hazardous substance (swallowing, inhaling, absorbing through the skin)
- the people who might be exposed to the substance.

3 **Evaluate** the best way to minimize these risks, by establishing what are called control measures to prevent exposure or, when this is not possible, to control exposure. There are several ways to prevent exposure
- stop using the substance or cut back its use
- find an alternative way to use the substance that will involve no exposure
- substitute a less hazardous substance
- substitute a less hazardous form of the same substance.

There are also several ways to control exposure:
- isolate or enclose the area
- use ventilation or exhaust extraction
- cut back the amount of exposure time
- limit the number of people who are exposed.

4 **Carry out** the control measures.

5 **Monitor** the activity to check that the control measures are in place and that they are doing the job properly.

6 **Review** the assessment regularly.

▶ **Figure 1C15** *Consulting Hazcards (which identify potential hazards in the use, storage and disposal of a substance) while carrying out a risk assessment.*

Managing hazards

Much of the work at the Johnson Matthey Technology Centre involves platinum salts, some of which are potentially hazardous in that exposure to them may cause platinum sensitization, producing asthma-type symptoms or rashes. As part of the COSHH regulations (see page 54) the company has a duty to identify and control the hazards associated with this substance.

Protecting employees

Those who work in the labs are protected by strict control measures determined by risk assessments. These measures may include substituting alternatives where possible, using glove boxes, decontamination, training in following written operating procedures, supervision of and encouraging a high level of discipline. Such control measures aim to keep exposure to a minimum.

All employees have frequent medical screenings to identify early stages of sensitivity. Any person who shows signs of sensitivity is removed from any potential exposure by changing his or her work. Experience shows that spotting symptoms early enough means that they can be arrested and often reversed.

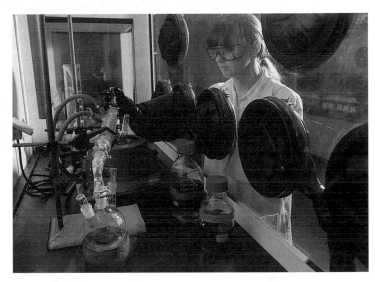

▲ **Figure 1C16** *A glove box protects an employee working with soluble platinum salts.*

Waste containing platinum salts

Once platinum salts are reduced to a metal they are no longer hazardous, so the first step is to reduce the salts to a metal. For this purpose the waste is sent to another branch of the company where it is refined back to a metal and recycled for further use.

Waste from platinum salts used in the bio-medical labs for cancer drugs is treated with magnesium under controlled conditions to reduce it to a metallic state. The metallic platinum then undergoes a refining process to remove impurities and produce a valuable product.

Maintenance in areas containing platinum salts

Before any maintenance work is done in an area where platinum salts have been used, a clean-up process is carried out by spraying the area with a diluted solution of an agent that reduces the salts to metal (such as sodium borohydride) and then the area is washed down with water. A permit to work is then issued (see page 59) specifying relevant precautions.

Checking that precautions work

Any area where platinum salts are in use is regularly monitored with swab samples, and air samples are collected and measured for the presence of the salts.

▼ **Figure 1C17** *Sampling air from the breathing zone of an employee working with platinum salts.*

Good communication

If someone knows all the Health and Safety Regulations by heart and is able to conduct the most efficient risk assessment in the company, but cannot communicate, that person becomes a hazard. Everyone must be open to what others know and have to tell them and must be willing and able to tell others what they know. It may be tempting sometimes to keep work secret and it can be boring to keep abreast of what others are doing, but working in isolation puts everyone at risk.

Here are some reminders of the importance of communicating with others in the lab.

Don't work alone

Dedicated scientists in the old films worked alone deep into the night on crucial projects, but what would have happened if something had gone wrong? Suppose there was an unexpected explosion or fire? Nowadays it makes sense to be sure there is someone within earshot who can help if there's trouble. When the green slime in the test tube suddenly comes alive it's a good idea to have someone else there, so that one person can call the police or fire brigade while the other stands watch.

Keep in touch with what others are doing

See what colleagues are up to. Someone may have discovered yesterday a previously unnoticed hazard in an operation that others are working on today. In a good lab such findings will be quickly passed on by the Health and Safety Officer, but if people can't be bothered to pay attention to the message they may not benefit from the warning.

When working on a group project it's even more important to communicate with others. How else will anyone find out that the chemical process expected to be ready by 3.00pm will not be ready until 4.00pm because one of the team was delayed in setting up the experiment?

Pay attention to 'Permit to Work' notices

Is it safe to begin work in a new situation? Suppose there are unusual circumstances going on: what changes need to be made in normal work practices? How will people be informed, for instance, that the electricity company are due to start drilling next door in two hours and the dust and vibrations might make the planned work unsafe?

The Permit to Work should answer these questions. This permit supplements usual Operating Procedures for temporary or unusual work and informs workers of all foreseeable hazards involved in the job to be done. People for whose benefit the Permit to Work is written are now part of a formal agreement with the management. They must read and obey what the permit says.

Report accidents

Someone must be told if an accident occurs or if something goes wrong – even if it does not seem serious. A lab worker might prefer, for instance, to keep quiet about having spilled some solution. After all, it might only have been a small spill and it was wiped up pretty quickly. Why make a fuss over nothing? Worse still, why get noticed and perhaps into trouble? But suppose it wasn't all wiped up. Suppose there was some hazard associated with the solution. It's not worth the risk to keep quiet about it. The Health and Safety Officer must be told; it's that person's job to know about all mishaps and to take the appropriate steps.

As for major accidents, of course these must be reported immediately. In fact it's the law that all major accidents be reported as soon as possible to the local office of the Health and Safety Executive. The scene of an accident should be left undisturbed because a safety inspector will want to examine it. Most labs will have specific procedures to follow in reporting an accident. Everyone should know in advance what these procedures are.

Ask for help

A lab is not the place for heroes, for people who go it alone with no need of help from anyone else. No one is there to prove how special they are; each person is part of a team. No one is expected to know everything. If people are in doubt about risks involved in a procedure, or about the precautions necessary for working with a particular substance, or about any potentially hazardous aspect of their work, they should ask for help. The Health and Safety Officer is the person who should be able to answer all these questions.

There are two reasons why people might hesitate to ask for help. For one thing they naturally don't want to look ignorant. In some circumstances ignorance may be something to be ashamed of, but there's something admirable about a person in a lab who knows he or she is unclear about something and has the guts to ask about it. The other problem is that asking for help may look like sucking up to the management. In school – and, unfortunately often at work too – people play the game of staying as far away as possible from people in authority. In a lab where the health and safety of many people may be at risk, it doesn't make sense to play games.

JM ⬡

Johnson Matthey Technology Centre

PERMIT TO WORK

AUTHORISED BY (Block Capitals):   **SIGNATURE:**
START DATE: **END DATE:**

NB: Duration of permit to be no more than 3 days.

ACCEPTANCE: I HAVE READ AND UNDERSTOOD THIS PERMIT AND I AGREE TO ABIDE BY IT AND BY THE JMTC SAFETY RULES:

NAME (Block Capitals)	SIGNATURE	DATE
_____	_____	_____
_____	_____	_____

EQUIPMENT/LOCATION:

DEFINITION OF WORK:

HAZARDS: Tick where relevant for the plant and its location:

Gas or Fumes	Steam	Fire & Explosion
Hydraulic Power	Hot Metal	Electricity
Pressurised Fluid	Radiation	Corrosive Fluid
Asbestos	Hot Fluid	Platinum Salts
Others – Specify		

SPECIAL PRECAUTIONS: (eg protective clothing)

ISOLATION: What method of isolation has been used for:

Gases
Electricity
Water
Other

THIS SECTION TO BE COMPLETED BY THE PERSON DOING THE WORK

The work **IS/IS NOT** complete and the equipment has been reconnected to:

Gases   YES/NO
Electricity   YES/NO
Water   YES/NO
Other process supplies   YES/NO

EQUIPMENT HANDED BACK BY: **RECEIVED BY:**

DATE:

▲ **Figure 1C18** *A Permit to Work Notice.*

Health and Safety are important issues outside the laboratory

This chapter has shown how comprehensive are the regulations governing laboratory environments. Proper training and the development of a sense of responsibility by everyone concerned mean that laboratories are safe places to work. They are at the cutting edge of thinking about health and safety. Another situation where health and safety must be paramount is the treatment of patients in hospitals and clinics.

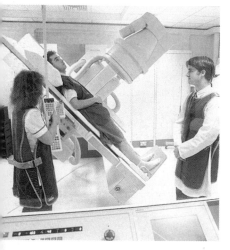

▲ **Figure 1C19** *Jamie in Room 5 of the X-ray department.*

A GNVQ student undertakes a clinical safety project

In the summer vacation of 1994, Jamie Davie, an Advanced GNVQ Science student at Yeovil College, spent three weeks in the X-ray department of Yeovil District Hospital, comparing the radiation dose given by the hospital's two X-ray machines; one old, the other new.

What follows are highlights from the report which Jamie prepared of his project. He was also asked to consider less 'scientific' aspects of X-ray procedures. This is typical of scientific analysis of technical procedures considered in the wider social and economic framework within which many scientists operate.

Extract from Jamie's report

```
Radiation doses

The aim of this project is to see if the new
X-ray machine which has been installed in
room 5, of Yeovil District Hospital X-ray
department is safer than the older machine in
room 4. It has other advantages over the old
machine. I will also give my view of the X-ray
rooms as a whole.
```

▼ **Figure 1C20** *Extracts from Jamie's diary.*

6 July, 1994
Today I watched endoscopic surgery. This is a very long procedure which involves the X-ray and surgical departments. The operation was to remove a stone which was blocking a patient's bile duct. This procedure, while being dramatic and uncomfortable at the time, does actually save the patient having surgery. It showed how busy it can get in the department and how important it is to be able to work as a team.

12 July, 1994
Today I was in room 4 collecting the data for the project. It is difficult because I'm only collecting data for barium enemas which are not as frequent as some other examinations. I also need some data for room 5 but there's been no opportunity to go into the room as yet.

13–22 July, 1994
The collection of data has been fairly easy and I haven't had to worry about getting help. I've just come in when the enemas were on and then gone home again when they are finished.

The variables in the exercise

1 Size and weight of the patient affect the amount of radiation used.

2 Different techniques used by different radiologists affect the radiation doses. The project was not long enough to use only one radiologist's results.

3 Magnification used for each patient varies, thus a variation in dose occurs.

4 Some patients may have more bowel tissue than others and thus take longer to look at. Again this causes variations in the radiation.

Results summary

Room 5
18 results with a total radiation dose
of 39 986 Gy cm^{-2}
Therefore the mean value of radiation doses
per investigation = 39 986/18 = 2221 Gy cm^{-2}

Room 4
28 results with a total radiation dose
of 141 849 Gy cm^{-2}
Therefore the mean values of radiation doses
per investigation = 141 849/28 = 5066 Gy cm^{-2}

◀ **Figure 1A 21** *Summary of the radiation doses recorded during the project.*

Advantages

Room 4 (old machine)
Nicely decorated (puts patients at ease)

Lower table (patients can more easily get on)
Wider table (patients feel more secure)

Room 5 (new machine)
Lower radiation
Better imagery
User friendly

Disadvantages

Room 4
Higher radiation dose
Lower image quality
Table too high (patients feel insecure)

Room 5
Very clinical (alarming to patients)
Table too narrow (ditto)

Conclusion

▲ **Figure 1C22** *The advantages and disadvantages of the two machine rooms.*

It can be seen from the data that the radiation from the machine in room 5 does give less radiation than that in room 4. It would have been better to continue with the project for longer to obtain more data and maybe even eliminate some of the variables.

Thoughts and actions

1 Who might be interested in the results of the following analyses and why?
   a The potassium ion concentration in soil.
   b The concentration of alcohol (ethanol) in blood.
   c The concentration of sulphur dioxide in air.
   d The percentage by mass of chalcopyrite in a rock sample.
   e The type of fibre in a tuft torn from a fabric.
   f The concentration of a steroid hormone in urine.
   g The concentration of nitrates in drinking water.

2 Analysts must work with samples which are representative of the bulk of the material from which they are taken. How should an analyst go about sampling when faced with the following problems? In each case identify the difficulty of taking appropriate small samples. Suggest ways of overcoming the difficulties.
   a Checking the purity of ammonium nitrate in a tanker full of the molten salt (see pages 4–5).
   b Measuring the chemical oxygen demand of river water (see pages 26–7).
   c Detecting banned drugs in the urine of athletes.
   d Investigating fragments of glass in the clothing of a victim of a hit-and-run accident.
   e Monitoring the quality of aspirin tablets made by a pharmaceutical company.

3 Draw up a table to give a summary of the analytical methods described in Chapter 1B. Use the heading suggested in Figure 1T1 and cover these methods:
   - chemical tests
   - IR spectroscopy
   - mass spectroscopy
   - nmr spectroscopy
   - thin-layer chromatography
   - gas-liquid chromatography
   - high-performance liquid chromatography
   - electrophoresis
   - colorimetry
   - acid–base titration
   - redox titration.

4 Which analytical methods would you recommend for solving the following analytical problems?
   a Checking the purity of citric acid supplied to a food manufacturer.
   b Identifying the food colours used in the orange coating of a chocolate drop.
   c Detecting abnormalities in the blood proteins of a sick patient.
   d Determining the structure of a newly synthesized molecule.
   e Finding out how the composition of petrol changes when in store.
   f Measuring the rate at which a drug is metabolized in the body and identifying the breakdown products.

5 Write balanced symbol equations, for each of the following word equations with the help of sections R10 and R11 in the Reference section. Classify the reactions as acid–base, redox, precipitation, or complex formation.
   a iron(s) + chlorine(g) $\longrightarrow$ iron(III) chloride(s)
   b zinc oxide(s) + sulphuric acid(aq) $\longrightarrow$ zinc sulphate(aq) + water(l)
   c nickel(II) ions(aq) + ammonia(aq) $\longrightarrow$ hexa-amminenickel(II) ions(aq)
   d iron(III) ions(aq) + zinc(s) $\longrightarrow$ iron(II) ions(aq) + zinc ions(aq)
   e ammonia(aq) + nitric acid(aq) $\longrightarrow$ ammonium nitrate(aq)

6 A brand of domestic bleach consists of 15% w/v sodium hypochlorite, NaClO. This means that there are 15 g of sodium hypochlorite in 100 cm^3 of solution. What is the concentration of the bleach solution in mol dm^{-3}?

7 A 0.100 mol dm^{-3} solution of sodium carbonate is used to standardize a solution of hydrochloric acid. 25.00 cm^3 of the sodium carbonate requires 22.25 cm^3 of the acid when titrated using bromocresol green as the indicator. What is the concentration of the acid?

▼ Figure 1T1

Analytical method	Qualitative, quantitative or both?	What can be determined with the help of the method?	Examples of applications of the method

8 A 0.800 g sample of iron ore is dissolved in acid. The iron is reduced to iron(II) and then titrated with 0.020 mol dm^{-3} potassium manganate(VII). The titre is 46.20 cm^3. What is the percentage, by mass, of iron in the ore?

9 Suggest possible identities for these salts from the results of the tests with the help of Figures R18.1 and R18.2 in the Reference section. Suggest one or two further tests to carry out in each case to confirm your conclusion.

  a Heating the solid produces a brown gas and a glowing splint re-lights when lowered into the test tube. Adding ammonia solution to a solution of the salt produces a white precipitate which dissolves in excess of the reagent.

  b Adding sodium hydroxide to a sample of a solution of the salt produces a brown precipitate which is insoluble in excess of the alkali. Adding silver nitrate to another sample of the solution gives a white precipitate.

  c This green solid colours a flame green and turns black on heating, giving off a gas which turns limewater cloudy white. The black solid dissolves in dilute sulphuric acid to give a blue solution.

10 a Write out the structure of an amino acid. Show how amino acids link together to form proteins by writing out the structure of a short length of a protein chain.

  b Figure 1T2 shows the results of paper chromatography to separate amino acids using a mixture of butan-1-ol, ethanoic acid and water as the solvent. Identify the three amino acids in the mixture with the help of Figure 1T3.

▶ **Figure 1T2**

Amino acid	R_f values for paper chromatography with a mixture of butan-1-ol, ethanoic acid and water
Alanine	0.38
Arginine	0.16
Glycine	0.26
Leucine	0.73
Tyrosine	0.50
Valine	0.60

▲ **Figure 1T3**

11 An organic liquid W contains carbon, hydrogen and oxygen only. Its mass spectrum is shown in Figure 1T4. The liquid boils at 56 °C. A drop of the liquid does not give a red precipitate with Fehling's solution but it does produce an orange precipitate with 2,4-dinitrophenylhydrazine (see Figure R16.1 in the Reference section).

  a What is the relative molecular mass of the compound?

  b Identify the organic liquid and write out its molecular formula and structure.

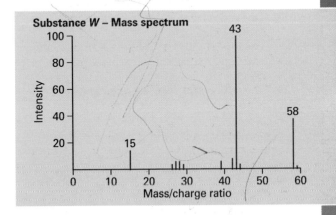

▲ **Figure 1T4**

12 An organic liquid X has the molecular formula $C_4H_{10}O$ and boils at 118 °C. Figure 1T5 shows the infra-red spectrum of X. X gives a neutral solution in water. Pure X reacts with sodium metal giving off hydrogen. Complete oxidation of X with acidified sodium dichromate(VI) produces an acid, Y, $C_4H_8O_2$, with a very unpleasant, rancid smell.

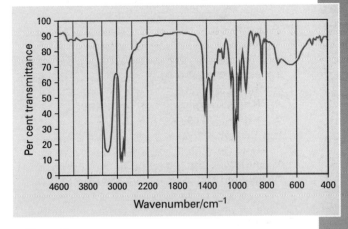

▲ **Figure 1T5**

  a Identify Y and X and write out their structures.

  b Identify the key peaks in the infra-red spectrum of X with the help of the table in Figure R24.1 in the Reference section.

13 Figure 1T6 is a low-resolution nmr spectrum of an organic compound Z consisting of carbon, hydrogen and oxygen. Z gives an orange-red precipitate with Fehling's solution. A solution of Z is neutral but oxidation of Z with acidified sodium dichromate(VI) produces an acid.

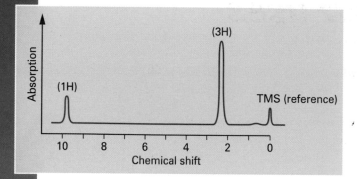

▲ **Figure 1T6**

a Identify Z and draw out its structure.
b Which atoms in the structure of Z are responsible for the peaks in the nmr spectrum? (See Figure R25.1 in the Reference section.)

14 An analyst determined the percentage of potassium in three brands of plant food for house plants. Figure 1T7 shows the five measurements made for each brand.

Brand	Results of measuring the percentage by mass of potassium as K⁺
A	4.93, 4.89, 4.71, 4.81, 4.74.
B	6.76, 7.91, 6.94, 6.71, 6.86.
C	4.72, 4.76, 4.68, 4.70, 4.69.

▲ **Figure 1T7**

a Determine the mean, median and range for each brand.
b What conclusions can you draw from these results about the three brands?

15 Generalization: 'all common carbonates are insoluble in water except for the carbonates of sodium and potassium'. With the help of Figure R20 in the Reference section, produce similar generalizations for nitrates, chlorides and sulphates.

16 Write a glossary of terms used to describe hazards to help people who need to understand Health and Safety regulations:
- explosive
- oxidative
- flammable
- toxic
- harmful
- pathogen
- irritant
- carcinogen
- mutagen
- teratogen
- harmful to the environment.

17 a Prepare to interview a member of staff responsible for health and safety by reading page 47 and noting a set of interview questions.
b Interview the member of staff and then write an article or report with the title: 'Who is in charge of Health and Safety?'

18 Read 'Managing hazards' on page 57. Identify:
a the hazards
b equipment used to protect people from hazards
c procedures designed to reduce the risk of harm
d methods of monitoring to check that the safety precautions are effective.

19 Prepare an illustrated briefing leaflet to get across the key messages about Health and Safety for a trainee technician starting work in a teaching laboratory.

20 a Write a news story for a local paper about an incident in a laboratory which you have experienced.
b Write a technical report analysing the same incident in the light of Health and Safety regulations.

21 Reflect on the work practices and procedures in the laboratories where you work.
a Do good communications (see pages 58–9) help to promote Health and Safety?
b Would the use of 'Permit to work notices' (see Figure 1C18) enhance safety? If so, devise a suitable format for a permit to work notice.

22 Design a form for recording risk assessments which covers the points included on page 56.

UNIT 2

Investigating materials and their uses

Materials on test

Up to scratch: setting standards at the BSI

When people go out shopping, they expect that everything they buy will be fit for use. No one wants shoes that wear out in a week, or a bicycle that collapses when sat on. The British Standards Institution sets standards for industry to follow. The right materials must be selected and tested so that everyone can be sure that their shoes and their bikes will last.

▲ **Figure 2A1** *Testing the strength of glass at the BSI. Window glass must be strong enough to withstand everyday impacts.*

BS 2592: 1973 Specification for thermoplastic flooring tiles: Qualities which need to be tested

Materials
Colour and finish
Dimensions
Stiffness
Resistance to impact
Indentation
Resistance to curling
   when wet

Steel for bridges, copper for electrical wiring, glass for windows, plastics for contact lenses – these are all materials with a purpose. They must be fit for the job for which they are intended. The British Standards Institution (BSI) is an independent organization which works with industry to set high standards for products so that customers know that what they buy will satisfy their requirements.

Good for customers ... good for manufacturers

Let's take an example. Imagine someone decorating a house who needs floor tiles for the kitchen or the bathroom. She may find tiles of just the right colour, but what else is important? The tiles must withstand boots, bicycles, tool boxes, toy cars, frequent wetting – perhaps with hot water or even more aggressive fluids. So it is very reassuring to know before buying that the tiles will all be the same size and shape, be hard and strong enough, waterproof, and made of a suitable material. Does the label say 'manufactured to comply with BS 2592'?

This statement is the manufacturer's claim that the tiles are suitably made, and of a suitable material, for use as floor tiles.

The British Standard allows manufacturers to sell their tiles, confident that they will last. It isn't practical to make some tiles, lay them in a real house and watch how they behave for fifteen years. But it is practical to have them tested to BS 2592. This doesn't say how to manufacture tiles, but it does describe the qualities that plastic floor tiles should have, together with simple tests that take only a few hours.

Whose standards?

Who wrote the British Standard for floor tiles? And who first thought it would be a good idea? Debbie Granville, a BSI press officer, explains.

'The answer to both questions is the same – it's the industry which asks for a standard, and works with us at the BSI to develop it. The companies who made floor tiles decided that it would be a good idea for them to agree about the important properties of floor tiles, and to publish this information. Then all tiles carrying the message "conforms to BS 2592" should reach a satisfactory standard, thus protecting the reputation of their industry.

'The BSI's role in all this was to co-ordinate the effort needed to obtain agreement between manufacturers and users, and to suggest other sources of helpful information – plastics manufacturers, architects and builders, specialists in materials testing. We organized discussions about the desirable characteristics of floor tiles, and ensured that there is a suitable test for each property. It takes about five years to get full agreement before publication of the standard.

'Since then, individual companies have made sure that their tiles are as good as, or better than, the quality described in BS 2592.'

Testing times

To match the standard, one test which the tiles must pass is the impact test. The standard lays down the procedure: the tile is supported on three steel balls, and a fourth ball is dropped on it. The tile is then examined for cracks.

The standard specifies the following:
size of test pieces: 150 mm square
number of test pieces: 2
temperature: $23 \pm 2\ °C$
size of falling ball: 25.4 mm diameter
mass of falling ball: $65 \pm 1\ g$
height of fall: 115 mm
point of impact: centre of tile

Each test is specified in detail. Tiles which fail any of these tests are unlikely to stand up to everyday wear and tear in today's homes.

The BSI kitemark is one of the UK's best-recognized Trade Marks. It is only attached to products which the BSI has tested and found satisfactory.

The CE mark shows that the product complies with all relevant EU directives.

The BSI Safety Mark, used primarily on electrical goods, shows that the product has been tested to ensure that it complies with necessary safety legislation.

▲ **Figure 2A2**

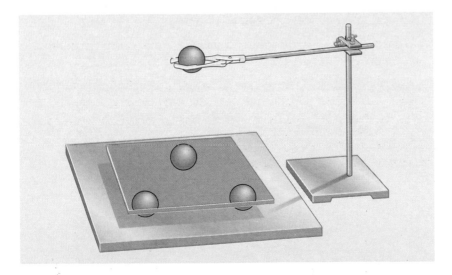

◀ **Figure 2A3** *The equipment for the impact test for tiles conforming to BS 2592.*

Fit for use

Giant cables over a metre thick support the graceful arching span of a suspension bridge. The bodywork of a car is pressed into shape to meet the latest aerodynamic design specifications. A can-opener slices into a tin of beans for a quick meal. All these are made of steel – different kinds of steel. What makes one kind of steel right for the cables, another right for the tin of beans?

Steel is iron with carbon (and other elements) in it. It's a material that has evolved over centuries, from a simple strong structural material to a material with many thousands of variations – stainless steel, structural steel, surgical steel .... Specialist suppliers stock many varieties from which customers can choose just the right kind, to meet their requirements.

There are millions of different materials available in the world today. Designers and engineers have to think about the circumstances in which the material will be used and who will buy the product. Then they can choose or design the material which is just right for the job.

Uses and choices

How to choose the right material? Start from what the material must do. Here are some examples which show the importance of getting the mechanical properties of materials right.

It's a hold-up: The cables of a suspension bridge are **in tension**. They are stretched by the weight of the bridge that they are supporting – the **load**. A **tensile force** acts within the metal cable.

The cables must be **stiff**. They must not stretch too much under the load. It would be no good if the weight of a few cars was enough to stretch the cables so that the roadway sank into the water below. And they must be **elastic** – they must return to their original length when the load is removed.

The cables must also be **strong**. In the course of their use, they will be subject to large loads – the weight of the roadway and the traffic, and the effects of high winds. They must be strong enough to withstand the greatest foreseeable load *without* breaking.

▶ **Figure 2A4** *New materials made it possible to design this motorized bicycle wheel ...*

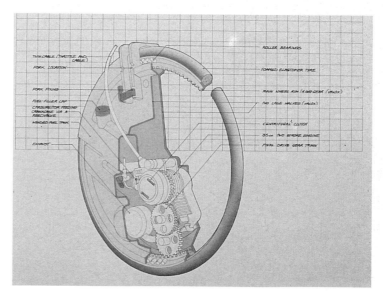

Under pressure: Many buildings are made of bricks. Each brick must support the weight of those above it. So every brick is being squashed – it is **in compression**. Too much load and, if the bricks are **weak**, they will crumble.

Stretching and bending: As an athlete bends and stretches, her clothes must stretch with her. They must be **flexible**, and they must be **elastic**, so that they return to their original shape when she straightens up. Because the textile fibres rub over one another, the fabric must be resistant to wear. It must also stand up to the **chemical effects** of sweat, deodorant and other substances.

Her shoes have polymer soles with air pockets, for extra elasticity. They must be very tough to stand up to repeated flexing.

On form: Clay is good for making cups and plates because it is easy to shape – it is a **plastic** material which has been used for thousands of years. But once it is fired, it is very different. Tap it, and feel how **hard** it is. Hit it hard, and it will shatter – it is **brittle**.

Other considerations

When making something with a complicated shape – think of a teapot – it's important to consider **ease** and **cost of fabrication**. The bodywork of a car must be formed to the right shape, so the metal must be fairly easy to deform, but that can lead to problems when one car hits another. There's a balance to be struck.

Looking good: There can be many different reasons for choosing one material rather than another for a particular use. As well as thinking about the desirable physical properties, a materials scientist must take into consideration the **cost**, **appearance** and **availability** of materials and their **impact on the environment**. The rest of this chapter looks at how a variety of properties are defined and measured, alongside detailed examples which show how materials are chosen to satisfy some demanding users.

◄ **Figure 2A5** ... *The wheel can be fitted to virtually any bicycle to turn it into a moped.*

Stretching and breaking

Stretching and breaking, squeezing and twisting, shaping and supporting. When forces act on materials, it is important to know how they will respond. By testing materials, their mechanical properties can be determined. Then it is possible to predict how they will behave in use.

▲ **Figure 2A6** *This tensile testing machine at the National Physical Laboratory can apply forces up to 200 000 newtons.*

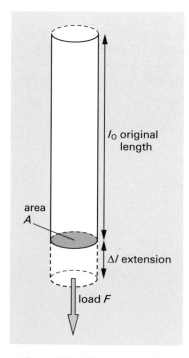

▲ **Figure 2A7** *Defining quantities when a specimen is under tension.*

Tensile testing

Tensile forces are stretching forces. Take a piece of any material, and it will stretch if both ends are pulled. Some materials are stretchier than others, and it is necessary to have a way of comparing one material with another.

In industry, a tensile testing machine is used to stretch samples of standard shapes. A large machine can apply forces of thousands of newtons, whereas a sensitive machine can pull the finest fibre with forces which are a fraction of a newton. As the sample stretches, a chart is produced which shows the **extension** (increase in length) of the sample against the **load** (the stretching force).

In order to compare one material with another, it would be difficult to insist that all samples were the same shape and size. It is simpler to define two new quantities, stress and strain.

A sample of any shape or size is stretched (put under tension) by attaching a load. The increase in its length shows the **strain** in the material. Strain is defined by

$$\text{strain} = \frac{\text{extension}}{\text{original length}} \quad \text{or} \quad \varepsilon = \frac{\Delta l}{l_0}$$

This equation allows for the fact that a long piece of material will stretch more than a short piece when subjected to the same loads. Strain ε has no units (but note that both extension and original length must be measured in the same units). Strain is often quoted as a percentage; a strain of 1% means that the sample has increased in length by 1% of its original length, i.e. $\varepsilon = 0.01$.

However a thick sample is harder to stretch than a thin one. To take account of this, the stress being applied is defined by

$$\text{stress} = \frac{\text{load}}{\text{cross-sectional area}} \quad \text{or} \quad \sigma = \frac{F}{A}$$

Units: $N\,m^{-2}$ or Pa (pascals)

Stress and strain are used to give a measure of the stiffness of the material. This is known as the **Young modulus** of the material, also known as the **elastic modulus**.

$$\text{Young modulus} = \frac{\text{stress}}{\text{strain}} \quad \text{or} \quad Y = \frac{\sigma}{\varepsilon}$$

The units of Y are $N\,m^{-2}$ or Pa. Since Y is often a very large quantity, its value is often quoted in MPa or GPa. (The symbol E is sometimes used instead of Y.) Values for a range of materials are given in the Reference section, R3.

Stretching metals

The graphs of Figure 2A8 show the Young modulus for three different metals. The convention is to plot stress on the y-axis. The initial, straight-line portions of these graphs show that for small loads, these metals obey **Hooke's Law**. Metal A is the stiffest, because the gradient is steepest. Metal C is the least stiff.

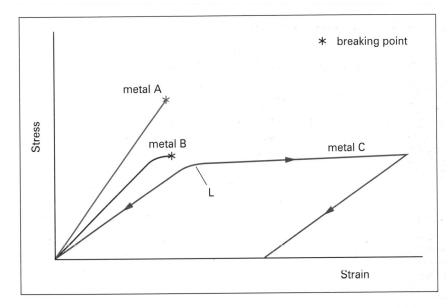

◀ **Figure 2A8** *Stress-strain graphs for three metals. The initial gradient of the graph represents the Young modulus for the metals.*

Usually, metals are elastic for small values of strain (up to 0.1%). This means that, provided the metal is not stretched by more than about 0.1% of its original length, it will return to its original length when the load is removed. If the strain is increased beyond this point (the **elastic limit** or **yield point** L), one of two things will happen. The metal may break (as for Metals A and B); alternatively, it may become permanently stretched. The metal shows plastic deformation, and when the load is removed, it does not return to its original length. This is shown on the graph for Metal C by the line returning to the x-axis. The value of the stress at the yield point is known as the **yield stress**.

In engineering applications it can be crucial to know about the yield point of a material. The stress in the steel ropes which support a suspension bridge must not exceed this point for the greatest loads that the bridge may sustain, or the bridge will be permanently damaged. On the other hand, to shape the sheet metal which forms the bodywork of a car, it is necessary to apply sufficient stress to pass the yield point.

Knowing values of the Young modulus for different materials allows a sufficiently stiff material to be selected for a particular application, and it is possible to calculate the amount a particular component will stretch under a given load.

Compression testing

Metals are not the only materials which can be stretched in order to determine their Young modulus. Polymers and ceramics, too, are important engineering materials. And materials can be tested in compression as well as tension. Figure 2A9 shows a concrete block being tested (to destruction!). Solid materials shrink as they are compressed; the Young modulus for compression is the same as for tension.

▼ **Figure 2A9** *A concrete block undergoing compression testing to destruction.*

Breaking point

When a metal such as hard steel is stretched or bent, it deforms elastically up to a point. Then it suddenly breaks or **fractures**. This is **brittle fracture**, and it usually leaves two pieces of metal with sharp edges.

A softer metal, such as copper or soft steel, deforms plastically before it breaks. It tends to become thinner at one point, and here the stress is greatest. Hence this is the point where the metal stretches most, and where it eventually breaks. Metals which can be deformed in this way are described as ductile, and their breaking is called **ductile fracture**.

There is more than one meaning to the term **strength** of a material. In general, this tells us about the stress it can withstand before either it becomes ductile or it breaks. For a brittle material, the **breaking stress** is the stress when it breaks; for a ductile material, the **yield stress** is the stress at the yield point, where it becomes ductile.

Stretching and compressing ceramics

Figure 2A10 shows the stress–strain graphs for two forms of glass. The graph is a straight line for cold glass, up to the point where it fractures. The gradient of this graph gives the Young modulus for glass, a brittle material which is elastic up to the point where it breaks.

▼ **Figure 2A10** *Stress–strain graphs for glass.*

The second line shows how the graph changes when glass is heated to the point where it softens. It behaves in a **plastic** way. When it is stretched, it gets longer and longer, but it does not return to its original length when the stress is removed.

Because ceramic materials are usually difficult to shape, they are often formed from a material which is initially plastic. Molten glass can be made into flat sheets by the float glass process, where molten glass floats on molten tin, or shaped into such items as glasses or bottles using moulds. When it is cooled, it retains its new shape. Similarly, clay is an easily shaped material because it is plastic; after firing, it is a rigid, elastic material.

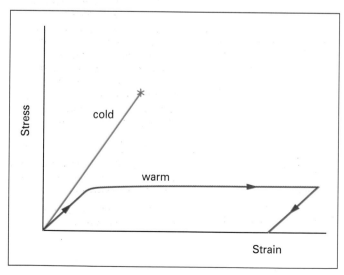

Because they are brittle, ceramics are typically rather weak in tension, but they can be much stronger in compression. Concrete, for example, can withstand high compressive stresses (up to 30 MPa) but tends to crack under relatively low tensile stress (1 MPa or less). Steel reinforcing rods are often included in concrete structures to strengthen regions which are likely to be in tension.

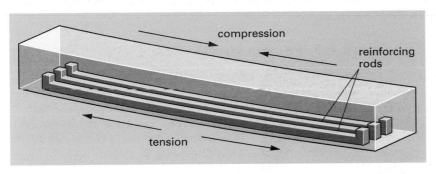

▲ **Figure 2A11** *Concrete has low tensile strength; the regions of a concrete beam that are in tension have steel rods included to give greater tensile strength.*

Polymers under tension

Polymers show two characteristic forms of behaviour: **glassy** and **rubbery**. A glassy polymer, such as Perspex, is elastic but brittle. A rubbery polymer can be stretched to high degrees of strain – perhaps as much as 400% – without breaking, and will return to approximately its original length when the stress is removed. Rubbery polymers become glassy when they are cooled down; this is discussed further on page 111.

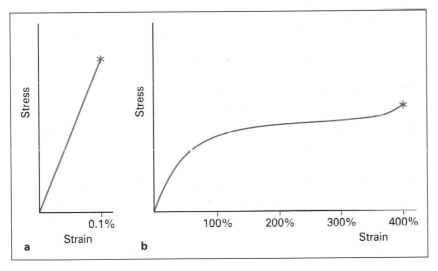

▲ **Figure 2A12** *Stress–strain graphs for a glassy and b rubbery polymers. Note the different strain scales.*

Materials scientists work to produce better materials – often stiffer, stronger materials which allow new solutions to problems. To achieve this, they must have an understanding of how the underlying structure of materials determines how they stretch and break. How changing the structure of materials can lead to improved mechanical properties is the subject of Chapter 2B.

'Lest there be any possible shadow of doubt, **strength** is not the same as **stiffness**. Stiffness or Young's modulus is concerned with how stiff, flexible, springy or floppy a material is. Strength is the force or stress needed to break a thing. A biscuit is stiff but weak, steel is stiff and strong, nylon is flexible and strong, raspberry jelly is flexible and weak. The two properties describe a solid about as well as you can expect two figures to do.'

J E Gordon, *The New Science of Strong Materials*

Wear it's at – materials for shoe soles

What is the best material for the soles of shoes? This is a deceptively simple question. But for a giant shoe manufacturer like Clarks, the answer isn't simply leather, rubber or a particular type of polymer. Shoes for different purposes may require different soling materials. And, as Peter Tazewell, technical manager with Clark International, says: 'It can all depend on the fashion designer.'

Designs on footwear

This doesn't mean that the designer will say that next year, shoes must have soles made of polyurethane – or polyvinylchloride (PVC) or ethylvinyl acetate (EVA) or rubber or another of the wide variety of materials that could actually be used. But the designs of shoes for sale next year (or the year after that) exercise a great influence on the material chosen for a shoe sole. A particular shoe may need very flexible soles. Or perhaps 5 cm thick platform soles are required, weighing no more than this year's 1 cm thick soles. Sports shoes have special requirements for different activities, as well as still needing to be fashionable.

Protective footwear for people working on building sites or in chemical plants, for example, poses yet another set of questions to the materials scientist whose job it is to ensure that these shoes are made from the most suitable materials.

Shoe sole science

Many of the questions posed by new shoe designs are scientific ones with scientific solutions. Peter Tazewell's responsibility is to translate the ideas of the designer into appropriate materials for the specific manufacturing process which will be used. These materials must offer the wide range of properties needed for a successful shoe sole.

So shoe scientists need to know about materials, mould making and production engineering. They must also know about the interaction between people and their shoes. The force a foot applies to a shoe may momentarily be as high as 50 times the weight of the wearer. It is not advisable to combine a stiff upper shoe with a very flexible sole. And the materials? Some polymers will always look 'cheap'; others can't stand up to high-speed stress; others can't reproduce a sharply detailed pattern.

▶ **Figure 2A13** *Peter Tazewell testing a shoe sole for resistance to tearing, elasticity, and the force required to separate or fracture the sole from the shoe. The equipment he uses is called an Instron Tensile Testing Machine.*

So how does a shoe scientist decide?
Peter Tazewell explains:

Property versus possibility

'Several different properties are likely to be important when selecting appropriate soling materials. And it's unlikely that a single material will have all of them at just the right level. In the end, choosing the best material often involves scoring each material against a list of criteria, and then a compromise is reached. Three "good" scores may outweigh two "very goods" and one "poor".'

Combining materials

'To give the desired combination of properties, soles may be made from two or more materials. A shoe-scientist will be able to distinguish between the properties needed in the main bulk of the sole and those essential only on the surface. We can bond a surface material (the outsole) to a lighter or cheaper material (the midsole) to achieve the result the designer wants and the consumer needs.'

These shoes are made for walking

'We use two general methods of testing. **Laboratory tests** give us a great understanding of the behaviour of the materials we use. But before a new shoe design goes into production, we also carry out **field tests**. At least 12 pairs are tested by a panel of people for whom the design is intended. These may be school children, nurses, office workers, milkmen, or indeed any group which reflects the type of wear to which the product will be subjected. They wear the shoes when they want to, in their everyday lives. They record what they do in them, how long they wear them on each occasion, and what they think of them. After a specific number of hours of wear, the shoes are sent back to us here at Clarks for professional inspection. Even one failure means a lot more work is needed on the design before it goes into production.'

What does a shoe scientist look for in a sole material?

Density Since every shoe sole has to be lifted with every footstep, its weight is important.

Strength Tensile and compressive, and also the ability to resist tearing.

Elongation How easily and how far will the material stretch before it breaks?

Resilience Will the sole absorb the shock as the foot hits the ground, and bounce back to help start off the next stride?

Hardness Will it resist damage caused by sharp stones? Will walking on rough, hard surfaces grind away the material?

Slip and grip Will the sole grip the ground to aid quick changes of direction?

Durability Leather soles need regular repair. Many modern soles are difficult (if not impossible) to repair, but can survive for very much longer than leather.

Water resistance Who wants water coming through the soles of his or her shoes?

Getting tough with wear and tear

A designer may choose a material with the right stiffness and strength for a particular use. It won't stretch or break when it is first used. But how will it behave in the long term? How will it wear, how hard will it be, how tough? Tests can measure these important properties of materials.

Hard stuff

The floor tiles discussed on pages 66–7 must be reasonably hard – they must stand up to furniture being dragged across them without showing scratches, and they must not dent easily when things are dropped on them. **Hardness** is the resistance of a material to **abrasion** or to **indentation**. In other words, the harder the material, the more difficult it is to scratch or to press a pointed object into its surface.

Although hardness is difficult to quantify, it is relatively easy to compare the hardnesses of two different materials. Moh's scale of hardness is based on scratching one material with another. Each material will scratch those with lower hardness values than itself. Hardness is related to the other mechanical properties of a material; a soft, ductile metal will have low hardness, because scratching and denting involve deforming the material.

There are several industrial methods in use for determining hardness, based on indentation tests. For example, in a Brinell test, a steel ball of standard size is pressed into the surface of a test specimen using a standard load. The area of the indentation is measured to assess the material's hardness. Other tests use different indentors (steel cone, diamond pyramid, needle), either pressed or dropped on to the surface, and the degree of indentation may be assessed by measuring the width or depth of the mark it makes.

If two manufacturers want to compare the hardnesses of their materials, they must use the same test. The table shows results for four polymers using three different tests. Notice that the rank order of hardness is not the same in all the tests. This makes it all the more important that manufacturers agree to work to, say, a British Standard which specifies the tests to be used. The test chosen would usually reflect the sort of damage which the material is likely to have to face up to in use.

▶ **Figure 2A14** *Some typical hardness values for plastics.*

Test type	Acrylic	Polystyrene	Polypropylene	Polyethene
Brinell	20	25	7	4
Vickers	5	7	6	2
Shore	90	74	74	70

Wear – and why

Wear happens when one object slides across another. The surfaces rub together, and gradually one or both of them is worn away. A hard material is likely to be more **wear resistant** than a soft one.

Adhesive wear: surfaces in contact tend to stick together.
Abrasive wear: occurs when bits of abrasive material become trapped between moving surfaces.
Corrosive wear: surfaces subject to chemical attack are rubbed.
Surface fatigue: materials are rubbed together under pressure.

Moh's scale	Standard mineral	Secondary standard
1	talc	
2	gypsum	fingernail
3	calcite	brass
4	fluorspar	knife blade
5	apatite	glass
6	feldspar	
7	quartz	
8	topaz	
9	corundum	
10	diamond	

◀ **Figure 2A15** *Moh's scale of hardness. If you cannot use the standard mineral, the secondary standard provides a suitable alternative.*

▼ **Figure 2A16** *A Brinell hardness tester, just one of several techniques for assessing the hardness of a material.*

Time and again

The wings of an aircraft flap up and down as it flies along. That's not how it flies, but it could put an end to the flight. The vibration of the wings mean that the material of which they are made is subjected to repetitively varying tensile forces. These forces are not big enough to break the wings but, after many repetitions, the effects can be serious. Tiny cracks may appear, and these can gradually grow until serious damage results. This damage after a long period of exposure to cyclical stresses is called **fatigue**.

In a similar way, if a material is subjected to a steady stress over a long period of time it may gradually deform. This is called **creep**. The aluminium and steel cables which hang between electricity pylons may stretch under their own weight, and they must be made strong enough to avoid this. (The steel core reinforces the aluminium, which is likely to creep.) The rotating parts inside a car engine or power station turbine are under high stress as they spin, and the metal gets softer as the temperature rises. This can lead to creep, perhaps with disastrous consequences.

Problems with creep and fatigue can be overcome by using tough materials. The tougher a material is, the more difficult it is to break it. It may be necessary to bend a piece of plastic back and forth repetitively before it will break – that's why plastic strips are frequently used as hinges, for example on children's lunch boxes. Similarly, tough fabrics are used for windsurfing sails. Even if the fabric is partly torn, a great deal of energy must be expended to rip it apart.

The **toughness** of a material is a measure of the energy needed to break it. Typically, tough materials have high breaking stress and do not break in a brittle way. In an industrial test of toughness, the sample is often a notched bar. A heavy pendulum swings down and breaks the bar; how high the pendulum swings afterwards shows how much of its energy has been transferred to the bar.

▶ **Figure 2A17** *A notched bar test measures the toughness of a material. The pendulum is shown in its initial, raised position.*

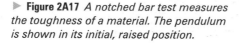

Precision precious metal

When they leave for home at the end of a day's work, the employees at Engelhard Engineered Materials go through a tight security check. The materials used at Engelhard include precious metals – the platinum used in making electrical resistance thermometers costs over £10,000 per kilogram. If platinum wire is to be used in high precision thermometers, it must be manufactured to very high standards.

The right metal

Platinum resistance thermometers are used increasingly in industry because they can be readily interfaced with electronic temperature indicators and controllers. They are based on the idea that the electrical resistance of a metal increases with temperature; platinum is used because it is a noble metal, so it does not easily corrode, and can be prepared to a very high degree of purity. The resistance of a length of platinum wire can therefore give a very accurate and reliable measure of temperature.

Standard platinum resistance thermometers are the world standard for measuring temperatures between 13.8 K and 1234.9 K.

At Engelhard, bars of platinum come from the melt room to the workshop where they are to be rolled and then drawn through a series of dies – hard blocks with increasingly narrow holes – until a very fine wire is produced. Eventually machines will wind the wire on to reels (like small cotton reels) to be sent to thermometer manufacturers, who will coil the wire into elements for thermometers. But how can Engelhard customers be sure that the wire they buy has the correct electrical properties? In the Physical Services Calibration Laboratory, Janet Taylor and two young technicians have the job of checking that the platinum will give wires whose resistance is within the permitted limits.

When a new bar of platinum arrives from the workshop, a number of thermometers are made from each end. It takes about five working days to make a set of thermometers and measure them. The process calls for great skill.

Janet explains what they are looking for in their test thermometers. 'We call the wire for thermometers "alpha wire", because we measure a key property, called α. This tells us how much the resistance of the wire increases for each one degree rise in temperature between 0 °C and 100 °C. If the platinum has the correct value of α, then thermometers made from the wire will agree with standard values over a wide range of temperatures.

'We control the resistance of the metal by doping with small amounts of other substances to get the right value of α. Platinum of the highest purity has an α–value of 0.003927. To meet British and German standards for thermometers, we must achieve an α-value of 0.003850.'

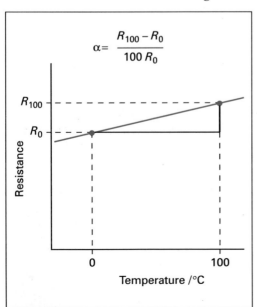

$$\alpha = \frac{R_{100} - R_0}{100\,R_0}$$

◀ **Figure 2A18** α is calculated from the gradient of the resistance–temperature graph.

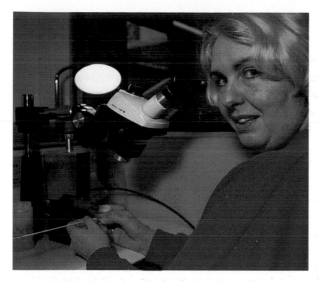

▲ **Figure 2A19a** *Janet Taylor leads the team at Engelhard, working to produce high precision materials for industrial thermometers.*

▲ **Figure 2A19b** *Jason Frame is operating the workshop's metal rolling machine.*

Testing times

Janet describes the sequence of operations involved in measuring the resistance of the wire and its α-value:

'I draw out the wire to a diameter of 0.15 mm, and coil it into a helix. We measure its resistance using a four-terminal technique, which eliminates the resistance of the leads. This involves welding two leads to each end of the test wire, so that each end has one lead for current and a second lead for voltage. We then pickle the coil in acid to remove any contamination, and seal it in a small glass tube with the leads sticking out at the ends. Because stress during handling increases resistance, the wire is heat-treated (annealed) to remove the stresses.

'As well as measuring the wire's resistance at ice-point (0 °C) and steam point (100 °C) to determine α, we also carry out a final test to find its resistance per unit length at 20 °C. This uses a "bridge" technique, in which a length of exactly 1 m of wire is clamped into one arm of a bridge circuit. The bridge is in a temperature-controlled box.

'We are very proud of the quality of the wires we supply. The German DIN standard requires an α-value of 0.003850 with a tolerance of ±12%. Our speciality is to offer a ±3% α-wire for precision thermometers.'

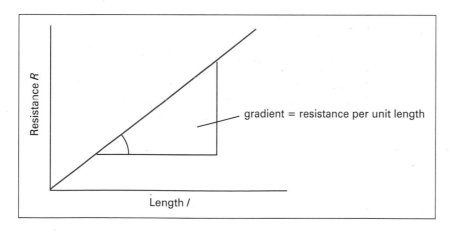

Resistance R / Length l — gradient = resistance per unit length

◄ **Figure 2A20** *The resistance of a wire is proportional to its length.*

Resistance to change

Many electrical devices – heaters, thermometers, sensors, transducers – make use of electrical resistance. Components must have the correct resistance, and this depends on the materials they are made from. As solid state electronics advances and circuits get smaller and smaller, it becomes increasingly important to know accurately the electrical properties of the materials being used.

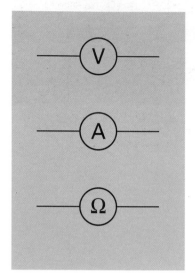

▲ **Figure 2A21** *Voltmeter, measures voltage (potential difference); ammeter, measures current; ohm-meter, measures resistance.*

Measuring resistance

The resistance R of a component is a measure of how difficult it is for a current to flow through it. Resistance is defined by

$$\text{resistance} = \frac{\text{voltage}}{\text{current}} \qquad R = \frac{V}{I}$$

Units: Ω (ohms) $1\,\Omega = 1\,\text{VA}^{-1}$

In the case of metal wires, it is often useful to know the wire's **resistance per unit length,** R/l; an example of this is the platinum wires supplied by Engelhard for making resistance thermometers (see page 78).

In order to determine R, it is usual to make measurements of both V and I. The British and European Standards require a 'four-terminal' method for specimens of low resistance. The current used must be low to avoid heating the specimen. Consequently, the voltage to be measured is also likely to be small.

For everyday measurements of R, an ohm-meter may suffice. A small, standard current flows through the component, and the meter measures the voltage required to maintain this current. The display gives a direct reading of resistance.

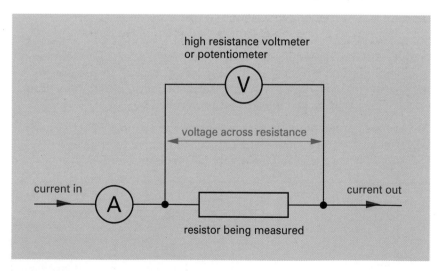

▲ **Figure 2A22** *Four-terminal method for resistance measurement. The current flowing in the voltage leads is zero (or negligible), so the ammeter can be relied on to measure accurately the current flowing through the specimen.*

Resistivity

Resistance is the property of an individual component or piece of material. But in order to compare the resistances of two materials, it is necessary to take into account shape and size. For a metal wire, resistance R is proportional to length l and inversely proportional to cross-sectional area A:

$$R \propto \frac{l}{A} \quad \text{or} \quad R = \frac{\rho l}{A}$$

where ρ is the **resistivity** of the material. The units of resistivity are ohm-metres ($\Omega\,m$); for metals, the value of ρ is usually of the order of $10^{-8}\,\Omega\,m$.

Alternatively, the **conductivity** σ of the material may be calculated; conductivity is the reciprocal of resistivity, with units siemens per metre:

$$\sigma = \frac{1}{\rho}$$

Units: $S\,m^{-1}$

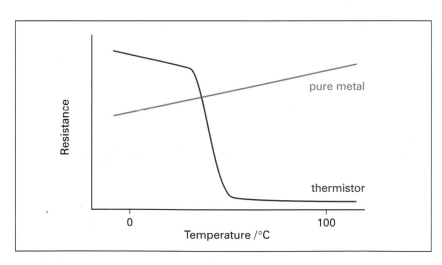

length l

1 unit of resistance

area A

double length = 2 units of resistance

double area = $\frac{1}{2}$ unit of resistance

▲ **Figure 2A23** *The resistance of a wire depends on its length* l *and cross-sectional area* A.

Semiconductors

Many electronic components, including transistors, integrated circuits and diodes, are made from semiconducting materials. These have electrical conductivity which falls between that of a good conductor such as a metal, and a good insulator such as a glass, ceramic or polymer. The conductivity of a semiconductor may be altered significantly by the process of 'doping', in which small amounts of impurities are added. This is discussed further on pages 120–21.

Changing resistance

The resistivity of metals increases gradually with temperature. This is made use of in resistance thermometers. **Thermistors** are semiconductor devices which are designed to have a resistance which changes dramatically over a narrow range of temperatures. They can be used as the basis of sensitive thermometers, since a small change in temperature can give a large change in resistance. They are also useful in control circuits, where their resistance changes at a critical temperature, and this can be sensed electronically (see page 290).

◀ **Figure 2A24** *The resistance of a pure metal increases by about one-third between 0°C and 100°C; the resistance of a thermistor may change by a factor of 100 over a range of 10 degrees. (This graph is for a negative temperature coefficient thermistor, whose resistance decreases with temperature.)*

pure metal

thermistor

Resistance

Temperature /°C

0

100

Keeping warm, staying cool

Hot things store energy. It can be difficult to keep the energy in something that is hot, and it can be difficult to keep energy out of things that need to stay cold. The water in a central heating system carries energy around the house; it must retain its energy in the tank, but release it in the radiators. Designing these components and choosing the right materials for them makes all this possible.

Heat capacity

It takes energy to raise the temperature of something. The greater the temperature rise, the more energy is required. For a particular object, the heat capacity C is the amount of energy required to raise its temperature by 1 °C (or 1 K).

$$\text{heat capacity} = \frac{\text{energy supplied}}{\text{temperature rise}} \qquad C = \frac{Q}{\Delta T}$$

Units: J K^{-1}

In some circumstances it is desirable for an object to have a high heat capacity; in others, a low value of C is wanted.

1 The plastic body of this electric kettle is chosen to have a low heat capacity. The kettle is designed to heat water; any energy which is supplied to raise the temperature of the kettle itself is wasted.

2 Plastic is used to make this ice-cube tray. When it is placed in the freezer, its low heat capacity means that its temperature will drop rapidly.

3 The bricks inside this storage heater have a high heat capacity. They are heated up at night, and release their store of energy during the day. If they had a low heat capacity, they would have to be heated up to a very high temperature, which might be dangerous in a domestic situation; the heater might also have to be much larger, making it bulky and unattractive.

4 Water is a convenient material for transporting energy around a house. The water inside a radiator has a high heat capacity, so the amount of energy stored in the tank, pipes and radiators is high. If the heat capacity was lower, the radiator would cool rapidly, and the water would have to be pumped back to the boiler much more rapidly.

5 The probe of the thermocouple thermometer has a low heat capacity. Any thermometer should have a small heat capacity compared to the object whose temperature it is measuring, so that the object's temperature is not significantly changed when the thermometer makes contact with it.

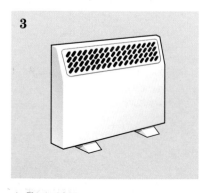

▲ Figure 2A25

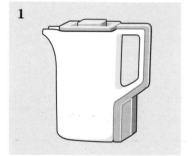

▲ Figure 2A26

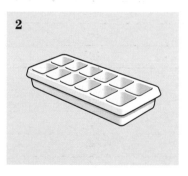

▲ Figure 2A27

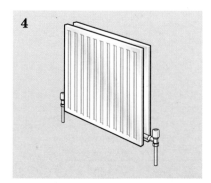

▲ Figure 2A28

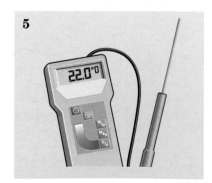

▲ Figure 2A29

Specific heat capacity

To describe the heat capacity of a material, rather than of a particular object, it is necessary to refer to its **specific heat capacity**, c. This is the amount of energy required to raise the temperature of 1 kg of the material by 1 °C (or 1 K). Hence to calculate the energy required Q to raise the temperature of mass m by an amount ΔT, the following relationship is used:

$$\text{energy required} = \text{mass} \times \text{specific heat capacity} \times \text{temperature rise}$$
$$Q = m\, c\, \Delta T$$

Water is notable for the high value of its specific heat capacity ($4200\,\text{J kg}^{-1}\,\text{K}^{-1}$). This makes it a very useful material for use in heating systems; oil might be used as an alternative, but its value of c is less than half that of water.

Energy supplies are expensive, and so it is important to consider the cost of the energy required in industrial processes. In many processes, materials are heated and then allowed to cool – for example, in the recycling of glass. This cost can be so high that it is cheaper to make new glass starting from fresh raw materials.

Measuring c and C

The principle of specific heat capacity measurements involves supplying energy (usually by means of an electrical heater) to an object or sample of material. The amount of energy supplied is determined from electrical measurements, and the temperature rise must also be found. Alternatively, the specimen may be heated to a known temperature, and then placed in water. When water + specimen have reached a uniform temperature, the final temperature can be used to calculate the energy which the specimen has supplied to the water (knowing the value of c for water). Hence the energy transferred from the specimen and its temperature change are both known, and so its heat capacity can be found.

In practice, care must be taken with the following points.

- The specimen must be uniformly heated; time must be allowed to minimize temperature differences within the specimen. If the temperature rise is over-estimated, this will lead to an **under-estimate** in the value of c.
- Account must be taken of energy supplied which does not heat the specimen; some heats the heater itself, and any insulating material. There are inevitable energy losses to the surroundings, no matter how good the insulation. This can give rise to an over-estimate of the energy, leading to an **over-estimate** in the value of c.

Material	Specific heat capacity c /J kg^{-1} K^{-1}
Water	4200
Oil	2100
Ethyl alcohol	2430
Mercury	140
Copper	390
Aluminium	900
Steel	~450
Concrete	3350
Granite	790
Glass	~840
Polypropylene	2100
Ice (−10 °C)	2220

▲ **Figure 2A30** *Specific heat capacities of selected materials.*

Duvets and ski jackets

Anyone buying a duvet is buying a lot of air. Duvets are good thermal insulators because the fabric of which they are made holds a lot of air, and air is a very good thermal insulator. At the Shirley Institute in Manchester, they have developed a machine called a togmeter to measure the **thermal resistance** of fabrics. In a togmeter, a sample of fabric is held, together with a standard sample for comparison, between a heated plate and a cold plate. The temperature difference across the fabric gives a measure of its thermal resistance.

Thermal resistance is measured in units called **togs**, where 1 tog is equal to $0.1\,\text{m}^2\text{KW}^{-1}$. Duvets are usually sold with a label indicating their tog-rating – typically 5 tog for a summer duvet, and 15 tog for winter weight. These units have been chosen so that they represent an increasing scale of 'warmth' for blankets etc., which customers can understand, and to give simple values – a typical medium-weight blanket has a tog rating of about 1.

▲ **Figure 2A31** *A Shirley togmeter in use, measuring the thermal resistance of a fabric sample.*

Area of house	U-value /$\text{W}\,\text{m}^{-2}\,\text{K}^{-1}$
Floor	0.45
Walls	0.45
Roof	0.25

▲ **Figure 2A32** *Maximum permitted U-values under Building Regulations (as at 1993).*

Building regulations

Architects and builders need to consider heat loss from the buildings which they design and build. The Building Regulations specify minimum standards for thermal insulation, and local authority inspectors check that these are being met. There are two types of specification. Firstly, there are limitations on the areas of windows and doors, since these represent prime sources of heat loss from buildings. Secondly, there are restrictions on the materials which may be used. Values of the maximum permitted **thermal conductance**, represented by the material's **U-value**, are given in Figure 2A32.

If a cavity wall material has a U-value of $0.5\,\text{W}\,\text{m}^{-2}\text{K}^{-1}$, this means that $0.5\,\text{W}$ of power will flow through $1\,\text{m}^2$ of the material for each $1\,\text{K}$ of temperature difference across the material. Note that these units are the reciprocal of those used in defining togs; builders need to be able to calculate the energy supply which will be needed to maintain the temperature of the inside of a house, so they need to know the rate at which energy will be lost.

Structure	U-value /$\text{W}\,\text{m}^{-2}\,\text{K}^{-1}$
Brick cavity wall, no foam	1.67
Cavity wall with foam insulation	0.44
Slate roof + plasterboard, no insulation	2.56
Slate roof + plasterboard, with 150 mm glass fibre	0.24
Concrete floor	0.42
Window: single-glazed	5.7
Window: double-glazed	2.8

▶ **Figure 2A33** *U-values of construction materials.*

Thermal conductivity

Togs and *U*-values are practical units for describing how good a material is at providing thermal insulation. They can describe complex materials – for example, fabrics which may be a mixture of different fibres, together with air, or wall materials, which may be a composite of brick, foam and air.

The scientific quantity to which these are related is **thermal conductivity**. In defining this quantity, it is necessary to consider a specimen of length l and cross-sectional area A – see Figure 2A34. One end is hotter than the other, so there is a flow of energy along the specimen.

If the temperature difference between the two ends is $\Delta\theta$, then there is a **temperature gradient** along the specimen given by

$$\text{temperature gradient} = \frac{\Delta\theta}{l}$$

The rate of flow of energy along the specimen, P, is proportional to the temperature gradient, and also to the cross-sectional area A. Hence

$$P = \frac{k\,A\,\Delta\theta}{l}$$

or rate of heat flow = thermal conductivity × area × temperature gradient.

Here, the constant of proportionality k is the thermal conductivity of the material. Values of k are given in Figure 2A35 and in the Reference section, Figure R3.2.

Insulating with air

Because air has very low thermal conductivity, it is a useful insulating material. A duvet is warm because its fibres or feathers trap air, and the air keeps heat loss to a low level. Similarly, most house insulation uses air, either trapped in cavity wall foam or in fibreglass or rockwool loft insulating material.

Convection currents can be established in air, and these can be a source of heat loss. Cavity wall foam prevents convection currents in the space between the two layers of bricks.

On a windy day, heat loss is greatly increased. This is because house insulation relies to a significant extent on the presence of a layer of still air next to the windows. This is typically 3 mm thick on a still day, giving 6 mm of still air as insulation. On a windy day, this still layer is blown away, taking heat with it and halving the insulating effect.

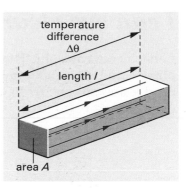

▲ **Figure 2A34** *Heat flow along a bar-shaped specimen. Note that the bar must be perfectly lagged (insulated), so that no energy escapes through the sides.*

Material	Thermal conductivity k /W m^{-1} K^{-1}
Aluminium	210
Copper	385
Iron	80
Steel	60
Brick	0.80 – 1.50
Concrete	1.40 – 1.50
Acrylic (e.g. Perspex)	0.17 – 0.25
Polyethene	0.33 – 0.52
Water	0.60
Air	0.024

▲ **Figure 2A35** *Values of thermal conductivity.*

I can see clearly now

Lenses control light. But which lens is right for the job? Lenses are found in cameras, plastic and glass spectacle lenses, contact lenses, the lenses in spy satellites that can read a newspaper from one hundred miles up. Lenses bend light – that is refraction. Controlling refraction is one way of controlling light.

Progress in optics

For some time, it seemed that optics – the science of controlling light – had reached a point where it was fully developed. However, the coming of lasers and optical communication systems has meant that there has been a great increase in work on new, high-quality optical materials. Fibre optic-cables criss-cross the globe. And a new generation of computers is on its way, in which light replaces electric currents for the speediest of high-speed computing power.

It is **refractive index** which controls the path of light. In a fibre optic-cable, monochromatic laser light – light of a single wavelength – travels inside a single plastic or glass fibre, thinner than a human hair. The material used must be of extreme purity – better than 99.999 999% pure – so that light entering one end of a fibre can be detected at the other end, hundreds of kilometres distant. In the most advanced fibres, the refractive index is graded, decreasing gradually from the centre of the fibre outwards, to ensure that a pulse of light stays as a tight pulse in its journey along the fibre.

Such high specifications require high standards – high standards of workmanship, and high standards of scientific understanding of the behaviour of light in transparent materials.

▶ **Figure 2A36**
Several optical fibres are wound together by this machine to make a single cable.

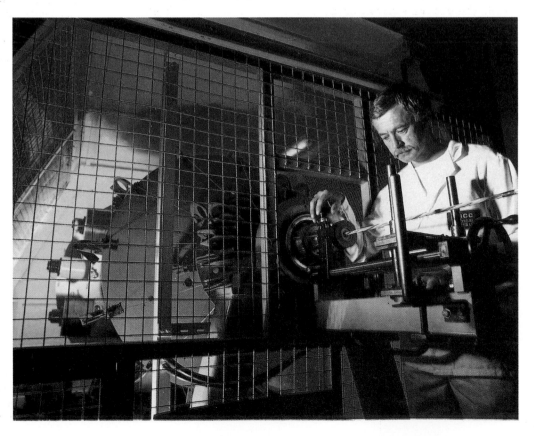

Refraction

Refraction is the bending of a ray of light when it passes from one medium into another. It happens because the speed of light is different in different materials. When light passes from air (fast) into glass (slower), it bends towards the normal. The degree of bending depends on the angle at which the ray strikes the glass. The greater the **angle of incidence**, i, the greater the **angle of refraction**, r. On leaving the glass, the ray is refracted back away from the normal.

Refractive index

The refractive index of a material is a measure of how much light slows down on entering the material from a vacuum (or air), where its speed is greatest. The refractive index of glass is about 1.5; this means that the speed of light decreases by a factor of 1.5 on entering glass.

It is not very convenient to measure the speed of light in different materials. Instead, practical measurements are based on Snell's Law, which involves measurement of the angles of incidence and refraction:

$$\text{refractive index } n = \frac{\sin i}{\sin r}$$

If a laboratory spectrometer is used, these angles can be measured to a fraction of a degree, and n can be calculated to an accuracy of ± 0.01. A more precise measurement can be made using a precision instrument such as an Abbé refractometer, which gives an uncertainty in n of ± 0.001 (see Figure 2A38).

An alternative way to find the refractive index of a transparent material involves immersing it in a liquid of known n. If the two refractive indices match, the test material will seem to disappear in the liquid. This technique is used for powdered or granulated materials, or when only a small amount is available, or when it is impossible to produce a specimen with a flat, smooth face.

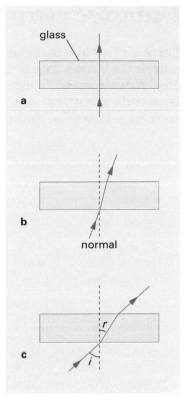

▲ **Figure 2A37** *a A ray of light entering glass along the normal continues along the normal. b, c The greater the angle of incidence, the more the ray is refracted. Note that angles i and r are measured relative to the normal, the line drawn perpendicular to the surface of the glass.*

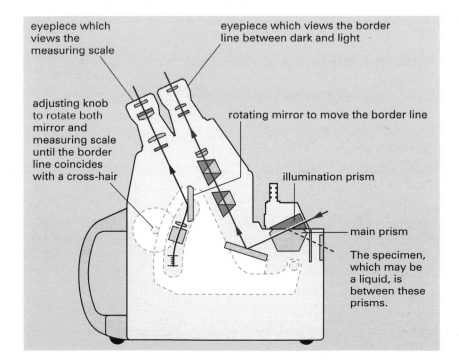

eyepiece which views the measuring scale

eyepiece which views the border line between dark and light

adjusting knob to rotate both mirror and measuring scale until the border line coincides with a cross-hair

rotating mirror to move the border line

illumination prism

main prism

The specimen, which may be a liquid, is between these prisms.

◀ **Figure 2A38** *This Abbé refractometer is one of several types of refractometer that uses the phenomenon of critical angle to measure refractive index.*

Material world

Earth to earth. All the materials we use come from the environment, and they all return there one day. Some, through rot and corrosion, return faster than we might like. Others outlast their usefulness and litter the environment for far too long. Materials scientists need to think about the effects of the environment on the materials they use, and the effects of their work on the environment.

From ore to scrap

Steel comes in thousands of varieties. Its basic raw materials are iron ore, limestone and coal. Quarrying and mining are activities which in themselves can scar the environment, leaving whole hillsides cut away and spoil heaps of waste material. A steel works produces waste of its own - slag and other effluent, waste gases and dust. A large plant like a steel works costs hundreds of millions of pounds, and is expected to last for 20 or 30 years. So the technology it uses and the environmental controls it incorporates may represent the standards of a generation ago.

Steel is one of the world's most widely used construction materials. It is used in transport, structural steel for buildings, white goods such as refrigerators and cookers, and a whole host of specialist areas - stainless steel sinks, surgical steels for medical instruments etc. Ultimately, all steel will corrode. At this stage, or earlier, it may be recycled, but for this to be feasible, it must be in a suitable condition. It may be inaccessible, perhaps because it is in the form of rods within concrete; it may be mixed with other materials such as plastics in the body of a car. The effort and energy required for recycling may not be justified. It may be better to start again from fresh raw materials. Making things from steel creates a lot of new scrap. For example, the scrap metal and plastic produced in the manufacture of a computer may weigh up to five times the weight of the computer itself.

British Steel has had to cope with the need for environmental improvements at its various steel works. It has put into operation a range of measures which reduce the impact of its activities on the environment.

Windblown dust from stockpiles	Use of water spraying and surface sealants to reduce dust
Dust, smoke and fumes from coke ovens	Fitting of hoods, ducting and washers
Iron oxide fume from blast furnaces	Fitting of extractors and fabric filters
Fumes from basic oxide steelmaking plants	Fitting of secondary extractors to existing plants, with electrostatic dust precipitators
Solvent emissions from paint plants	Pre-painted sheet steel ensures controlled disposal of solvents by incineration
Energy consumption	Recovery of hot air from coolers, controls to ensure complete combustion
Coke production	Coal and oil used directly in blast furnaces

Energy costs

Aluminium is an expensive metal. It is smelted using electricity, and electricity generation is an inefficient, wasteful process. So why should anyone consider using aluminium for car bodies?

The initial cost of aluminium for a car body is over twice that of steel. However, aluminium is much lighter, and this makes for greater fuel economy. The gain in mpg as a consequence of the weight reduction means that the price difference can be recovered after about 7000 miles. For a car that travels 100000 miles in its lifetime, the total energy savings could be as much as 30 times the additional energy consumed in manufacturing the aluminium as compared with steel.

The problem that remains is to convince the consumer that a product which is initially more expensive is worth buying because of the long-term savings in running costs.

Recycling – the best policy?

Recycling and reuse of materials is obviously desirable. But it isn't always the best policy. It takes energy to collect, transport and recycle waste materials. It can be more energy-efficient to start again from scratch, or find ways to improve materials so that they last longer in the environment, or find ways to do without the product in the first place.

▲ **Figure 2A39** *Rust to rust – the life cycle of steel, from steelworks ...*

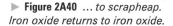

▶ **Figure 2A40** *... to scrapheap.*
Iron oxide returns to iron oxide.

Concrete proposals

Icy roads need salt, and salt spells danger to concrete. Just one salt-damaged concrete beam can lead to roadworks which cause traffic chaos for weeks. At the Building Research Establishment, scientist Kate Hollinshead has been studying the effect of chloride ions on the steel reinforcement of concrete. Her work can help to keep traffic flowing smoothly.

▲ **Figure 2A41** *Dr Kate Hollinshead took a chemistry degree at the Imperial College, before she specialized in Applied Electro-chemistry at Loughborough University of Technology. She went on to carry out research on corrosion problems in roads and bridges before joining the Building Research Establishment. Here she is at work, using an electrochemical probe on a concrete beam at the BRE test site.*

Rusty spaghetti

Many large structures are built of reinforced or prestressed concrete. These structures act as giant composites carrying forces of compression. Concrete is weak in tension, so steel rods carry the tension forces. Usually, concrete provides an alkaline environment (pH 12–13) for the steel, protecting it from rusting. The steel is said to be in a passive state.

At the motorway interchange at Gravelly Hill, Birmingham (Spaghetti Junction), salt used for de-icing attacked the steel, causing rusting. Rust occupies a larger volume than steel, and so the concrete may split. Salt can also cause pitting and local thinning. Stress concentrations in pitted regions of steel can build up so that they exceed the breaking stress of steel, even when the general level of stress is low and the structure appears quite safe.

Kate Hollinshead and her colleagues in the Metals Section of the Building Research Establishment have a range of instruments dedicated to detecting and monitoring corrosion. They use an outdoor exposure site to simulate the actual environment of a structure. Early detection of problems can save the cost and disruption caused when a major structure fails.

Outside in

Kate Hollinshead describes one technique used in the battle against corrosion.

'An electrochemical probe on the outer surface of reinforced concrete can reveal whether the hidden steel is rusting. We use a probe as shown in Figure 2A42. The saturated copper/copper sulphate electrode (CSE) forms one half cell, called the reference electrode. The interface between the steel and the concrete makes up the other half of the electrochemical cell. Moisture within the concrete between the CSE and the steel provides a conducting path, and the circuit is completed by a high resistance voltmeter connected between the CSE and the steel reinforcement.

'When the steel is corroding, the electrochemical cell acts like a battery, giving a high electromotive force (EMF, voltage). The higher the voltage, the more active is the corrosion.

'We use computer software to map the corrosion under the surface of reinforced concrete. Chloride ions tend to cause small areas of steel to suffer severely – chloride is said to be aggressive. The ions dissolve in the pore solution of the concrete where they can break down the passivity of the steel. The computer map (Figure 2A43) shows a test slab with a high concentration of chloride ions in the left-hand half.'

▼ **Figure 2A42** *This electrochemical cell generates an EMF which increases with the state of corrosion of the steel.*

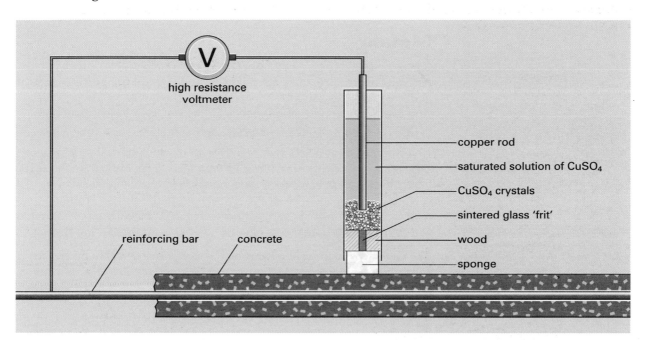

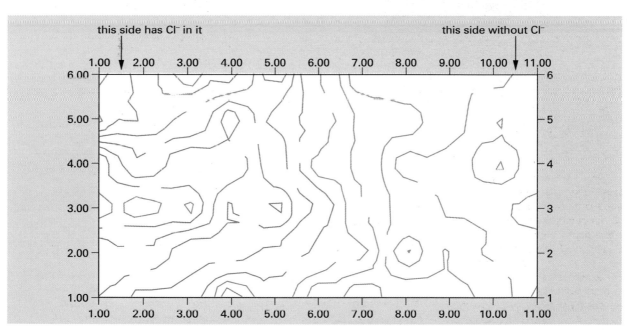

▲ **Figure 2A43** *This computer-drawn contour map shows the variation of EMF (in mV) for a concrete slab; the left-hand half has a high concentration of chloride ions. High voltages reveal active corrosion.*

▶ **Figure 2A44** *Electrode potentials reveal the state of steel corrosion.*

CSE potential /mV	Condition
<200	passive
200 – 350	passive/active
>350	active

Chemical corrosion

A material which has all the right physical properties may turn out to be a bad choice if it is attacked by chemicals while in use. Choosing a more expensive material may well be justified if it makes it possible to produce a component which will last much longer, require less maintenance and give better value over the whole life of the product.

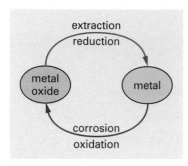

▲ **Figure 2A45** *The cycle of metal extraction and corrosion.*

Metals

Corrosion tends to turn metals back to oxides, which is how they occur naturally in ores. Iron ores are relatively abundant in the Earth's crust and blast furnaces can turn iron oxides into the metal on a large scale. As a result iron and its alloys, steels, are widely used for construction of cars, buildings, bridges and many other products.

Unfortunately iron reacts very readily with oxygen and water. When iron and steel corrode they turn into rust which is a form of hydrated iron(III) oxide. Rust is permeable to air and moisture so the metal goes on corroding underneath the rust. Corrosion costs the British economy many millions of pounds per year providing a big incentive for research and development to find cost effective methods for preventing rusting.

The usual way to prevent rusting is to coat the metal with a barrier to keep out air and water. The barrier can be a film of oil, a layer of paint or a coating of plastic. Galvanizing coats iron with zinc, a more reactive metal which corrodes in preference to iron. In a similar way steel pipelines are connected to blocks of magnesium buried in the ground to give them extra protection.

Other metals, such as chromium and nickel, are much more resistant to chemical attack, but they are expensive. Stainless steel is an alloy consisting of about 74% iron, 18% chromium and 8% nickel. Like iron, chromium reacts with oxygen but the oxide is not hydrated and it forms a thin, impermeable layer on the surface of the metal which stops any further reaction.

Aluminium is another metal which resists corrosion because of an oxide layer on its surface. Anodizing is an electrolytic process which thickens the oxide layer sufficiently for anodized aluminium to be used out of doors without further protection. Freshly anodized aluminium adsorbs dyes so it is possible to colour the metal for decoration.

Copper and lead are metals which are much less chemically reactive than other metals, so much so that they are used as roofing materials. There are still many homes with lead plumbing. In hard water areas this is not a problem because salts in the water react with the metal surface forming insoluble lead salts which stop further attack. In areas where the water is soft the metal slowly dissolves and there is a risk of lead poisoning.

Polymers

Chemically, polythene is one of the simplest polymers. Polythene molecules are essentially very long hydrocarbon chains (see page 108). Like the hydrocarbons in petrol, polythene burns but tends not to react with reagents such as acids and alkalis or mix with water. The general inertness of the plastic makes it suitable for storing some chemicals as well as for food bags and wrapping film.

The behaviour of natural rubber shows that cross-linking (see page 109) can affect how polymers behave when mixed with other chemicals. Raw rubber dissolves completely in a hydrocarbon solvent such as methylbenzene. Cross-linking rubber by vulcanization with sulphur stops the polymer molecules mixing freely with solvent molecules.

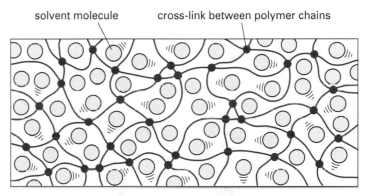

▲ **Figure 2A46** *Rubber dissolves in a solvent.*

Vulcanized rubber does, however, absorb solvents because after cross-linking the material becomes a three-dimensional network which can stretch to make room for solvent molecules between the polymer chains. Modern disposable nappies are much more effective because they include granules of highly absorbent polymers designed to swell and take in large amounts of water.

Because polymers can absorb small molecules, it is very important to choose the right type of plastic container when storing liquid fuels, lubricants, household chemicals and drinks. Early plastic bottles for fizzy drinks could not be stocked for long because the carbon dioxide molecules leaked out through the polymer chains.

The development of soluble laundry bags is an innovation which shows that it is sometimes desirable to have a polymer with a limited life. Hospital workers can put infected linen into the bags, seal them and then put them straight into washing machines without further handling in the laundry. The bags consist of a grade of polyvinyl alcohol which is impermeable to bacteria but soluble in hot water.

▲ **Figure 2A47** *Vulcanized rubber swells in a solvent such as methylbenzene by absorbing small hydrocarbon molecules.*

Ceramics

It is not just that glass is transparent that makes it suitable for test tubes and other chemical apparatus, glass has a high melting point, and above all it is very resistant to chemical attack. Glass, like many other ceramics, consists of oxides so it cannot burn.

Materials which are difficult to melt or change in any way by heating are **refractories**. Some industrial processes take place at very high temperatures. A furnace lining of a refractory ceramic material is essential because anything else would soon melt or burn away.

Fireclay is the raw material for making refractory bricks. Some industries need more specialized materials, such as pure silicon dioxide or magnesium oxide. Molten glass and the slags formed during smelting are very corrosive when red hot and they would quickly eat away ordinary bricks made of fireclay.

▲ **Figure 2A48** *Relining a steel furnace with refractory bricks.*

Packing salad cream

If a company producing mustard decides to increase its range by selling a special brand of salad cream, it may start by designing the actual product – the taste and consistency must be just right. But they must also design a container which will allow it to stand on a shop or supermarket shelf in good condition for a certain time – its shelf-life.

The science of packaging

Food scientists need to know about chemistry and microbiology. Food packaging and preservation are closely linked. So any design for a salad cream container, including the choice of material, must take into account all the physical, chemical and biological properties of the cream.

The Institute of Packaging at Melton Mowbray in Leicestershire has information to help design all kinds of packaging. Standard lists of properties and other details of all the available materials are filed in their library. How does the salad cream company decide?

Physical state: Salad cream is a viscous liquid.

General properties: Salad cream is sticky, odorous, perishable, and potentially corrosive (because of the acids – acetic and citric – which it may contain).

▶ **Figure 2A49** *When choosing a packaging material for a new product, designers must take into account the product's state and properties.*

Physical state
Gas
Runny liquid
Viscous liquid
Paste
Liquid + solid
Powder
Granules
Tablets
Solid block
Capsules

General properties
Corrosive
Toxic
Odorous
Volatile
Perishable
Sticky
Corrodible
Fragile
Abrasive
Easily scratched

Providing protection

During the salad cream's shelf-life, the bottle must prevent leakage and contamination from outside. But is there anything else which salad cream should be protected from? Is it sensitive to temperature changes, moisture changes and chemical changes? How does it behave if exposed to oxygen, to odours and to light?

The emulsion of fat, oil and water may break down with time. Light can catalyse the oxidation of fats, and this may cause fading. Microbiological changes affect the flavour, appearance, quality and wholesomeness of the salad cream. Acids in the cream may react with the material of the bottle. And all foodstuffs deteriorate biochemically with time, however well protected.

The answers to these questions leave the salad cream company with just a few choices of container. A steel or aluminium can will be ruled out. Salad cream is used a little at a time, and cans are difficult to reseal. That's why foodstuffs like ketchup, honey and vinegar are not packed in cans. Another reason is that most food packed in cans is actually cooked inside the can before it leaves the factory.

In the end, the choice is between a glass or plastic bottle. Glass is traditionally used. It is cheaper than plastic, but plastic is lighter and much less likely to break.

▲ **Figure 2A50** *A modern plastic bottle is a complex product. For these bottles, the decision was taken to use a laminated plastic called 'Lamicon', produced by the Metal Box Company. This is a composite of five layers of plastic. It is blown into shape inside a mould, which can be used to give a distinctively shaped bottle. The inner and outer layers are water and acid resistant (often of polypropylene or polythene), and the central barrier layer of ethyl vinyl alcohol resists the passage of oxygen and oils. Some barrier materials allow the manufacturer to fill the bottles with mayonnaise which is still hot from the production line.*

A mouthful of metal

False teeth, fillings and dental plates – all of these face a hostile environment, inside our mouths. And nowadays there are artificial hip-joints, pacemakers, heart valves and more, all technological products designed to survive inside the human body, to help us survive. What properties must these materials have to do their jobs in this demanding environment?

Open wide

Teeth must be strong. They are subject to quite severe mechanical stresses. The muscles of the human jaw are capable of crushing teeth together with as much as 600 newtons of force. This is roughly equivalent to the force experienced by the feet of an average build adult jumping off a table. So the tooth replacement materials used by dentists for fillings and false teeth have to stand up to that kind of impact as well as the daily grind of chewing which causes the tooth surface to wear. The cleaning of teeth also wears away the surface, especially if the more highly abrasive smokers' toothpastes are used.

Tooth replacement materials also have to perform despite being continuously exposed to the wide variety of chemicals that can be found in saliva and the even wider variety that we temporarily add to our mouths as we eat and drink. Acids are most potentially damaging. Fruits can be very acidic and some soft drinks have a pH of between 2 and 3. After drinking a can of cola, many people are aware that their teeth feel less smooth and slippery. This isn't because the cola has left a deposit on the teeth. It's because some of the mineral on the surface of the teeth has dissolved in the acidic liquid. Teeth only survive cola drinking because minerals from saliva are re-deposited on the tooth once the mouth returns to normal pH. Tooth replacement materials will not necessarily be re-mineralized in this way.

Dental materials

Metals are ideal for taking the heavy loads of chewing. Gold is particularly good because it is strong enough to take the impact of chewing and yet soft enough to wear a little, so that it wears at the same rate as the surrounding teeth and can last a lifetime. Amalgam is a mixture of mercury with other metals – silver, tin, zinc and copper. It has similar thermal expansion properties to natural tooth, so these fillings usually fit well. However, there are worries about the toxicity of amalgam materials, and most people don't like the appearance of metal fillings, so these are usually reserved for back teeth.

Porcelain, a ceramic, is used for making artificial teeth and crowns. These can look wonderfully natural, although getting them to look right is as much an art as a science. Porcelain can be made to have the translucence and slight touch of fluorescence seen in natural teeth. It can be made sharp, and it stays sharp. However, it is brittle and not as strong as amalgam or gold. Its expansion does not match that of natural teeth.

Composites of plastic and inorganic material are ideal for filling front teeth because they can be made of a colour that matches the patient's own teeth. They are soft as they are placed in the mouth and then rapidly harden. These materials are poor conductors of heat, so that the nerve is not affected by hot drinks. However, these materials cannot withstand severe mechanical stress, so they are not usually recommended for filling back teeth.

A Scottish vet fits elderly sheep with stainless steel false teeth so that they live longer. It's cheaper than buying new sheep.

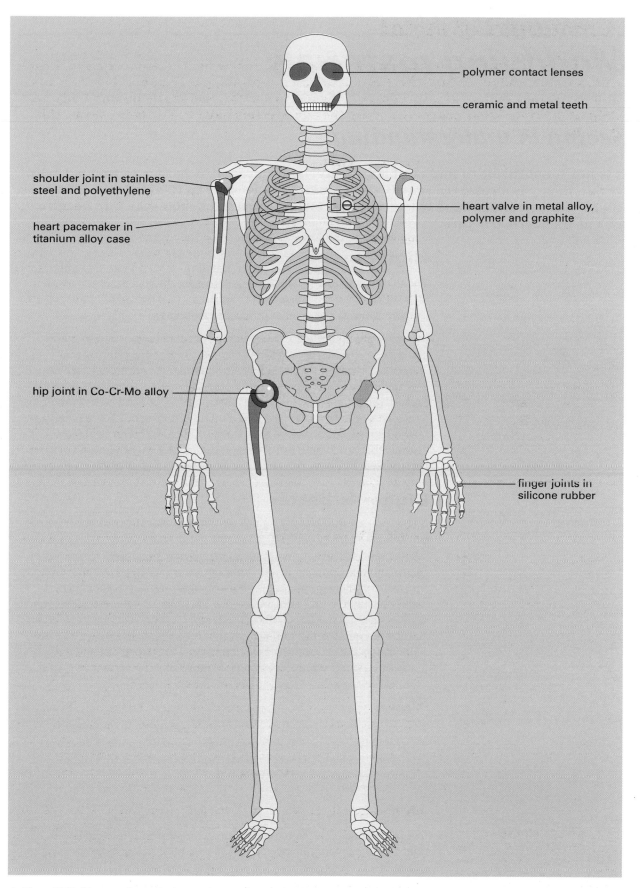

polymer contact lenses

ceramic and metal teeth

shoulder joint in stainless steel and polyethylene

heart pacemaker in titanium alloy case

heart valve in metal alloy, polymer and graphite

hip joint in Co-Cr-Mo alloy

finger joints in silicone rubber

▲ **Figure 2A51** *More and more advanced materials are finding their way into the human body.*

Modifying materials

Seeing is understanding

It is not too difficult to find out how a material behaves. It is harder to find out why. Dr Sue Impey is a research scientist at Cranfield University in Bedfordshire. She says, 'If you want to understand why a material behaves in a particular way, you need to look at its microstructure.'

High power

The microstructure of a material is its structure on a scale too small to be seen with the naked eye. This can mean at the level of atoms, or on a larger scale, at the level of grains or crystallites.

Information about a material's microstructure is important in many industries – health care, food, electronics, heavy engineering and chemicals. Work in the School of Manufacturing and Industrial Science at Cranfield involves making and modifying new materials, developing protective surfaces with thin coatings, examining failures and materials which do not behave as expected. So Sue Impey needs to be able to see how materials and surfaces have been treated, and details like the crystal structure of a metal and even the arrangement of atoms within the crystals. But how can she hope to see such fine detail?

Bigger is better

A vital tool for investigating microstructure is the electron microscope. While an optical microscope magnifies up to 1000 times, an electron microscope can achieve magnifications greater than 5000 times. An optical microscope uses visible light with a wavelength of about 500 nm. An electron microscope uses a beam of electrons in place of light. Its wavelength is 0.1 nm ($1 \, nm = 10^{-9} \, m$). This tiny wavelength allows much greater resolution – far smaller details can be seen. The electron beam also gives a good depth of focus, so that a rough surface can be clearly seen from top to bottom at the same time. That is why scanning electron microscope photographs often look dramatically three-dimensional.

SEM

A scanning electron microscope looks at surfaces. The finely-focused electron beam scans rapidly over the specimen. Secondary electrons produced at the surface are collected and converted into a signal to produce an image on a TV screen.

TEM

In a transmission electron microscope, a broad electron beam passes right through a very thin specimen (10 to 200 nm). The beam is scattered depending on the material's thickness and composition. This machine makes it possible to magnify up to hundreds of thousand of times, so that the atomic planes in the crystal structure of the material can be examined.

EPMA

Where the electron beam hits the surface of the specimen, X-rays are emitted. The electron probe microanalyser detects these X-rays; their wavelength allows the chemical elements present to be determined. So the surface, structure and composition can be found. It's a very useful way to begin understanding why a material behaves the way it does.

Learning to fly

Sue Impey can use all the machines in the department, but the newer machines are easier to operate because their controls have been simplified. The older machines look rather like aircraft cockpits!

'It can take a student just a few hours to learn how to use the simplest machine. But the real skill is in deciding what to look for in a specimen, and then interpreting what you see. The image may be so magnified that it's difficult to understand what you're looking at.'

◀ **Figure 2B1** *Sue Impey at the controls of an electron microscope. After working as a chemist in the pharmaceutical industry, she turned to materials science. For her PhD, she studied the best way of recycling aluminium (for example, drink cans), and how to get the most metal out of the process.*

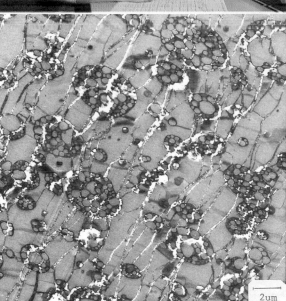

▲ **Figure 2B2** *The microstructure of a polymer containing rubber particles. This electron micrograph shows that the polymer is weakened by tiny cracks; however, the rubber particles have successfully prevented the cracks from spreading throughout the material.*

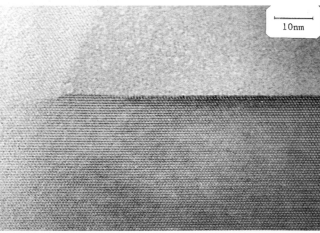

▲ **Figure 2B3** *A plane of atoms in a ceramic crystal. This electron micrograph shows a boundary between grains in the material.*

Metals

The discovery of production methods for metals such as bronze and iron was a great advance in technology – the Stone Age was replaced by the Bronze Age and then the Iron Age. Nowadays, metals are used for a great range of applications. Perhaps the most striking property of metals, for which there is no real substitute, is their electrical conductivity. This property gives a clue to the underlying structure of metals.

Free electrons

Metals: Typical properties
State: solid at room temperature – exception: mercury
Electrical conductivity: high
Thermal conductivity: high
Stiffness (Young modulus): generally high
Strength: variable
Toughness: generally high – brittleness often caused by impurities
Opaque to light

Four-fifths of the elements in the Periodic Table are metals. To understand why they show metallic behaviour, it is necessary to understand the way in which atoms are arranged in a metal and the bonding between atoms which holds a solid piece of metal together.

Typically, the atoms of a metal are arranged in a regular structure. They lie in straight rows, the rows form flat planes, and the planes make up a regular three-dimensional array. Such a regular array is called a crystalline structure. It is not obvious, looking at the outside of a piece of metal, that there is a regular atomic arrangement inside. However, this can be revealed using electron microscopy or X-ray diffraction. Figure 2B4 shows an electron microscope image of the crystalline structure of a metal.

▶ **Figure 2B4** *This electron microscope photograph shows the regular arrangement of atoms in a gold crystal. The distance between the centres of the gold atoms is 0.204 nm.*

The atoms of a metal are bonded strongly together. Metallic bonding arises when metal atoms are brought together; electrons break away, and become free to move about within the material. The atoms that have lost electrons are now positively charged ions, and it is these ions that form the regular array. The delocalized ('free') electrons are attracted to the ions, because of their opposite electric charge, and so they act as a glue, holding the metal together.

The free electrons within a metal give it its high electrical and thermal conductivity. They are free to move within the metal, and so they provide an effective mechanism for transferring electrical or thermal energy. This is discussed in more detail on page 118.

Grain structure

In general, the crystalline structure of a metal is not visible. However, there are occasions when metal crystals can be seen with the naked eye. For example, the thin zinc layer which protects the steel of a galvanized bucket often appears as a patchwork of areas of different shades of grey. Each of these areas is a separate grain or crystallite of zinc; in each grain, the metallic atoms are arranged in uniform rows over distances which may be as great as a centimetre or two. In neighbouring grains, the rows are arranged with different orientations, and this gives rise to some grains appearing darker than others.

Grains arise because metals have usually formed from molten metal. As the hot liquid cools, it starts to solidify. Tiny crystals start to grow at many points within the liquid; eventually, all of the liquid becomes solid, and every tiny crystal has become a grain within the solid. Usually, it is necessary to cut, polish and etch a piece of metal to reveal its inner grain structure.

Crystal defects

In principle, metals are strong. In order to break a metal, the strong metallic bonding within the material must be overcome. However, a metal is often weakened by the presence of defects within its regular crystalline structure. Figure 2B6 shows five important types of crystalline defects which affect the mechanical properties of metals. An understanding of how to control these defects allows materials scientists to design improved metals which have better mechanical properties.

▲ **Figure 2B5** *The grain structure of brass shows up in this photograph taken with polarized light using an optical microscope. Magnification × 550.*

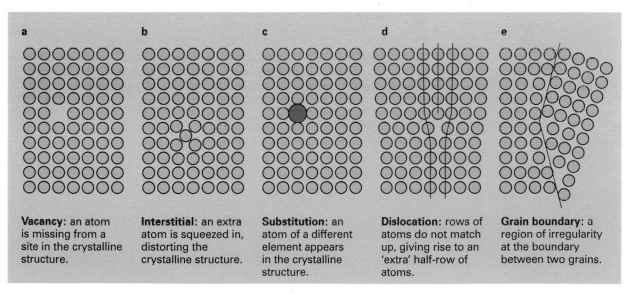

a	b	c	d	e
Vacancy: an atom is missing from a site in the crystalline structure.	**Interstitial:** an extra atom is squeezed in, distorting the crystalline structure.	**Substitution:** an atom of a different element appears in the crystalline structure.	**Dislocation:** rows of atoms do not match up, giving rise to an 'extra' half-row of atoms.	**Grain boundary:** a region of irregularity at the boundary between two grains.

▲ **Figure 2B6** *Five types of defect which appear in regular crystalline structures.*

Weak metals

In order for metals to be shaped, they must be ductile or molten. However, a ductile metal is a weak metal. There is a balance to strike between having a metal which is soft enough to be shaped and yet which is strong enough to be useful.

Metals are weak because of some of the defects in their structure. A perfect metal crystal is strong; the metallic bonding holds the atoms tightly together. However, in practice, dislocations in the crystal structure make it weaker by a factor of as much as 1000. To change the shape of a piece of metal, it is necessary for the atoms to be rearranged. Dislocations make it possible for planes of atoms to slide over one another relatively easily. Since there are increasing numbers of dislocations at higher temperatures, metals become weaker and softer as they are heated; i.e. their yield stress is reduced and the range of ductility is extended.

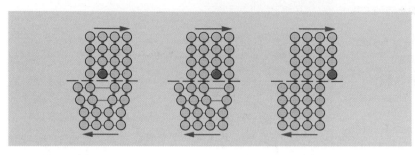

▲ **Figure 2B7** *A dislocation in a metal crystal makes it easy for planes of atoms to slide sideways over each other. This is a major source of weakness in metals.*

Stronger metals

To make metals stronger, it is necessary to prevent the movement of dislocations. There are several ways of doing this.

Work hardening

If a piece of iron is hammered, it becomes stronger (and harder). The hammering introduces many more dislocations, which become tangled together so that they are less likely to move. Work hardening comes about in many different ways; for example, when a metal is bent, or if it is drawn through a die to form a wire.

Annealing

This technique is used to reduce the number of dislocations in a metal. The metal is kept at a temperature below its melting point for some time, so that any dislocations have a chance to move out of the crystal structure. It is gradually cooled so that it retains its softness.

Alloying

By mixing in atoms of a different metal, the crystal structure is disrupted. The movement of dislocations relies on a regular structure, so alloying increases strength. (Carbon atoms in steel act in this way to increase the strength of iron.)

Quenching

If a piece of steel is heated to a sufficiently high temperature, its crystal structure changes. If it is then plunged into cold water (quenched), carbon atoms have insufficient time to move and are trapped within the structure. The result is a distorted, irregular structure in which it is difficult for dislocations to move, and so the metal is stronger. Quenching is the opposite process to annealing.

Long-life steels

Steel is vulnerable to corrosion. There are many established processes for preventing steel from rusting – for example, galvanizing, in which steel is coated with a protective coating of zinc. In the past, many items were first fabricated and then galvanized. Nowadays, many consumer products and even buildings are made of steel which has been covered at the steelworks with a complex series of layers of protective coatings. As many as four different coatings may be applied to each side of the steel sheet, and the final layer may include a desired colouring.

Colorcoated steel: used for cladding on steel-framed industrial buildings.

Stelvetite steel: used for video recorders, computers, kitchen appliances.

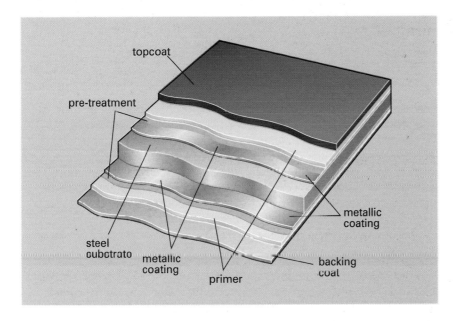

◀ **Figure 2B8** *Layer sequence of colorcoated steel.*

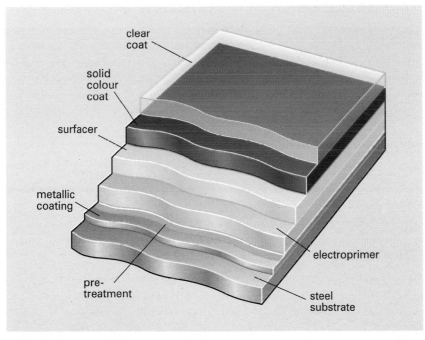

◀ **Figure 2B9** *Layer sequence of stelvetite steel.*

Ceramics

Many traditional ceramic materials are based on clay. Pottery and bricks are made from clay which has been mixed with other materials and then fired in a kiln to give a hard, strong, brittle material. Nowadays, there is an increasing range of engineering ceramics which have been developed to work in demanding situations – at high temperatures, as high-voltage electrical insulators, inside the human body and at the heart of computers.

Ceramics: Typical properties
State: high melting point solids
Electrical conductivity: low
Thermal conductivity: variable
Stiffness: high
Strength: high in compression, low in tension
Toughness: low because brittle (but new ceramics are much tougher and less brittle)
Can be opaque or transparent

Forming and firing

There are two ways to make a china cup: put the clay in a mould or, for the skillful, shape it on a spinning potter's wheel. Firing the clay in a kiln results in a product which is much stronger than the clay from which it was made. Clay has many tiny mineral grains in it; when it is fired, these grains partially melt. A glassy material spreads between the grains and holds them together when the clay cools down. This process of forming a solid material by pressing grains together and heating is called sintering.

Sintering is an ancient process which reaches its most refined form in the production of some of the modern ceramics which have been developed for high-tech engineering applications. For example, ceramic parts are used in some vehicle engines, because they can operate at higher temperatures than metals. The hotter an engine is, the more efficiently it can run. So ceramic coatings such as zirconium oxide are sprayed on to the cylinders and piston heads of some diesel engines. Turbine blades may be made from ceramics sintered from powder at high temperatures and pressures.

When ceramic materials are made from powders, they often retain a grainy texture. The boundaries between grains are likely to be weaker than the material from which the grains are made, and so the grain boundaries are regions of weakness. The material is likely to break between the grains.

▶ **Figure 2B10** *The grainy structure of this specimen of alumina (aluminium oxide, Al_2O_3) reflects the fact that it has been formed from particles of powder.*

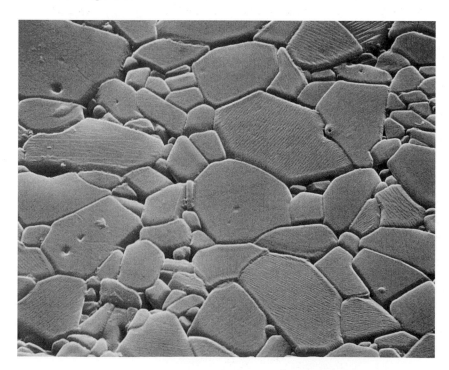

Bonding in ceramics

Ceramic materials are non-metallic and inorganic. They are generally oxides, carbides or nitrides. Figure 2B11 shows the formulae for some engineering ceramics, together with their melting points. Because they have such high melting points, ceramics are very important as refractories (furnace and kiln linings, for example). Many ceramics are oxides so, unlike metals and polymers, they do not burn in air – they are already oxidized.

Material		Melting point /°C
Ceramics		
Aluminium oxide (alumina)	Al_2O_3	2054
Magnesium oxide (magnesia)	MgO	2800
Zirconium oxide (zirconia)	ZrO_2	2770
Boron carbide	B_4C	2450
Silicon carbide	SiC	2650
Boron nitride	BN	3000
Silicon nitride	Si_3N_4	1900
Titanium nitride	TiN	2950
Molybdenum silicide	$MoSi_2$	2030
Metals		
Iron	Fe	1535
Nickel	Ni	1453
Aluminium	Al	660

◀ **Figure 2B11** *Composition and melting points of some engineering ceramics. (Some metals are included for comparison.)*

Ceramics with ionic giant structures

Some ceramics form when reactive metals, which tend to form positive ions, combine with reactive non-metals, which tend to form negative ions. The oppositely charged ions attract each other and build up a giant lattice held together by **ionic bonding**. Magnesium oxide is an example of a ceramic with this type of structure.

Ceramics with covalent giant structures

Silicon carbide is not as hard as diamond (a form of **carbon**) but harder than **corundum** (a crystalline variety of aluminium oxide). Hence its common name, carborundum, which suggests a material with in-between properties. In industry, all three materials are used as abrasives for cutting and grinding. They all have similar structures. They consist of giant, three-dimensional networks held together by covalent bonds.

Covalent bonds are strong bonds. They have a definite length and direction, so a covalent structure is rigid and hard to deform or melt. Another feature of covalent bonds is that the bonding electrons are localized, so there are no charged particles which are free to move and carry an electric current.

Glasses

There is no such thing as glass – but there are many different glasses. Some glass is found naturally, formed when the heat of a volcano melts silica in the form of sand. But glass technology involves much more than this – modern glasses are complex materials made by combining a range of substances to achieve useful properties – glasses to withstand high temperatures, rapid heating and cooling, intense radiation and much more. There is even glass which isn't transparent.

Making glass

Glass is usually made by melting together a mixture of substances at a temperature of about 1500°C. Soda-lime glass (see Figure 2B13) is a general purpose material, suitable for making windows, bottles, drinking glasses etc. Unless high-purity raw materials are used, it is likely to be coloured pale blue or green, as can be seen by looking at a sheet of glass edge-on.

Glass must be cooled quickly to give a transparent material. The resulting atomic structure is often described as **amorphous**; it is a somewhat disordered structure compared to the orderly crystalline arrangement of other ceramic materials. If cooled more slowly, tiny crystals have time to form, and the glass is likely to have an opal, non-transparent appearance.

Borosilicate glasses (e.g. Pyrex) consist mainly of silica and boric oxide. They can withstand rapid heating and cooling (high resistance to thermal shock) and so are useful for cooking dishes, chemical plant and laboratory apparatus.

▶ **Figure 2B12** *Many kinds of glass are made from a mixture of substances. Their structure is irregular; it retains some of the randomness of the structure of the liquid from which it formed.*

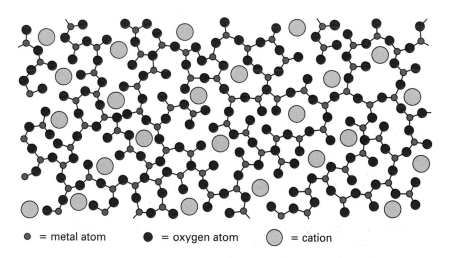

● = metal atom   ● = oxygen atom   ◯ = cation

▶ **Figure 2B13** *Typical chemical analysis for soda-lime glasses.*

Compound in glass	% present	Chemical formula	Source
Silica (silicon dioxide)	70–74	SiO_2	SiO_2 in sand
Sodium oxide	12–16	Na_2O	Na_2CO_3, soda ash
Calcium oxide	5–11	CaO	$CaCO_3$, limestone
Magnesium oxide	1–3	MgO	$MgCa(CO_3)_2$
Aluminium oxide	1–3	Al_2O_3	impurity in sand
Ferric oxide	~0.1	Fe_2O_3	impurity in sand

Breaking glass

Glass is a brittle material. To break glass (and many other ceramic materials), it is enough to scratch the surface and then use a small force. The scratch widens into a crack which spreads rapidly through the bulk of the material. (All brittle materials break in a similar way, although the imperfections are not always on the surface.)

Glass is weak because its surface is usually covered in cracks and other flaws. This reduces its strength by a factor of 100 or more, below that which would be expected if its strength was determined by the strength of the bonds between ions in its structure. These cracks were investigated in the 1920s by A. A. Griffith at the Royal Aircraft Establishment at Farnborough. Griffith was able to show that stress within a material is concentrated around a crack (see Figure 2B14) and that, although the material might generally be well below the theoretical level of breaking stress, at the tip of a crack the stress might be magnified 100 times.

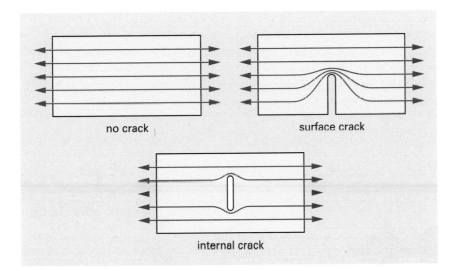

no crack

surface crack

internal crack

◀ **Figure 2B14** *The stress within a piece of glass is highly concentrated around the tip of a crack.*

Strengthening glass

There are two general ways of strengthening glass, to overcome the weakness introduced by Griffith cracks. They both rely on the idea that ceramics are generally weak in tension (because of the cracks) but strong in compression (because compression closes up the cracks).

In **thermal toughening**, the glass is heated, and then the surface is rapidly chilled so that it does not have time to shrink as it cools. The interior cools more slowly, and shrinks more than the surface. When the entire piece is cool, the interior is permanently in tension, and the surface permanently in compression. This technique is used in making some car windscreens; it is sometimes possible to see the pattern of the cold air jets used to cool the surface. The glass is tougher because the surface is in compression. Any crack which starts on the surface will automatically close up, rather than propagating through the material. See the previous paragraphs on this page.

In **chemical toughening**, a hot glass article is placed in contact with a hot salt. This is chosen so that small ions dissolve out from the surface of the glass, and larger ions replace them from the salt. When the glass is cooled, the larger ions keep the surface in a state of compression.

Polymers or plastics?

Polymers are materials made from long chain molecules. Materials technologists can control the properties of polymers in many ways – by changing the chemical composition, by changing the length of the chains, by rearranging the molecules to change the microstructure, by mixing in other substances. The final products are known as plastics.

Long chain molecules

There are many naturally-occurring polymers: cellulose, which forms the structure of wood, and rubber are examples. However, the development of a vast range of synthetic polymers means that polymers can be thought of as twentieth-century materials.

Polymer molecules are long, thin and flexible, free to coil and twist like a long metal chain or a Christmas garland. Consequently, they don't pack together very well. Sometimes they do pack in an orderly, crystalline way, but often the microstructure of a polymer is irregular (amorphous).

Polymer molecules are formed from groups of smaller molecules, called monomers, which link together in the process of polymerization. Each molecule typically consists of 1000 to 10 000 of these units joined together, although the number may be as high as 100 000. Figure 2B15 shows two ways of representing the structure of polythene, formed from ethene monomers C_2H_4.

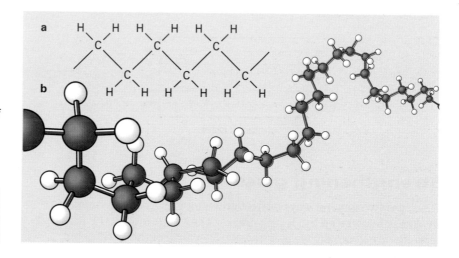

> **Figure 2B15** *The structure of polythene.* ***a*** *This 2-dimensional representation shows how the atoms which make up a polythene molecule are bonded to their neighbours.* ***b*** *This 3-dimensional representation gives a more realistic impression of the shape of a polythene molecule. The long molecule is flexible because it can rotate about individual covalent bonds between carbon atoms.*

Note: The correct systematic name for polythene is **polyethene**.

> **Polymers:**
> **Typical properties**
> State: mostly solid at room temperature
> Electrical conductivity: good insulators
> Thermal conductivity: good insulators; polymer foams are excellent insulators
> Stiffness (Young modulus): low
> Strength: low
> Transparency: depends on microstructure
> Density: lower than metals, ceramics

> **Silicones** are a group of polymers based on a chain of alternating silicon and oxygen atoms. Silicones are used for lubricants, gaskets, electrical insulators and body implants. They and the vast majority of carbon-based polymers are synthetic – products of the worldwide chemical industry.

Strong and weak bonding

Polymers tend to be weak materials. One way to increase their strength is to extrude or draw the material out; in these processes, the long chain molecules are rearranged so that they become aligned in a parallel structure (Figure 2B16). Why does this make the material stronger?

Atoms *within* a polymer chain are joined by covalent bonds. These are strong bonds, and make it difficult to break the molecule. However, the bonds *between* molecules are much weaker. This means that it is relatively easy to pull a polymer material apart by overcoming these weak bonds between the molecules.

Many plastic bags and plastic drinks cups are made from drawn or extruded polymers. They are often easy to tear in one direction, but much stronger in a direction at 90°.

Controlling strength and stiffness

The strength and stiffness of a polymer depend on its molecular structure and on the nature of the bonding both within and between its molecules. Polymer chemists control polymer properties by altering: chain length, chain branching, interchain forces and cross-linking.

Chain length

A polymer such as polythene lies between two extremes. At one end of the spectrum is methane gas consisting of small separate molecules able to move with almost complete freedom because they are affected only by very weak, intermolecular forces. At the other extreme is diamond where there is no freedom of movement because all the atoms are held in a giant structure by strong covalent bonds.

In polythene the atoms are covalently bonded into long molecular chains so they have less freedom than methane molecules but much greater freedom than atoms in diamond since only weak forces act between the chains. The covalent bonds in the linear polythene chains are directional, but rotation about the bonds is possible. So the chains are flexible and can slither about in tangled coils. Breaking a piece of polythene involves pulling chains from an entangled mass which gives the polymer greater strength than it would have simply from weak intermolecular forces between short sections of neighbouring chains.

Chain branching

There are two methods for making polythene and they produce plastics with slightly different properties. Low-density polythene has numerous short side chains branching off from the main chain. These stop the chains aligning so the material is only about 75% crystalline. High-density polythene, on the other hand, has regular chains with no branching. The chains pack together in a regular way giving almost 100% crystallinity and a material which is harder, stronger and denser.

Forces between chains

Polythene is non-polar and the forces between the chains are the weakest kind of van der Waals attraction between transient dipoles (see page 123). In polyester there are carbon–oxygen bonds which are polar. The attraction between permanent dipoles gives rise to stronger intermolecular forces.

Polymers with regular chains and strong interchain forces are often good fibre-forming polymers. This is particularly true of nylon in which there is the possibility of hydrogen bonding between neighbouring chains.

Cross-linking

Thermosetting polymers harden on heating because cross-links form between the polymer chains. Cross-links are covalent bonds which hold together the polymer chains much more strongly than weak intermolecular forces (Figure 2B17).

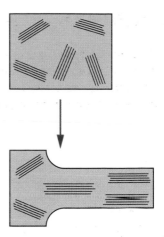

▲ **Figure 2B16** *Drawing or extrusion tends to align long chain polymer molecules. The resulting material is weak in one direction but strong at right angles.*

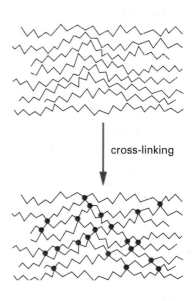

cross-linking

▶ **Figure 2B17** *Without cross-links, this polymer is flexible and weak. Cross-links give it stiffness and strength.*

Thermoset and thermoplastic

Different types of polymer behave differently when heated. This is made use of in the ways in which they are formed into useful objects.

Thermoplastic polymers are solid when cold. Heating softens or even melts them, so they can be moulded into different shapes. Like candle wax, they can be remelted and processed again and again.

Thermoplastics such as polythene, polypropene and PVC are normally supplied as tiny chips or powders which can be melted and forced, under pressure, into closed moulds. This process of **injection moulding** is how plastic buckets, crates, bottles and many other items are made.

Even more thermoplastics are extruded. Molten plastic is squeezed through a shaped die to create a continuous strip with a constant cross-section. All plastic strips – car trim, draught seal, curtain track – are made like this. But the **extrusion** process can also be varied to make hollow sections such as pipes, very thin sheet, and even to put the insulation on to electrical wire.

▼ **Figure 2B18** *Methods of forming plastics:* ***a*** *injection moulding,* ***b*** *extrusion,* ***c*** *thermoforming.*

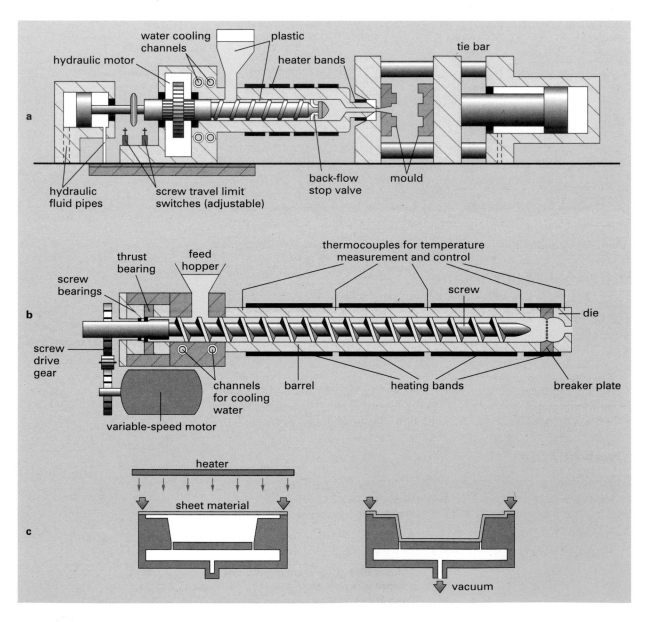

Thermoplastics such as acrylic (e.g. Perspex) are often hard, brittle materials when cold. However, when they are warmed, they become soft and rubbery. They change at the **glass transition temperature**. This is made use of in the **thermoforming** process. For example, bath manufacturers may be supplied with large flat sheets of thermoplastic. These are heated until they become rubbery, and then stretched over an open mould. They retain the bath shape of the mould when they cool down.

Thermoset polymers are created by heat. A mould is filled with a thermosetting polymer, and this is then heated. Chemical reactions occur in which strong bonds form between the polymer chains. This cross-linking creates a strong, stiff material. It is sometimes said that an object made of a thermoset plastic consists of just one giant covalently bonded molecule.

Thermoplastics		
PE	polythene	boxes, buckets, bowls, bags, bottles, baths and anything else beginning with b
PP	polypropene	
PVC	polyvinyl chloride	drains, gutters, tiles, electrical insulation, window frames, coating steel
PS	polystyrene	thermal insulation, toys and models, yoghurt pots
Nylon	polyamide	engineering components, textile fibres
Acrylic	polymethyl methacrylate	baths, signs, glass replacement
Thermosets		
PF	phenol formaldehyde	electrical fittings, saucepan handles
MF	melamine formaldehyde	tableware, composite worktops
	polyester	textile fibres, matrix for reinforced plastics – cars, boats, tanks
PU	polyurethane	cushions, thermal insulation

▲ **Figure 2B19** *The right plastic for the job.*

Fillers e.g. chalk, china clay	To make plastics cheaper, stiffer, harder
Reinforcement e.g. glass or carbon fibres	To increase strength and stiffness, reduce thermal expansion
Plasticizers	To soften and make rubbery
Flame retardants	To reduce flammability
Pigments	To create coloured plastics

▲ **Figure 2B20** *Making plastics from polymers – some useful additives.*

Polyurethanes: a polymer family

Polyurethanes may be as stretchy as a rubber band, or hard and rigid enough to make chairs and tables. Some are so dense that they sink in water, while others are so light that their buoyancy in air must be taken account of when they are weighed. This tremendous variation in properties is achieved because 'polyurethane' refers to a family of polymers whose molecular structures and microstructures are similar, but not identical.

Making boots while making plastic

Manufacturing polyurethane articles is unlike most plastics manufacturing processes. Manufacturers of, say, polyurethane Wellington boots don't buy polyurethane in bulk, to be melted or reshaped. Rather, they buy the raw materials which react to form polyurethane, mix them together so that they react, and then put the mixture into a Wellington-shaped mould. The reaction in the mould creates the solid polymer in the shape of a boot; one minute after mixing, the completed boot can be removed from the mould.

The raw materials used to make polyurethanes are isocyanates and polyols.

Isocyanates are a family of chemicals with two or more isocyanate ($-NCO$) groups. For example, diphenylmethane diisocyanate has the structure:

$$OCN-(C_{13}H_{10})-NCO$$

Isocyanate groups are chemically very reactive; in particular, they react readily with hydroxyl ($-OH$) groups. Care must be taken to ensure that these substances do not come into contact with water, including the moisture in someone's skin.

Isocyanates are made from crude oil.

Polyols are another chemical family, the polymeric alcohols. An example is butanediol, which has the structure:

$$HO-(CH_2)_4-OH$$

They have different numbers of hydroxyl ($-OH$) groups; thus diols have two $-OH$ groups, triols have three, etc.

Polyols are made from organic materials such as oil or sugar beet.

When a polyol and an isocyanate are mixed, the resulting chemical reaction between the $-OH$ and the $-NCO$ groups forms the urethane linkage ($-OCONH-$) which is bonded to a polyol molecule at one end and to an isocyanate molecule at the other. A long chain of alternating molecules results, complete with cross-linking.

Because there are extensive families of these two chemicals, a wide range of different polyurethanes can result. A pure diisocyanate with a diol, for example, creates a tangle of threadlike molecules – the perfect structure for a rubbery polymer that can be stretched to three or four times its original length. Using triols and triisocyanates gives a complex network of chains and cross-links, a much stiffer material more suitable for making furniture.

Some applications of polyurethanes

Fibres for athletic clothes (e.g. Lycra)
Sports goods
Thermal insulation in fridges and buildings
Electrical insulation
Car components
Computer cabinets
Shoe soles
Buoyancy aids
Mattresses and upholstery
Paints
Artificial hearts
Fabric coatings

Density control

Polyurethane foam can be made for such uses as cushions and thermal insulation. The technique uses the fact that the reaction in which polyurethanes are formed is exothermic, and the heat released can be put to good use. To make a foam, a liquid with a low boiling point (e.g. a hydrofluoroalkane) can be mixed with the polyol. During the reaction, the liquid boils, filling the polymer with bubbles of gas. The polyurethane swells up as it turns from a liquid mixture to a solid + gas polymer composite.

An alternative method of expansion is to add a controlled amount of water to the polyol. This reacts with the isocyanate to produce bubbles of carbon dioxide which expand to create a foam plastic. The final volume may be as much as 40 times the volume of the solid polymer.

Composite control

Polyurethane chemistry has a third trick to demonstrate. For a few seconds during the reaction, the surface of the material is sticky enough to act as an adhesive. This is used in car seats, where the fabric cover is used to line a mould, and then the polyurethane foam is formed so that it sticks to the fabric to make a complete upholstered seat.

Refrigerators have polyurethane foam formed between the outer steel shell and the inner plastic lining. The whole structure is held together by the insulating polyurethane foam.

▼ **Figure 2B21** *Polyurethanes can be created with a variety of stiffnesses and densities, making them suitable for a wide range of applications.*

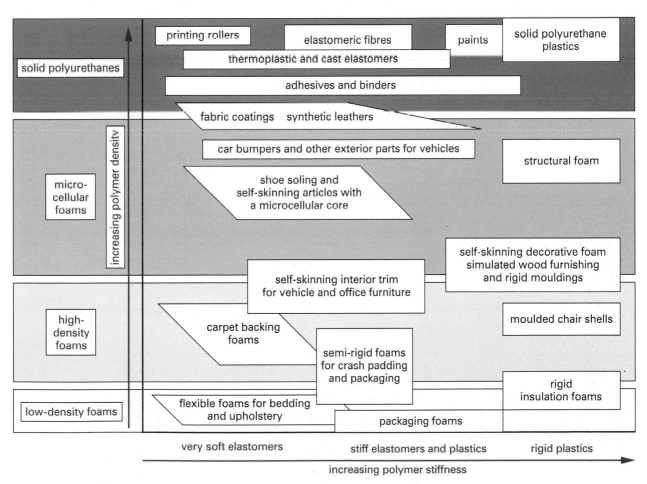

Composite materials

Composites are a general class of materials, made by combining two or more different materials in order to benefit from the desirable properties of both. Some everyday materials are composites; modern composites such as fibre-reinforced plastics have been developed to solve some very demanding technological problems.

Familiar composites

Wood has grain. Its fibres lie lengthways within the material, and this makes wood weak along the grain. It is much stronger across the grain. (Try cutting an ice lolly stick – it's easier lengthways.) To make **plywood**, a composite material, manufacturers cut very thin slices of wood and glue them together so that the grains of alternate layers are at right angles to one another. A new material is created which is strong in both directions.

Steel is strong and stiff, but dull to look at and liable to corrode. It can be coated with plastic – often PVC – to make a composite material as strong as steel but resistant to corrosion. Millions of tons of **plastic-coated steel** are used each year to make the walls and roofs of factories and warehouses. Zinc is a soft, weak metal, but it does not corrode. **Galvanized (zinc-coated) steel** is a composite material which gains its strength from steel and its corrosion resistance from zinc.

What properties are needed for a worktop in a kitchen or laboratory? It must be strong and stiff – 10 to 20 mm of plywood or chipboard will provide the strength. And it must be hard, heat resistant, withstand water and other liquids, scratch resistant, and easily wiped clean – just the sort of properties provided by polymeric materials such as melamine-formaldehyde. So the polymer is used to impregnate a layer of paper, giving a surface which is stuck on to the chipboard. The result is a **composite worktop**.

Fibre reinforcement

This may be the oldest way to make a composite material. For thousands of years, bricks have been made which contain straw to prevent them cracking as the clay dried in the sun. Today, 'fibreglass' dinghies and racing-car bodies, 'carbon' fishing rods and tennis rackets, radomes and car bumpers are the technological descendants of those ancient bricks. Fibre-reinforced composites are discussed in more detail on pages 116–17.

Solid + gas

Gases (such as air) are useful because of their low thermal conductivity – they are excellent for insulation. However, a gas needs to be held in place, and trapping it in a foam is how this can be done. Many plastic foams are used as thermal insulation; the solid skeleton that contains the bubbles of gas is most commonly polyurethane, phenol formaldehyde or polystyrene. As much as 97% of the volume may be gas.

The most heat resistant material ever is probably the ceramic 'wool' used to make the tiles which cover the outside of the space shuttle, to protect it from the high temperatures generated during re-entry to the Earth's atmosphere. The wool consists of extremely fine fibres of silica, a ceramic which is itself a very poor thermal conductor. Ninety-five percent of the volume is air from the thin surrounding atmosphere, making the tiles as lightweight as cotton wool.

During re-entry, the surface temperature of the tiles reaches 1500°C, hot enough to melt steel, but the inside of the shuttle remains cool.

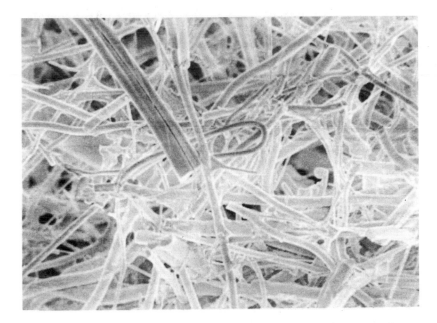

◀ **Figure 2B22** *The heat resistant tiles of the space shuttle are a composite of silica fibres and air, seen here using an electron microscope.*

Filled composites – some examples

Material	Matrix	Filler	Nature of composite
Plasticized PVC	PVC	oily substance	rubbery polymer, used for protective clothing, electrical cable insulation, pond liners
Concrete	sand and cement	gravel	tough, strong material, relatively cheap
Cermets	metal	ceramic	hard, strong, tough – e.g. tungsten carbide ceramic in cobalt metal for cutting tools
Polythene	polythene	cellulose	largely biodegradable plastic – used for carrier bags

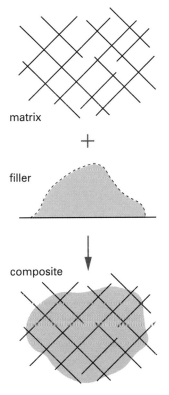

▲ **Figure 2B23** *In a filled composite, a matrix material provides the structure which holds a filler material in place (see table).*

Fibres for strength

Fibre-reinforced composite materials are one of the great success stories of materials engineering. These materials, made of carbon, glass or polymer fibres embedded in a solid matrix, have replaced metals in a wide range of applications, and new materials and applications are still being developed. But we think of carbon, glass and polymers as relatively weak materials. So what is it that makes these composites so attractive?

Comparing strengths

The strength of fibres depends on making use of the strong covalent bonds between atoms in the structure. There are three types of fibre in general use.

Carbon fibres consist of graphite, a material in which layers of carbon atoms are strongly bonded together. The layers are only weakly bonded together (by van der Waals forces) so it is necessary for the layers within a fibre to lie along the axis of the fibre. In practice, the fibres are not as strong as they might be because of the presence of grain boundaries between tiny crystals, and imperfect alignment of the layers within the fibre.

Glass fibres are made from E-glass, a sodium silicate glass with additives; their strength derives from the strength of the covalent bonds between silicon and oxygen atoms. They are coated with an organic polymer called *size* which aids bonding to the matrix and prevents damage to their surface, which would lead to weakening. Not the best fibres, but cheap!

Kevlar fibres are a polymer; their precise composition is a trade secret, but they are probably poly (paraphenylene terephthalamide). The fibres are drawn out so that the carbon chains lie along their length. The strength of the fibres then derives from the strength of the carbon-carbon covalent bonds.

Figure 2B24 gives details of the mechanical properties of these fibres, compared to steel. It can be seen that their strength is comparable with that of steel; their great advantage lies in their low densities. (Notice that some of these properties are very variable, dependent on the details of the production process.)

▶ **Figure 2B24** *Mechanical properties of some fibre materials. Relative density is the ratio of density to the density of water.*

Property	Units	Steel	Carbon fibres	E-glass fibres	Kevlar fibres
Diameter	$\times 10^{-6}$ m	—	7 to 9	8 to 14	12
Relative density		7.9	1.8	2.6	1.5
Young modulus	GPa	207	390	75	125
Tensile strength	GPa	2.3	2.5	2.0	3.2

Fibre composites in production

There are several different approaches to producing items made from fibre-reinforced composites. Figure 2B25 shows a tennis racket being made with a woven carbon-fibre textile; a polymer matrix is injected into the mould, filling the space in and around the fibres. Other rackets are made by injecting molten polymer filled with short carbon fibres into a mould. The fibres align themselves along the length of the racket, giving maximum strength in the most useful direction.

Fibres for strength

The matrix material is a 'resin' (usually polyester or epoxy but sometimes nylon). This is much weaker than the fibres; however, the presence of fibres greatly increases its strength by preventing brittle fracture. A crack tending to break the matrix is diverted and rendered ineffective when it reaches a fibre.

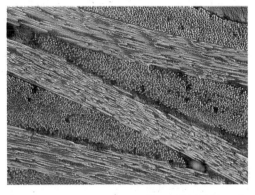

▲ **Figure 2B25** *A carbon-fibre reinforced polymer tennis racket is removed from its mould.*

▲ **Figure 2B26** *This micrograph reveals the structure of a woven glass-fibre reinforcement material. Short glass-fibres are lined up to form threads; criss-cross threads give a structure which is strong in all directions.*

Stronger than metals?

Fibre-reinforced composites are useful because they give high strength for low density. Figure 2B28 shows how they compare with metals; on a 'weight-for-weight' basis, the best composite materials can beat metals for both strength and stiffness.

▶ **Figure 2B27** *A crack is prevented from propagating right through the matrix by the presence of high-strength fibres.*

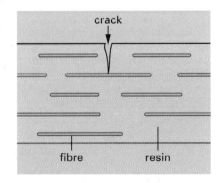

▼ **Figure 2B28** *Comparing FRP composite materials with metals. Specific strength is tensile strength / relative density; specific Young modulus is Young modulus / relative density.*

Material	Relative density	Strength /GPa	Young modulus /GPa	Specific strength /GPa	Specific Young modulus /GPa	Some uses
Steel	7.9	2.0	207	0.25	26	
High strength Al alloy	2.8	0.5	70	0.18	25	
Long carbon fibres in one direction and epoxy matrix	1.6	1.4	220	0.875	138	aircraft, sports gear
Long random glass fibres and polyester matrix	1.6	0.11	9	0.07	6	boats, car bodies
Short random glass fibres and nylon matrix	1.5	0.21	14	0.14	9	nuts and bolts, hooks, machinery

Good conductors

Metals are good conductors of electricity. They are also good thermal conductors. Both depend on the presence of conduction electrons. But some non-metals which are bad electrical conductors are good thermal conductors. How can this be?

Conduction in metals

Metals are held together by metallic bonding. Free electrons (conduction electrons) are free to move about within the metal, and they may transfer electrical energy or thermal energy through the material.

The free electrons within a metal are sometimes referred to as an electron 'gas', because they move about rapidly at speeds of millions of metres per second. This means that there is the possibility for a very rapid transfer of energy within a metal, by means of these fast-moving electrons.

For **electrical conduction**, there must be a **potential difference** (voltage) between the two ends of a piece of metal (Figure 2B29). Electrons at the negative end have more electrical potential energy than at the positive end. They flow towards the positive end, transferring electrical energy through the metal. (Note that, since **electric current** is the flow of positive charge, and electrons are negatively charged, it follows that the current flow is in the opposite direction to the electron flow.)

If an electron collides with an ion of the metal, it will share its energy with the ion; thus the metal itself gains energy. The ion vibrates more; that is, the temperature of the metal increases. This is the mechanism whereby the **electrical resistance** of the metal means that energy is transferred to the metal.

▶ **Figure 2B29** *Electrical energy is transferred by conduction electrons through a metal. There is a general flow of electrons towards the + end. Collisions between electrons and ions transfer energy to the metal.*

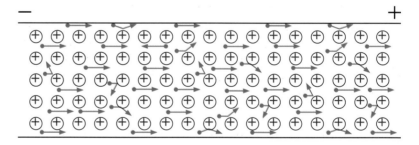

For **thermal conduction**, it is necessary to have a **temperature gradient** within the material. At the warmer end (Figure 2B30), the ions are vibrating more than at the cooler end. Collisions between electrons and ions transfer energy between electrons and ions; at the warmer end, there is a net transfer of energy from ions to electrons; at the cooler end, there is a net transfer from electrons to ions. As a result, there is a flow of energy from the warmer end to the cooler end, carried by the electrons.

▶ **Figure 2B30** *The conduction electrons transfer energy from the warmer end of a piece of metal to the cooler end; the electrons help to spread the energy more uniformly within the material. Note that the electrons leaving the hot end have more energy than those returning from the cold end.*

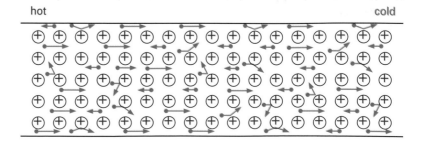

Electrical conduction in non-metals

Non-metals do not have free electrons; their electrons are localized, because they are involved in covalent and ionic bonding. Consequently, non-metals are not good electrical conductors.

It is true, however, that there is no clear dividing line between metals and non-metals. Typically, in a metal, each atom gives up about one electron to the conduction electron gas. There are other materials which do have conduction electrons, but which are not as good conductors as metals. For example, graphite (a form of carbon) has some delocalized electrons which are free to move within planes of carbon atoms. Graphite is therefore a fairly good conductor of electricity.

Semiconductors are materials with a very low concentration of free electrons. They have high electrical resistivities at room temperature, but they become better conductors as the temperature rises. Thermal energy enables electrons to break free, and the resistivity of the material decreases. This is in contrast to metals, whose resistivity increases with temperature. (The electrical conductivity of semiconductors can be controlled by the addition of impurities – see page 120.)

Thermal conduction in non-metals

Without the presence of conduction electrons, there must be another mechanism to explain thermal conduction. Again, a temperature gradient is necessary – see Figure 2B31. At the warmer end of the material, the atoms have more thermal energy and so they are vibrating with greater amplitude. Because atoms are bonded to their neighbours (by covalent or ionic bonds), there is a general sharing of energy between neighbouring atoms as they jostle together. This sharing of energy results in a gradual transfer of energy through the material.

The thermal conductivity of a non-metal thus depends on the bonding between neighbouring atoms. In diamond, the carbon atoms are joined by stiff covalent bonds, and vibrations are transmitted rapidly through the material. The thermal conductivity of diamond is higher than that of any other material, including metals.

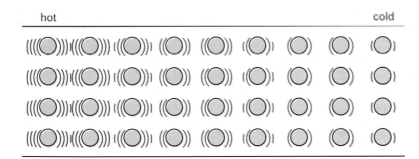

▲ **Figure 2B31** *In a non-metal, vibrations of atoms transfer thermal energy through the material.*

Values of a range of electrical and thermal properties of metals and non-metals are given in the Reference section, R3.

Semiconductors

It is said that this is 'the Silicon Age'. Many of the electronic devices in everyday use would be impossible without semiconductors. These materials, often based on silicon, are essential for the transistors and integrated circuits which are at the heart of information processing systems – computers, hi-fis etc.

High purity materials

Silicon, from Group IV of the Periodic Table, is a semiconductor; so are some Group III–V compounds such as gallium arsenide, GaAs. Every year, the electronics industry makes use of thousands of tonnes of these materials, processed to exceedingly high purity, with less than one impurity atom for every billion silicon atoms, and in the form of highly perfect single crystals with very low concentrations of dislocations. Ironically, once these high purity crystals have been prepared, their electrical properties are changed by making them impure.

Semiconductors are not insulators, but nor are they such good electrical conductors as metals. They are covalently bonded materials; the crystal structure of silicon is represented in Figure 2B32a. Each silicon atom is bonded to four neighbours, so that all four of its outermost electrons are involved in bonding. At room temperature, a very few of these electrons gain enough energy to break free and become delocalized within the material. Since roughly one atom in a billion contributes a conduction electron in this way, the resistivity of silicon is roughly a billion times greater than that of a metal.

The conductivity of a semiconductor can be increased by the process of **doping**, in which small concentrations of impurity atoms are added to the pure material. If the impurity is from Group V, it has one more electron than is needed to bond with neighbouring silicon atoms; this electron is then free to move within the material – it is a conduction electron (Figure 2B32b).

A doping impurity from Group III has one electron too few for bonding; there is therefore a 'hole' in the electronic structure of the material. This hole, the *absence* of an electron, can move through the material. It acts in many ways like a positively charged conducting particle (Figure 2B32c).

▼ **Figure 2B32** *a In pure silicon, each atom is covalently bonded to four neighbours, so few electrons are available for conduction.*
b In n-type silicon, an impurity is used as dopant which has one more electron than silicon; this electron is free to contribute to the material's conductivity.
c In p-type silicon, the dopant has one electron too few to satisfy the bonding requirements. The hole which results acts as a positively charged particle, capable of carrying electric current through the material.

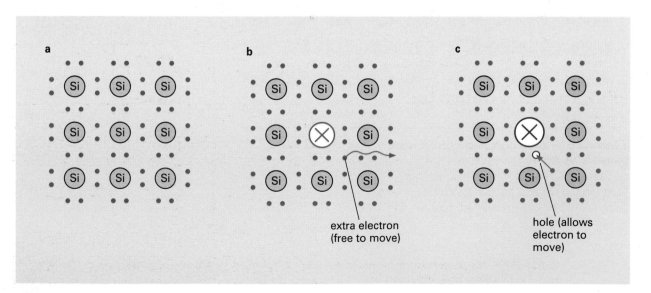

extra electron
(free to move)

hole (allows
electron to
move)

Energy bands

One way to depict the behaviour of metals, semiconductors and insulators uses energy band diagrams as shown in Figure 2B33a. These show the possible energies of the electrons within the material.

In a solid, electrons may have certain values of energy but not others. Electrons whose energies fall within the range labelled **valence band** are involved in the bonding of atoms, and are not able to move within the material. Those in the **conduction band**, however, are free to move throughout the material. There is a forbidden **energy gap** between the two bands; electrons cannot have energies in this range.

In this metal, the valence band is full and the conduction band is half full. The electrons in the conduction band can move freely, so the metal is a good conductor (Figure 2B33b).

In this semiconductor, the valence band is full and the conduction band is empty (Figure 2B33c). One electron is shown gaining enough energy to enter the conduction band; the material has a very low conductivity. (In an insulator, the gap between the two bands is too great for electrons to jump the gap at room temperature.)

In this doped n-type semiconductor, the dopant atoms have introduced electrons at an energy level within the forbidden gap. These electrons can easily rise to the conduction band, and so the conductivity is increased (Figure 2B33d).

In this doped p-type semiconductor, the dopant atoms have introduced a permitted energy level into the forbidden gap. An electron from the valence band can jump up to this level, leaving a hole in the valence band. This allows the movement of electrons within the valence band, and again the material conducts (Figure 2B33e).

▼ **Figure 2B33**

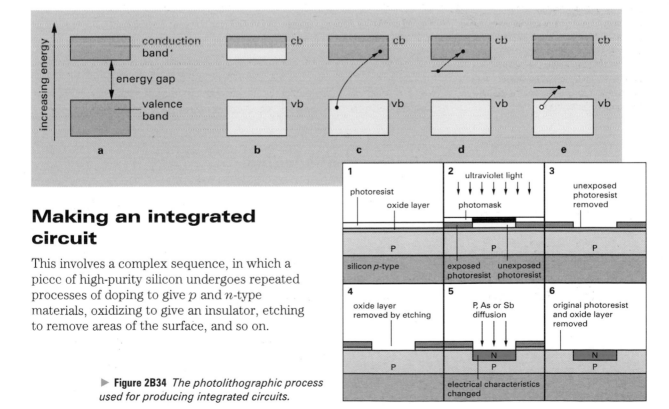

Making an integrated circuit

This involves a complex sequence, in which a piece of high-purity silicon undergoes repeated processes of doping to give p and n-type materials, oxidizing to give an insulator, etching to remove areas of the surface, and so on.

▶ **Figure 2B34** *The photolithographic process used for producing integrated circuits.*

Bonding within and between molecules

Materials scientists use models to explain the properties of materials in terms of structure and bonding. The structure of a material is a description of the arrangements of atoms. Theories of bonding are attempts to account for the forces which hold the atoms together.

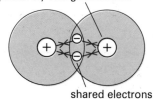

positively charged nucleus

shared electrons

▲ **Figure 2B35** *Sharing electrons to form a covalent bond in a hydrogen molecule. The shared negative electrons attract the two positively charged nuclei.*

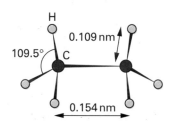

▲ **Figure 2B37** *The shape and size of an ethane molecule.*

▶ **Figure 2B38** *Single, double and triple bonds in some covalently bonded molecules. Each line represents a shared pair of electrons.*

Strong bonding within molecules

Covalent bonding

When non-metal atoms combine to form molecules, they do so by sharing electrons (see Figures 2B35 and 36). Molecules have a particular shape because covalent bonds have a definite length and there are fixed angles between the bonds (see Figure 2B37).

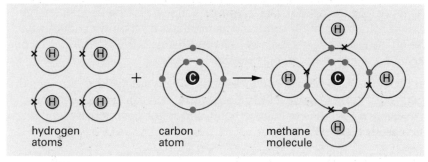

hydrogen atoms   carbon atom   methane molecule

▲ **Figure 2B36** *Sharing electrons to form covalent bonds in a methane molecule. Dots represent the electrons from hydrogen and crosses the electrons from carbon. In reality all the electrons are the same.*

Figure 2B38 shows that covalent bonding can give rise to double and triple bonds. Figure 2B39 lists the numbers of bonds formed by some common atoms.

$$H-H \qquad H-Cl \qquad H-\underset{\underset{H}{|}}{\overset{\overset{H}{|}}{C}}-H \qquad O=O \qquad \underset{H}{\overset{H}{\diagdown}}C=C\underset{\diagdown H}{\overset{\diagup H}{}} \qquad N\equiv N$$

Dative covalent bonding

Usually each of the two atoms contributes one electron to the shared pair which makes up the covalent bond. Some molecules, however, have so-called lone-pairs of electrons (see Figure 2B40).

$$H-\underset{\underset{H}{|}}{\overset{..}{O}}: \qquad CH_3-\underset{\underset{H}{|}}{\overset{..}{O}}: \qquad H-\underset{\underset{H}{|}}{\overset{..}{N}}-H \qquad CH_3-\underset{\underset{H}{|}}{\overset{..}{N}}-H$$

▲ **Figure 2B40** *Examples of molecules with reactive lone-pairs of electrons.*

These molecules can form a **dative covalent bond** in which both the shared electrons come from one of the two atoms. Once formed, dative bonds are indistinguishable from normal covalent bonds (see Figure 2B41).

Element	Number of covalent bonds
Hydrogen, H	1
Halogens, Cl, Br, I	1
Oxygen, O	2
Nitrogen, N	3
Carbon, C	4

▲ **Figure 2B39** *The numbers of covalent bonds formed by atoms.*

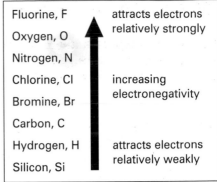

Figure 2B41 *Dative covalent bonding to form the oxonium ion. The short arrow represents a dative covalent bond.*

Fluorine, F	attracts electrons relatively strongly
Oxygen, O	
Nitrogen, N	
Chlorine, Cl	increasing electronegativity
Bromine, Br	
Carbon, C	
Hydrogen, H	attracts electrons relatively weakly
Silicon, Si	

Figure 2B42 *A list of elements in order of electronegativity.*

Polar covalent bonds

In a hydrogen molecule both atoms are the same and they share the bonding pair of electrons equally. In many compounds, however, there are covalent bonds between unlike atoms and often one atom has a much stronger attraction for the electrons. One atom has a slight negative charge because it has a greater share of the electrons. The other atom has a slight positive charge because it has lost some of its share of electrons. The result is a polar covalent bond with a positive end and a negative end – a minute electric **dipole**.

Figure 2B43 *Non-polar and polar molecules. The Greek δ signifies a very small fraction. The charges in polar molecules are a fraction of the full charge on a positive or negative ion.*

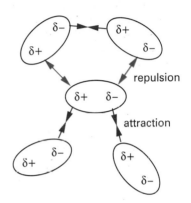

Figure 2B44 *Attractive and repulsive forces between molecules with dipoles. The overall effect is weak bonding holding the molecules together.*

The electronegativity scale (Figure 2B42) compares atoms by showing how strongly atoms in molecules attract electrons. Figure 2B43 shows several examples of polar and non-polar molecules. Compounds which are polar are often more reactive with aqueous reagents such as acids and oxidizing agents than are non-polar compounds

Weak bonding between molecules

Attractions between dipoles

The small positive and negative charges in polar molecules mean that they attract each other – but weakly. The weak bonding between molecules holds them together in liquids and solids.

It is less easy to see why there should be attractive forces between non-polar molecules such as hydrocarbons. Without such forces there would be no molecular liquids such as hexane or molecular solids such as polythene. The explanation is that the electrons in molecules are in constant agitation, setting up temporary, flickering dipoles. Overall the effect is to produce a weak bond between molecules. Larger molecules with more atoms and electrons attract each other more strongly than small molecules, so methane, CH_4, is a gas, hexane, C_6H_{14}, is a liquid while eicosane, $C_{20}H_{42}$, is a solid.

Hydrogen bonding

Hydrogen bonding is the strongest of the types of weak bonding between molecules. Hydrogen bonding affects compounds in which hydrogen atoms are covalently bonded to one of the three highly electronegative elements at the top of the list in Figure 2B42: fluorine, oxygen or nitrogen.

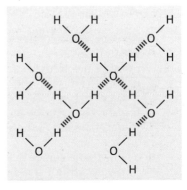

Figure 2B45 *Hydrogen bonding in water.*

Thoughts and actions

1 The following items are likely to be sold with a kitemark or other indication that they have been tested to appropriate standards:
   ■ a 13A mains plug
   ■ a child's doll
   ■ car tyres.
   a For each of these, suggest why it is desirable that they should have been tested.
   b Suggest properties of each which might be the subject of tests.
   c It has been suggested that the existence of standards reduces the chance of innovation, and can lead to reduced standards because manufacturers do not improve their product beyond the minimum standard. What do you think?

2 Look at the motorized bicycle wheel shown on pages 68–69. How are the materials chosen appropriate to the design? The wheel was designed in 1985, but is rarely seen. Why do you think this might be?

3 Laboratory containers are made of a range of metals, ceramics and polymers. What are the factors which determine the choice of material? Under what circumstances would you choose to use:
   a a stainless steel beaker in preference to one made of glass
   b a glass Petri dish, or trough, in preference to one made of plastic
   c a nickel crucible in preference to one made of porcelain?

4 Sketch stress–strain graphs (on the same axes) for two metals: metal A is stiffer and stronger than metal B; metal B is brittle, but metal A shows plastic deformation.

5 On pages 74–75, Peter Tazewell describes how Clarks develop new shoe designs. Two types of tests are involved; laboratory tests and field tests.
   a What is the difference between these two types of test?
   b Why do both play an important part in the development of the shoe design?

6 a Polythene comes in two forms, high and low density. Study the data for the mechanical properties of polythene on page 486. How do the two forms differ in density, strength and stiffness?
   b These differences arise during the production and processing of the material. How can the different microstructures of the two forms account for their different properties?
   c Make the same comparison for iron, mild steel and stainless steel.

7 On pages 78–79, you can read about the procedure used to make high-precision wires for resistance thermometers. There are several steps involved; draw a flow chart to show the procedure.

8 It is easier to measure the thermal conductivity of a metal than of an insulating material such as the fabric used to make a ski jacket. Why is this?

9 Many of these yoghurt pots can be split easily from top to bottom, but they are much stronger if you try to break them horizontally. What does this suggest about the arrangement of molecules within the material?

If one of these pots is heated in a pressure cooker with water at 120°C for a few minutes, it is likely to collapse to a flat disc. What does this suggest about how these pots are manufactured?

▲ Figure 2T1

(Before trying this experiment, it is advisable to eat the yoghurt.)

10 Ceramics are materials which have been traditionally used to make crockery, sinks and toilets. However, modern ceramics have found uses in many high-tech applications. (There are several examples mentioned in this book.) Write a short article describing some of these recently-developed uses of ceramics.

11 Study the data given for the properties of solid materials on page 486 of the Reference section, and decide whether you agree with the following statements.
   a Metals are denser than polymers.
   b Metals are stronger than non-metals.
   c Metals are stiffer than polymers.

12 Aluminium is an alternative to steel for the construction of car bodies. There are energy-saving advantages in the use of aluminium – see page 89. However, the initial cost is higher than for steel. It has been suggested that there should be a government subsidy to cut the price of aluminium cars and thereby to encourage their use.
  a Who would benefit from such a subsidy, and who would lose out? Think about:
  - consumers
  - taxpayers
  - electricity producers
  - petrol companies
  - steel and aluminium producers
  - car manufacturers
  - the environment.
  b Should there be such a subsidy?

13 What is the difference between a *polymer* and a *plastic*? Give examples to illustrate the distinction.

14 All metals that are good electrical conductors are also good thermal conductors. However, a non-metal may be a poor electrical conductor but a good thermal conductor. Explain how this can be.

15 Here are some pairs of words which describe materials and which are easily confused. Write short paragraphs to make clear the distinction between them, giving appropriate examples of materials that are:
  - *elastic* and *plastic*
  - *stiff* and *strong*.

16 To answer this question, you will need to make use of values of thermal conductivity and conductance given on pages 84–85.
  a Calculate the rate of flow of heat through $1\,m^2$ of brick wall, 10 cm thick, when there is a temperature difference of 10 °C across it.
  b Calculate the rate of flow of heat through $1\,m^2$ of brick cavity wall, without foam, with the same temperature difference.
  c Explain the difference in these results.

17 Everyone knows that glass is easily broken. So it is surprising to find that glass fibres are used as the reinforcement in some of the strongest composite materials available. Write an article of no more than 150 words to explain this apparent paradox.

18 Diamond is a very unusual material. It is a better thermal conductor than any other material; its Young modulus is six times that of steel; it is an excellent electrical insulator. These properties are related to its underlying structure. How?

19 A kettle for use on a gas hob is usually made of metal. An electric kettle, with an element inside, may be made of metal or plastic. Discuss these choices of material. Refer to the following properties of the materials:
  - stiffness
  - strength
  - thermal and electrical conductivities
  - thermal capacity.

20 Concrete is a composite material. Its properties vary according to its composition. In particular, the type of gravel used can vary widely.

Type of gravel	Density /kg m^{-3}	Compressive strength /MPa	Use
Vermiculite	500	1	insulation
Foamed slag	1800	20	floor slabs
Limestone	2400	10–70	general construction purposes
Magnetite	3850	50	ballast for underwater pipes
Lead	8900	20	radiation shielding

▲ **Figure 2T2** *Concrete and its uses.*

How does each type of gravel shown in Figure 2T2 result in an appropriate type of concrete for the uses stated?

21 Figure 2T3 shows the stress–strain graph for a hypothetical material. Use the graph to deduce:
  a the strain in the material when the stress is 50 MPa
  b the yield stress of the material
  c the Young modulus of the material
  d the breaking stress.

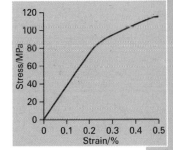

▲ **Figure 2T3**

22 Are the following failures a consequence of lack of stiffness or lack of strength?
  a Your leg breaks in a sporting accident.
  b A chair sags badly when you sit on it.
  c A car tyre bursts.
  d A heavily-laden car scrapes the road when going over a bump.

23 The box on page 75 lists some important properties of the materials used for shoe soles. Select three of these properties and design laboratory tests which will allow you to measure or compare these properties for some samples of suitable materials.

24 Polyurethanes have a great range of uses, because of the way in which their composition can be controlled. This allows the density and stiffness to be controlled. For some of the uses shown in Figure 2B21 (page 113), explain why the values of density and stiffness are appropriate.

25 Imagine that you are a manufacturer of high-quality cutlery. You are involved in developing a new British Standard for cutlery. You have to attend a meeting where you and other manufacturers will meet with staff of the British Standards Institute to discuss the new standard. Prepare a draft proposal to put to the meeting. You should list:
- the items which might be tested
- the properties which might be tested
- suggested procedures for these tests.

26 These five sentences describe structure and bonding in materials.
- A sea of electrons around a crystalline giant structure of positive ions.
- An amorphous molecular structure with strong bonds between atoms in the molecules but weak bonds between molecules.
- A crystalline giant structure of positively and negatively charged ions.
- A crystalline giant structure of atoms held together by strong bonds with a definite length and direction.
- An amorphous giant structure with covalent bonds between some atoms and ionic bonds between others.

a For each sentence choose a material which matches the description.

b For each of your chosen materials account for one of its properties in terms of structure and bonding.

27 Imagine that you are preparing a lecture for young people about metals which you plan to enliven with simple illustrations, models and demonstrations. The theme of your lecture is summed up by this quotation written for adults.

'The ways in which metals stretch, bend, become permanently deformed, and eventually break, are of crucial importance in determining the uses which we make of metals. It is therefore a prime task of metallurgists to determine how these phenomena depend both on the atomic and on the grain structure of a metal, so that they may see how to produce metals with the most useful combinations of qualities.'

a Choose a range of interesting examples to illustrate your lecture.

b Suggest suitable demonstrations.

c Prepare an outline of the lecture in note form.

28 Long chain molecules in plastics, such as polythene, nylon and polyvinylchloride, are held together by relatively weak intermolecular forces – similar to the forces between the molecules in candle wax, ice and sulphur. How then do scientists account for the useful mechanical properties of plastics?

29 There are problems involved in the use of plastics. Imagine the 'life' of a plastic bag, or any other plastic article, as having three phases as shown in Figure 2T4. Discuss the advantages and disadvantages of using plastic objects at each stage of their 'life'.

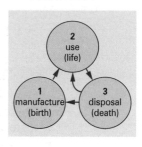

▲ **Figure 2T4**

30 A technician was given a section of metal piping and asked to find the metal's specific heat capacity. She had no thermometer, and no means of measuring energy supplied. Making the most of equipment to hand, she proceeded as follows:

She weighed the pipe.	*Mass of pipe = 1600 g.*
Then she put 1 litre of cold water in an electric kettle, and switched on.	*Time for water to come to the boil = 2 min 20 sec.*
She refilled the kettle with 1 litre of cold water, added the pipe, and switched on.	*Time for water to come to boil = 2 min 40 sec.*

a Make an estimate of the specific heat capacity of the metal. (Specific heat capacity of water = $4200\,\mathrm{J\,kg^{-1}K^{-1}}$)

b Is your answer an overestimate or an underestimate?

c Suggest one metal which the pipe could *not* be made of. (See page 486.)

31 Using a laboratory spectrometer, a student investigates the refractive index of a glassy polymer. Figure 2T5 shows a record of the angles measured when a ray of light is shone into a block of the polymer.

a What are the values of the angle of incidence i and the angle of refraction r?

b What is the refractive index of the polymer?

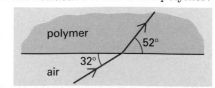

▶ **Figure 2T5**

UNIT 3

Obtaining new substances

Natural and synthetic chemicals

How natural?

Advertisers know that one of the best things you can say about a product is that it is natural. People like the idea of things being natural and hate the idea of them being synthetic. But what do these ideas really mean? Over the last few centuries, chemists have learned a great deal about how to extract chemicals from nature, how to modify those chemicals and how to use raw materials from nature to construct totally new synthetic chemical compounds.

Life in industrialized countries has been totally transformed by this knowledge of chemistry. People depend on chemical knowledge, even when they believe they are pursuing 'naturalness'. So-called 'natural' yogurt and 'natural' spring water come in synthetic plastic containers. Many people prefer clothes made of natural fibres like cotton and wool but they clean them with products created by the chemicals industry. Clothes may have 'natural' colours like beige and olive but the dyes responsible for these colours are as synthetic as the ones used to make clothes hot pink or bright orange.

The fact is, nature is very often improved by the use of synthetic chemicals. Wood is a valuable natural material but it is far more useful if it is given a coating of paint or varnish. Hair with a 'natural' shine has very likely been cleaned with a detergent, coated with a conditioner and perhaps coloured with a synthetic dye. Fresh 'natural' food is only part of our diet. There is no way we could have the quantity and variety of food we enjoy if it weren't for the technology which allows us to process, package and store food. This technology relies on the use of many synthetic chemicals.

▶ **Figure 3A1**
Gathering, processing and storing herbs from "Das Kreüterbuch oder Herbarius" Augsburg 1534.

▲ **Figure 3A2** The 'perfumer's organ' is the laboratory area where the stock of mostly synthetic fragrance ingredients are stored. Today the perfumer has a palate of 3000 fragrances to choose from when mixing a new perfume.

Over the years humans have discovered ways of using many of the natural substances created by living things. Willow bark was used for centuries as a treatment to relieve pain. It worked because it contains the chemical salicin. Chemists were able to produce a much better pain reliever by synthesizing a very similar chemical, aspirin, which is not only more effective, but also causes less stomach irritation than the compound produced by willow trees.

Among the most highly valued chemicals produced by nature are those with a fragrance. In the Middle Ages, the petals of rose, jasmine, lavender and other fragrant flowers were placed between layers of animal fat, which absorbed the chemicals responsible for the smell. The fat could then be used as a hair cream. Over the years, as the art and science of perfumery grew more sophisticated, perfumers produced extremely expensive mixtures of fragrant natural oils to be used and enjoyed by the wealthiest people.

By the 19th century, four strong smelling chemicals produced by animals had become important ingredients in the perfumers' mixtures. 'Musk' was obtained by killing a male musk deer during the rutting season and removing a golf ball sized gland from the base of its anus. 'Civet' was squeezed from the anal sac of captive bred civet cats. 'Castoreum' was pressed from the anal gland of the beaver. 'Ambergis' was obtained from balls of pale gray material that are produced in the intestines of sperm whales. Sometimes these balls, which could be as large as a football, were found washed up on the seashore.

Today, most fragrant chemicals used in the making of perfume are synthetic. Chemists can make substances chemically identical to those produced in nature at a tiny fraction of the cost.

Chemical synthesis

Analytical chemists use their knowledge of the behaviour of chemicals to detect their presence and measure their concentration. Synthetic chemists also need a wide knowledge of chemical behaviour so that they can synthesize new substances by modifying or building up chemical structures in predictable ways.

Chemicals change in many ways: they melt and evaporate, they dissolve in solvents, and they undergo a variety of reactions. When chemicals react, chemical bonds break and new bonds form as atoms rearrange to produce new materials.

Many of the different chemical compounds that make up our environment are not reacting at the moment or, if they are changing, they are reacting extremely slowly. However, every one of these chemicals will react, in the right conditions. For example, the cellulose that makes up the pages of this book is not reacting. If a match is put to the paper the cellulose would quickly react with the air producing carbon dioxide and water.

Heating is one of the commonest ways to get reactions started. Raising the temperature makes atoms and molecules move and vibrate faster so that it is more likely that bonds between atoms will break and start a chemical change (see Chapter 6B, pages 330–31). When a flame touches a piece of paper, for example, it heats up the cellulose and oxygen molecules providing the energy needed to start them burning.

The key to synthesizing chemical compounds is being able to create exactly the right conditions to break certain bonds and cause other bonds to form. Hundred of years of experimentation have provided chemists with the basic knowledge of how this can be done. They can predict how chemicals such as metals, acids, salts and alcohols will behave when mixed with other chemicals under controlled conditions.

The challenge synthetic chemists face is to create a compound with a given structure. It may be a completely new compound or it may be a natural compound which is only available in small quantities from natural sources and therefore very expensive. Sometimes, the only way to establish the precise structure of a natural compound is to synthesize it. If the natural compound has a complex structure, analytical chemists are often only able to narrow down its structure to a range of possible structures. Synthetic chemists must then attempt to create each of the suggested structures to see which one has the same properties as the natural compound.

The structure of cortisone, for example, was confirmed in 1951 by the American chemist Robert Woodward who completed its synthesis in more than 40 steps. Woodward led a group of researchers at Harvard University, where the team achieved many notable firsts including the synthesis of cholesterol in 1951, strychnine in 1954 and chlorophyll in 1954.

▼ **Figure 3A3** *The brilliant synthetic organic chemist, Robert Woodward, who was born in Boston, USA in 1917.*

Discovering a method of synthesizing a compound involves looking at the structure of the compound and considering how other chemical compounds could be rearranged or made to combine to create that molecular structure. Often there are a number of possible ways of getting to the desired structure (Figures 3A4 and 3A6).

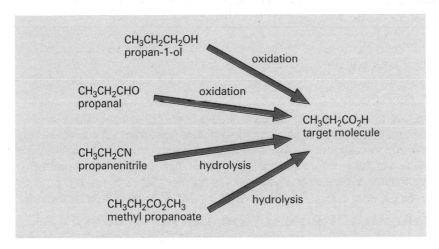

▲ **Figure 3A4** *Alternative one-step reactions for making propanoic acid.*

More complex compounds must often be synthesized in more than one step. For example, the local anaesthetic, benzocaine, can be produced by the oxidation of ethyl 4-nitrobenzoate. The problem is that ethyl 4-nitrobenzoate is not readily available and must itself be synthesized. In fact, a common synthesis of benzocaine has four steps.

There may also be two or more routes to an inorganic compound as illustrated by the two methods of making titanium dioxide (Figure 3A6). Titanium dioxide is manufactured in the UK on Humberside and on Teesside but by different methods. Titanium dioxide is one of the whitest substances known and is much superior to the traditional whiteners such as chalk, china clay and zinc oxide. Its principal uses are as a paint pigment, for making plastics opaque and as a whitener for paper.

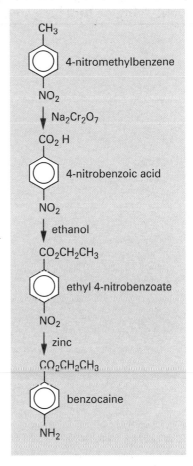

▲ **Figure 3A5** *A four-step synthesis of the anaesthetic benzocaine.*

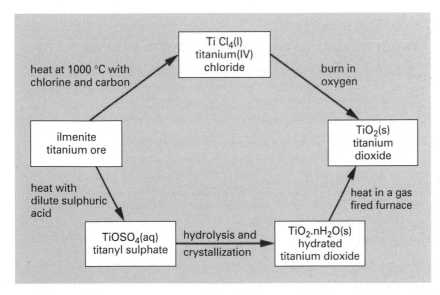

▲ **Figure 3A6** *Alternative routes from titanium ore to the white pigment titanium dioxide.*

Designing a procedure

Selecting a reaction or series of reactions to synthesize a chemical is known as choosing a 'synthetic route'. Synthetic chemists must then find the procedures which create the optimum conditions for each of those reactions to occur.

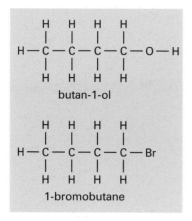

▲ **Figure 3A7** *Structures of butan-1-ol and 1-bromobutane.*

▲ **Figure 3A8** *Cooling the reaction mixture while adding concentrated sulphuric acid.*

Planning a synthesis involves a lot of informed guesswork and perfecting the conditions to get the best yield is often a matter of trial and error.

Creating the right conditions for a reaction to take place is seldom a matter of just mixing together the chemicals in the balanced equation. Chemists must create conditions which force the reagents to make the right contributions. They have found, for example, that a mixture of sodium bromide and concentrated sulphuric acid brings about the one-step synthesis of 1-bromobutane from butan-1-ol. Adding sodium bromide and concentrated sulphuric acid in excess makes sure that as much of the alcohol reacts as possible.

Keeping the reaction under control

Another aim is to find a procedure that makes the reaction occur at a convenient speed. A reaction that occurs too quickly can be a safety problem if, for example, the reaction is exothermic or gives off a gas. A reaction that takes several days to complete is obviously not ideal either. Adding concentrated sulphuric acid to the reaction mixture during the preparation of 1-bromobutane is highly exothermic so the reaction flask must stand in ice cold water while the acid runs in (Figure 3A8).

Reactions between molecules are often slow because covalent bonds are strong bonds. Raising the temperature speeds up the reaction. For many reactions, a 10 °C rise in temperature roughly doubles the rate (see pages 330–31). Once all the reagents for making 1-bromobutane are in the flask, the mixture is heated for about 45 minutes (see Figure 3A9). A reflux condenser prevents loss of volatile reactants and products. Any vapours escaping from the flask cool, condense and run back from the condenser into the flask.

Theoretical and percentage yields

In designing a procedure for synthesizing a compound, chemists aim to make each reaction as efficient as possible. A perfectly efficient reaction would convert 100% of the starting materials to the desired product. Such a reaction would be said to produce a 100% yield.

No reaction is 100% efficient and some reactions give lower yields. There are several reasons why the overall yield may be low.

- In some cases, low yield is due to the reaction being 'incomplete'. A proportion of the starting chemicals remains unreacted. Even with excess of sodium bromide and concentrated sulphuric acid, some unchanged butan-1-ol remains.
- Another problem is 'side reactions'. These are reactions that occur alongside the desired reaction that use up the reagents to create chemicals (called by-products) that are not the desired product. The main reaction on heating butan-1-ol with concentrated sulphuric acid forms 1-bromobutane, but some of the alcohol may be dehydrated to an alkene or converted to an ether.

■ A third common reason for a low yield is difficulty in separating the pure product from the reaction mixture. Some of the product is left behind and there are further losses during the purification stages. Purifying 1-bromobutane, for example, involves distilling the product from the reaction mixture, treating it with concentrated hydrochloric acid in a tap funnel (Figure 3A11) to remove unreacted butan-1-ol then with sodium hydrogencarbonate solution to remove traces of acid, drying it with anhydrous sodium sulphate, filtering off the drying agent and finally redistilling.

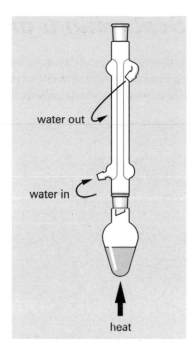

▲ **Figure 3A9** *Heating under reflux to prevent loss of volatile reactants and products.*

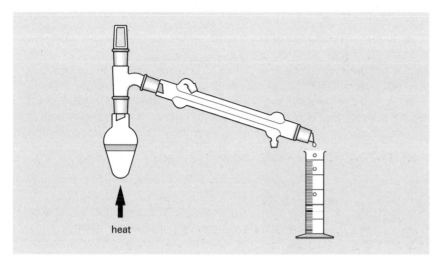

▲ **Figure 3A10** *Distilling off the product from the reaction mixture.*

Example

What is the theoretical yield of 1-bromobutane from $7.5\,cm^3$ of butan-1-ol? What is the percentage yield if the actual yield of pure product is $6.8\,g$?

Answer

The reaction converts one mole of butan-1-ol to one mole of 1-bromobutane.

$$C_4H_9OH(l) \xrightarrow{\text{NaBr/conc. } H_2SO_4} C_4H_9Br(l)$$

Molar mass of butan-1-ol = $(4 \times 12) + (10 \times 1) + 16 = 74\,g\,mol^{-1}$
Molar mass of 1-bromobutane = $(4 \times 12) + (9 \times 1) + 80 = 137\,g\,mol^{-1}$

So theoretically the yield from $74\,g$ of butan-1-ol should be $137\,g$ of 1-bromobutane.

The density of butan-1-ol is $0.81\,g\,cm^{-3}$, so the mass of alcohol used $= 7.5\,cm^3 \times 0.81\,g\,cm^{-3} = 6.1\,g$.

The theoretical yield of 1-bromobutane $= 6.1\,g \times \dfrac{137}{74} = 11.3\,g$.

If the actual yield is $6.8\,g$, the percentage yield $= \dfrac{6.8\,g}{11.3\,g} \times 100\% = 60\%$.

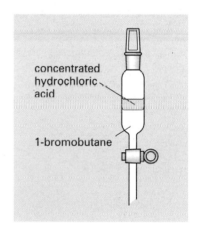

▲ **Figure 3A11** *Removing unchanged butan-1-ol by shaking with concentrated hydrochloric acid in a tap funnel.*

mass/g
= volume/cm^3 × density/$g\,cm^{-3}$

Separating and purifying products

During a chemical synthesis it is often difficult to avoid creating mixtures of chemicals. A reaction of two chemicals rarely produces just the desired product. The flask usually contains a confusing mixture of the starting materials and by-products.

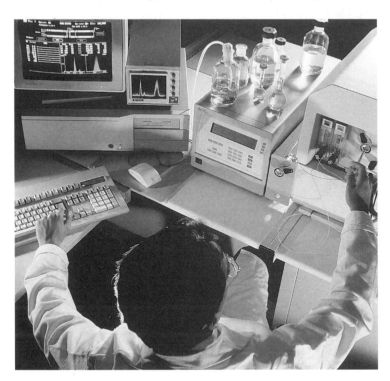

▲ **Figure 3A12** *A scientist injects a sample into a mass spectrometer used for protein analysis. The computer stores and displays the analytical data.*

The key to a successful synthesis is often the development of a procedure designed to separate the product from the rest of the reaction mixture. It is sometimes also necessary to separate intermediates after each step of a multi-step synthesis.

The separation of chemicals is possible because each different chemical compound behaves in a unique way. A knowledge of this behaviour allows chemists to develop techniques to separate chemicals and to establish the purity of the products. These techniques are not only used to separate the product of a synthesis from a reaction mixture, but to separate natural products from mixtures of chemicals found in nature.

Vast reference books and databases exist which give the characteristics of the millions of different chemicals that have been isolated from nature or synthesized in the laboratory.

Separation methods based on solubility

Crystallization

One way substances differ is in their solubility. If the desired product is in solution with other chemicals, one method of separation is to create conditions in which the product crystallizes while the other chemicals stay in solution. Then the product can be removed by filtering the liquid. This technique is used in the preparation of pure potassium iodate, a primary standard for volumetric analysis of oxidizing agents.

Figure 3A13 outlines the procedure for making potassium iodate on a small scale from iodine and potassium hydroxide.

$$3I_2(s) + 6OH^-(aq) \longrightarrow IO_3^-(aq) + 5I^-(aq) + 3H_2O(l)$$

As Figure 3A14 shows, potassium iodate is much less soluble than potassium iodide and so it crystallizes on cooling. Using a Buchner funnel and a pump to lower the pressure in the filtration flask speeds up filtration.

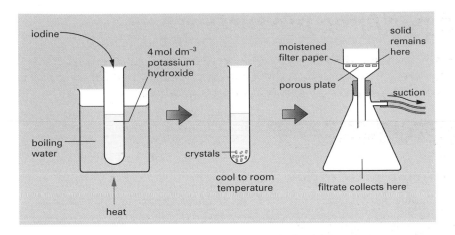

◀ **Figure 3A13** *A procedure for making potassium iodate.*

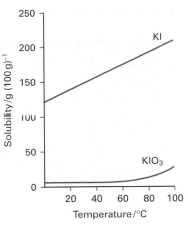

▲ **Figure 3A14** *The change in solubility of potassium iodate and potassium iodide with temperature.*

Solvent extraction

The product can also be separated from the reaction mixture if it dissolves in a solvent in which the other chemicals are insoluble. This is **solvent extraction**. For example, organic syntheses are often carried out in an aqueous reaction mixture but produce a product which is more soluble in an organic solvent. The solvent is added to the aqueous solution in a stoppered funnel. On shaking, most of the product dissolves in the organic solvent. After the mixture has settled, the water and solvent form two distinct layers which can be run off in turn from a separating funnel. More solvent can then be added to the aqueous solution and the procedure repeated several times until virtually all the desired product has been extracted.

Some seaweeds concentrate iodine from the sea to a remarkable extent. The *Laminariaceae* seaweeds can contain as much as 800 parts per million of iodine in fresh weed which they take in as iodide ions from seawater with an iodine concentration of only 0.05 parts per million.

The procedure for extracting iodine involves drying the seaweed, heating to burn it and then converting it to an ash. The next step is to boil the ash with water to extract soluble potassium iodide. Filtering removes insoluble parts of the ash. Acidifying with dilute sulphuric acid and then adding dilute hydrogen peroxide oxidizes the iodide ions to iodine which can be extracted from the aqueous solution by shaking with a hydrocarbon solvent (Figure 3A16).

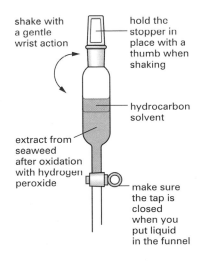

▲ **Figure 3A16** *Solvent extraction to obtain iodine.*

▲ **Figure 3A15** Laminariaceae *seaweed.*

Separation methods based on differences in boiling point

Seaweeds are not the only plants that are a valuable source of chemicals. Traditionally people have turned to plants for food flavours, perfumes, drugs and dyes. Cooks and chemists have discovered ways to use different parts of plants as a source of flavour and chemicals: peppermint from leaves, ginger from roots, mustard from seeds, nutmeg from fruits and cloves from buds.

Steam distillation

Heating plant material directly to distil off the chemicals does not work. The compounds either decompose or burn. Distilling in steam, however, makes it possible to separate plant chemicals without destroying them.

Steam distillation drives off from plant materials the oily chemicals which do not mix with water. The oils distil over in steam just below 100 °C – well below the boiling point of the oil.

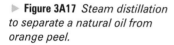

▶ **Figure 3A17** *Steam distillation to separate a natural oil from orange peel.*

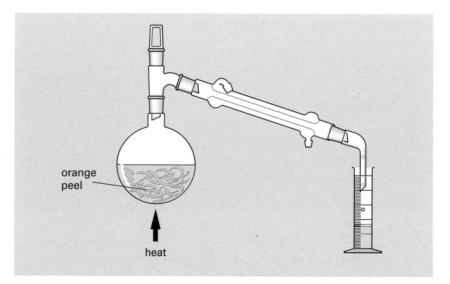

orange peel

heat

Steam distillation can be used to separate oils from orange peel, cloves, thyme or fennel (Figure 3A17). The distillate consists mostly of water mixed with some oil. After steam distilling orange peel, the oil can be extracted from the distillate by solvent extraction with dichloromethane in a separating funnel.

Simple distillation

Solvent extraction produces a relatively pure solution of the product but it is then usually necessary to dry the extract to get rid of traces of moisture and then to remove the solvent.

If the product has a higher boiling point than the solvent and is not damaged by heating, this can be done by heating to evaporate the solvent. Simply evaporating the solvent is wasteful and hazardous so it is better to distil off the solvent. The condensed solvent can then be collected and re-used. This approach is possible for the oil from orange peel. The main ingredient of the oil is a hydrocarbon, limonene, which boils at 176 °C. The solvent, dichloromethane, boils at 40 °C.

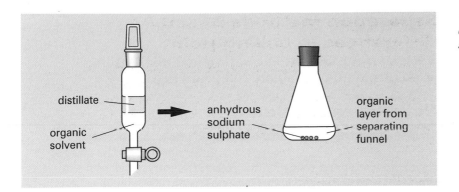

◀ **Figure 3A18** *Procedure for obtaining a purified oil after steam distilling.*

Fractional distillation

Fractional distillation is often the final stage when purifying a liquid from a synthesis, or from a plant extract. The technique separates liquids with different boiling points.

The mixture boils in a distillation flask as in simple distillation but, instead of going directly to a condenser and receiver, the vapour rises into a vertical fractionating column.

As the vapour travels upward, most of it condenses and collects on surfaces inside the fractionating column. Some of the condensate flows downward and may drip back into the distillation flask but rising hot vapour also causes some of the condensate to evaporate again and travel further up the column. Even if the liquids in the mixture have boiling points which are close together, there is a higher concentration of the more volatile liquid higher up the fractionating column.

Packing a fractionating column with glass spheres or rings increases the surface area inside the column and makes sure that the rising vapours and falling liquids mix well. This improves the separation in the column.

For a good separation, fractional distillation must be carried out slowly to make sure that there is a temperature gradient up the column. With care it is possible to distil over liquids one at a time from the mixture. At any moment the thermometer at the top of the column records the boiling point of the liquid condensing around its bulb and passing over into the condenser.

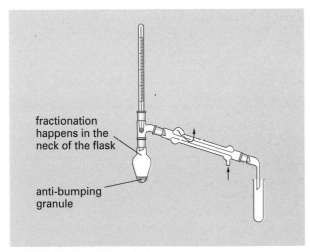

▲ **Figure 3A19** *Small-scale apparatus for fractional distillation being used to purify limonene from orange peel.*

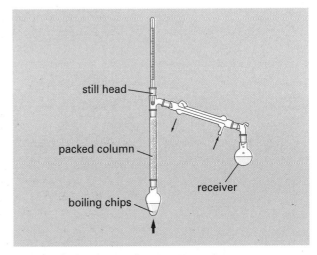

▲ **Figure 3A20** *A packed fractionating column for a more efficient separation.*

Fragrances from flowers

The French perfume industry began using solvent extraction and distillation procedures to obtain fragrant oils from flowers about 200 years ago.

Solvent extraction

Chopped up raw plant material was stirred into a solvent, usually benzene, which is immiscible in water. After filtering off the mass of vegetable matter and removing the water, the fragrant oil was extracted from the benzene by simple distillation. This involved boiling the solution and directing the benzene vapour into a condenser where it cooled, condensed and dripped into a collection vessel. The benzene could then be used again.

Only a tiny amount of fragrant oil was obtained from each extraction. It takes five tonnes of rose blossom to produce a kilogram of rose oil and eight million jasmine blossoms to produce a kilogram of jasmine fragrance.

Today, benzene cannot be used for safety reasons but there is another problem with using benzene to collect fragrances. Heating the solution of benzene and fragrant oil to remove the solvent often damages or evaporates some components of the delicate mix of chemicals that make up the fragrant oil.

Nowadays, a liquified gas, like butane or carbon dioxide, is often used as a solvent by the perfume industry. The solvent extraction procedure is done in a pressure vessel at a pressure high enough to keep the solvent liquid. After filtering, there is no need to heat the oil and solvent mixture to distil off the solvent. The pressure is simply reduced and the solvent boils leaving behind a cool and intact preparation of fragrant oil.

▼ **Figure 3A21** *Harvesting lavender in Norfolk.*

▲ **Figure 3A22** *Steam distillation to extract oil of lavender.*

Steam distillation

Lavender grows well in light, well-drained soils. It flourishes on the Mediterranean coast and was harvested by the Romans to scent their baths. Today lavender is used in perfumes, soaps, talcs and many other everyday products.

Before World War II, English perfumers relied on French growers for lavender, but the war cut off supplies and created an opportunity for Linn Chivers, a market gardener, who had already spotted the commercial possibilities of growing lavender in Britain.

He and a local landowner went into partnership to start a business in 1932 and had already managed to interest one of the big perfume companies by 1936. They brought over traditional copper stills from France to distil the oil. A visiting chemist and expert in perfumery, Horace Avery from Leicester, was able to let them into the secret of an 18th-century formula for lavender perfume.

The company was renamed Norfolk Lavender Limited in 1941 and, once the war was over, continued to develop looking to expand its markets not just in Britain.

Figure 3A22 shows the equipment now used at Norfolk lavender to steam distil the oil from the flowers after harvesting.

Testing the purity of products

Absolute purity can never be achieved, but the chemist has many ways of establishing how pure a chemical sample is and separating the desired chemical from the surrounding impurities. Again these techniques are based on the principle that chemical compounds behave in unique ways. They have unique characteristics.

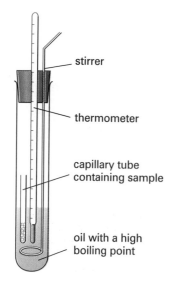

stirrer

thermometer

capillary tube
containing sample

oil with a high
boiling point

▲ **Figure 3A23** *Test-tube method for measuring the melting point of an organic solid.*

Melting points

Pure, crystalline organic compounds usually have sharp and specific melting points somewhere in the range 30 °C to 300 °C. Melting points are very sensitive to impurities and even small amounts can lower the melting point by several degrees. Also impure solids often soften and melt over a range of temperatures. All this means that watching samples melt and recording the melting point can help both to check on the identity of a product and to test its purity.

Chemists have developed techniques to measure the melting points of very small samples of chemicals. Two techniques are illustrated by Figures 3A23 and 3A24.

▶ **Figure 3A24** *Electrical apparatus for measuring melting points.*

Boiling points

The simplest way to measure the boiling point of a liquid is to distil it in an apparatus fitted with a thermometer to measure the temperature of the vapour passing over into the condenser (Figure 6B19).

Pure liquids have sharp boiling points but boiling points alter significantly with variations in atmospheric pressure. They may also fluctuate erratically if there are impurities in the liquid. This makes it more difficult to use boiling points to identify chemicals or check their purity.

Chromatography

Thin-layer chromatography (TLC) provides a quick and easy way of finding out whether or not a product is pure (see page 29). Impurities separate on the TLC plate and show up as separate spots. It is sometimes possible to identify the impurities with TLC by including pure samples of likely impurities and comparing the R_f values (see Figure 1B11) of the impurities with those of compounds included for comparison.

Planning a synthesis

Chemists have worked out procedures for the synthesis of hundreds of thousands of different chemical compounds. The result is an often complex and highly precise recipe for making a chemical which is published in academic papers, reference books and as part of patent applications for the production of new chemicals.

Reference books often offer a choice of synthetic routes. Factors to consider when making the choice of route include:

- the cost of the starting materials, the reagents, and the equipment
- the possible hazards associated with the chemicals and the practical techniques
- the complexity of the methods and the level of skill needed to complete the synthesis successfully
- the number of steps in the synthetic route
- the efficiency of the reaction at each step and the implications this has for the scale of operations at the start to ensure a reasonable yield.

Some chemical synthesis procedures give plenty of instructions and advice. Others assume that the person carrying out the synthesis is experienced enough to work out the details of the amounts of reagents, what equipment to use and what safety procedures are necessary.

▼ **Figure 3A25** *A paper in the 29 July 1993 edition of* Nature *describing the synthesis of chemicals which might help to treat ovarian cancer.*

Design, synthesis and biological activity of protaxols

K. C. Nicolaou[*]**, C. Riemer**[*]**, M. A. Kerr**[*]**, D. Rideout**[†] **& W. Wrasidlo**[‡]

[*] Department of Chemistry, The Scripps Research Institute, 10666 North Torrey Pines Road, La Jolla, California 92037, and Department of Chemistry, University of California, San Diego, 9500 Gilman Drive, La Jolla, California 92093, USA
[†] Department of Molecular Biology, The Scripps Research Institute, 10666 North Torrey Pines Road, La Jolla, California 92037, USA
[‡] Drug Discovery Unit, The Scripps Research Institute, 10666 North Torrey Pines Road, La Jolla, California 92037, USA

TAXOL[1-6] is a product isolated from the Pacific yew tree (*Taxus brevifolia*) and is a potent microtubule-stabilizing agent which has recently been approved for treatment of otherwise intractable ovarian cancer. Despite taxol's therapeutic promise, its aqueous insolubility (<0.004 mg ml^{-1}) hampers its clinical application. Here we report the design, synthesis and biological activity of a series of taxol-releasing compounds (protaxols) with improved pharmacological properties. These prodrugs were designed to increase their aqueous solubility and allow for taxol release under basic or physiological conditions. We demonstrate the stability of these prodrugs at pH $\leqslant 7$ and their ability to release taxol in a basic medium. Taxol-like microtubule-stabilizing activity[7-9] appears after the release of taxol. *In vitro* these prodrugs have cytotoxic properties against tumour cell lines comparable to those of taxol; moreover, human plasma catalyses the release of active taxol. These protaxols have greater potential as anticancer agents than the parent compounds taxol and taxotere (Fig. 1a).

Structure–activity relationships and variations in solubility of taxol have been investigated through substitution at the C-2′ hydroxyl group[10-13], but new taxols are needed with improved pharmacological properties. We therefore designed two types of structure (I and II in Fig. 1b). As the C-2′ hydroxyl group is the most convenient site to attach designed functional domains

in which the accelerating effect of higher temperatures and pH on taxol release was demonstrated. Table 1*a* includes the half-lives of six of these compounds at pH 7.5 and 9. As seen from these data, for compounds of type I the rate of taxol release increases with the electron-withdrawing ability of the aryl substituents, whereas for type II derivatives, the rate of release increases with the electron-withdrawing nature of the linking heteroatom. This illustrates the capacity for fine-tuning the rate of release of taxol according to a desired set of conditions using simple chemical principles.

Significantly, incubation of compound 5 in human plasma at 37 °C accelerates the release of taxol (half-life $t_{1/2}$ ~100 min) when compared to taxol release in aqueous media at the same pH and temperature (Fig. 2*b*). This indicates that taxol release from this compound (5) is being assisted by factors present in human plasma and suggests that it may be effective *in vivo*.

Tubulin polymerization to microtubules is promoted by GTP, whereas CaCl$_2$ causes depolymerization of microtubules back to tubulin (Fig. 3*a*). Taxol allows and promotes this type of microtubule assembly and, furthermore, it stabilizes microtubules against CaCl$_2$-induced depolymerization (Fig. 3*b*). Protaxol 5 was tested for its ability to stabilize microtubules formed from tubulin as a result of the action of GTP. This agent failed to prevent CaCl$_2$-induced disassembly of microtubules at the initial stages of the experiment (Fig. 3*c*), but showed increased potency with prolonged exposure times, as would be expected from the slow release of taxol, reaching a level comparable to that of taxol when conversion to taxol was essentially complete (Fig. 3*d*). Similar results were obtained with several other protaxols (Table 1). These findings are in agreement with the previously reported loss of activity resulting from blocking the C-2′ hydroxyl group[10-13].

The protaxols were tested against a broad range of cell lines, including the multiple-drug-resistant ovarian cells OVCAR-3, and lung (H-322) and leukaemia (MOLT-4) cells, to assess their cytotoxicity, cell-type selectivity, and duration of action. Comparison with taxol itself revealed that not only were potencies similar, but so also were selectivities against various cell lines. This is consistent with a mechanism of action dependent on taxol release, rather than the derivative itself having intrinsic activity. Furthermore, taxol was isolated and its identity confirmed from

A synthesis for indigo

Indigo is the dye used to give blue jeans their characteristic colour. It has been used as a dye since at least 3000 BC, and is made from an extract of leaves from plants of the genus *Indigofera*. In 1883, the German chemist Adolf Baeyer announced that, after more than 20 years research, he had determined its molecular structure.

Once the dye's structure was known it became possible to synthesize it from simpler and more easily obtained starting materials. Even so it was not until 1897 that the first commercially viable process came on stream. Figure 3A26 is a version of the last three stages of this first practicable synthesis of the dye.

▼ **Figure 3A26** *A synthesis of indigo.*

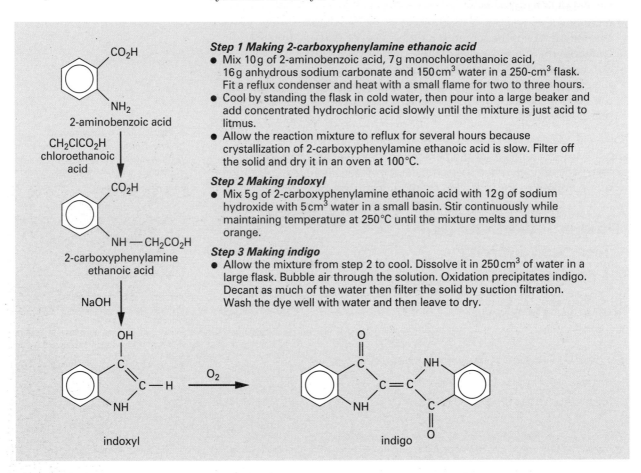

Step 1 Making 2-carboxyphenylamine ethanoic acid
- Mix 10 g of 2-aminobenzoic acid, 7 g monochloroethanoic acid, 16 g anhydrous sodium carbonate and 150 cm³ water in a 250-cm³ flask. Fit a reflux condenser and heat with a small flame for two to three hours.
- Cool by standing the flask in cold water, then pour into a large beaker and add concentrated hydrochloric acid slowly until the mixture is just acid to litmus.
- Allow the reaction mixture to reflux for several hours because crystallization of 2-carboxyphenylamine ethanoic acid is slow. Filter off the solid and dry it in an oven at 100 °C.

Step 2 Making indoxyl
- Mix 5 g of 2-carboxyphenylamine ethanoic acid with 12 g of sodium hydroxide with 5 cm³ water in a small basin. Stir continuously while maintaining temperature at 250 °C until the mixture melts and turns orange.

Step 3 Making indigo
- Allow the mixture from step 2 to cool. Dissolve it in 250 cm³ of water in a large flask. Bubble air through the solution. Oxidation precipitates indigo. Decant as much of the water then filter the solid by suction filtration. Wash the dye well with water and then leave to dry.

Planning the synthesis

Find out about the chemicals needed

Before carrying out the first step of the indigo synthesis, it is worth knowing that monochloroethanoic acid is corrosive and poisonous and so is concentrated hydrochloric acid. When setting up and checking the reaction, eye protection and protective gloves are needed and step 2 should be carried out in a fume cupboard.

Knowledge of the chemicals also helps in the selection of the equipment used. The heating needed to carry out the first step of the indigo synthesis cannot be done in a flask or beaker that is open to the air. During the heating, reagents will evaporate and a reflux condenser is needed to prevent them escaping.

If the reagents or solvents give off flammable gases during the reaction, it is not safe to use a flame. The reaction vessel should be heated with an electric hotplate or heating mantle or placed in a bath of hot water, steam or oil (depending on the temperature required).

Determine the amounts of different reagents to use

This depends on how much product is required. The equations for the steps of the synthesis show how many moles of starting reagents are required for each mole of product.

In the indigo synthesis, two moles of 2-aminobenzoic acid and chloroethanoic acid are needed, in theory, for every mole of indigo produced.

In practice the amounts of 2-aminobenzoic acid and chloroethanoic acid required to make a certain amount of indigo also depend on the efficiency of each step of the synthesis. It is unrealistic to assume the reactions will give a 100% yield. If there are three steps to the synthesis and each step only gives a yield of 80%, more than twice as much of the starting reagents is necessary than the equations suggest.

If some of the reagents are very cheap and easily available, it is often a good idea to add excess amounts of them to the reaction vessel so as to use as much as possible of the more expensive reagents. In the third step of the indigo synthesis, air is used to oxidize indoxyl. Air is readily available and there is no need to limit the amount used.

Adding the right amount of other reagents, such as solvents and catalysts, is often a matter of trial and error. The amounts cannot be worked out from the equation using molar masses. A reference book describing the procedure for a reaction usually gives the concentration of catalyst that needs to be present in the reaction mixture. From this, it is possible to work out the amounts of catalyst which will result in a good yield.

Draw up a schedule for the synthesis

A synthesis is a sequence of stages. During some of them chemists have to work, during others they may only have to watch and sometimes they just have to wait. Some of the stages take longer than others. It helps to study the procedure for each reaction, to work out what has to be done and when. This helps to make good use of available laboratory time.

The first step of the synthesis of indigo requires quite a bit of work to set up, then there is gap of two or three hours while the reaction mixture refluxes. After adding the concentrated hydrochloric acid there is an even longer wait while the product crystallizes. This stage doesn't need watching and is probably best left over night.

List the reagents and equipment needed at each stage

It is important to plan ahead by examining the procedure to see what will be needed and make sure it will be available when required.

▲ **Figure 3A27** *Anna Denny doing an organic synthesis using a non-aqueous solvent. The equipment consists of a reflux condenser on a multinecked round bottom flask, which is placed in a heating mantle, and a dropping funnel. The condenser and funnel are equipped with calcium chloride guard tubes to keep moisture out.*

Synthesizing organic chemicals

Organic synthesis

The challenge for organic chemists is to find ways to synthesize valuable products from simpler chemicals.

The strategy

Paradoxically the starting point for planning an organic synthesis is the **target molecule** – the desired product. A study of its carbon skeleton and functional groups makes it possible to devise a synthesis from simpler and more readily available **starting materials**. Several steps may be necessary on the way to the final product. The strategy is to work back from the target molecule until suitable starting materials are identified.

Starting materials must be cheap and easily available. In practice this means that most are derived from the simpler hydrocarbons from the petrochemical industry, although natural products from plants and animal sources may also be useful.

Reagents

Chemists have built up a huge bank of knowledge about the reagents and conditions needed to convert one compound to another. Figure 3B3 summarizes some of the important reactions of propene. Alkenes such as propene make useful starting materials for synthesis because they are much more reactive than the corresponding alkane. Simple alkenes are available cheaply on a large scale from the petrochemical industry (see Figure 3B1).

▼ **Figure 3B1** *Naphtha is one of the products from the fractional distillation of oil. It can be used to make motor fuel or to produce chemicals.*

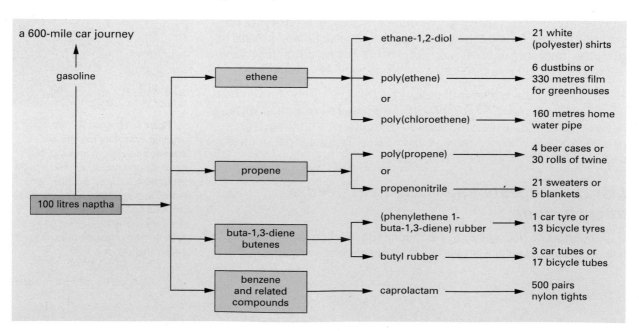

Challenges

There is often no one correct solution to a synthetic problem. Several routes may be equally possible and the problem is to select the optimum route, which involves the minimum number of steps each with high yields, small quantities of valueless by-products and all at an acceptable cost. Health and safety as well as economics are also factors which have to be considered when devising a commercial synthesis.

Most reactions of carbon compounds are accompanied by side reactions forming by-products as well as the main product. In organic reactions a yield of 90% is excellent, 80% is extremely good and even a yield as low as 50% may be acceptable.

It is often essential to check that reagents required for one step in the synthesis do not react with other groups present in the molecule. When they do it may be necessary to protect these groups while the desired reaction is carried out. Also, it may be necessary to carry out a multi-step synthesis in a particular order in case a change made in an earlier step of the process changes the reactivity of the molecule in a way that blocks a later step.

The American chemist, Russell Marker faced these challenges when seeking a route for making an abundant supply of progesterone, one of the steroid hormones in contraceptive pills. He discovered a route beginning with the natural steroid diosgenin for which the Mexican wild yam is an excellent source.

In the final stages of the synthesis Russell had to convert an alcohol to a ketone and then shift a double bond to a new position (see Figure 3B2). The problem was that oxidizing agents, such as sodium dichromate(VI), attack double bonds as well as —OH groups. What he chose to do was add bromine to the double bond, then oxidize the —OH group. Heating with zinc metal removed the bromine atoms reforming the double bond. Once the C=O group was in place, all that was needed to encourage the double C—C bond to shift to the new position was an acid catalyst.

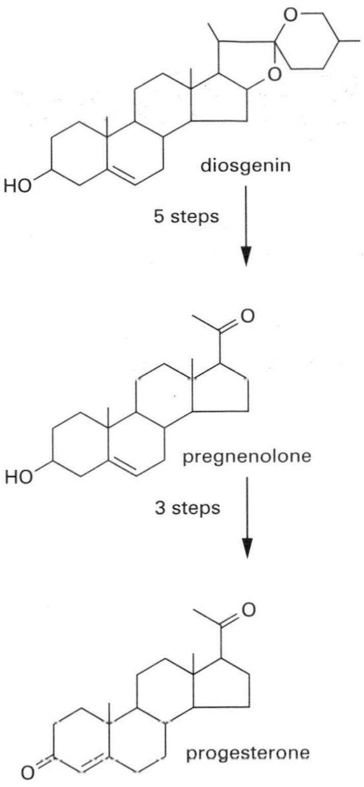

▲ **Figure 3B2** *Steps in the synthesis of a steroid – progesterone.*

▼ **Figure 3B3** *Some reactions of propene.*

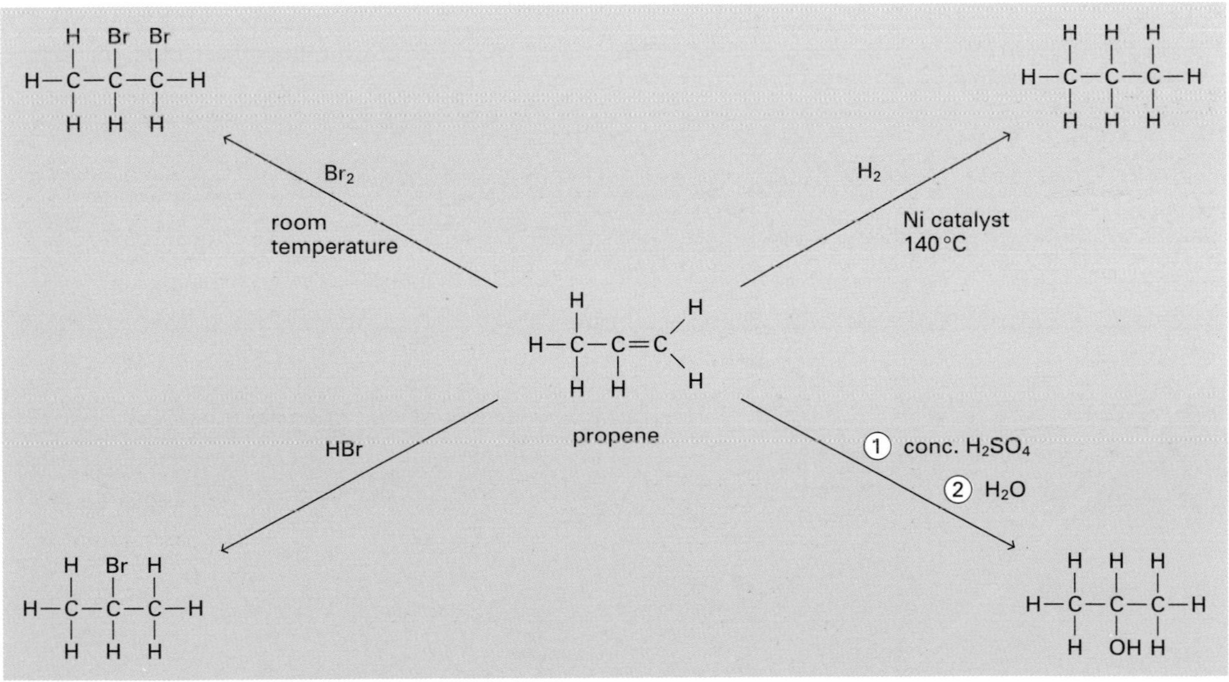

Ibuprofen

The Boots company developed Ibuprofen as a drug to help people who suffer from rheumatoid arthritis; these people are in pain because of inflammation round the joints. The story of the discovery of this drug illustrates the benefits of a thorough knowledge and understanding of organic synthesis.

When they tested Ibuprofen Boots found that as well as being anti-inflammatory it was also a pain reliever (analgesic) and helped to reduce temperature (antipyretic). So it turned out to be a rival to aspirin. When first released in 1969, Ibuprofen was only available with a doctor's prescription but it has proved effective and safe and so people can now buy it over the counter in a lower-dose form from a pharmacist, as Nurofen.

▼ **Figure 3B4**

Name/ code	Structure	Activity relative to aspirin		
		Anti-inflammatory	Analgesic	Antipyretic
Aspirin	OCOCH_3 CO_2H	1	1	1
10335	$(CH_3)_3C\;\;CH_2CO_2H$	4	2–4	4
10499	CH_2CO_2H	3	10	4
Ibufenac	$(CH_3)_2CHCH_2\;\;CH_2CO_2H$	2–4	2–4	4
Ibuprofen	$(CH_3)_2CHCH_2\;\;CHCO_2H$ $\;\;\;\;CH_3$	16–23	30	20

Boots chemists worked on the development of the new drug for a long time. During that time they tested lots of compounds, including those shown in the table (Figure 3B4) which compares the effectiveness of a range of compounds to aspirin.

For a short time during the 1960s, Ibufenac was available on prescription in Europe and the UK but it had to be withdrawn because of side effects. The next modification to be given widespread testing was compound 10499 but it produced rashes in about 20% of patients and so it too had to be withdrawn. It took 30 years from the start of the research programme to the launch of Nurofen on the open market.

▼ **Figure 3B5** *Stages in the development of a new drug.*

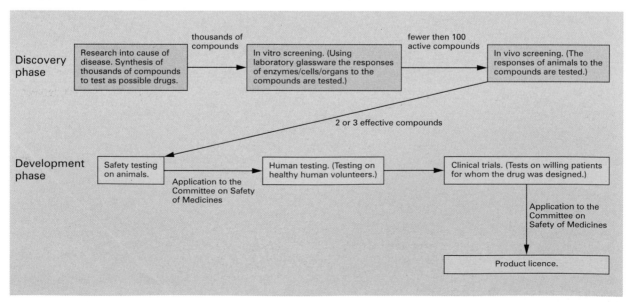

The process of research and development is long and slow, so it costs a pharmaceutical company a vast amount of money to bring a new drug to market. The company therefore takes out patents in many countries to protect its discovery and prevent other firms making and selling the drug except under licence. Patents only last for a limited number of years so the company hopes to be able to sell enough of the drug to recover its costs and make a profit before the patent runs out.

Figure 3B6 shows a possible laboratory synthesis of Ibuprofen which illustrates many of the chemical reactions described on pages 148–55 in this chapter. This is a laboratory route and not the procedure used to manufacture the drug, which is also a multi-step process but with fewer stages.

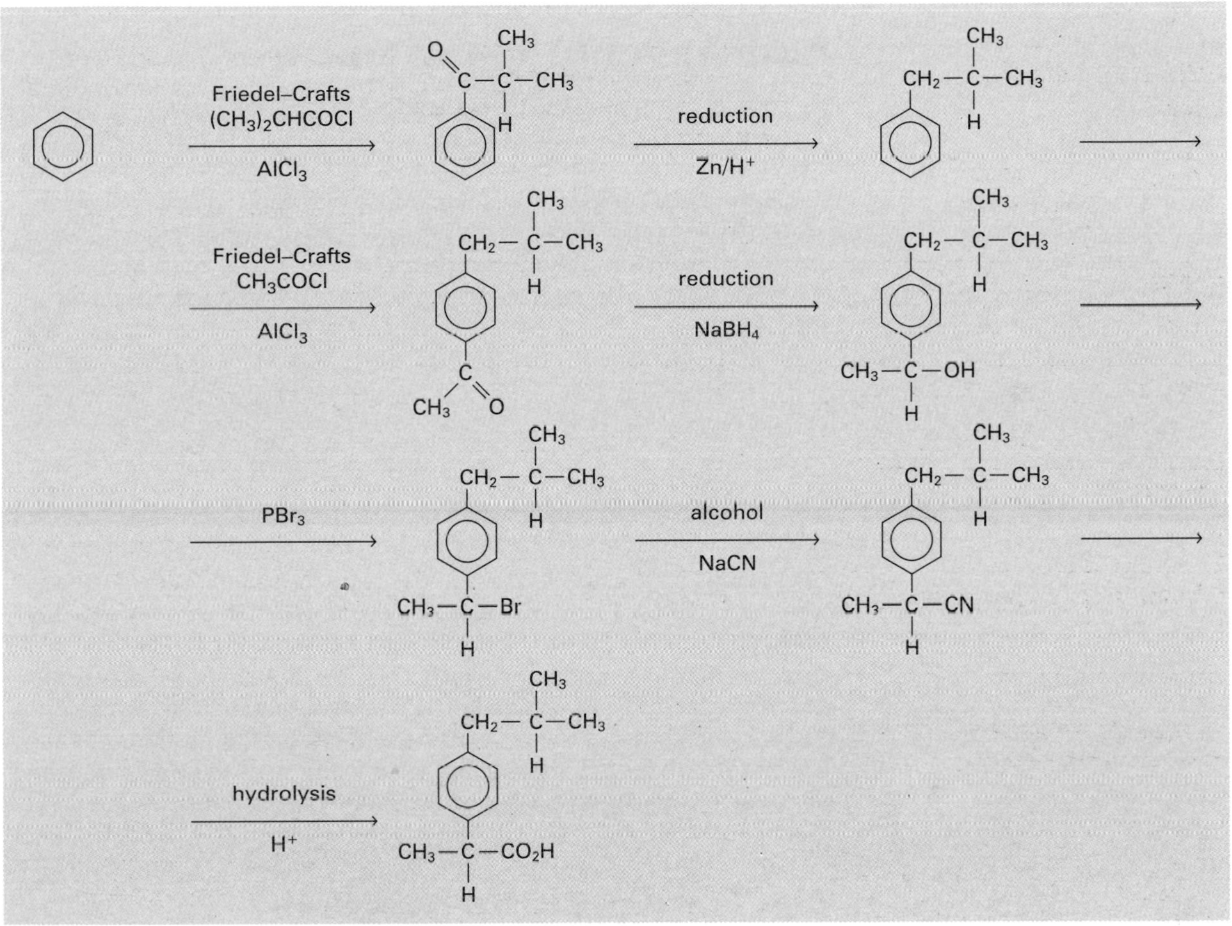

▲ **Figure 3B6** *A possible laboratory synthesis of Ibuprofen.*

The action of drugs is closely linked to their molecular structure. Nowadays a research team looking for alternatives to an existing treatment might start with the structure of an established drug and explore ways of changing it to produce a superior product. Much of the early planning can be done with the help of computers to model drug structures on the screen and match them to likely receptor sites in the body. This can help to eliminate many possibilities and draw up a short list of likely candidates for synthesis and testing.

For a research compound to become a marketed product it has to cross three critical barriers: it has to meet a definite therapeutic need; it has to be scientifically and technically possible to develop and manufacture the product; and there has to be a big enough market to ensure that the development work will be commercially viable.

Reactions to build up a carbon skeleton

The enormous range of carbon compounds is the result of the ability of carbon atoms to join together to form chains and rings. Chemists have reported over seven million carbon compounds, but fortunately they have found that they can understand them in terms of a carbon skeleton supporting one or more functional groups.

When setting out to build up a more complex molecule, such as Ibuprofen, organic chemists have to select suitable reactions for adding carbon atoms to the basic skeleton of the starting material. Chemists have devised many ways to do this illustrated here by the polymerization of alkenes, the Friedel–Crafts reaction and the use of cyanide ions.

Addition polymerization

The typical reactions of alkenes are addition reactions involving the double bond. The addition of bromine is used as a test for unsaturated hydrocarbons (see page 15 and Figure R16.1 in the Reference section). Under the right conditions it is possible to persuade alkene molecules to add to each other to create very long chains of carbon atoms. This process of **addition polymerization** gives rise to polymers such as polythene, PVC, polystyrene and acrylics (for more details see pages 156–7).

$$nCH_2 = CH_2 \longrightarrow ---CH_2-CH_2-CH_2-CH_2-CH_2-CH_2----$$
ethene – monomer   poly(ethene) – polymer

Polythene comes in two forms: a low density form ($0.92\,g\,cm^{-3}$) used for carrier bags or bin liners and a high density form ($0.96\,g\,cm^{-3}$) which is more rigid and suitable for bleach bottles and milk crates. The low density form is the product of a high-pressure method of polymerizing ethene gas. During polymerization side branches grow from the main chains, which prevent the molecules packing together neatly in the solid. The alternative route to the higher density plastic produces unbranched chains by passing ethene gas at atmospheric pressure into a solution containing small amounts of a catalysts formed from $TiCl_4$ and $(C_2H_5)_3Al$.

The Friedel–Crafts reaction

Organic chemists have established a tradition of naming reactions after the people who discovered them. Such a reaction is the Friedel–Crafts reaction named after two chemists, Frenchman Charles Friedel and American James Crafts. Together they worked out a method for introducing side chains into benzene rings by forming carbon–carbon bonds. This is now an important reaction in laboratories as well as in the petrochemical and fine chemicals industries.

As sometimes represented, benzene has three double bonds in its structure (see page 16), so at first sight it seems that it should be highly reactive like the alkenes. In fact, benzene is far less reactive than alkenes and does not easily take part in addition reactions.

The essence of the Friedel–Crafts family of reactions is that by using a suitable catalyst, some halogen compounds can be made reactive enough to attack and **substitute** into the benzene ring replacing a hydrogen atom with a side chain.

One example is the substitution of a group with three carbon atoms into benzene using 2-chloropropane and the catalyst aluminium chloride, $AlCl_3$.

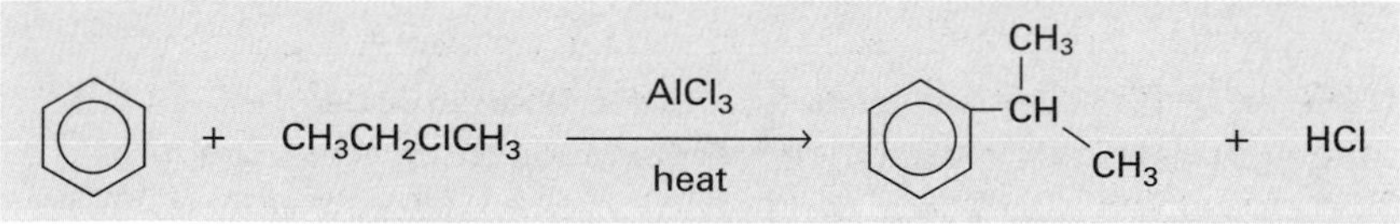

The Friedel-Crafts reaction can also produce ketones when an acid chloride reacts with a benzene ring. Aluminium chloride is again the catalyst (see also Figure 3B6).

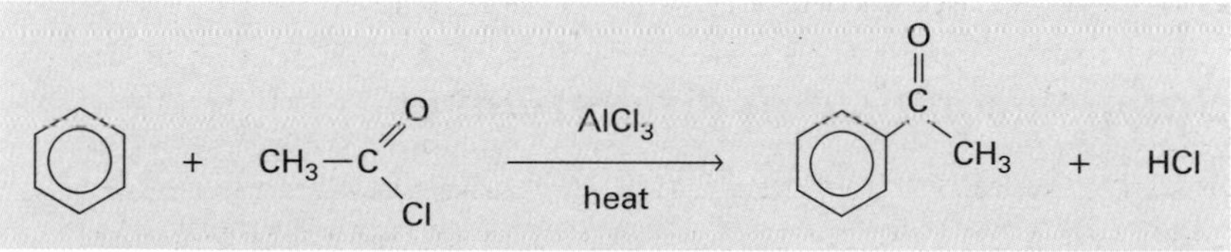

Cyanide reactions

Under the right conditions, cyanide ions replace halogen atoms in organic compounds forming carbon–carbon bonds. Heating 1-bromopropane with a solution of sodium cyanide in ethanol brings about a **substitution reaction** which adds a carbon atom to the molecule.

$$CH_3CH_2CH_2Br + Na^+CN^- \xrightarrow{\text{heat}} \underset{\text{butanenitrile}}{CH_3CH_2CH_2CN} + Na^+Br^-$$

The product (a nitrile) is not the target molecule but it is easily converted to other more useful products. **Hydrolysis** converts nitriles to acids. Hydrolysis reactions use water to break chemical bonds, usually with the help of an acid or an alkali to act as a catalyst.

$$CH_3CH_2CH_2CN + 2H_2O + H^+ \xrightarrow[\text{with acid}]{\text{heat}} \underset{\text{butanoic acid}}{CH_3CH_2CH_2CO_2H} + NH_4^+$$

Reduction converts nitriles to amines. Hydride ions from lithium aluminium hydride are a suitable reducing agent.

$$CH_3CH_2CH_2CN \xrightarrow[\text{Li AlH}_4\text{ in ether}]{H^-} \underset{\text{1-aminobutane}}{CH_3CH_2CH_2CH_2NH_2}$$

Organic halogen compounds as intermediates

Chemists have discovered ways to introduce functional groups into organic molecules and then to convert one group to another. They use these reactions to add the reactive groups they need to the basic carbon skeleton. Reactions involving halogen compounds as intermediates are particularly useful. The use of nitriles in synthesis is one example (see page 149) but there are many others.

There are remarkably few naturally occurring organic halogen compounds. The few which are known include the thyroid hormone thyroxin (which is an iodine compound) and the chlorine compound, chloromethane, produced by some algae in the sea. What this means is that almost all organic halogen compounds must be made synthetically.

Methods used to introduce halogen atoms

Halogen compounds from alkenes

The characteristic reactions of alkenes are addition reactions. Alkenes react readily with aqueous hydrogen bromide at room temperature. Prop-1-ene adds hydrogen bromide to form 2-bromopropane (see Figure 3B3).

Alkenes also form dibromo-compounds when they react at room temperature with a solution of bromine in an organic solvent (see Figure 3B3).

Halogen compounds from alcohols

There are two main ways of replacing an —OH group by a halogen atom. The main reagent in the first method is a hydrogen halide (HCl or HBr) as illustrated by the synthesis of 1-bromobutane (see pages 132–3). The reagents used, sodium bromide and concentrated sulphuric acid, react to make hydrogen bromide. The substitution reaction is effectively a reaction between the alcohol and hydrogen bromide.

This type of reaction goes much more readily when the —OH group is attached to a carbon atom at a branch in the carbon skeleton. Simply shaking the tertiary alcohol (see box on page 151) 2-methylpropan-2-ol with concentrated hydrochloric acid, HCl(aq), at room temperature quickly produces 2-chloro-2-methylpropane (Figure 3B7).

> **Halogenoalkanes**
> The common halogens are chlorine, bromine and iodine. When halogen atoms replace hydrogen atoms in alkanes the result is a halogenoalkane.

> **Names**
> The name of a halogenoalkane is derived by adding chloro, bromo or iodo to the related alkane. Numbering the carbon atoms makes it possible to distinguish isomers.
>
> CH_3–CH_2–CH_2Cl
> 1-chloropropane
>
> CH_3–CH_2Cl–CH_3
> 2-chloropropane

▼ **Figure 3B7** *Stages in the preparation of 2–chloro–2–methylpropane.*

Shake 20 cm³ of 2-methylpropan-2-ol with 70 cm³ of concentrated hydrochloric acid in a stoppered flask for about 20 minutes until an upper layer of product forms.	Transfer to a separating funnel and run off the aqueous layer. Add 20 cm³ of 0.1 mol dm⁻³ sodium hydrogencarbonate. Stopper and shake, taking care to release gas as the pressure builds up in the funnel. Run off the aqueous layer and repeat the treatment until no more gas forms.	Transfer the product to a small conical flask and add a little anhydrous sodium sulphate as a drying agent. Stopper and leave to stand for a few minutes.	Filter the product into a small distillation flask. Distil the liquid and collect the fraction boiling between 50°C and 52°C.

The second method uses a phosphorus compound such as phosphorus tribromide, PBr_3, usually made in the reaction flask by mixing red phosphorus with bromine.

Reactions of compounds with halogen atoms

Substitution

Figure 3B8 describes three useful reactions of halogenoalkanes. They are all substitution reactions in which the halogen atom is replaced by another functional group.

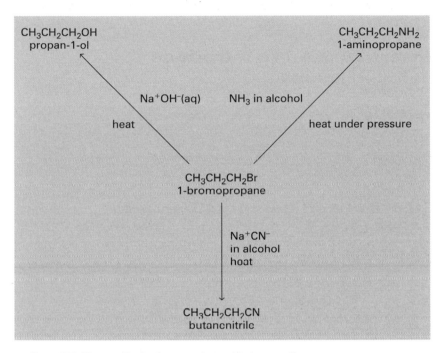

▲ **Figure 3B8** *Three substitution reactions of halogenoalkanes.*

In these ways halogenoalkane reactions make it possible to build up molecules by forming C—C, C—O and C—N bonds.

Elimination

Another reaction of halogenoalkanes is a good method for introducing double bonds into complex molecules. The reagent is potassium hydroxide dissolved in ethanol instead of in water. Under these conditions the change is an **elimination** reaction. Both a hydrogen and a halogen atom split off from the molecule. The reaction goes more readily with secondary and tertiary halogenoalkanes.

$$(CH_3)_3CBr + K^+OH^- \longrightarrow CH_3C{=}CH_2 \text{ (with } CH_3 \text{ branch)} + K^+Br^- + H_2O$$

(CH₃)₃CBr   +   K⁺OH⁻ ⟶ CH₃C=CH₂   +   K⁺Br⁻   +   H₂O
2-bromo-2-methylpropane   methylpropene

Three types of structure

- Primary – the halogen atom is attached to a carbon atom linked to **one** other carbon atom:
  $CH_3—CH_2—CH_2—CH_2Br$
  1-bromobutane

- Secondary – the halogen atom is attached to a carbon atom linked to **two** other carbon atoms:
  $CH_3—CH_2—CH_2Br—CH_3$
  2-bromobutane

- Tertiary – the halogen atom is attached to a carbon atom linked to **three** other carbon atoms:
  $$CH_3—CHBr—CH_3$$
  with CH_3 branch
  2-bromo-2-methylpropane

Alcohol reactions

Alcohols are useful chemicals, they are also reactive and feature as intermediates in many organic syntheses.

Methods used to introduce —OH groups

Figure 3B9 summarizes some of the methods used in synthesis to add —OH groups to organic molecules.

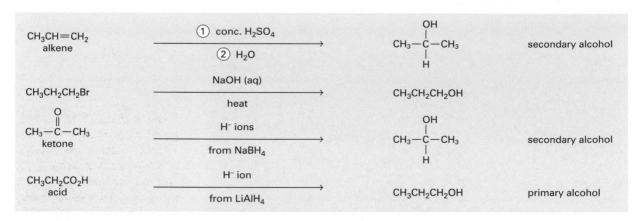

▲ **Figure 3B9** *Reactions which introduce —OH groups into organic molecules.*

Reactions of compounds with —OH groups

Oxidation

An acidic solution of sodium dichromate(VI) oxidizes primary alcohols such as propan-1-ol first to an aldehyde and then to a carboxylic acid. The reaction can be used to make an aldehyde if the product is separated from the reaction as it forms. This prevents further oxidation to the acid.

$$CH_3-CH_2-CH_2OH \xrightarrow{\text{warm with acidified sodium dichromate(VI)}} CH_3-CH_2-\textbf{CHO}$$
propanal (an aldehyde)

Prolonged heating of the alcohol with an excess of the oxidizing agent in a flask fitted with a reflux condenser makes sure that it is all converted to the acid.

$$CH_3-CH_2-CH_2OH \xrightarrow{\text{heat with excess acidified sodium dichromate(VI)}} CH_3-CH_2-\textbf{CO}_2\textbf{H}$$
propanoic acid

Oxidation of secondary alcohols, such as propan-2-ol, produces a ketone. It is hard to oxidize a ketone further because it involves breaking a C—C bond.

$$CH_3-CHOH-CH_3 \xrightarrow{\text{heat with acidified sodium dichromate(VI)}} CH_3-\overset{\displaystyle O}{\underset{\displaystyle \|}{C}}-CH_3$$
propanone

Carbonyl compounds

The carbonyl group, $>C=O$ features in aldehydes and ketones.

In an aldehyde the carbonyl group is at the end of the carbon chain. The aldehyde with three carbons is propan**al**.

CH_3CH_2CHO

In a ketone the carbonyl group appears between two carbon atoms in the chain. The ketone with three carbon atoms is propan**one**.

CH_3COCH_3

Substitution

Hydrogen halides and phosphorus halides react with alcohols replacing the —OH group with a halogen atom. These reactions are described on pages 150–1.

Elimination

Heating an alcohol with phosphoric acid produces an alkene by an elimination reaction which splits off water molecules. Another name for this reaction is **dehydration**.

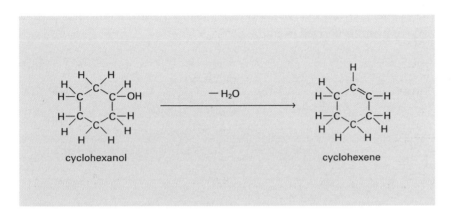

cyclohexanol   cyclohexene

Figure 3B10 shows how this reaction converts cyclohexanol to cyclohexene.

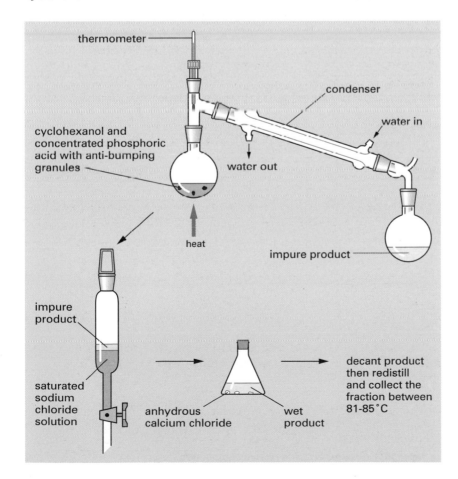

thermometer

condenser

water in

cyclohexanol and concentrated phosphoric acid with anti-bumping granules

water out

heat

impure product

impure product

saturated sodium chloride solution

anhydrous calcium chloride

wet product

decant product then redistill and collect the fraction between 81-85°C

◄ **Figure 3B10** *Converting cyclohexanol to cyclohexene.*

Shorthand

Writing out the full structures of cyclohexane and cyclohexene is tedious. Chemists draw a skeleton structure showing just the C—C bonds.

cyclohexane

Looking at this they assume that there will be a carbon atom at each apex and as many hydrogen atoms as necessary to make sure that each carbon atom forms four covalent bonds.

Carboxylic acids and their derivatives

Many natural products contain carboxylic acid groups including all the fatty acids in our diet. Chemists have a toolkit of reactions to convert the acid functional group into related compounds which are valuable in themselves or useful in synthesis.

The chemical industry manufactures carboxylic acids on a large scale as a source of chemicals for use in foods (as preservatives and flavourings), in perfumes, in solvents and as raw materials for polymers.

Figure 3B11 shows the chemical relationships between ethanoic acid and compounds derived from the acid.

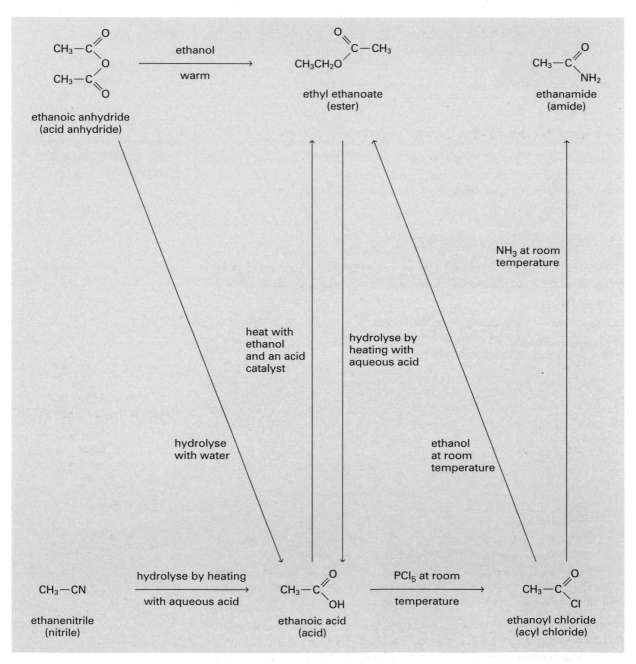

▲ **Figure 3B11** *Ethanoic acid and related compounds.*

Esters

Esters help to make up the subtle flavours of ripe fruits. Even pure esters on their own have fruity tastes and smells. Pear drops, for example, owe their flavour to the ester 3-methylbutyl ethanoate. Intriguingly the same ester is a component of a chemical signal (or pheromone) produced by a honey bee to warn other bees of danger.

Esters form directly when an alcohol reacts with an acid linking the two molecules together and splitting off a molecule of water. The reaction is very slow unless there is an acid present to act as a catalyst.

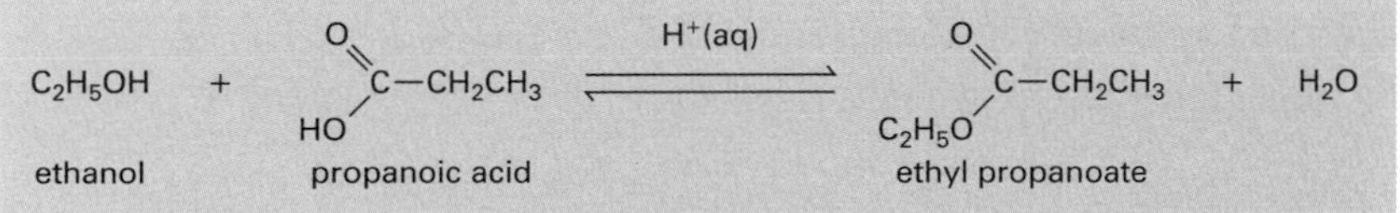

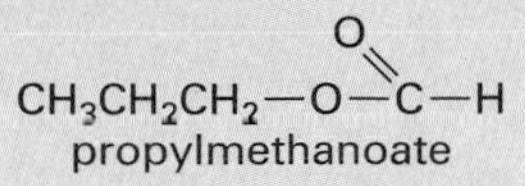

Often it is easier to make an ester with the help of an acid chloride or an acid anhydride (as shown in Figure 3B11).

Esters from 2-hydroxybenzoic acid

There are two functional groups in 2-hydroxybenzoic acid: an —OH group and an acid group. This means that it has two ways of turning into an ester and it turns out that both ways can produce chemicals with useful medical properties.

Making oil of wintergreen

People suffering from aches rub on creams containing oil of wintergreen. The oil is absorbed through the skin and it helps to lower inflammation and relieve pain.

The acid group in 2-hydroxybenzoic acid forms the ester, oil of wintergreen, directly when heated with methanol in the presence of concentrated sulphuric acid to act as the catalyst.

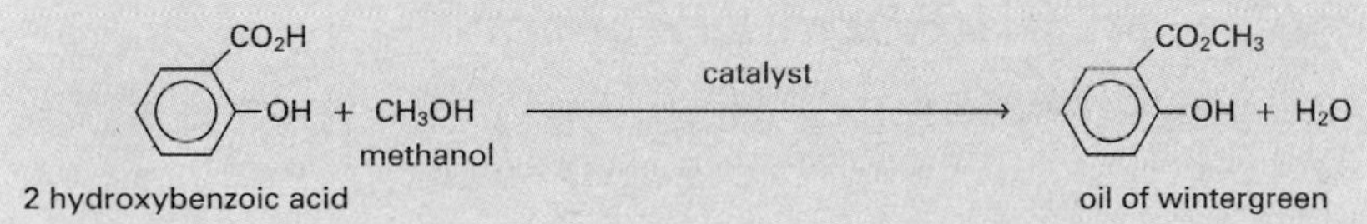

Making aspirin

Aspirin was the first synthetic drug and it is still one of the most widely used medicines. Pharmaceutical companies make over 4000 million tablets each year in the United Kingdom. People take aspirin for feverish colds, headaches and rheumatism. Doctors also prescribe small regular doses for some patients to ward off heart attacks.

Compounds with —OH groups attached to a benzene ring do not form esters easily by reacting with an acid. For this reason the manufacture of aspirin is based on the reaction of 2-hydroxybenzoic acid and ethanoic anhydride.

Naming esters

The alcohol methanol reacts with propanoic acid to form the ester methylpropanoate. Propan-1-ol and methanoic acid form propyl methanoate.

$$CH_3CH_2CH_2-O-\overset{O}{\overset{\|}{C}}-H$$
propylmethanoate

▼ **Figure 3B12** *Making aspirin.*

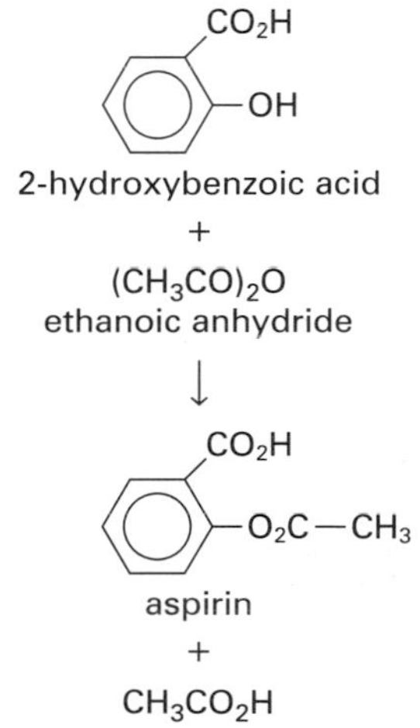

Making polymers

Big things like houses can be made quickly and efficiently when built from many identical units like bricks. The same is true of big molecules. Polymers are huge molecules consisting of long chains of smaller molecules that can bond together.

Natural and synthetic polymers

A wide range of biopolymers make up the structural parts of living things. Plants synthesize carbohydrate polymers such as cellulose, but animals rely on the more versatile protein polymers such as keratin, collagen and chitin. Many of the structural materials and fibres from living things consist of biopolymers. Wood, paper and cotton are made up of carbohydrate polymers. Wool, horn and ivory are made of protein polymers.

Cellulose nitrate, first made in the mid-19th century, is often called the first synthetic plastic but it is actually just a modification of the biopolymer in wood. The same is true of the first artificial fibre, cellulose acetate which came a few years later. The first truly synthetic polymer was developed by Leo Baekland who mixed phenol and methanal and heated them under pressure. He produced a new material which was stiff, light, reasonably strong, easy to mould and an electrical insulator. Baekland did not understand the chemical nature of this new material or how it had formed but he knew a good thing when he saw it. He called the plastic 'Bakelite'. In 1910 he formed a company to manufacture the product and became very wealthy.

Not surprisingly, this inspired many other chemists to try mixing combinations of organic chemicals. A few succeeded in producing new materials but the real advance only came once they understood that the new chemicals were the result of reactions which could link small molecules together in very long chains.

It was the Du Pont research chemist, Wallace Carrothers who, in 1931, added several new words to the chemists' vocabulary: polymer, monomer and polymerization. He was the first to distinguish between the two types of polymerization: addition and condensation polymerization.

PVC – an addition polymer

Small molecules with double bonds are the monomers which add together in long chains to form addition polymers.

PVC is perhaps the most versatile of addition polymers with a staggering variety of uses. There are three stages to the manufacture of PVC:
- making the monomer (vinyl chloride)
- polymerization
- blending the polymer with other chemicals to produce a wide range of products.

The starting point for making the monomer is ethene which first adds chlorine and then changes it to chloroethene (vinyl chloride) on heating.

$$CH_2{=}CH_2 \xrightarrow{60\,°C} CH_2Cl{-}CH_2Cl \xrightarrow{530\,°C} CH_2{=}CHCl$$

ethene $\qquad\qquad$ 1,2-dichloroethane $\qquad\qquad$ chloroethene (vinyl chloride)

Vinyl chloride is a gas at room temperature and pressure, but for the manufacture of PVC it is processed as a liquid under pressure. Polymerization takes place inside high-pressure chambers at a temperature between 50 °C and 70 °C. The liquid monomer is dispersed in water with an organic peroxide to start the process. As the vinyl chloride polymerizes, tiny solid particles appear and are allowed to grow until they are slightly smaller than the grains of granulated sugar. At this point any unchanged monomer is removed by lowering the pressure and allowing the vinyl chloride to vaporize. The recovered monomer is compressed, condensed and recycled.

Centrifuges separate the water from the product which is then dried in a stream of hot air to produce a free-flowing white powder. High speed blending mixes the polymer grains with selected additives. Fast moving blades heat the mixture by friction and create a homogeneous melt with all the ingredients evenly mixed.

Blended with one set of additives, PVC can be melted down and turned into sheets of clear film for wrapping food. Other additives make it into the brightly coloured opaque plastic of children's waterproof boots or the stiff, hard plastic of credit cards or the tough frames that hold panes of glass in double glazed windows.

Polyester and polyamide – condensation polymers

Carothers's research group at Du Pont worked on the first truly synthetic fibre which was a condensation polymer they called Nylon. Condensation polymerization usually involves two monomers each with two functional groups at each end of their molecules. The molecules link in chains by splitting off a small molecule such as water or hydrogen chloride. Nylon is a polyamide, one of two important classes of condensation polymers.

$$n HO_2C(CH_2)_4CO_2H + n H_2N(CH_2)_6NH_2 \longrightarrow -[-OC(CH_2)_4CONH(CH_2)_6NH-]_n- + (2n-1)H_2O$$
$$\text{nylon– 6,6}$$

The other main class of condensation polymers is polyester. Molecules with two —OH groups (such as ethane-1,2-diol) form polyesters with molecules which have two carboxylic acid groups (such as benzene-1, 4-dicarboxylic acid).

Developing a new fungicide

Every year, farmers around the world spend about \$5 billion on chemicals to protect their crops from infection by fungi. In the next few years, the British bioscience company Zeneca plans to launch a new fungicide which they believe will capture a significant slice of this market. The systematic IUPAC name for the new chemical is methyl (*E*)-2-{2-[6-(2-cyanophenoxy)pyrimidin-4-yloxy]phenyl}-3-methoxyacrylate. Until it is given a shorter chemical label it is known as ICIA5504 or 5504 for short.

▲ **Figure 3B13** *Powdery mildew fungi growing on a grape vine.*

▶ **Figure 3B14** *First reported structure of Strobilurin A.*

John Clough was one of the team of chemists at Zeneca's research labs at Jealott's Hill, Berkshire, who invented 5504. As John explains, the key to inventing useful new agricultural chemicals is deciding where to look and then working very hard in the lab and the greenhouse.

'The story of 5504 began in 1981 when one of my colleagues saw a scientific paper written by researchers at the University of Kaiserslautern in Germany. A group of small fungi that live on rotting wood get the upper hand on their competitors by producing chemicals which inhibit the growth of other fungi. The German scientists had isolated one of these chemicals and found that it works by blocking energy processing inside the competing fungi's mitochondria. They called the chemical Strobilurin A and reported its chemical structure as looking like this:

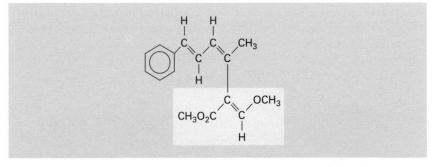

'When we tried to synthesize this chemical in the laboratory, we found that the compound's molecular structure really looked like this:

▲ **Figure 3B15** *Real structure of Strobilurin A with toxophore indicated in a box.*

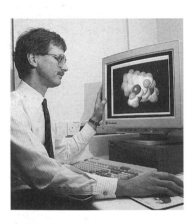

▲ **Figure 3B16** *John Clough studying an image of Strobilurin A.*

'This may seem like a subtle difference, but it meant that we had to completely revise our ideas about the three dimensional shape of Strobilurin A. An accurate understanding of this shape is essential if we are to design molecules which will work in the same way as Strobilurin A. The molecules we make have to be a similar shape so that they will bind to and block the same enzyme active site (see page 333) in the energy processing machinery of fungi. Molecules of the wrong shape simply won't fit.

'Once we had synthesized a sample of the compound we could conduct tests to find out if it had any promise as a fungicide. Would it inhibit the growth of the kinds of fungi that cause the most serious damage to a variety of crops? The answer was: "Yes, sort of". We found that even very low concentrations of Strobilurin A inhibited the growth of these fungi, and we were extremely interested to see that it was effective against several important strains of fungi that are resistant to other fungicides. The problem was that it only worked when applied to fungi growing on agar plates in a dimly lit laboratory. It had no effect on the same kinds of fungi growing on plants in the greenhouse. This suggested to us that Strobilurin A is destroyed by sunlight. We then went on to confirm this in the lab using a lamp to simulate sunlight.

'The next step was to synthesize a large number of chemically related compounds. We speculated, correctly as it turned out, that the methyl 3-methoxyacrylate group was the part of the Strobilurin A molecule which was important for fungicidal activity, the "toxophore" as we call it. We set out to prepare compounds which still contained this group but which would be less sensitive to sunlight than the natural compound. We didn't want to produce compounds that would be too robust, however, or they would persist for too long in the environment and could inhibit the growth of harmless or useful fungi.

'The most efficient way to synthesize a large number of related compounds is to find a synthetic route which can branch off in many directions. We chose routes which produced the toxophore at quite an early stage. We then used different reactions to add a variety of structures. These are some of the molecules we synthesized.

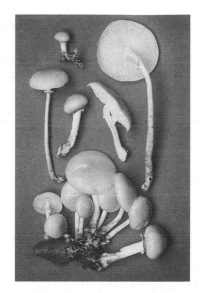

▲ **Figure 3B17** *The toadstool fungus which is the natural source of Strobilurin A.*

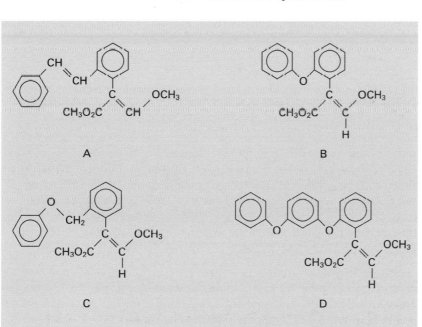

A

B

C

D

▲ **Figure 3B18** *Molecular structure of a variety of compounds tested.*

'We tested each for fungicidal activity, first in the laboratory, then in the greenhouse and then on crops growing under field conditions. Compound A, which is a Stilbene, looked promising. It had excellent activity in the greenhouse but did not perform well enough under field conditions. All in all, we synthesized and tested almost 1500 compounds before we came up with 5504, which really did seem to be a winner.

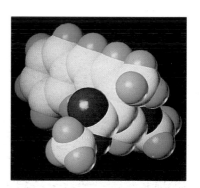

▲ **Figure 3B19** *Colour computer graphic of three-dimensional structure of Strobilurin A. Carbon atoms are white, oxygen red and hydrogen blue.*

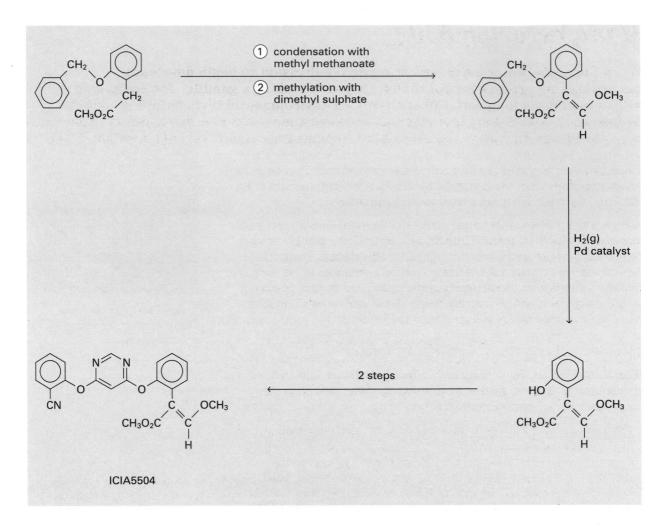

ICIA5504

'There are already more than 150 different fungicides on the market so any new one faces stiff competition but we believe that 5504 has properties that make it better for some uses than any fungicide already on the market. The main advantage is that it is effective against a wide range of the really damaging fungal diseases. For example, there are two key fungal infections that damage vines. Currently, vineyard owners give their crops two different treatments or spray them with a mixture of fungicides to protect against both diseases. 5504 is the first fungicide that can control both pests. There is a similar situation with two diseases that damage rice crops, rice blast and sheath blight. Again, 5504 is the first fungicide that controls both.

'Today, however, it is not good enough for a new fungicide simply to be good at killing fungi. We have to find out what else it may kill. Pesticides are released into the environment so we must carry out tests on any new one to find how long it will persist in the environment, how quickly it is broken down by, for example, sunlight and soil bacteria. We must also find out if it will leach into the groundwater and learn what effect the compound is likely to have on fish, invertebrates and other types of organisms. And, of course, we have to find out what effect it will have on the humans who will be exposed to it. Early tests showed no adverse effects, no causes of concern at all, so Zeneca's Senior Management decided that it would be worth investing several million more pounds carrying out the next stage of its development, working out how to manufacture the compound in bulk.'

Manufacturing 5504

When Zeneca's senior management made the decision to begin developing a manufacturing process for ICIA5504, they were taking a gamble. The compound had to undergo a long series of toxicity and environmental tests before it could be licensed for sale. Taking this risk was necessary, however, because it can take several years to design a process and assemble the plant for manufacturing a new chemical.

Zeneca wanted to be able to start selling the new product as soon as it was licensed so it had to start preparing for its manufacture years before the company knew if a licence would even be granted.

All being well, 5504 will be produced by the Fine Chemicals manufacturing organization within Zeneca, which has manufacturing facilities at Grangemouth in Scotland and Huddersfield in England. A team of chemists was assigned to investigate a number of synthetic routes and produce a commercially viable manufacturing process. Only occasionally is the synthetic route devised by the research chemist suitable for scaling up for manufacturing the product.

When the most favourable route has been selected, more detailed development work beings. Patrick McNeilly, one of the process chemists at Zeneca's Process Technology labs in Huddersfield explains how a chemist must take a number of factors into account when working towards a suitable manufacturing process.

'Agricultural chemicals have to be sold at a sensible price which means that the cost of manufacture has to be kept as low as possible. Zeneca has to be able to sell the product at a profit to get a return on their investment in research and the building of the manufacturing plant. There is however a limit on how much farmers will pay. They will not buy the product unless they make a profit from the increased yield of their crops.

▼ **Figure 3B21** *Patrick McNeilly with the pilot plant which was built to test the process before scaling up to manufacturing.*

▲ **Figure 3B22** *'The vessels and pipework used in the bulk manufacture of a compound are much larger than those used in a research lab but they are essentially the same. If a few hundred milligrams of a substance can be synthesized in a lab, the same reaction in a 10 000 litre reactor can produce several tonnes of the stuff.'*

'To keep the cost of manufacture down, we need a synthetic route that is efficient. The better the yield, the more tonnes of product we get for every tonne of reagent and solvent we use. But process chemists must also consider the number of synthetic steps involved and the cost of the reagents. In research labs, chemists often use expensive dried solvents. We have to avoid these when designing a process that will use many litres of solvent and tonnes of starting materials.

'Another important factor is time. Designing processes that deliver the greatest amount of product in the shortest time possible reduces costs and allows Zeneca to meet higher demands for its products. Economizing on time means taking into account each type of operation involved. Filtration is one operation we have to look at closely. In a laboratory, grams of solid can be filtered in a moment but on a plant scale it could take days if small particles of solid clog up the pores of the filter. If we need a filtration step, we have to determine if it will be a problem and, if it is, do something about it. Sometimes, by changing the precipitation conditions, it is possible to reduce the proportion of small particles, allowing filtration to go on at a reasonable speed.

'The cost of safety also has to be put into the equation. Zeneca has a special hazards group that looks at all our proposed processes in detail to determine if there are potential problems and to recommend steps to ensure the process can be operated safely.

'We have to consider the potential hazards of each reaction. If a reaction is strongly exothermic we have to consider ways to control the temperature of the reaction mixture. Cooling down several thousand litres of liquid quickly is not a straightforward operation. We could invest in technology to do so but we prefer to avoid the problem, if possible, by choosing a method which does not involve such an exothermic reaction. We also have to take into account the hazardous nature of some of the reagents including their toxicity. Dimethyl sulphate, which was used in the original method of synthesizing 5504 is very toxic and we only use it if absolutely necessary. The route we have devised for manufacturing the fungicide does not use this reagent.

'Another factor to take into consideration is waste. In chemical plants, waste chemicals are called "effluents" and they all have to be treated before being disposed of in the environment. Virtually every chemical reaction produces effluent but we aim to design processes that create effluents that are not a problem to treat and to create as little effluent as possible. This not only benefits the environment but also cuts the company's treatment costs

'When we have to use a solvent other than water we normally recycle it. In one of the 5504 stages, we use toluene. We use it in one batch then distil it off and use it again for the next batch. Aqueous waste is normally neutralized and then filtered to remove salts. We dispose of the salts in a landfill site. The rest of the solution undergoes biotreatment by the local water authority.

'As data from the environment and toxicity tests built up, it looked more and more as though 5504 would be granted a licence. The synthetic route for the manufacture was chosen and a team of scientists and engineers assigned to each step of the synthesis. Each reaction had to be carefully scrutinized and the conditions perfected to make the reaction take place as quickly as possible with the best possible yield.'

Making inorganic compounds

Why make inorganic compounds?

It is obvious why scientists manufacture organic compounds, like aspirin or polyester, but why produce inorganic compounds, like aluminium chloride or iron(II) sulphate?

Here are some possible reasons.

- Many inorganic compounds are active ingredients of useful products, such as copper(II) sulphate – an agricultural fungicide, and silver bromide – the light sensitive material in photographic films. There are also valuable inorganic polymers, such as silicone oils, greases, rubbers and resins.
- Inorganic compounds are made and then used as starting materials for other industrial processes. For instance, millions of tonnes of sulphuric acid are manufactured in Britain each year. Most people are unaware of this because most of it is reused to make a wide range of common materials, including fertilizers, paints and detergents. Similarly, aluminium chloride is manufactured, on a smaller scale, and used as a catalyst for processes to make organic chemicals.
- Many inorganic compounds are used as fillers and additives, to dilute the active ingredients of a product and give the required properties such as texture or colour. Thus, dicalcium phosphate (DCP) is the abrasive in toothpaste and various metal oxides are the additives which colour glass.
- Other compounds are essential reagents for chemical analysis, either to detect whether or not a substance is present or to estimate its concentration. Thus, silver nitrate is used to detect chloride ions and to measure chloride concentrations.

All in all, inorganic chemicals are not 'laboratory curiosities', they are commercially valuable and socially useful.

▶ **Figure 3C1** *Some of the uses of sulphuric acid. The percentages show how the acid is used in the UK.*

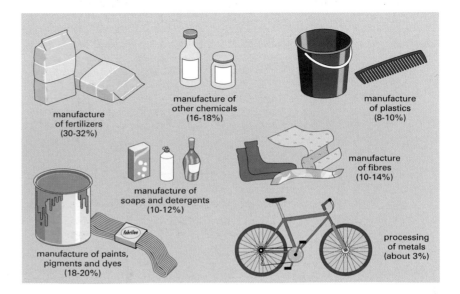

manufacture of fertilizers (30-32%)

manufacture of other chemicals (16-18%)

manufacture of plastics (8-10%)

manufacture of soaps and detergents (10-12%)

manufacture of fibres (10-14%)

manufacture of paints, pigments and dyes (18-20%)

processing of metals (about 3%)

Planning inorganic syntheses

Choosing the type of reaction

These guidelines help to suggest reactions for preparing inorganic compounds.

- To make a metal oxide, consider heating the metal hydroxide, carbonate or nitrate. Heating calcium carbonate, $CaCO_3$, in a furnace is the industrial method for making calcium oxide, CaO.
- To make a soluble salt (such as a metal chloride, nitrate, sulphate or phosphate), consider an acid-base reaction. An acid can be neutralized with a metal oxide, hydroxide or carbonate. Copper(II) sulphate, for example, can be made by neutralizing sulphuric acid with copper(II) oxide or copper(II) carbonate.
- To make an insoluble salt, consider mixing solutions of two soluble salts which will produce the product by precipitation. Mixing solutions of silver nitrate and sodium chloride, for example, precipitates silver chloride.
- To make a chloride which hydrolyses in water, consider oxidizing the element (metal or non-metal) with chlorine. A stream of chlorine gas, for example oxidizes hot silicon to make the fuming liquid, silicon tetrachloride.
- To make an oxoacid, consider:
  - oxidizing a non-metal with concentrated nitric acid – for example, nitric acid oxidizes iodine to iodic acid, HIO_3
  - the reaction of an oxide of a non-metal with water – for example, sulphur trioxide reacts with water to make sulphuric acid
  - starting with a salt of the acid and adding a stronger acid – for example adding concentrated sulphuric acid to calcium phosphate to make phosphoric acid, H_3PO_4.
- To make a co-ordination compound, consider starting with a 'simple' compound of the metal and adding a reagent to complex with the metal ion. Ammonia solution, for example, reacts with copper(II) sulphate solution to form tetraammine copper(II) sulphate.

Oxoacids
Examples of oxoacids are: sulphuric acid, H_2SO_4, phosphoric acid, H_3PO_4 and nitric acid, HNO_3. Each oxoacid consists of hydrogen combined with a non-metal element and oxygen.

Recognizing reaction types from equations

- Many acid–base reactions (see page 8) follow the pattern:
  acid + base $\longrightarrow$ salt + water. For example,
  $$H_2SO_4(aq) + MgO(s) \longrightarrow MgSO_4(aq) + H_2O(l)$$

- A redox reaction involves changes in oxidation number (see page 10). For example,
  $$2CuCl_2(aq) + Na_2SO_3(aq) + H_2O(l) \longrightarrow$$
  $$2CuCl(s) + Na_2SO_4(aq) + 2HCl(aq)$$

- A hydrolysis reaction involves a compound reacting with water and splitting into two or more products. For example,
  $$PCl_5(l) + 4H_2O(l) \longrightarrow H_3PO_4(aq) + 5HCl(g)$$

- A co-ordination reaction (see page 13) involves the formation of a complex compound, in which one, two, four or eight molecules or ions bond to a central metal ion. For example,
  $$CuSO_4(aq) + 4NH_3(aq) \longrightarrow [Cu(NH_3)_4]SO_4(aq)$$

Extracting and purifying inorganic compounds

A preparation does not end when a reaction has given the desired product. The product must then be separated from the other substances in the reaction mixture. It may then have to be purified further.

Add concentrated hydrochloric acid to a solution of about 10g borax (hydrated sodium tetraborate) in 100cm³ water until the solution is strongly acid.

↓

Cool the solution in an ice bath.

↓

Filter to separate the crystals.

↓

Wash them on the filter with a little ice-cold water. Then allow to dry.

↓

Convert boric acid to boron oxide by heating about 2g of the acid in a crucible. Weigh the crucible and contents before heating. Cool and reweigh from time to time. Continue heating until the weight stops changing (constant weight).

▲ **Figure 3C2** *Flow diagram for making boric acid and boron oxide.*

Two routes to boric acid

The final steps in alternative preparations of boric acid illustrate two common methods of extraction. Boric acid is a weak acid used as a mild antiseptic, for example in eye lotions. It is also converted to boron oxide which is an ingredient of heat resistant, borosilicate glasses.

One route to the acid starts by adding hot sulphuric acid to calcium borate ore. This produces a hot solution of boric acid and a precipitate of solid calcium sulphate. Vacuum filtration removes the solid calcium sulphate before heating to evaporate some of the water. Boric acid crystallizes as the hot, concentrated solution cools. Filtering separates the crystals which can be washed with a little cold water and dried. In a similar way boric acid, and then boron oxide, can be made from borax on a small laboratory scale (see Figure 3C2).

An alternative approach is necessary to obtain boric acid from natural brines drawn from lakes rich in dissolved borates. A suitable method is solvent extraction. The lake water is mixed with a hydrocarbon solvent containing a complexing agent. The dissolved borates form a complex which is more soluble in the hydrocarbon layer than in water. Impurities remain in the aqueous layer, and are pumped away. Treating the organic layer with dilute sulphuric acid breaks down the borate complex and precipitates boric acid. The acid is then filtered, washed and dried.

The boric acid obtained is not completely pure from either source. It can be purified further by recrystallization from water (see Figure 3C3).

▼ **Figure 3C3** *Recrystallization is sometimes used to purify inorganic compounds, although not as frequently as in organic chemistry.*

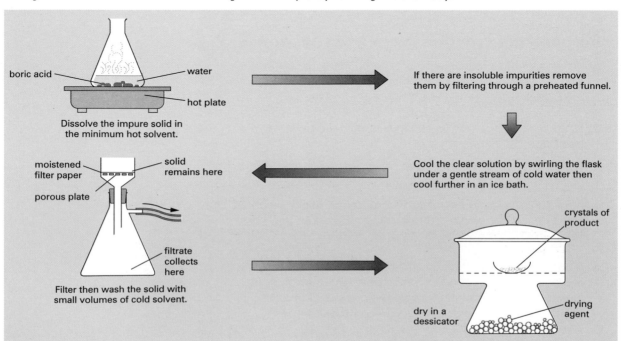

boric acid — water — hot plate

Dissolve the impure solid in the minimum hot solvent.

If there are insoluble impurities remove them by filtering through a preheated funnel.

moistened filter paper — solid remains here — porous plate — filtrate collects here

Filter then wash the solid with small volumes of cold solvent.

Cool the clear solution by swirling the flask under a gentle stream of cold water then cool further in an ice bath.

crystals of product — dry in a dessicator — drying agent

In general, inorganic compounds are separated by filtration, if insoluble, or by evaporation and crystallization, if soluble.

Solvent extraction is usually restricted to difficult inorganic separations, as it requires expensive solvents and reagents and is complex.

Some chlorides, however, have relatively low melting and boiling points, and can be extracted and purified by other methods, such as distillation and sublimation. For instance, titanium(IV) chloride is a liquid and can be separated from other chlorides by fractional distillation. On the other hand, aluminium chloride is one of the solids which **sublimes**, meaning that it changes directly to vapour on warming and the vapour returns directly to solid on cooling (see pages 172–3).

Tests for purity

Chemists use a mixture of qualitative and quantitative tests to check the purity of inorganic compounds:

- spot tests – to show if particular impurities are present. For instance, adding a solution of potassium thiocyanate is a very sensitive test for traces of iron impurities

- titrations – to measure the amount of product in a sample to compare the mass of product in the sample with the total mass of material.

Example

Titration of a $0.691\,g$ sample of borax ($Na_2B_4O_7.10H_2O$) required $29.50\,cm^3$ of $0.120\,mol\,dm^{-3}$ hydrochloric acid. What is the percentage purity of the borax?

Answer

The amount of acid used to neutralize the borax

$$= \frac{29.50}{1000}\,dm^3 \times 0.120\,mol\,dm^{-3}$$
$$= 3.54 \times 10^{-3}\,mol$$

From the equation, $2\,mol$ HCl react with $1\,mol$ borax
$$B_4O_7^{2-} + 2H^+ + 5H_2O \longrightarrow 4H_3BO_3$$
The amount of borax in the sample $= 0.5 \times 3.54 \times 10^{-3}\,mol$
$$= 1.77 \times 10^{-3}\,mol$$
The molar mass of borax $= 381.4\,g\,mol^{-1}$
Mass of borax in the sample $= 1.77 \times 10^{-3}\,mol \times 381.4\,g\,mol^{-1}$
$$= 0.675\,g$$
Percentage of borax in the sample $= \dfrac{0.675\,g}{0.691\,g} \times 100\% = 97.8\%$

In general chemists do not use melting and boiling points to check the purity of inorganic compounds because they are too high for convenient measurement; in any case many inorganic compounds decompose on heating. The use of chromatography to test purity is also less common in inorganic chemistry.

Making salts

The pages of laboratory catalogues offer a very wide range of salts for use as chemical reagents. The usual route for making a soluble salt is to neutralize an acid (see page 9). Insoluble salts, such as the silver halides in photographic films (see page 298) are made by mixing solutions of two soluble salts.

Making soluble salts

Figure R20.1 in the Reference section shows whether or not a salt is soluble or insoluble. Three general reactions of acids are used to make soluble salts:

$$\text{metal oxide/hydroxide} + \text{acid} \longrightarrow \text{salt} + \text{water}$$
$$\text{metal carbonate} + \text{acid} \longrightarrow \text{salt} + \text{carbon dioxide} + \text{water}$$
$$\text{metal} + \text{acid} \longrightarrow \text{salt} + \text{hydrogen}$$

Figure 3C5 shows a procedure for making a soluble salt. This procedure is suitable if the solid used to neutralize the acid does not react with water or dissolve. Adding an excess of the solid makes sure that all the acid reacts. Filtering removes the excess solid. As a result the solution formed only contains the salt, which can be separated by evaporation and crystallization.

▼ **Figure 3C4** *Part of a page from a catalogue showing the cost and purity of a range of salts of copper.*

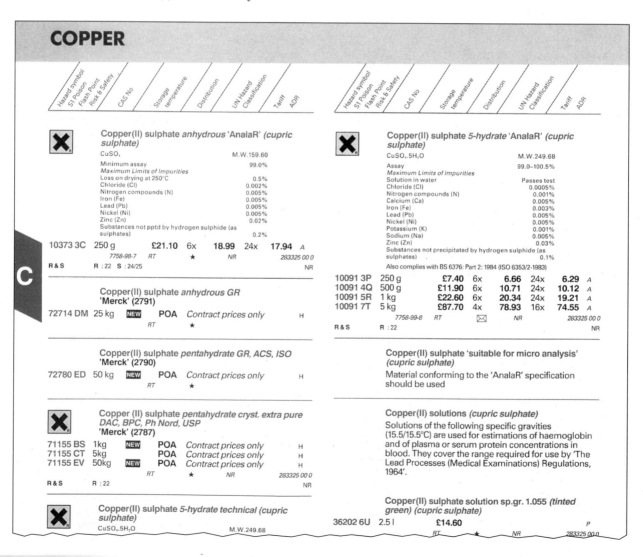

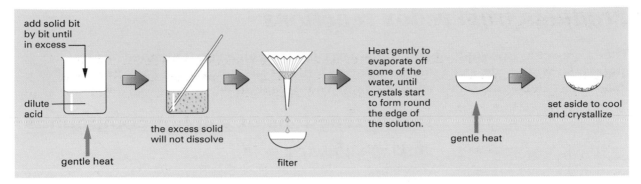

Figure 3C6 shows a suitable procedure for making a soluble salt by neutralizing an acid with a base which is soluble in water and so cannot be removed by filtering if added in excess. Instead the procedure starts with a titration to find the exact volume of acid needed to react with a certain volume of the base solution.

▲ **Figure 3C5** *A method for making soluble salts by neutralizing an acid with an insoluble metal oxide or hydroxide, or an **insoluble** metal carbonate or a metal which does not react with water.*

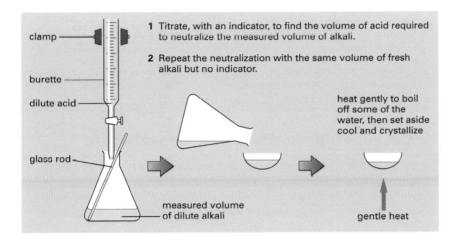

1 Titrate, with an indicator, to find the volume of acid required to neutralize the measured volume of alkali.

2 Repeat the neutralization with the same volume of fresh alkali but no indicator.

heat gently to boil off some of the water, then set aside cool and crystallize

◀ **Figure 3C6** *A method for making a soluble salt by neutralizing an acid with a **soluble** metal hydroxide or carbonate.*

Making insoluble salts

Figure 3C7 shows a small–scale procedure for making a sample of an insoluble salt. The choice of soluble salts depends on the product required. To make silver bromide, mix solutions of silver nitrate and sodium chloride. Silver bromide precipitates (see page 12) leaving a solution of sodium nitrate, which can be washed away as the product is purified.

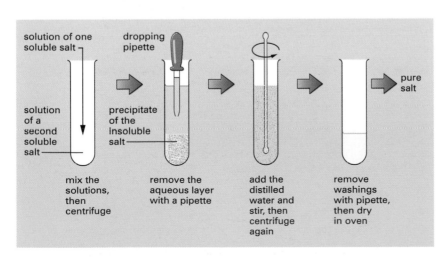

◀ **Figure 3C7** *A method for making an insoluble salt from two soluble salts.*

Products from redox reactions

The large-scale inorganic chemical industry is based on a small number of raw materials: water, air, salt (sodium chloride), limestone, phosphate rock and sulphur. Processing these materials involves many redox reactions.

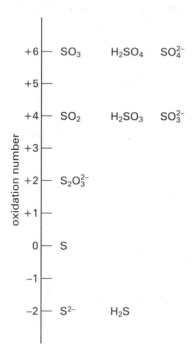

Figure 3C8 *Oxidation states of sulphur compounds.*

Redox reactions of sulphur compounds

Making sulphuric acid

More sulphuric acid is made than any other compound (see pages 342–50), but many other sulphur compounds are needed on a smaller scale, such as sodium thiosulphate which is used as a fixer in photography.

Changing one sulphur compound to another often involves changes in the state of oxidation of the element (Figure 3C8). It takes a redox reaction (see pages 10–11) to change the oxidation number of an element in a compound.

To produce sulphuric acid, sulphur is first oxidized to sulphur dioxide, and then further oxidized to sulphur trioxide. Sulphur trioxide reacts with water, under carefully controlled conditions, to make the acid.

$$S(s) \xrightarrow{\text{burn in air}} SO_2(g) \xrightarrow{\substack{\text{combine with oxygen} \\ \text{over a } V_2O_5 \text{ catalyst}}} SO_3(g) \xrightarrow{\substack{\text{dissolve in sulphuric} \\ \text{acid, then add water}}} H_2SO_4(l)$$

Making sodium sulphite and thiosulphate

Dissolving sulphur dioxide in a solution of sodium carbonate produces sodium sulphite; a colourless, crystalline compound used in the paper, brewing and textile industries. Sodium sulphite can also be converted to sodium thiosulphate by heating with powdered sulphur, as shown in Figure 3C9.

Figure 3C9 *A procedure for making sodium thiosulphate.*

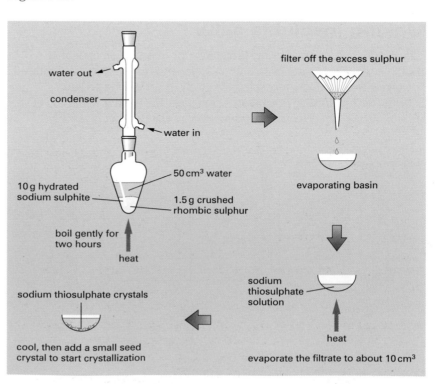

Redox reactions of metals

Metals such as vanadium, chromium, manganese, copper and iron form colourful compounds in a range of oxidation states. Some of the compounds are valuable chemical reagents such as potassium dichromate(VI) and potassium manganate(VII), which are powerful oxidizing agents in acid solution. Others are important industrial chemicals such as vanadium(V) oxide for the manufacture of sulphuric acid.

Redox reactions of iron compounds

Iron forms two series of compounds: iron(II) and iron(III) compounds. Iron(II) compounds are generally green while iron(III) compounds are yellow or brown. The colours of rust and red sandstone rock are both due to the presence of forms of iron(III) oxide.

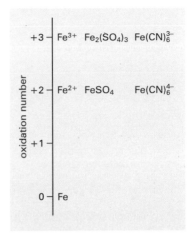

▲ **Figure 3C10** *Oxidation states of iron compounds.*

The solution to a laboratory problem

Iron(II) sulphate is cheap and readily available. Commercially it is available from the solutions remaining after sulphuric acid has been used to clean steel. Iron metal reacts with dilute sulphuric acid to make iron(II) sulphate which then crystallizes as a **hydrate**, $FeSO_4.7H_2O$.

Iron(II) sulphate is the active ingredient in 'iron tablets' used to treat anaemia; it is also added in trace amounts to fertilizers as well as being the starting point for making the artists' pigment, Prussian blue.

As a laboratory reagent, iron(II) sulphate has the disadvantage that, once in solution, it reacts with oxygen from the air and changes to iron(III) sulphate. Adding sulphuric acid to the solution slows down the change but chemists have discovered that it is more effective to use a **double salt**, ammonium iron(II) sulphate which crystallizes from a solution containing equal chemical amounts of ammonium sulphate and iron(II) sulphate.

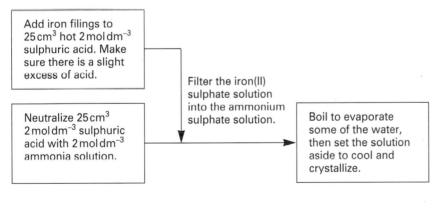

◀ **Figure 3C11** *Flow diagram for the production of ammonium iron(II) sulphate.*

In solution the double salt is indistinguishable from a mixture of ammonium sulphate and iron(II) sulphate, but in the solid the ammonium, iron and sulphate ions pack in a distinctive way together with water molecules to form crystals which are quite different from either of the simple salts.

Another double salt of iron, ammonium iron(III) sulphate, belongs to the family of **alums** used for water treatment and as mordants to fix dyes to cloth. Iron alum can be made by oxidizing iron(II) sulphate to iron(III) sulphate with nitric acid, then adding an equivalent amount of ammonium sulphate and crystallizing the solution.

Alums

Alums are double salts with the general formula: $M^I_2SO_4.M^{III}_2(SO_4)_3.24H_2O$. M^I is a metal ion with a single positive charge such as Na^+, K^+, or NH_4^+, while M^{III} is a metal ion with a 3+ charge such as Al^{3+} or Fe^{3+}.

Making aluminium chloride

Durham Chemicals is part of the Harcros Chemical Group and is based in Birtley, County Durham. At Durham Chemicals, the letters AAC stand for 'anhydrous aluminium chloride', or just as appropriately for 'an acknowledged catalyst'. Its hidden help lies in speeding up the production of a wide range of useful materials including polymers, pigments, pharmaceuticals, dyes and detergents (see page 147).

Raw materials

There are three possible routes to AAC (Figure 3C12). They use route 1 at Durham Chemicals.

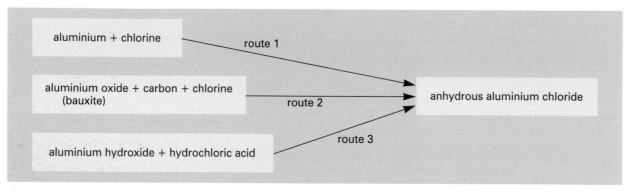

▲ **Figure 3C12** *Three routes to AAC.*

Route 1 is a redox reaction in which chlorine oxidizes aluminium:

$$2Al(s) + 3Cl_2(g) \longrightarrow 2AlCl_3(s)$$

Route 2 is also a redox reaction:

$$Al_2O_3(s) + 3C(s) + 3Cl_2(g) \longrightarrow 2AlCl_3(s) + 3CO(g)$$

Route 3 is an acid-base reaction:

$$Al(OH)_3(s) + 3HCl(aq) \longrightarrow AlCl_3(aq) + 3H_2O(l)$$

'We use aluminium and chlorine, because we can start with very pure raw materials and obtain a pure product by a direct process,' says Richard Goulding, Business Manager at Durham Chemicals.

Route 2 would have the advantage of starting with bauxite, which is a relatively cheap ore, but the lower cost of raw materials would be more than offset by the greater technical complexity of the process.

Route 3 would also use cheap raw materials and avoid the hazard of using highly toxic chlorine gas. The yield of AAC, however, would be very small. This is because the solid obtained would be hydrated aluminium chloride, $AlCl_3.6H_2O$. Attempts to drive off water by heating the solid would result in hydrolysis. The water would attack the aluminium chloride and turn it back into aluminium hydroxide (the reverse of the reaction shown for route 3).

Sublimation
This is the change of state from solid to vapour and back to solid without passing through the liquid state. The process can be use to purify substances such as aluminium chloride and iodine.

Making AAC on a laboratory scale

Figure 3C13 illustrates a small–scale method for making AAC by route 1. Dry chlorine gas, from a small cylinder, or gas generator, passes over hot aluminium turnings.

The reaction is very exothermic, so once it starts it keeps the metal hot without further heating.

$$2Al(s) + 3Cl_2(g) \longrightarrow 2AlCl_3(s) \qquad \Delta H = -1408\,kJ$$

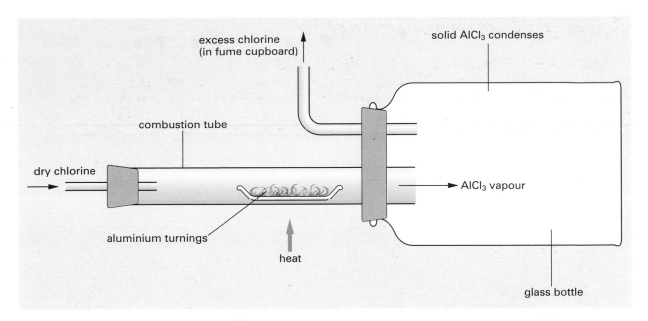

▲ Figure 3C13 *Making AAC on a laboratory scale.*

The AAC forms as a vapour, in the hot tube, and condenses to a solid in the cold bottle. This happens because AAC is a substance that sublimes. The solid turns directly to vapour on warming and the vapour returns directly to a solid on cooling.

Scaling up to a manufacturing process?

The large-scale process for making AAC is very similar to the laboratory procedure. At the Durham Chemicals plant there are a large number of reactors, arranged in two rows, each connected to its own condenser.

'We must maintain supplies of aluminium and chlorine, to keep the reactors going continuously,' says Operations Manager, Bill Taylor.

'Our storage tanks each contain up to 35 tonnes of liquid chlorine. We evaporate the liquid so that we can pass chlorine gas into excess molten aluminium. In this way we make sure that the reaction uses up pretty well all of the highly toxic chlorine.

'We manage to convert 99.8% of the chlorine into AAC. Scrubbers absorb the small amount of remaining gas, absorbing traces of chlorine from the outlet gas in sodium hydroxide solution.

▲ Figure 3C14 *Bill Taylor checking the stockpile of aluminium ingots at Durham Chemicals.*

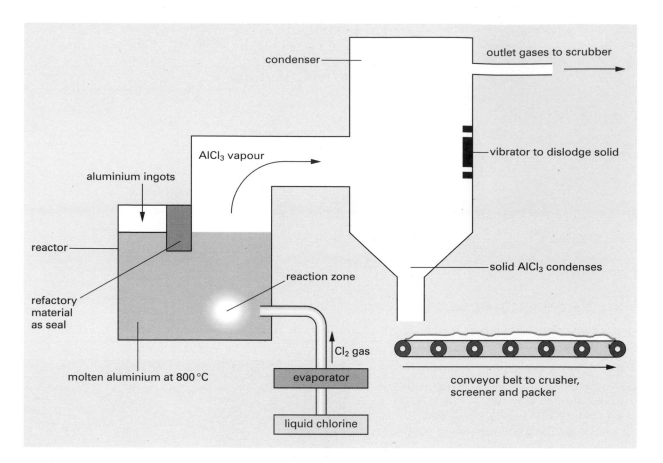

The diagram is labelled, clockwise from top: condenser, outlet gases to scrubber, vibrator to dislodge solid, solid AlCl₃ condenses, conveyor belt to crusher, screener and packer, liquid chlorine, evaporator, Cl₂ gas, molten aluminium at 800 °C, refactory material as seal, reactor, reaction zone, aluminium ingots, AlCl₃ vapour.

▲ **Figure 3C15** *Making AAC on a large scale.*

▼ **Figure 3C16** *Loading aluminium ingots into a reactor.*

'We have designed our plant to make sure that we waste very little energy,' notes Bill Taylor.

'The reaction between chlorine and aluminium is so exothermic that we have to cool the reactors. We do this by pumping water through a cooling jacket. We can then use the hot water to:

■ warm the evaporator, where liquid chlorine evaporates
■ warm the sodium hydroxide solution for the scrubbers
■ to heat all our buildings in cold weather.

'Controlling the reactor temperature is very important if we are to make sure that we make a quality product. If the temperature gets too high, we find that the AAC is contaminated with traces of metallic aluminium. What happens at a higher temperature is that the reaction produces small amounts of aluminium(I) chloride along with the normal aluminium(III) chloride. When aluminium(I) chloride cools, it splits up, forming AAC and aluminium.'

$$3AlCl(g) \longrightarrow AlCl_3(s) + 2Al(s)$$

As Bill Taylor explains, 'On a large scale we have had to work out how to dislodge the solid AAC from the inside of the condensers. What we do is to shake the sides of the vessels with vibrators driven by compressed air. We switch on the vibrators once during each 8 hour shift. Before vibrating, the crystals inside a condenser look something like a coral reef.

'We crush the crystals of AAC and then screen (sieve) them to produce the variety of particle sizes which our customers need. We sell AAC as powder, small grains or large grains. We despatch the product in containers ranging from 16 kilogram bags up to 22-tonne road tankers.'

Handling AAC

AAC fumes in moist air because aluminium chloride reacts with water vapour in air, forming highly corrosive hydrogen chloride gas. This could be a formidable problem for producers and users. Fortunately people have been able to develop safe procedures for storing, transporting and using AAC. The production plant and containers are firmly sealed against air. AAC carried in road tankers is blanketed with dry nitrogen.

Durham Chemicals provide their customers with Safety Data Sheets, in line with a European Union directive, describing hazards and safe procedures.

Economic aspects

'The demand for AAC has remained fairly constant over recent years, but the price has been more volatile,' reflects Richard Goulding.

There is a steady demand because AAC is used in such a wide range of processes. Fortunately for Durham Chemicals, some uses have expanded while others have contracted. The demand for AAC in Western Europe is about 40 000 tonnes. There have been recent fluctuations in the price because, for an industrial chemical, the demand is relatively small and so a change in the amount produced by one manufacturer has a significant effect on the balance of supply and demand. The price of AAC is also affected by changes in the cost of aluminium.

Quality, safety and the environment

Local residents were anxious about the storage of chlorine and the production of AAC near their homes when the plant was first planned and built. Since then, confidence in safety precautions and safeguards against pollution have increased and neighbourly relations were further strengthened by a site Open Day, in September 1994.

Brian McCartney, Quality Assurance Manager at Durham Chemicals, is concerned to develop of 'an all–embracing quality umbrella, covering product quality, safety and the environment'. Product quality is assured by production and analysis procedures that meet British Standard 5750. Safety procedures meet the requirements of the Health and Safety Executive. As regards environmental factors, AAC production has been designated an Approved Process by HM Inspectors of Pollution, who investigate the impact of any solid residues, liquid effluents or gaseous emissions.

Durham Chemicals will follow one of the two proposed routes to demonstrate high environmental standards. The company will aim to qualify for either British Standard 7750 or recognition within the European Community's Eco-Management and Audit System (EMAS) scheme.

Products from complex-forming reactions

Some complex compounds, such as the artists' pigment Prussian blue, are useful products; others are laboratory curiosities; many are interesting to make because they are colourful compounds. Complexes have a part to play in medicine too including a platinum complex which is a very effective anti-cancer drug.

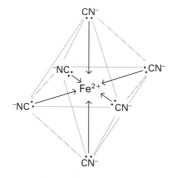

▲ **Figure 3C17** *The structure of the hexacyanoferrate(II) ion. Each of the six cyanide ions carries a 1– charge so the overall charge on the ion is 4–.*

Iron complexes

Potassium hexacyanoferrate(II), $K_4[Fe(CN)_6]$ is a yellow, crystalline solid obtained on a laboratory scale by treating iron(II) sulphate with potassium cyanide. Oxidation with chlorine produces a dark red solid, potassium hexacyanoferrate(III), $K_3[Fe(CN)_6]$. In both these compounds six cyanide ions form dative covalent bonds (see pages 122–3) with each iron ion.

Mixing a solution of potassium hexacyanoferrate(III) with a solution containing iron(II) ions produces an intensely coloured, deep blue precipitate of the pigment Prussian blue.

In another complex of iron, three ethanedioate ions each form two bonds with a central iron(III) ion. This complex is easy to make simply by mixing a solution of iron(III) chloride with a calculated amount of a solution of potassium ethanedioate. The complex salt, $K_3[Fe(C_2O_4)_3]$ crystallizes when the mixture is allowed to stand.

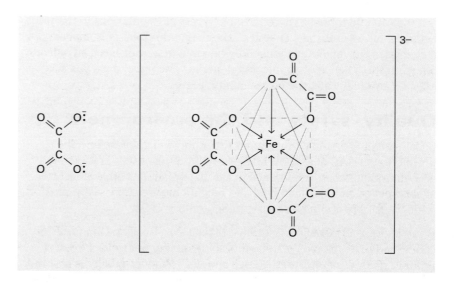

▶ **Figure 3C18** *An ethanedioate ion and the complex formed between iron(III) ions and ethanedioate ions.*

Monastral blue

Today the most widely used blue pigment is probably Monastral blue used to colour plastics, paints and enamel. The pigment is bright, the blue colour does not fade and a little of the pigment goes a long way.

The story of the discovery of the pigment began in 1928 at a Scottish dyeworks which manufactured a chemical needed to make dyes by passing ammonia through molten phthalic anhydride in a iron vessel lined with glass. Both phthalic anhydride and the product, phthalimide, are white but someone spotted that there were traces of a blue substance in some batches of the compound. The colour seemed to be forming around parts of the vessel where the lining was damaged. Analysts found that the substance had a definite composition including 12.6% of iron together with carbon, hydrogen and nitrogen.

Further study showed that the blue compound was an interesting complex closely related to the natural porphyrin rings in haemoglobin and chlorophyll. Four nitrogen atoms in a porphyrin ring can bind to a central metal ion (see Figure 3C19).

They called the new compound iron phthalocyanin. Chemists led by R. P. Linstead at Imperial College London took up research into this substance and other related compounds. They made a range of phthalocyanins and after a few years realized that copper phthalocyanin was a very stable compound of more than academic interest. By 1939, ICI was marketing the copper compound as Monastral blue.

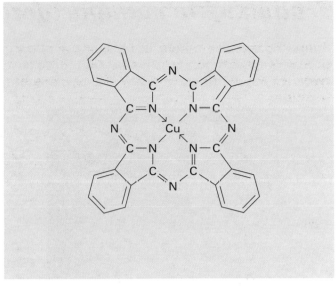

▲ **Figure 3C19** *The structure of copper phthalocyanin.*

Cisplatin

The discovery of the drug cisplatin began with another chance discovery, this time by a research team studying the effect of electric fields on the growth of bacteria in the early 1960s. Barnett Rosenberg, and his group at Michigan State University grew bacteria in electric fields between platinum electrodes. To their surprise they found that the effect was to inhibit cell division but not to stop cell growth.

Chemists usually assume that platinum is inert and so when Rosenberg tried to explain his observations he did not expect to find that his choice of electrodes was responsible for the effect. After studying many other possible factors, however, he finally reported that it was traces of a platinum compound in solution which were responsible for stopping cell division.

Once isolated the compound proved to be a complex ion with the formula $Pt(NH_3)_2Cl_2$ in which both chlorine atoms are on one side of the complex and both ammonia molecules on the other. This is the *cis-*isomer rather than the alternative structure of the *trans-*isomer (Figure 3C20) – hence the name cisplatin.

Rosenberg's research team realized that a compound which inhibited cell division could be a valuable drug to treat cancer. After many years of testing and clinical trials cisplatin was approved for medical use in the USA in 1978 and in the UK in 1979.

Unfortunately the drug is toxic and has unpleasant side-effects, so research has continued in a quest for new compounds which are equally effective but less toxic. Between 1965 and 1985, chemists synthesized over 2000 compounds with structures similar to cisplatin of which just one, carboplatin, has been approved as a drug.

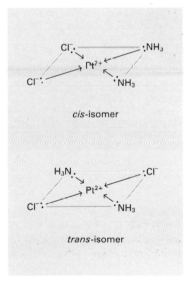

▲ **Figure 3C20** *The structure of cisplatin (which is an anti-cancer drug) and its isomer, the trans complex which does not affect cell division.*

Scaling up to manufacture zinc chelate

Traces of zinc are essential for healthy plant growth. Zinc deficiency can lower the yield and quality of many crops, including cotton, cereals and citrus fruits. Farmers avoid this by adding a soluble zinc compound to the crop as a leaf spray.

The trouble is that 'simple' zinc compounds such as zinc sulphate cannot be mixed with the various herbicides, insecticides and other fertilizers which the farmer also needs to apply. The 'simple' zinc compound is liable to react giving a precipitate and making spraying an impossibility. Several spraying operations would be necessary.

'The answer', says Nick Poulton, Quality Manager of Rhône-Poulenc in Gloucester, 'is to use a complex compound of zinc, which we call zinc chelate. Forming a complex with edta allows the zinc to be mixed with herbicides, fertilizers, etc. without reacting, so that only one spraying operation is needed.

'We make the chelate by the reaction between a zinc salt and edta. I can explain some of the factors we have to take into account when scaling up a process by comparing what we do here with the preparation of the chelate on a laboratory scale.'

◀ **Figure 3C21** *This picture shows a zinc deficiency in a pear tree alongside a healthy leaf.*

▲ **Figure 3C22** *An edta molecule surrounds a metal ion like the claws of a crab. Hence the name* **chelate** *which comes from the Greek word for a claw.*

Edta
The initials edta stands for the older name of the compound: **e**thylene**d**iamine**t**etra**a**cetic acid. Chemists generally use the abbreviation **edta** because the full name is so long. The structure of the compound is:

$$HO_2CCH_2 \qquad\qquad CH_2CO_2H$$
$$N-CH_2-CH_2-N$$
$$HO_2CCH_2 \qquad\qquad CH_2CO_2H$$

The modern systematic name for the acid is 1,2-bis[bis(carboxymethyl)amino]ethane. A useful shorthand for the salt is H_4Y as only the four hydrogen atoms from the carboxyl groups (CO_2H) are acidic.

The laboratory preparation of zinc chelate

Storage and supply of reagents

The starting materials: solid zinc sulphate, solid edta, sodium hydroxide solution and purified water are available from bottles on the laboratory shelves.

The amounts needed are small and easily transferred by hand: a few grams of each solid and a few cubic centimetres of solutions.

The reaction

The first step is to make a solution of edta by stirring the solid with water in a beaker and heating the mixture to about 70°C, using a Bunsen burner or a hotplate.

Adding solid zinc sulphate with a spatula starts the reaction. The zinc ion is strongly attracted to the edta, because of the number of bonds it can form, and so it reacts to form the chelate.

Next, adding a measured volume of sodium hydroxide solution, from a measuring cylinder, gives a solution of zinc chelate, $Na_2(ZnY)$, where (ZnY^{2-}) is the complex ion. The sodium salt with the complex is soluble in water.

Filtering

Filtering removes solid impurities from the original zinc sulphate which is often supplied as a relatively impure compound. Vacuum filtration speeds up the process.

Separating the solid chelate

Evaporating the filtrate and then setting it aside to crystallize produces crystals of solid zinc chelate.

Manufacturing a batch of zinc chelate

Storage and supply of reagents

Rhône-Poulenc use several tonnes of powdered zinc sulphate to make each batch of chelate solution. The compound arrives in 25 kg bags, about the size of a typical sack of potatoes. The company makes its own edta and stores it also in 25 kg bags. Each batch needs several tonnes of edta. The sodium hydroxide solution is drawn from a bulk storage tank that supplies several processes on the site. Between one and three 18-tonne road tankers stock up this tank each week.

One of the plant operators adds the zinc sulphate and edta to the reactor. Liquids are easier to handle. Pipes bring the sodium hydroxide solution and water to the reactor so they are 'on tap'.

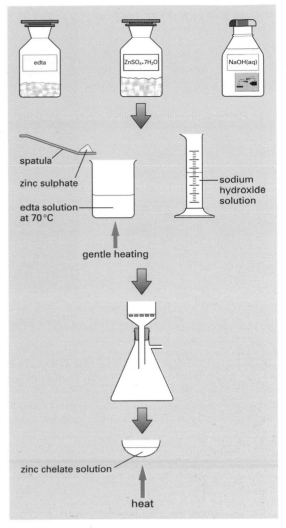

▲ **Figure 3C23** *Stages in the laboratory preparation of zinc chelate.*

The reaction

The reactor is a stainless steel cylinder, about 3 metres high and 2.5 metres in diameter – about the size of a room. This is vast compared to a typical laboratory beaker.

Mixing the reactants on this scale requires an agitator like the paddle of a giant food mixer. Steam flows through a jacket surrounding the reactor to heat the contents to 70 °C.

The operators turn on a valve to let water into the reactor. Next they add 40 bags of edta followed by 29 bags of zinc sulphate. On this scale, it is important to keep the mixture mobile so that the agitator does not become stuck in a thick slurry. This is done by adding a portion of the sodium hydroxide solution to form some zinc chelate in the early stages. This is soluble and so will give a solution which can be easily stirred. This whole sequence of additions is repeated several times until the full amounts of zinc sulphate and edta have been added.

▼ **Figure 3C25** *Cleaning the filter.*

The reaction is exothermic and so the flow of steam through the heating jacket is reduced to make sure that the temperature of the mixture does not rise above 90 °C.

Filtering

A pump forces the hot liquid through a cloth filter. This is a suitable way to remove a small amount of solid impurities from a solution. This is pressure filtration rather than the vacuum filtration used in the laboratory method.

Separating the solid chelate

The filtrate flows to a heated storage tank which feeds a spray drier.

In the drier a spray releases fine aerosol droplets into a blast of hot air from a gas burner. The water vaporizes rapidly leaving particles of dry powdered chelate, which fall like a snowstorm on to a metal bed and then into a hopper and into a bag. In 24 hours a typical spray drier can treat thousands of litres of solution and produce several tonnes of dry powder, packed in 25 kg bags.

Rhône-Poulenc export most of the spray dried powder to the USA, the Middle East and other parts of the world as a solid containing about 10% zinc. For customers in Britain and Europe they omit the drying stage and sell the chelate as a solution containing about 7% zinc. This is cheaper to produce, but more expensive to transport.

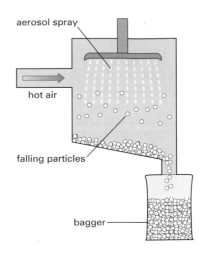

▲ **Figure 3C26** *Diagram of a spray drier.*

◀ **Figure 3C27** *Bagging up the product.*

Batch or continuous?

Rhône-Poulenc use a batch process to manufacture zinc chelate because the demand is seasonal and is insufficient to keep the plant operating all year. Batch production has the advantage that the same plant can be used to produce different chelates at other times.

'If demand were to increase, continuous production would be considered', speculates Nick Poulton.' A continuous process is technically more complicated and the capital cost of installing the plant is therefore greater. Once installed, automation means that labour costs are lower while the production per year is higher because of the continuous flow of product. It is possible to repay the capital costs over a period of years providing there is a large enough market for the amount of material produced. Building a technically excellent plant is useless if we cannot sell the product.'

Thoughts and actions

1 'How natural?' on pages 128–9 suggests that people like the idea of things being natural and hate the idea of them being synthetic. Imagine that you have been taken on by the chemical industry to organize a media campaign to counter this prejudice.
   a Devise a plan for your campaign.
   b Prepare drafts, notes or sketches of selected parts of your campaign (such as posters, leaflets, feature articles, public speeches, advertisements in the media or press notices).

2 a Read the introduction to chemical synthesis on pages 130–33. Work with a photocopy of the text. Use different colours of pen or pencil to underline or ring parts of the text which tell you what chemists know about:
   ■ the purposes of synthesis
   ■ the behaviour of chemicals
   ■ ways of controlling the behaviour of chemicals
   ■ strategies for planning syntheses
   ■ problems which affect the success of syntheses
   ■ successful examples of syntheses.
   b Use your labelled text to write a 200 word abstract of the ideas in these four pages.

3 a Find examples of each of these types of *inorganic* compound: oxide, halide, salt of oxo-acid and co-ordination compound. Name each example and give its formula.
   b Give reasons for preparing the compounds you have named in a.

4 With the help of examples and equations, explain how you can recognize these types of reactions in *inorganic* chemistry:
   ■ acid–base   ■ hydrolysis
   ■ redox   ■ complex formation.

5 a Find examples of each of these types of organic compound: alcohol, carboxylic acid, ester, amide, polymer. Name each example and give its formula.
   b Give reasons for preparing the compounds you have named in a.

6 a Summarize, in the form of a flow diagram (such as Figure 3B7), the preparation of 1-bromobutane described on pages 132–3.
   b Why is the yield of the product only about 60% of the theoretical yield?

7 With the help of examples and equations, explain how you can recognize these types of reactions in *organic* chemistry:
   ■ acid–base   ■ substitution
   ■ redox   ■ elimination
   ■ hydrolysis   ■ addition
   ■ dehydration   ■ condensation.

8 Give an example of the use of each of these extraction methods being used to separate or purify a product from a naturally occurring material or from a reaction mixture:
   ■ sublimation   ■ simple distillation
   ■ evaporation   ■ fractional distillation
   ■ crystallization   ■ solvent extraction.
   ■ decantation
   ■ filtration (under normal and reduced pressure)

9 a Give an example to explain how these techniques can be used to test the purity of a compound:
   ■ measuring the melting point
   ■ measuring the boiling point
   ■ using chromatography
   ■ carrying out a titration.
   b Summarize the advantages and disadvantages of these methods and the extent to which they can be used with organic and inorganic compounds.

10 Choose one of the procedures described in a flow diagram (see Figures 3B7, 3C2, 3C11).
   a Devise a detailed worksheet, with diagrams, giving step-by-step instructions for carrying out the preparation.
   b Carry out a risk assessment for the procedure, as if you were going to do the preparation.
   c Write an equation for the reaction and calculate the theoretical yield starting with the quantities stated in the flow diagram.

11 a Calculate the mass of iodine needed to react with $4.0\,mol\,dm^{-3}$ potassium hydroxide solution (see Figure 3A13).
   b Calculate from the equation the masses of potassium iodate and iodide formed using the procedure shown in Figure 3A13.
   c With the help of Figure 3A14, estimate the temperature at which crystals would start to form on cooling the solution produced by the reaction. Would you expect the crystals to consist of one of the two iodine compounds or a mixture of them?

12 Study Figure 3B4 in the account of the development of ibuprofen on pages 146–7.
 a Why do you think that the activity of aspirin is given as 1 in each column?
 b Apart from aspirin, which functional groups do the compounds have in common?
 c Which parts of the ibuprofen molecule seem to be effective in helping to relieve the symptoms of arthritis?
 d What are the structural differences between ibufenac and ibuprofen?

13 Use molecular models to work through the stages of the laboratory synthesis of ibuprofen in Figure 3B6.
 a Name the starting material.
 b Identify the two hydrocarbons in the sequence of changes.
 c Identify examples of compounds with these functional groups:
   ■ alcohol   ■ carboxylic acid
   ■ ketone   ■ halogen compound.
 d Identify the reaction steps which increase the number of carbon atoms in the structure.

14 Summarize the reactions of alkenes and halogenoalkanes by making a large copy of Figure 3T1.
   ■ Illustrate the functional groups in the flow sheets by including structures of examples in the boxes.
   ■ Add arrows linking the boxes, and beside each arrow write the conditions needed to convert the starting compound to the product.
   ■ Under each arrow, write the type of reaction taking place.

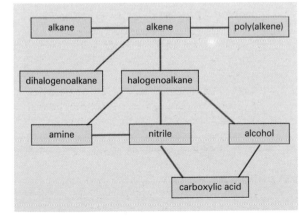

▲ Figure 3T1

15 How would you make these compounds using ethanol as the only organic starting material:
 a ethylamine
 b ethyl ethanoate
 c ethanamide.

16 Guided by the leading questions, suggest a two-step or three-step route for making the target molecule from the specified starting materials in a–d. Write down your suggested routes as a flow diagram giving structural formulas with the reagents and conditions for each step.
   ■ What are the structural formulas of the target molecule and the starting material?
   ■ Does the target molecule have the same number of carbon atoms as the starting material?
   ■ What is the functional group in the target molecule?
   ■ What reactions can be used to introduce this functional group?
   ■ Which of the possible intermediates can be made from the starting material (in one or two steps)?
 a butanoic acid from 1-bromobutane (in two steps)
 b butanoic acid from propan-1-ol (in three steps)
 c 1,2-dibromobutane from butan-1-ol (in two steps)
 d pyruvic acid, $CH_3.CO.CO_2H$, from 2-bromopropanoic acid (in two steps).

17 Plan a two-step synthesis of ethyl propanoate from a carboxylic acid and an alcohol in which you first convert the acid to an acid chloride and then mix the acid chloride with the alcohol.
 a Write out a reaction scheme for the synthesis giving the reagents and conditions.
 b Calculate the starting quantities required to make 10 g of the ester assuming that you get a 60% yield at each stage.
 c Describe the procedure you would follow with details of apparatus, procedures and safety precautions.

18 Use molecular models to examine in detail the reaction used to make nylon-6,6 (see page 157). Convince yourself that:
   ■ nylon is a polyamide
   ■ that the polymerization involves condensation reactions.

19 Strontium is below calcium but above barium in group 2 of the Periodic Table. Strontium occurs naturally as celestite (strontium sulphate) and strontianite (strontium carbonate). Strontium salts give a brilliant red flame colour and can be used in fireworks, signal flares and tracer bullets.

Strontium oxide can be made from the sulphate in three steps.
   ■ step 1 – heat the sulphate with carbon to make the solid sulphide and carbon monoxide gas

- step 2 – treat the sulphide with sodium hydroxide solution to make strontium hydroxide and a solution of sodium sulphide
- step 3 – separate the hydroxide, purify it and then heat to convert it to the oxide.

a Write equations for the three steps, including state symbols.

b Identify the type of reaction taking place in each step.

c What are the essential safety precautions when carrying out step 1?

d Outline the essential practical steps after step 2 to obtain pure, dry strontium oxide in step 3.

e Calculate the theoretical yield of strontium oxide from 4.6 g of strontium sulphate.

f Describe the procedure you would follow to make strontium chloride from strontium carbonate.

20 Sodium chloride can be converted to sodium thiosulphate in three stages.

$$\underset{\text{step 1}}{NaCl} \rightarrow \underset{\text{step 2}}{Na_2CO_3} \rightarrow \underset{\text{step 3}}{Na_2SO_3} \rightarrow Na_2S_2O_3$$

a Step 1 is a large scale industrial process (see pages 351–5). What is the overall equation for the reaction?

b Write equations for steps 2 and 3 (see page 170). Identify the type of reaction taking place in each step.

c What are the uses of sodium thiosulphate? (See for example page 299.)

21 a How do Durham Chemicals justify their chosen route for making anhydrous aluminium chloride (see pages 172–5)?

b Describe the factors which Durham Chemicals have to take into account when scaling up the manufacture of anhydrous aluminium chloride.

c Why is sublimation an appropriate way of separating aluminium chloride from the reaction mixture in both the laboratory and industrial procedures?

22 a Use molecular models to represent the structures of cisplatin and transplatin (see page 177).

b *Cis*- and *trans*- forms are also possible in organic compounds with double bonds. Make models of the *cis*- and *trans*- forms of but-2-ene.

c Make a model of the zinc–edta complex to show how six atoms in edta can cluster round and bond to the central metal ion.

23 Copy and complete Figure 3T2 to compare the laboratory preparation of zinc chelate with the large-scale industrial method.

24 Compare the reasons for synthesizing compounds for the pharmaceutical industry (see pages 146–7) and for the agrochemical industry (see pages 158–160). What are the similarities? What are the differences?

25 Imagine that you are a copy editor working on the text of 'Developing a new fungicide' (see pages 158–160). You decide that it would be improved by a series of sub-headings. Devise a series of headings to help a reader follow the story. (You may find it helpful to add notes to a photocopy of the text.)

Feature	Laboratory process	Industrial process
Starting materials		
Relative quantities in a batch		
Reaction vessel		
Method of transferring solids		
Method of transferring liquids		
Method of mixing		
Method of heating		
Method for removing impurities		
Method for obtaining the solid from solution		

▲ Figure 3T2

UNIT 4

Obtaining products from organisms

Working cells

Raise animals, grow plants, culture microbes and change the world

Agriculture, horticulture, and biotechnology are ways of cultivating other living things for human benefit. Ultimately they all harness solar energy to produce organic materials. Ecologically and economically they are the most important techniques we possess.

Farming and the human population

▼ Figure 4A1 Hunting and gathering are still carried out on a vast scale. Fish, marine invertebrates, and whales are hunted. The photograph below shows traditional shrimp fishing in Belgium.

A few people – like some of the aborigines of 'Crocodile Dundee' country in Australia's Northern Territory – still obtain food by hunting animals and gathering plants. So long as people remain 'hunter gatherers' (Figure 4A1), their numbers are limited by what nature can provide. The point of farming is to increase food supply by domesticating livestock and cultivating crops.

Agriculture, horticulture, and biotechnology

Human beings exploit other living things in many different ways. The word **agriculture** means 'cultivation of the fields'. But the term is used broadly for large-scale raising of livestock and growing of crops. People who practise agriculture are of course 'farmers'.

Farmers are of different kinds. **Pastoralists** raise animals like cattle and sheep which feed largely on grass; while arable farmers (or **arablists**) raise 'field' crops like cereals, potatoes, and broad beans.

Commercial **foresters** are also farmers in a way. They grow fast-growing trees such as spruce and eucalyptus just as arablists grow wheat. Commercial trees take 15 to 30 years to grow while cereals take only a few months, but the principle is the same.

Horticulture is the science and art of growing high-value crops intensively – like lettuce or spices or gladioli. It is probably the oldest form of farming. Some hunter-gatherers, as in New Guinea, cultivate gardens of fruits and beans (Figure 4A2) The Aztecs raised beans and squashes. Today, horticulturalists in countries like Israel and Holland employ high technology, from artificial control of daylength to computerized irrigation, to raise high value crops like avocados and bulbs.

Biotechnology just means 'technology based upon living things' – defined in this broad way it could include agriculture and horticulture. But biotechnology normally implies 'high-tech' manipulation of living material in a laboratory or factory (Figure 4A3).

▲ **Figure 4A2** *Gardens in New Guinea.*

Thus biotechnology now embraces what used to be called **industrial microbiology** – the use of 'microbes' (bacteria and fungi) to produce all kinds of fermented foods and drinks, as well as drugs such as antibiotics, and other industrial materials (see page 196). But nowadays biotechnology may also imply culture of cells and tissues taken from multi-celled organisms (including humans), for example, to produce various kinds of antibodies. The biotechnologist may also employ **free enzymes** – that is, enzymes taken out of the living cells that produce them. Such free enzymes are used in modern detergents.

Increasingly, too, microbes and other cells employed in biotechnology are first subjected to genetic engineering (see page 200). That is, new genes are introduced into them so that they can carry out totally novel functions.

In theory, almost every kind of material that is now produced by the chemical industry might be produced by cultured microbes or other cells. Traditional chemistry employs high temperature and pressures, requires a great deal of energy, and often generates enormous pollution. But biotechnology methods operate at ordinary temperatures and need not produce pollution (although in practice all industries can be polluting).

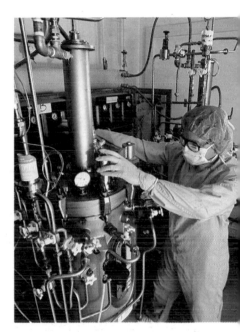

▲ **Figure 4A3** *Production facility for biotechnological manufacture.*

Harnessing sunlight

Plants and some bacteria tap solar energy directly by the process known as **photosynthesis** (see page 206). They use this energy to convert carbon from carbon dioxide gas and hydrogen from water into complex organic materials such as carbohydrates. From these they build their own structures and supply themselves with materials for respiratory energy transfer. Animals and microbes live by consuming the organic materials made by plants.

Solar power is 'renewable energy'; after all, the Sun rises every day. Thus, if they are carried out well, agriculture, horticulture, and biotechnology can be truly 'sustainable' industries. But if done badly, they waste land, pollute the surroundings, and destroy wildlife.

Traditional biotechnology

Cheese is made by fermenting the solids in milk by using 'lactic acid bacteria' and sometimes other bacteria and fungi as well. It is one of the oldest food technologies and yet it can be called biotechnology because microbial fermentation is involved. There are still cheesemakers who combine elements of traditional craft practice with the latest scientific know-how.

Charlie the cheesemaker

After travelling the world for a year or two, aged 25 and wondering what to do with the rest of his life, Charlie Westhead had a flash of inspiration. He would make farmhouse cheese! Now, aged 31, he makes cheeses, Greek yoghurt, and crème fraîche for the world-renowned Neal's Yard, which sells speciality cheeses and other fine foods in London's Covent Garden. He and his colleagues, Liz Harris and Margaret Collins, are good at it. Neal's Yard's fromage frais won first prize at the 1991 International Cheese Show. 'Fromage frais' is a farmhouse cheese sold very young, without maturing.

The Neal's Yard 'creamery' is in Kent, 30 miles from London. Inside its buildings, where the yoghurts and cheeses are made, every surface including floors and walls, and every vessel, is carefully scrubbed. Old-style cheese makers relied on wild bacteria and fungi to ferment the milk. But every microbe employed in modern creameries has been carefully bred for the purpose and is bought in as a commercial 'culture'.

'Hygiene is the key', says Charlie. 'It's not so much a matter of diseases (although cheeses can carry unpleasant bugs, such as *Listeria*) but of making sure that no wild microbes get in and spoil the recipes.'

Charlie buys in 200 gallons a week from a herd of Friesian cows and 100 gallons a week from a flock of white Swiss Saanen goats. From the cows' milk he makes two cheeses (as well as the 'fromage frais'), **Wealden Round**, made with layers of herbs, and **Finn**, which has a white mould on the outside like the French cheeses, Brie and Camembert. From the goats' milk he makes **Perroche** – sold very young, and rolled in herbs; and **Ragstone**, named after the local hills. Ragstone, like Finn, is sold with a white coat of mould.

The cheese making process

The milk of all mammals contains fat, protein (mainly casein, but also other proteins), plus lactose ('milk sugar'), and minerals (including lots of calcium). They are all suspended and dissolved in water. The amount of solids in milk varies enormously from species to species but in cows' and goats' milk they make up about 12% of the total – so nearly 90% is water.

'We use unpasteurized milk', says Charlie, 'so first we "thermize" it – which means heating it rapidly to 63°C. This gets rid of bacteria like *Staphylococcus* which sometimes infect cows' udders. Then when the milk has cooled to around 30°C we add "starter culture" and "rennet".'

The first step in cheese making is to coagulate the protein and in particular casein which means making it form a spongy mass. This spongy structure holds on to most of the fat in the milk, plus some of the sugar and minerals. The whole semi-solid mass of coagulated protein, fat, and the rest is called **curd**. The liquid left behind – water plus the rest of the sugar, minerals, and a little of the fat – is **whey**. Cheese is made from the curd. Stage one, then, is to prepare the curd.

This is done by adding 'starter culture' and 'rennet' to heat-treated milk. Starter culture includes 'lactic acid bacteria' – in this case *Lactococcus* – which convert the lactose in the milk into lactic acid. This acidity causes some coagulation. Rennet is traditionally prepared from the stomach lining of young calves, and contains the 'protease' enzymes that calves produce to help digest their mothers' milk. But Charlie uses a 'rennet' made with 'vegetarian' protease enzymes prepared from a mould, *Mucor meihei*. Whatever their source, these enzymes coagulate casein faster than acid alone would do.

If Charlie is making Ragstone or Finn he also adds cultures of *Penicillium* mould at this stage (the same group of fungi that yield penicillin). Later, as the finished cheese matures, this mould grows to form the white surface coating.

After 20 hours the bacterial culture and the rennet have done their work and turned the milk in its white 10-gallon bucket into a sloppy, creamy mixture of curds and whey like cold custard. Charlie first slices the curds into cubes, about 4 cm across. The cubes are then piled into polythene moulds shaped like one-pint beer glasses, but with holes in the sides, out of which the surplus whey can flow away. As the whey 'exudes' the volume goes down and more cubes are added; and so on until no more whey runs out and the curds are soft but solid. They are then left to drain for another 16 hours.

After that, if the cheese is a simple one like Perroche, there's only one stage left: putting it in brine for about 10 minutes. The brine is a saturated solution of sea-salt and it dries the cheese, adds flavour – because it sinks in over the following 24 hours, and improves the shelf life.

Perroche is now effectively ready for sale – but for most cheeses there is one more vital stage. They must be matured. During maturation enzymes in the bacteria of the starter culture and from the original milk continue to break down fats and proteins, producing aromatic products such as fatty acids which give each cheese its characteristic flavour. Many are matured for months – in all kinds of different circumstances, hung in a basket under an olive tree, or in the cool and dark of some French cave. But Ragstone and Finn are ready for sale after just 10 days' maturation in a cold room at around 12 °C.

Cheeses of all kinds

There are thousands of different kinds of cheese. Ewe's milk is used in the French blue cheese Roquefort and water buffalo's in Mozzarella. Different kinds and combinations of lactic acid bacteria can be used to start the culture, including *Lactobacillus* and *Streptococcus*, plus an additional range of yeasts and fungi.

The starter culture may be introduced at different temperatures and cut or stirred in different ways, and the finished cheese may be given many different shapes or coverings ('rinds'), both of which affect the way they dry; and of course different cheeses are matured for different lengths of time. Finally, they may be herbed, spiced, or smoked.

'All these techniques', says Charlie, 'are variations on the same basic theme. Prepare a curd with starter bacteria and rennet, separate it off, decide how much whey you want to leave in, brine it, and then let it mature.'

> 'Then we have to separate the curd from the whey. In fact, the method of separation, and the amount of whey removed, is the cheese-making recipe.'

How cells divide

The cells of plants, animals, and fungi divide in two ways. Most of the time they divide by *mitosis*, to produce two daughter cells that are just like the parent cell. Reproductive cells are generated by a more complicated process, *meiosis*, to produce eggs and sperm.

Mitosis

Plants, animals, and fungi are called **eukaryotes**: that is, their cells contain nuclei (see page 362). In eukaryotic cells, genes are carried on **chromosomes**. Each chromosome consists of a *single*, but extremely long, 'macromolecule' of DNA, which in parts is wound around special proteins that hold it in place.

Every nucleated cell in every animal, plant, or fungus carries two complete sets of chromosomes. One set was originally inherited from the mother, and one from the father. A normal body cell, with two sets of chromosomes, is said to be **diploid**. Each species has its own characteristic number of chromosomes. Human beings have 46 chromosomes – two sets of 23. Chimpanzees have 48 – two sets of 24.

When a cell divides its usual aim is to produce two daughter cells that are very like itself. In fact they may not be the same, because some cells divide to produce daughters that become more specialized than themselves. For example, stem cells in the bone marrow divide to produce different kinds of blood cell (see page 374).

▼ **Figure 4A4** *The process of mitosis.*

But it is important that daughters contain exactly the same **genes** as the parent cell. This is achieved by **mitosis** (Figure 4A4).

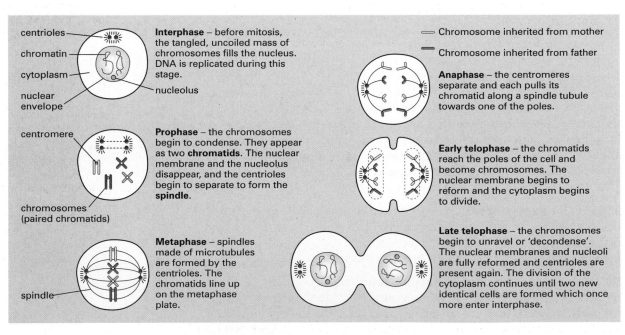

centrioles
chromatin
cytoplasm
nuclear envelope
nucleolus

Interphase – before mitosis, the tangled, uncoiled mass of chromosomes fills the nucleus. DNA is replicated during this stage.

centromere

Prophase – the chromosomes begin to condense. They appear as two **chromatids**. The nuclear membrane and the nucleolus disappear, and the centrioles begin to separate to form the **spindle**.

chromosomes (paired chromatids)

spindle

Metaphase – spindles made of microtubules are formed by the centrioles. The chromatids line up on the metaphase plate.

Chromosome inherited from mother
Chromosome inherited from father

Anaphase – the centromeres separate and each pulls its chromatid along a spindle tubule towards one of the poles.

Early telophase – the chromatids reach the poles of the cell and become chromosomes. The nuclear membrane begins to reform and the cytoplasm begins to divide.

Late telophase – the chromosomes begin to unravel or 'decondense'. The nuclear membranes and nucleoli are fully reformed and centrioles are present again. The division of the cytoplasm continues until two new identical cells are formed which once more enter interphase.

Meiosis

This is how specialist sex cells within the **ovary** or the **testis** produce **gametes**: eggs or sperm. In meiosis each parent sex cell divides to form four gametes, each of which contains only one set of chromosomes (Figure 4A5). Cells with only one chromosome set are said to be **haploid**.

Prophase I – each chromosome appears in the condensed form with two chromatids. *Homologous pairs* of chromosomes associate with each other. These are equivalent chromosomes inherited from the two parents.

Metaphase I – the spindle forms and the pairs of chromosomes line up on the metaphase plate. **Crossing over** occurs.

Anaphase I – the centromeres do not divide. One chromosome (pair of chromatids) from each homologous pair moves to each end of the cell. As a result the chromosome number in each 'cell' is half that of the original.

Telophase I – the nuclear membrane reforms and the cells begin to divide. In some cells there may be a period of brief or prolonged interphase. During this interphase there is *no replication* of DNA.

Metaphase II – new spindles are formed and the chromosomes, still made up of pairs of chromatids, line up on the metaphase plate.

Anaphase II – the centromeres now divide and the chromatids move to the opposite ends of the cell.

Telophase II – nuclear envelopes reform, the chromosomes return to their interphase state and DNA replication occurs, giving four daughter cells each with half the chromosome number of the original diploid cell.

▲ **Figure 4A5** *The process of meiosis.*

During late prophase a process takes place which is the key to heredity: **crossing over** (Figure 4A6).

As the sets of four chromatids (formed from each pair of chromosomes) lie side by side, two from different chromosomes may become intertwined. They will exchange DNA. The result is that two of four chromatids contain the same DNA (genes) as the original chromosomes, and two contain a new mixture of genetic material. Thus, some gametes will have different combinations of genes from the parent organisms which produced them.

Meiosis consists of two cell divisions to produce four daughter cells each of which contains only **one** (haploid) set of chromatids (doubled up to whole chromosomes in the ensuing interphase).

Bacteria are quite different. Their cells have no nuclei, they are **prokaryotes**. Instead their DNA forms a single chromosome. They also have an indefinite number of small pieces of DNA known as **plasmids**. The DNA in the chromosomes and plasmids simply divides. There are no elaborate whole chromosome movements as in the nucleated cells of eukaryotes.

▶ **Figure 4A6** *Recombination and crossing over.*

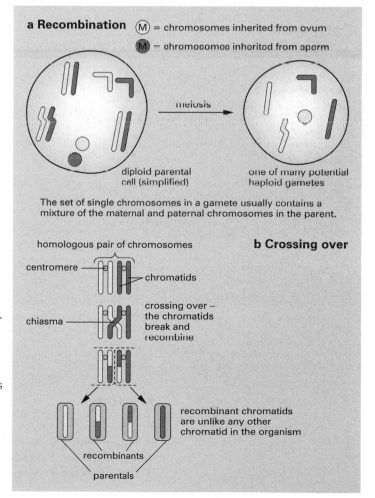

a Recombination Ⓜ = chromosomes inherited from ovum
Ⓜ = chromosomes inherited from sperm

diploid parental cell (simplified) → meiosis → one of many potential haploid gametes

The set of single chromosomes in a gamete usually contains a mixture of the maternal and paternal chromosomes in the parent.

b Crossing over

homologous pair of chromosomes

centromere — chromatids

chiasma — crossing over – the chromatids break and recombine

recombinant chromatids are unlike any other chromatid in the organism

recombinants

parentals

DNA and protein synthesis

Genes determine the physical attributes and some behaviour of living things. They are made of DNA which provides a code for the construction of proteins. Proteins, in turn, make up much of the structure of living tissue and act as biological catalysts (enzymes) which largely control the functions (metabolism) of an organism.

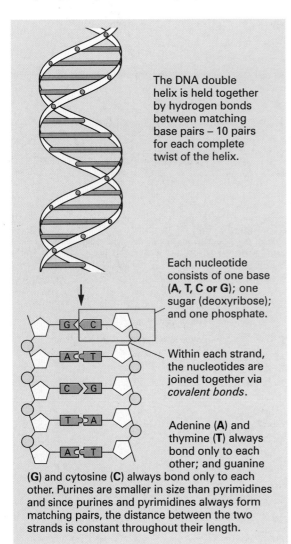

The DNA double helix is held together by hydrogen bonds between matching base pairs – 10 pairs for each complete twist of the helix.

Each nucleotide consists of one base (**A, T, C or G**); one sugar (deoxyribose); and one phosphate.

Within each strand, the nucleotides are joined together via *covalent bonds*.

Adenine (**A**) and thymine (**T**) always bond only to each other; and guanine (**G**) and cytosine (**C**) always bond only to each other. Purines are smaller in size than pyrimidines and since purines and pyrimidines always form matching pairs, the distance between the two strands is constant throughout their length.

▲ **Figure 4A7** *The DNA double helix.*

Genes are made of DNA

The idea that the attributes (**characters**) of organisms are determined by particular 'factors' was discovered by Gregor Mendel in the 1860s (see page 216). Early 20th century biologists renamed these factors **genes**.

In 1902 Archibald Garrod, an English physician, proposed that genes operate by making enzymes. He studied the inherited disease **alkaptonuria**, whose sufferers produce urine that turns black in air. He found that the disease was caused by a single mutant gene and that its symptoms were produced by lack of a particular enzyme.

In the 1950s it became clear that genes controlled the production of all kinds of proteins – not just enzymes. But until the 1940s most biologists thought that genes themselves were also made of protein. Then experiments showed that genetic information could be passed between bacteria by DNA, but not by protein.

DNA itself was discovered in Switzerland in the early 1870s, in cell nuclei, but for a long time it was thought unimportant. Biochemists in the early 20th century worked out its rough chemical structure. They found it contained molecules of the sugar, **deoxyribose**; phosphate radicals (Pi); and four kinds of 'base': two **purines** known as adenine (**A**) and guanine (**G**), and two **pyrimidines** known as thymine (**T**) and cytosine (**C**). A single sugar, phosphate and 'base' combined together form a **nucleotide**.

When biologists realized that DNA *was* the stuff of genes, they set out to discover its exact structure and how it works. In 1953 Francis Crick and James Watson proposed that DNA molecules consist of two nucleotide chains wound round each other, and lying end to end. This structure is called a 'double helix' (Figure 4A7).

The fact that **A** bonds only to **T** and **G** bonds only to **C** makes it simple for DNA to multiply (**replicate**) itself accurately. First, the two helices separate to form two separate chains. Then each single helix forms a 'template' for the new chain that forms alongside. Each new chain is bound to have the same structure as the one that had been there before. Hence one double helix divides into two single chains which form two doubles, each of which is an exact copy of the original double helix.

The production of proteins

DNA stays in the nucleus but protein production occurs in the cytoplasm, in **ribosomes**. A second form of nucleic acid, known as **RNA**, provides the necessary links between nuclear DNA and the ribosomes.

RNA is broadly similar to DNA: it consists of a chain of nucleotides. It differs from DNA in four ways:

- the sugar in each nucleotide is ribose rather than deoxyribose. In fact RNA is short for **ribonucleic acid**
- the base **uracil** replaces thymine
- each RNA molecule consists only of a single chain
- RNA molecules are much shorter than DNA molecules.

RNA molecules are formed when needed in the same way as a new DNA strand is formed. Two strands of DNA double helix separate, and a piece of RNA is formed as a 'mirror image' of one of the separated DNA strands. The code in the DNA is said to be **transcribed** on to RNA. The process is therefore called **transcription** (Figure 4A8).

The code on the RNA is then **translated** into protein (Figure 4A9). Three different kinds of RNA are needed for protein synthesis. The ribosomes themselves contain **ribosomal RNA** or **rRNA** which joins the amino acids together to form protein chains. Each amino acid is ferried into position by its own particular kind of **transfer RNA** known as **tRNA**. The message from the DNA, to tell the ribosome which kind of protein is required, is brought by **messenger RNA**, or **mRNA**, which travels out of the nucleus to the ribosomes.

The genetic code

How does DNA tell the ribosome in which order to assemble amino acids in the proteins? How does the **genetic code** work?

The genetic code was 'cracked' by Francis Crick and Sydney Brenner in 1961. They showed that the code depends on the sequence of nucleotides in the DNA. Although the nucleotides simply form an uninterrupted sequence, they are 'read' as if they were groups of three.

Each group of three is called a **codon**. Since there are four different nucleotides in each chain, there are 64 different possible arrangements of groups of three, $4 \times 4 \times 4 = 64$. All the thousands of proteins in nature are made from just 20 or so different amino acids. So there are more than three times as many possible codons as there are amino acids to code for. In practice, most amino acids can be coded by more than one codon. Some codons also act as 'punctuation marks' to indicate where each gene begins and ends.

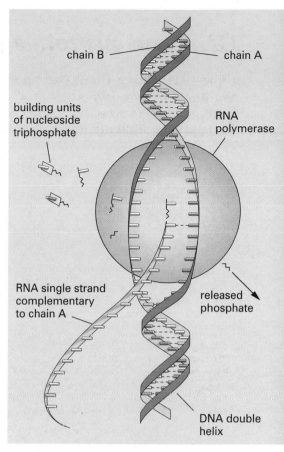

▲ **Figure 4A8** *RNA being synthesized against a template of single strand DNA.*

▼ **Figure 4A9** *Protein synthesis.*

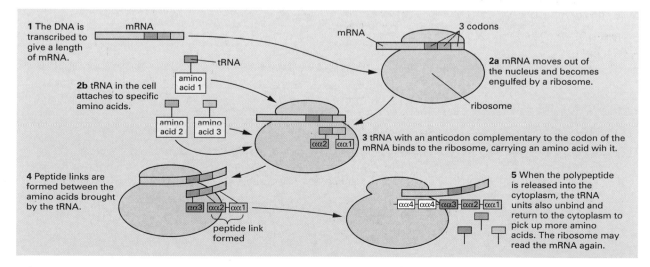

Growing microbes and cell culture

Most bacterial, animal and plant cells multiply by binary fission. A parental cell divides into two approximately equal daughter cells which separate and lead an independent existence. Yeasts including the baker's yeast, *Saccharomyces cerevisiae*, multiply by budding off smaller daughter cells.

Growing cells in the laboratory

A single bacterium like *Escherichia coli*, which is found in the human gut, can grow into two identical cells in under 20 minutes. These two daughter cells can become four cells in a further 20 minutes. If that doubling carried on for two days, the resultant bacterial colony would contain over 10^{40} cells and be bigger than the Earth. Clearly, the absence of planet-sized colonies of bacteria suggests that such growth rates cannot be sustained for long periods. However, it does occur for shorter times, particularly under artificial culture conditions. Indeed, there are bacteria that can double in around ten minutes.

Growth by constant doubling is an example of **exponential** growth. Fungi, algae and other micro-organisms besides bacteria can grow exponentially. So can animal, human and plant cells, although their doubling times are measured in tens of hours rather than minutes. All these cell types are used in **biotechnology** to produce substances such as antibiotics, human proteins, enzymes, vitamins, and other chemicals. The patterns of cell growth are fundamentally similar for all cell types.

▶ **Figure 4A10** *Patterns of cell growth in culture. The duration of each phase will vary from culture to culture but the pattern is similar for all types of organism.*

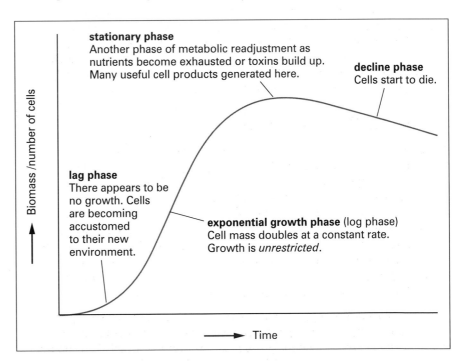

stationary phase
Another phase of metabolic readjustment as nutrients become exhausted or toxins build up. Many useful cell products generated here.

decline phase
Cells start to die.

lag phase
There appears to be no growth. Cells are becoming accustomed to their new environment.

exponential growth phase (log phase)
Cell mass doubles at a constant rate. Growth is *unrestricted*.

Biomass /number of cells

Time

The way cells grow is influenced by both external factors and features peculiar to themselves. For instance, larger and more complex animal and plant cells reproduce and organize themselves more slowly than smaller, simpler microbial cells: they grow more slowly as a consequence. External factors like nutrition, temperature, pH, and gas availability also affect cell growth.

Temperature

Cells growing in culture are **temperature-sensitive**. Roughly speaking, for every 10 °C rise in temperature, the organism's growth rate doubles. However, above an optimum temperature, the rate at which cells die also increases. Thus each organism type has an optimum temperature for growth: it is 37 °C for animal and human cells, and for microbes, like *E. coli*, that inhabit man. Fungi, yeast and soil-borne bacteria prefer temperatures around 25–30 °C. There are bacteria which inhabit deep-sea vents, however, that thrive at temperatures above 100 °C: they cannot grow at ordinary temperatures.

pH

An organism's growth in culture also varies with pH, the optimum value reflecting the environment from which the organism originally came. Buffer solutions are used to maintain the optimum pH in small-scale artificial cultures while on a larger scale, acid and alkaline solutions can be added to the culture to adjust the pH.

Nutrients

Food provides growing cells with a source of energy and chemicals for the synthesis of the materials of which they are made. Many microbial cultures thrive on sugars (typically glucose) and simple mineral salts. Human and animal cells require extensive vitamin and protein supplements as well. Nutrition can have a profound effect on cell cultures. In some biotechnology processes, cells are deliberately starved to induce them to produce substances, like antibiotics, not generated when the cells are growing (**secondary metabolites**). Oxygen is a particularly important nutrient for most cultures because it is necessary for the release of energy in cellular respiration. It can be a particularly difficult nutrient to supply, especially in large-scale cultures.

Basic culture techniques

The simplest form of cell culture is batch culture; cells grow in a jar of liquid nutrients. An inoculum of cells is added to a vessel containing fresh, liquid medium in which the cells can grow. Batch cultures are usually aerated to provide oxygen and maintained at a constant temperature. They are also constantly mixed either by shaking or via an internal impeller to prevent nutrients running out in local areas within the container. As the cells grow, they exhaust the nutrients, growth slows and eventually stops. During batch culture everything is changing: the amount of organism, the concentration of nutrients, the concentration of product and of waste materials generated by the organism.

A continuous culture method such as the **chemostat** is technically more complex but simpler to analyse than a batch culture. In the chemostat, fresh nutrients are continuously added to the culture vessel. The volume of the system is kept constant by removing culture fluid, including the growing cells, at the same rate. After a while, the rate at which cells are added through growth equals the rate of cell removal. The system is then at **equilibrium**. The cells are growing at a constant exponential rate and the concentration of cells, nutrients, products and waste products is constant. By varying the rate at which nutrients are added, the growth rate of the cells can be controlled.

The range of microbial products

During World War I, large amounts of acetone were needed to make the explosive, cordite. Supplies of acetone were scarce. But a chemist, Chaim Weizmann, discovered that a bacterium, now called *Clostridium acetobutylicum*, could produce huge amounts of acetone and another valuable compound, butanol, from cheap materials like molasses. The aceto-butanol fermentation marked the beginning of the modern era of biotechnology – micro-organisms could be harnessed for industrial chemistry.

Primary metabolites

Acetone and butanol are examples of **primary metabolites**, compounds which organisms use while they are growing. Ethanol (common alcohol) is another primary metabolite. Alcohol is something yeast cells produce when they grow on sugar but have no oxygen. The equation for the production of ethanol is:

$$C_6H_{12}O_6 \longrightarrow 2C_2H_5OH + 2CO_2$$

In order to produce ethanol, therefore, brewers starve yeast cells of oxygen by putting them in a large fermentation tank. One of the basic tricks of all biotechnology is to identify those growth conditions which persuade micro-organisms to produce as much of the desired product as possible. That can be done by adjusting the temperature of the fermentation, or its pH, or by altering the types of nutrients that are supplied. In other cases biotechnologists must select, or create, an organism which is particularly suited to the job.

Production of amino acids, another group of primary metabolites, depends heavily on **mutant** organisms which over-produce the compounds. Mutant *Corynebacterium* species may produce more than 50% of their own mass as amino acids such as lysine, which is used as a nutritional supplement in animal feed and human food or the flavour enhancer, monosodium glutamate.

Corynebacteria also produce phenylalanine, an amino acid which is now in great demand to make the sweetener, **aspartame** (Nutrasweet). The explanation for such over-production is often that a mutation in a gene for a key enzyme blocks the conversion of the amino acid into a related essential compound. The organism tries harder to make that compound but succeeds only in producing more of the amino acid.

Before genetic engineering, biotechnologists used ultraviolet radiation or chemicals to induce random genetic changes in the DNA of organisms to develop over-producing strains. Now, recombinant DNA methods provide a more direct way of achieving the same end.

Secondary metabolism products

Antibiotics like **penicillin**, **cephalosporin** and **streptomycin** are produced by micro-organisms, too. These are secondary products. They are produced when the organism is not growing exponentially. In general, their chemical structures are complex and their natural functions a mystery. It may be that antibiotics help organisms compete in challenging environments. All of the commercially important antibiotics (and 90% of the others) are produced by organisms that live in soil, either **filamentous fungi** or a type of filamentous bacteria called **actinomycetes**. The organisms used for commercial antibiotic production are highly developed strains; they can produce over 50 grams of antibiotics per litre of culture, 50 000 times more than their undomesticated counterparts. However, these days, not all antibiotics are produced by micro-organisms. Chemists have become very adept at mimicking the microbe's synthetic skills. In other cases, for example in most types of penicillin, the organisms only do part of the job: they produce the core of the molecule while chemists add a specialized side-chain (**semi-synthetic penicillins**).

Drug companies have screened vast numbers of micro-organisms and samples of soil in the hope of finding new antibiotics. They have found only a few. Now the companies are looking at their samples again, using new tests with genetically engineered organisms which produce human proteins. Many of these proteins are associated with human disease. By detecting compounds made by the soil bacteria, which bind to those proteins, the drug companies hope to discover, not antibiotics, but compounds that might cure AIDS, cancer, brain disease or other conditions. The molecules that microbes synthesize may not always make ideal drugs. But they provide a 'lead compound', a skeleton upon which chemists can build the drugs of the future.

Enzymes

Micro-organisms' synthetic abilities depend on enzymes. But micro-organisms also produce enzymes that break down biological materials. These have many uses. Modern 'biological' washing powders contain as many as four separate enzymes: a **protease** to break down proteins, a **lipase** for fats, an **amylase** to release starch, and a **cellulase** which restores whiteness to cotton fabrics. Other enzyme formulations soften paper pulp, remove hair from leather, or produce a 'stone-washed' effect in jeans. Microbial **pectinases** are used extensively in the fruit and vegetable processing industry while **phytase**, which breaks down phosphorus compounds in plants, can make animal feed more nutritious.

Whole organisms

In other fermentations, the required product is the micro-organism itself. Bakers and brewers require live yeast. Preparations of *Rhizobium* bacteria are used as a form of 'green' fertilizer: once sprayed over a field, the organisms can help legume plants to fix atmospheric nitrogen (see page 236). Mycorrhizal bacteria are used by foresters to help newly planted young trees take root and acquire essential nutrients. *Bacillus thuringiensis* is a 'green' insecticide: it contains crystals of a protein that is toxic to caterpillars but not to any other part of the food chain. All these products are produced by fermentation and then distributed (usually) as dried preparations.

Commercial manufacture of cell products

A micro-organism or a genetically engineered cell that produces a drug or an enzyme, will be of no commercial value unless it produces enough at the right quality and at the right price. Laboratory systems are not necessarily devised with these factors in mind and must therefore be modified or adapted for industrial biotechnology.

How much? How valuable?

Commercial processes are not always bigger than laboratory operations. Some protein drugs from genetically engineered organisms are produced in culture vessels that are only 1–10 litres in volume, roughly the same size as many laboratory fermentors. Only gram or kilogram amounts of specialized human proteins are needed.

However, commercial production usually needs laboratory operations to be scaled up. For instance, enzymes are needed in larger quantities – often tonnes per year. Microbial processes for chemicals and animal feeds may produce hundreds of thousands of tonnes of product per year.

In general, the value of the product – and therefore, the money that can be spent producing it – varies inversely with the amount produced. The more you need, the cheaper it has to be. Some human protein drugs can cost well over £10 000 per gram; enzymes can cost less than £100 per kilogram; the microbial animal feed, Pruteen, produced by Zeneca Bioproducts, costs less than £2.00 per kilogram.

Scaling up

The simplest method of scaling up is to copy the laboratory technique. For example, in the early days of penicillin manufacture, the antibiotic was produced by inoculating many thousands of small flasks with the producer fungus.

One of the most successful human protein drugs, **erythropoietin** (EPO) is produced in much the same way that penicillin originally was. Thousands of small roller bottles, similar in appearance to milk bottles with screw tops, are inoculated with mammalian cells. The bottles are rolled slowly by robots and the cells grow on the inside surface of the bottle, excreting EPO into the culture medium. Strict rules controlling the production of human drugs make it difficult for a company to alter the principles of its pilot laboratory production process once a drug has been approved as a medicine.

Another way of scaling up processes is to increase their volume. To produce 1000 times as much of a product, you could grow 10 litres of the culture in a small fermentor instead of 10 millilitres in a flask or test-tube.

The difficulty with this approach is that increasing the volume can change the culture conditions. The temperature, pH and nutrient concentrations can be fairly easily duplicated in a larger vessel. However, providing oxygen (as air) is more difficult. All other things being equal, the rate at which oxygen can come into a culture is proportional to the area of the culture in contact with air. But when the culture volume increases 1000-fold, the surface area increases only 100-fold.

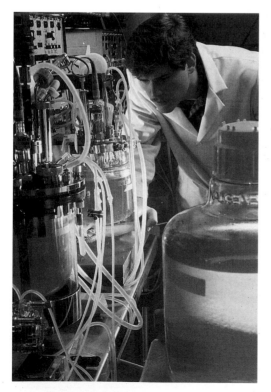
▼ **Figure 4A11** *Production of erythropoietin.*

To overcome this difficulty, large scale microbial processes usually have air injected into them, and the culture is rapidly mixed with a kind of propeller. In the largest or most dense fermentations, heat production by the organisms themselves can be a problem. Most large fermentors have a water jacket outside or a cooling system inside the vessel to keep the temperature constant.

Microbial cells are pretty tough and can withstand the beating they receive when mixed in a fermentor. However, biotechnologists cannot always use microbes. Many human proteins, for instance, have to be produced by mammalian cells. Mammalian cells, unlike microbes, are not protected by cell walls and, being fragile, cannot withstand rapid mixing. For this reason, it is not possible to grow mammalian cells at the same density as microbial cells.

Mammalian cells present **bioprocess engineers** with another problem. Some of these cells only grow when attached to solid surfaces. The problem can be overcome and cells grown in liquid culture, by growing them on beads made of glass or polymers. Each bead provides both attachment sites for the cells and protection from the ravages of the culture environment. More surface area and protection can be given if the beads are porous. The cells grow on both the inside and outside surfaces of the beads.

Improving the organisms

Improving producer organisms by **genetic engineering** has now become an essential part of scaling-up. When it first became possible to produce human proteins in mammalian cells by genetic engineering, researchers thought they would have to culture huge numbers of cells. They designed bioreactors of every shape and size: huge columns; short, squat, bioreactors; reactors that let the cells grow as an artificial skin on membrane filters.

In the event, those designs were not really needed: instead of producing thousands of times more cells, each cell could be persuaded, through genetic engineering, to produce thousands of times more protein. Genetic engineers designed producer strains that contained hundreds of copies of the relevant gene. They altered that gene so that it was very efficiently transcribed into messenger RNA which, in turn, was very efficiently translated into protein. They engineered extra amino acids onto the protein. These act as signals to ensure that the protein is exported from the cell into the surrounding growth medium, rather than being retained by the cells. It could therefore be more easily recovered. Most commercial processes therefore use relatively small and simple conventional fermentors.

Before they amend commercial processes, companies always consider carefully the productivity benefits against possible disadvantages. Each time companies change a drug production process, for example, the regulatory authorities worry that changing the process will change the product and cause some unforeseen side-effects. They insist that companies re-test their products every time they modify or change production.

Genetic engineering

Genetic engineering is a way of adding, removing or controlling the biological function in an organism through its genetic material, usually DNA. It can be a very precise process (although it is not always so). Its principles are much the same whether applied to viruses, bacteria, fungi, plants, animals, insects or human beings.

Breaking and re-assembling DNA

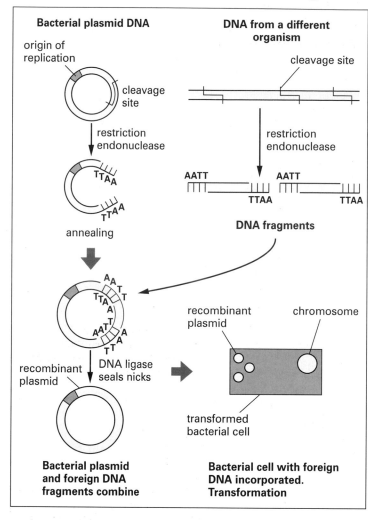

▲ **Figure 4A12** *Action of restriction endonucleases and ligases in DNA cutting and reassembly.*

To be able to handle DNA easily, genetic engineers need to cut it into small pieces. In the 1970s **restriction endonucleases** were discovered. These are produced by bacteria to protect themselves against invasion by viruses known as **bacteriophages** (**phage** for short). The enzymes cut the invading phage DNA at specific sites where there is a particular DNA sequence. This means that phage strains are 'restricted' in the types of bacteria which they can successfully invade. Importantly, for genetic engineers, a given restriction enzyme will always cut a given piece of DNA at precisely the same point.

Many restriction enzymes have now been isolated. Each is named after the bacterium in which it was found. Thus, *Eco*RI was the first (I) restriction enzyme isolated from *Escherichia coli* strain R; *Bam*HI comes from *Bacillus amyloliquefaciens* strain H; and *Hin*dIII was the third enzyme found in *Haemophilus influenzae*.

The most useful kinds of restriction enzymes for genetic engineers cut DNA at four- or six-base 'palindromic' sites (where the sequence in one strand is identical to the sequence in the other). When the enzyme cuts the DNA at such sites, it produces 'sticky ends' of single-stranded DNA. By base-pairing, these 'sticky ends' can join onto other pieces of DNA which have been cut with the same restriction enzyme. Here is a method which not only cuts DNA precisely but also allows it to be joined together in new combinations. The result is 'recombinant DNA'.

The original associations between 'sticky ends' were loose and the 'recombinant' molecules were unstable. Genetic engineers found another enzyme, piece of **DNA ligase**, to join permanently two DNA molecules whose 'sticky ends' were already associated. In effect, this enzyme seals the join between the two molecules and creates a genuinely stable 'recombinant' molecule.

Basic recombinant DNA technology can produce in a test-tube any arrangement of genes in a piece of DNA. It can splice together DNA from closely or distantly related species. It can link DNA that has been chemically synthesized. It can combine DNA sequences that code for proteins with DNA elements that control how much protein will be produced in cells, and when.

DNA cloning

The other part of genetic engineering, **DNA cloning**, occurs when a recombinant DNA molecule is re-introduced into a living organism. There are many ways of doing this.

A common method which works with microbial, plant and animal cells alike, is called **transformation**. When DNA is mixed with living cells, it can enter them. Cell walls and membranes resist DNA entry but it can be enhanced, by adding calcium ions, by applying electrical shocks (a process known as **electroporation**) or, as is often done in plants, by removing the cell wall (generating **protoplasts**).

Another approach that is widely applied is to use **vectors**. These are natural infectious agents (such as viruses) which have been adapted as carriers of recombinant DNA. Their harmful functions have been removed so that when they infect a cell, they do not kill it, but merely carry a piece of recombinant DNA into it. The bacterium *Agrobacterium tumefaciens*, for instance, is a **pathogen** (disease-causing organism) which naturally causes crown gall disease in many plants.

Genetic engineers have adapted part of the pathogen, the **Ti plasmid**, to serve as a vector for carrying genes into plants. **Plasmids** are small rings of DNA which can replicate independently within the cells in which they exist. Natural bacterial plasmids are used extensively in bacterial genetic engineering. Shuttle plasmids that have been adapted to reproduce (**replicate**) in more than one host are particularly useful. **Retroviruses** (viruses whose genes are composed of RNA) are used as vectors in the genetic engineering of humans, **gene therapy**.

DNA can even be injected directly into the nucleus of a single recipient cell through a fine glass needle. This is the most successful method for genetic engineering of animal cells. Once inside the nucleus, the injected DNA combines with the animal's own DNA. This type of approach has led to the development of sheep, goats, cows and mice which produce human proteins in their milk (**transgenic** animals).

▼ **Figure 4A13** *One way of delivering recombinant DNA to a cell. Plasmid engineering with* Agrobacterium tumefaciens.

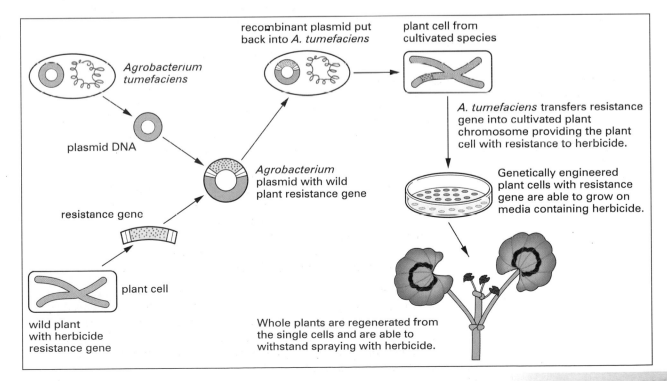

recombinant plasmid put back into *A. tumefaciens*

plant cell from cultivated species

Agrobacterium tumefaciens

plasmid DNA

Agrobacterium plasmid with wild plant resistance gene

resistance gene

plant cell

wild plant with herbicide resistance gene

A. tumefaciens transfers resistance gene into cultivated plant chromosome providing the plant cell with resistance to herbicide.

Genetically engineered plant cells with resistance gene are able to grow on media containing herbicide.

Whole plants are regenerated from the single cells and are able to withstand spraying with herbicide.

Restraints on using genetically engineered organisms

Genetic engineering is a highly regulated activity. In 1975, those at the forefront of genetic engineering met in the American town of Asilomar. At that time, the process of genetic engineering was young, and the scientists involved considered that too little was known about the impact of moving genes between organisms to allow all types of experiment to proceed. They specifically banned experiments that involved putting cancer-associated genes into micro-organisms.

Physical containment

The recommendations from Asilomar and other scientific meetings became formal rules controlling the way genetic engineering experiments should be performed. Government bodies outlined specific precautions to be taken to prevent the escape of genetically engineered organisms from the laboratory. For instance, experimenters had to wear surgical gowns, caps, masks, gloves and boots rather than just laboratory coats. They had to change their clothes in a room that served as a kind of air lock before they left the laboratory, so that any organisms on the lab wear would remain inside the laboratory. The windows of the laboratory had to be sealed and the waste from the sinks sterilized.

Air-flows in laboratories were carefully filtered and controlled. Experiments were performed under hoods which sucked the air away from the experimenter. Air inside the laboratory was maintained at a pressure lower than that outside so that if anyone opened a door, the air would come into the laboratory from the outside rather than escape from the laboratory.

In the most extreme cases – where human disease-causing organisms were being genetically manipulated – the experimenters had to shower and have their laboratory clothes sterilized each time they left the laboratory.

Collectively, these precautions constitute **physical containment**. They are all ways of preventing organisms leaving the controlled environment of the laboratory.

Physical containment also applies to the manufacturing plant for genetically engineered vaccines, drugs, and other products. Physical containment has to be applied not only where the organisms are grown, but also in the down-stream processing steps used to purify the protein, or other desired substance, and in the product testing areas.

Increasing knowledge of the risks and familiarity with the techniques of genetic engineering has allowed relaxation of some of these precautions in recent years. Some experiments can now be performed under near normal laboratory conditions.

Biological containment

In some applications genetically engineered organisms have to leave the laboratory to perform their work. Clearly, physical containment is no longer possible. People or animals injected with genetically engineered vaccines cannot remain in the lab; similarly, microbial fertilizers, insecticides or soil-treatment preparations need to be sprayed on land if they are to be useful. The organisms in these applications are **deliberately released**.

In order to minimize any risks, and to reassure the public that appropriate precautions are being taken, researchers have developed methods of **biological containment** for such products.

The crudest form of biological containment – killing cells – was used for the first deliberately released microbial product approved for sale, a microbial insecticide produced by the Californian firm, Mycogen. The product was a strain of *Pseudomonas* bacterium which contained the genes for, and produced large amounts of, an insecticide toxin from another bacterium, *Bacillus thuringiensis*. Mycogen produced the cells in a fermentor, killed them, and sold them ready for spraying on the fields.

Other methods of biological containment are more subtle. Various 'suicide' mechanisms can be used to control the growth of living genetically engineered organisms in natural environments.

Pseudomonas putida is a bacterium that can use toxic organic chemicals in the soil as food, thereby removing them from the environment. It can eat the chemicals because it possesses a set of enzymes which can break them down. These enzymes are made when a group of genes are turned on by the presence of the toxins (a genetic switch).

Through genetic engineering scientists can put the organism's vital survival metabolism under the control of the same switch. This produces an organism that can grow when, and only when, toxic compounds are present. When sprayed on polluted soil the bugs will happily remove the pollutants. But when they complete their task, they will be unable to grow. Similarly, if the bacteria are washed away by the rain, or taken on the feet of animals or birds to other, unpolluted environments, they will not grow there.

Some people have concerns that, even though organisms themselves cannot spread, their genetically engineered DNA might. These concerns, too, can be addressed by biological containment.

The toxin-degrading genes of *P. putida*, for instance, are contained on a plasmid, a form of genetic element that readily passes from one organism to another. However, with the aid of a little more genetic engineering, the plasmid can become a 'poison chalice'. A gene that codes for a toxin can be incorporated into the plasmid. The *Pseudomonas* host is protected from the toxin by an immunity gene which is placed on its chromosome.

However, if the plasmid passes to another bacterium the toxin will kill the new, unprotected host. In killing its new host, the plasmid, in effect, destroys itself.

Working plants

Cricket bats: four plants from three continents

The West Indian cricketer, Brian Lara, hit 501 runs in a famous innings in 1994. He faced a hard, heavy ball hurled at him very fast – and flicked, hooked, cut or drove it to the boundary, perhaps 70 metres away. Such power came partly from his own strength and timing but was also helped by the extraordinary suppleness, spring, and resilience of his bat. These qualities arise from the subtle interplay of materials from four very different plants from widely scattered parts of the world.

Properties of plants

The main part of the cricket bat, the **blade**, is made from the trunks of willow trees. Of all the many kinds of willow just one variety of one species is favoured: the variety *coerulea* of *Salix alba*, the white willow. These 'cricket bat willows' are typically grown along river banks in Essex, Norfolk and Suffolk, where they reach a height of 20 metres within twelve to fifteen years. Then they are cut into lengths of about 70 centimetres, which are split into wedges or 'clefts', and left to season for eight to twelve months. They are then roughly shaped into blades with a circular saw, and after another seasoning they can be cut to their final shape by hand. The blades are compressed by machine to strengthen them and reveal any weaknesses. Finally a 'V' is cut in the top of the blade to accommodate the handle.

Two very different plant materials are employed to make the handle. The first is **rattan**, which is wood from the trunk of palm trees in the genus *Calamus*. Most palms grow as straight tall trees like the coconut or oil palms. But *Calamus*, oddly, is a climbing plant from Southeast Asia; and as with most climbers, its stems are extremely springy. For extra spring, the bat maker employs not one but up to sixteen separate strips of rattan stem in the handles, arranged in four groups of four.

Between each group of rattan strips the bat maker inserts material from yet another plant: **rubber**. Natural rubber can be made from sticky sap known as latex which is produced by many species from various plant families. But the best latex producer, and the most widely grown, is *Hevea brasiliensis* – a tree that came originally from Brazil but is now grown on a vast scale in Southeast Asia, particularly Malaysia. The trees are grown in plantations. The farmers cut 'Vs' in the bark, and the latex runs out and is caught in containers tied to the tree. The latex is then hardened and stabilized chemically to form rubber. The reddish wood of the rubber tree can also make fine furniture and veneers.

The fourth plant traditionally employed is **linseed** or **flax**, *Linum usitatissimum*. Its seeds are oily, and the oil is extracted by pressing. The raw oil, applied to the blade of the bat, keeps it springy and prevents rot. (Alternatively, modern bats may be surfaced with fabric or treated with polyurethane varnish.) *L. usitatissimum* for oil is mainly grown in Argentina. So South America has at least three stakes in the game of cricket: rubber, linseed, and many fine players from Guyana. (Incidentally, stumps and bails are made from **ash**; and the leather ball has a **cork** interior.)

Willows are related to poplars and aspens within the family **Salicaceae** (pronounced Sally-case-ee). In all, this family contains around 350 species. There are nineteen species of willow in Britain alone. Most are scrubby trees or bushes, but poplars make taller trees. Willow twigs are used for baskets, and farmers now grow them on marginal land for woodchip or fuel. Willow bark yields tannin for tanning leather, and drugs such as aspirin. Poplar is the main timber for matchsticks. The straight 'Lombardy' poplars are grown as windbreaks.

Palm trees, family **Palmae**, belong to the group of flowering plants known as monocotyledons, the group that includes grasses, lilies, and orchids. The Palmae are extremely varied, with about 2780 species. Most grow in the tropics, sometimes in humid rainforest but also in deserts, swamps, and high mountains. Many are valuable, including the coconut which yields oil, **copra** (which is the white flesh of the coconut) and the fibre **coir** from the husks. Other palm products include palm oil, dates, sago, raffia (fibres from a palm leaf) and hard timber, while many are planted for their ornamental value. *Calamus* gives rattan and malacca cane, used for walking sticks.

The rubber tree, *Hevea brasiliensis*, belongs to the enormous plant family, the **Euphorbiaceae** (pronounced Yew-forb-ee-ase-ee), with 300 genera and more than 500 species. Most are tropical, but the family includes the common spurge plants of Britain. Besides the rubber plant, other valuable 'euphorb' species yield **cassava** (also known as **manioc** or **tapioca**) which is a valuable staple food; **castor oil**; **tung oil** (used in varnish and paints); 'vegetable tallow' (used for soaps); purgative drugs; dyes; timber; and many ornamental plants, including *poinsettia*.

Linseed belongs in the family **Linaceae**: a small group, with only about 300 species. *Linum usitatissimum* is the most valuable, but other *Linum* species are grown as garden plants. The vascular bundles of the stem of the linseed plant form extremely strong fibres known as flax, which are used for linen fabric and high-quality papers, including cigarette paper. *Linum usitatissimum* for fibres is mainly grown in Europe.

▲ **Figure 4B1** *Lombardy poplars in England.*

▲ **Figure 4B2** *Coconut plantation in The Philippines.*

▲ **Figure 4B3** *Caster oil fruit growing in Thailand.*

▲ **Figure 4B4** *Linseed field in Shropshire.*

Photosynthesis

By photosynthesis green plants and some bacteria harness the energy of the Sun to convert inorganic materials – carbon dioxide and water – into carbohydrates. Photosynthesis is at the root of all the most significant food chains.

The basic chemistry of photosynthesis

The overall chemistry of photosynthesis can be represented as follows:

$$CO_2 + H_2O + \text{light energy} \longrightarrow CH_2O + O_2 \qquad \textbf{(1)}$$

In this equation CH_2O is a general formula which represents any kind of carbohydrate. Carbohydrates are extremely varied, and include a vast range of sugars, plus starch and cellulose. But they are all based on combinations of the basic unit CH_2O – so CH_2O can stand for any of them.

One particularly important carbohydrate is glucose, a sugar, whose molecules contain 6 CH_2O units – giving the formula $C_6H_{12}O_6$ (see page 19).

Because glucose is so important, the equation for photosynthesis is sometimes given as:

$$6CO_2 + 6H_2O \longrightarrow C_6H_{12}O_6 + 6O_2 \qquad \textbf{(2)}$$

In practice, the biochemistry of photosynthesis is immensely complicated, and involves a variety of pigments and helper molecules. But the essentials are as follows.

Chlorophyll is the key molecule

Chlorophyll is the pigment that gives plants their green colour. The pigment acts like the photoelectric cells found in solar-powered cars and pocket calculators. It transfers energy from the Sun (**solar energy**) into **electrons**. Chlorophyll is contained within organelles known as **chloroplasts**, which are found mainly in leaves.

▼ **Figure 4B5** *The chemistry of the chlorophyll molecule is critical for photosynthesis.*

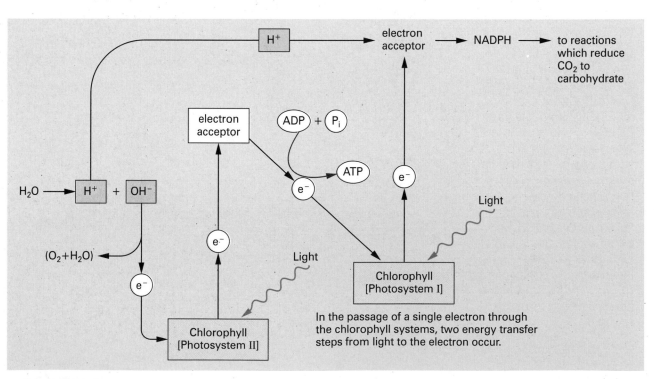

In the passage of a single electron through the chlorophyll systems, two energy transfer steps from light to the electron occur.

Splitting water

The electrical energy captured by chlorophyll is then passed on to various helper molecules and finally is used to split water:

$$2H_2O + \text{electrical energy} \longrightarrow 4H^+ + O_2 \qquad (3)$$

The water is supplied to the leaf mainly from the soil – through the roots and up the conducting **xylem** vessels. The oxygen produced is either used by the plant for respiration, or escapes into the atmosphere. Without photosynthesis, there would be no oxygen gas in the atmosphere at all.

Making carbohydrate

The hydrogen that is split from the water is joined to carbon dioxide from the air to make carbohydrate. This stage can be represented:

$$CO_2 + 4H^+ \longrightarrow CH_2O + H_2O \qquad (4)$$

It can be seen that putting equations **(3)** and **(4)** together gives equation **(1)**, because the $4H^+$ in **(3)** and **(4)** cancel out. The carbon dioxide used at this stage comes from the air.

The leaf as a site for photosynthesis

When the stomata open to allow CO_2 in, they also allow water to escape, and a plant will die if it loses too much water. So the stomata are surrounded by **guard cells**, like lips which open wide only when the light is bright, and close when it is not. But on very bright days plants may lose water faster than they can bring it from their roots, and then the leaves will wilt. Fortunately, when the leaves do wilt, the stomata automatically close; so this is a last ditch safety measure.

Summary points

- **The chief element in the plant** – and all living things – is **carbon** from carbon dioxide in the atmosphere.

- **The oxygen** in carbohydrate also **comes from the CO_2**. It does *not* come from water. In photosynthesis light energy is used to split water – not to split CO_2.

- **Photosynthesis is a reduction process**. That is, carbon dioxide is reduced to carbohydrate by adding hydrogen to it.

- **Photosynthesis is an exercise in transferring energy from the Sun to chemicals**. Chlorophyll transfers the energy from sunlight to electrons. The electrons then bring about chemical changes which convert carbon dioxide and water into carbohydrates.

▼ **Figure 4B6** *The role of the leaf in photosynthesis.*

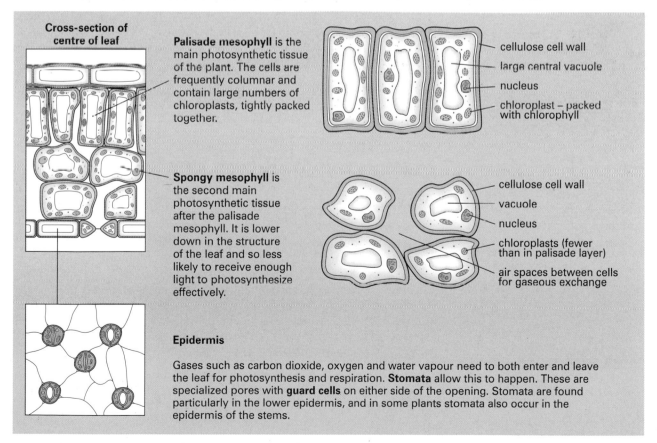

Cross-section of centre of leaf

Palisade mesophyll is the main photosynthetic tissue of the plant. The cells are frequently columnar and contain large numbers of chloroplasts, tightly packed together.

- cellulose cell wall
- large central vacuole
- nucleus
- chloroplast – packed with chlorophyll

Spongy mesophyll is the second main photosynthetic tissue after the palisade mesophyll. It is lower down in the structure of the leaf and so less likely to receive enough light to photosynthesize effectively.

- cellulose cell wall
- vacuole
- nucleus
- chloroplasts (fewer than in palisade layer)
- air spaces between cells for gaseous exchange

Epidermis

Gases such as carbon dioxide, oxygen and water vapour need to both enter and leave the leaf for photosynthesis and respiration. **Stomata** allow this to happen. These are specialized pores with **guard cells** on either side of the opening. Stomata are found particularly in the lower epidermis, and in some plants stomata also occur in the epidermis of the stems.

What plants need

If crops are to germinate, grow, and ripen at the right time, then the following parameters must be attended to: light, temperature, nutrients, soil structure, soil pH, moisture, availability of CO_2, and space for the plant to grow. Modern technology allows growers to provide perfect conditions for any kind of crop in any country: aubergines and bananas could be grown in heated greenhouses on top of Scottish mountains. In practice production costs must be justified by the value of the produce.

Each parameter must operate within an optimum range. If any one falls below a certain critical value or threshold, then growth stops. On the other hand, for any one parameter there is a maximum, above which no further input is useful. Only if *all* parameters are optimal can the plant realize its full biological potential, and grow at its maximum rate. If any one parameter is too low, then growth is slowed. Whichever one is lacking is called the **limiting factor**. For example, crops in the semi-arid tropics have abundant light and heat but are often limited by the supply of water and sometimes of nutrients.

Sunlight

All crops need light for photosynthesis and unless they receive enough in a growing season they will not reach saleable size and perhaps will not ripen. Thus maize needs 1000 hours of sunlight in the season to ripen the grain.

Many crops also regulate their growing cycles according to day length. Thus British varieties of wheat will not ripen their grain until the days start to grow shorter – indicating that summer is ending.

Temperature

Many crops, including fruit blossoms and some grasses for pasture, are killed by frost. Only a few tropical crops, such as sorghum, can tolerate prolonged temperatures much above 45 °C. But between these lethal extremes, every 10 °C rise in temperature roughly doubles the rate of photosynthesis. So under the same light conditions, a plant might grow almost twice as fast at 30 °C as at 20 °C. In general, as with light, a plant needs to enjoy a certain minimum number of hours above a critical temperature if it is to grow sufficiently and ripen.

Fertilizer

Plants obtain their principal nutrient – carbon – from the air. They obtain other nutrients mainly through their roots. The ones needed in greatest amounts are **nitrogen** (N), used in making proteins and nucleic acids; **phosphorus** (P), which is incorporated into many vital molecules including nucleic acids and some lipids (fats); and **potassium** (K), which regulates the electrical properties of cell membranes. But plants also require a great many other elements including iron, copper, cobalt, molybdenum, and manganese. These vital elements are needed only in very small or **trace** quantities.

Nutrients can be given as '**artificial**' fertilizers, or in **organic** form, as compost or manure. Extra nitrates and ammonia are also supplied by **nitrogen fixation** (see page 236).

Soil

Clay is made from very small particles, so clay-rich soils have a **close** texture. They hold water well but they may become waterlogged, and wet clay soils are also slow to warm up in spring. But they retain nutrients very well and some plants, like roses, prefer a clay soil.

Sand has much bigger particles than clay and sandy soils are 'light' or **open**. They drain quickly so they do not become waterlogged, but they tend to become too dry. Crops like carrots prefer a sandy soil.

If clay, sand, and organic material are evenly mixed then the resulting soil is called a **loam**. Good loams hold water and nutrients well (because of the clay and organic materials) but also drain reasonably well (because of the sand). Hence a loam is a good all-purpose soil.

pH

If the **pH** of the soil is wrong – too acid or too alkaline – then plant roots do not absorb nutrients efficiently. Most crops prefer a fairly neutral soil (around pH 7.0) – so growers tend to apply lime every three years or so to neutralize acidity built up by adding fertilizers. Rain tends to be slightly acid (pH around 5.5) because it picks up carbon dioxide as it falls, which creates weak carbonic acid. But in industrial countries the pH of rain may fall to 3.0 or less because it contains oxides of sulphur (such as SO_4^{2-}) from power stations and oxides of nitrogen (such as NO_2^{2-}) from internal combustion engines. Such 'acid rain' is a serious pollutant.

Water

All plants need water which they obtain mainly through their roots. All except a few specialist plants such as cacti are distressed if the soil dries completely. But few tolerate being flooded or 'waterlogged'. Plant roots need oxygen for respiration and too much water excludes air and 'drowns' them. In temperate countries, soils that are too wet also tend to be cold. Many crops worldwide are irrigated, via channels of water from the river, or by sprinklers.

Carbon dioxide

Most crops pick up all the carbon dioxide they need from the surrounding air. But if a plant has plenty of light and warmth, and all the water and nutrients it needs, then lack of CO_2 may become the limiting factor. So growers of high-value crops in greenhouses sometimes pump in extra CO_2. Field crops may also be short of CO_2 on good summer days but they rarely justify the cost of supplying extra amounts.

Space

Finally, each plant must have enough **space** to grow. If plants are too crowded then they **compete** for light and nutrients and no individual grows well. Seedlings are often far too crowded and must be thinned. But too much room can be bad, too. In the same plot it may be better to grow, say, 100 cabbages to three-quarters of their maximum size, than grow 50 cabbages to their full size. Then again, timber trees generally grow straighter and taller if they are crowded because then they have to 'reach' upwards to the light.

Selecting appropriate plants

Human beings are known to eat parts of about 3000 different plant species, but only about 170 food crops are grown on a large commercial scale. Many more are grown for animal feed, fibres, timber, medicines, perfumes, and other uses (see pages 212–13). But there are about 250 000 species of flowering plant. So only about one in 80 species is grown commercially. What determines which ones are grown?

What grows where and why?

Many crops are dual purpose, like cotton and linseed, each of which supplies both fibres and oil; or multi-purpose, like oak trees which provide high-class timber, tannin for treating leather, and acorns for feeding pigs, while 'cork oaks' provide cork. Most commercially grown species are flowering plants, or angiosperms, but many timber crops and a few others are conifers or gymnosperms.

The world's most important crops, the big-seeded grasses known as **cereals**, are good examples of what grows where and why. The main types are **wheat**, **rice**, **maize**, **barley**, **rye**, **oats**, **sorghum**, and various **millets**. In some cases, each crop is represented by several different species; and each species in turn may be subdivided into many (sometimes scores) of different varieties. Thus, nowadays, two main species of wheat are grown, *Triticum aestivum*, which is bread wheat, and *Triticum durum*, used for pasta, like spaghetti and lasagne. Each crop has been developed from wild grass species taken from different environments; and each modern crop retains a preference for a set of conditions similar to those experienced by its wild ancestor.

Wheat, which is the most widely grown food crop of all, prefers a temperate to sub-tropical climate, not arid but not too wet. Scotland, Northeast England and East Anglia provide ideal conditions and produce some of the highest yields in the world – sometimes averaging around 7–8 tonnes of grain per hectare. North America, which is far bigger, produces much more wheat but yield per hectare is only half that of Britain. Durum wheats are grown in hotter, drier conditions than are usual in Britain.

The world's **rice** crop is slightly smaller than that of wheat, but most rice is eaten direct while a lot of wheat is fed to livestock. Rice therefore feeds more people. In contrast to wheat rice likes wet, tropical conditions and indeed the young crops are flooded to create paddy fields.

Maize, the third biggest cereal crop, is multi-purpose. It is a staple food crop in Central and South America and parts of South Africa, but the grain also provides oil ('corn oil') and animal feed. It prefers warmer, drier climates than wheat. The grain will not ripen with less than about 1000 hours of sunshine per season. So British farmers grow maize to harvest while still unripe – feeding the whole plant to livestock.

Barley is valuable mainly for animal feed and for fermenting into beer and whisky (see page 196). It is also eaten as a staple, for example in Tibet, as it will grow on lighter soils and at higher altitudes than are ideal for wheat. **Rye** and **oats** are crops that can tolerate harsh or wet conditions. Rye is still favoured in Eastern Europe while oats was the traditional staple of Scotland. But oats can tolerate a wide range of conditions and are also grown in hot dry countries like Mexico.

Rye is used to make whisky, and its long stems make fine thatched roofs. Oats contain high-quality dietary fibre and are finding new favour as a health food.

Sorghum and millet are extremely important in the vast, hot, dry areas of the world known as the **semi-arid tropics**; for example in the 'Sahel' region of Africa along the south of the Sahara desert, and in much of India. Both are drought tolerant, but millet is more hardy and is grown when conditions are too harsh even for sorghum.

Yield

The **yield** is the amount of usable material that the crop produces per unit area. Breeders and other scientists in Britain have worked to increase wheat yield per hectare by five or six times in this century (from about 1–2 tonnes per hectare in 1900).

Yield is not simply related to the size of the plant. In fact modern wheats are only about waist-high or less, while a donkey could have disappeared in many old-fashioned wheats. It has been more important to raise the **harvest index**: the mass of the usable crop (say grain) relative to the whole crop (which includes straw).

Yield, economics and overall efficiency

In western farming, what really counts is **efficiency**, which in this context means the **overall cost of the inputs** divided by the **overall value of the output**. To grow a modern crop you need labour, machinery, fertilizers and pesticides, which all cost money. To produce high yields per hectare you need to take more trouble; for example, to increase labour costs or invest in capital equipment. This is worthwhile if the land is expensive. But if the land is very cheap then it can pay to spend less on raising yield per hectare, and simply spread out more. High-cost, high-yield farming is said to be **intensive**. The more spread out approach is **extensive**.

Resistance to pests and diseases

Crop plants are much more genetically uniform than wild ones, and are grown together in large numbers. This makes them extremely susceptible to pests including insects such as aphids (greenfly and blackfly), mites (such as red spider mite), nematodes (such as potato cyst nematode, *Globodera*), fungi (such as potato blight, *Phytophthora*), and diseases caused by bacteria and viruses. Yields of sorghum in Africa are typically reduced by a third just by mildew.

These can often be countered with **pesticides** such as pyrethrins, and sometimes by various **biological controls** (for example, introducing parasitic wasps to kill aphids, especially in glasshouses). But such controls have many disadvantages and it is always better to provide crops that are as resistant as possible to infection.

Crops, like all plants, adopt many mechanisms for resisting pests and diseases. A thick waxy **cuticle** on leaves may repel some fungal attack. Aphids are deterred by hairy leaves on potatoes. Many crops produce specific proteins which limit virus attack, or toxins or repellents to drive away insects. 'Resistance' mechanisms depend on possessing the appropriate genes. Increase of resistance occupies much of the time of plant breeders and is a most important task for genetic engineers (see page 200).

The things which plants provide

Plants are wonderful chemists. They produce a vast range of organic materials: to build their own structure; to provide themselves with energy; to lay down food stores in the seeds for their own offspring; and to attract animal pollinators and repel pests and pathogens. Plants produce these commodities for their own benefit. But human beings then make use of them. Some of the major categories of plant products are as follows.

Foods

Plants are the major source of human food worldwide. Most people in industrial countries obtain about 40% of their total energy, more than 60% of their protein, and up to 75% of their fat from animal products (meat, milk and eggs, plus fish). But all those animals are ultimately fed by plants – mostly grass, cereals, and pulses. Even so most people in the world obtain more than 80% of their energy and most of their protein and fat directly from plants.

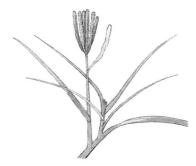

▲ **Figure 4B7a** *Cereals* *are the most important food crops (for instance, millet).*

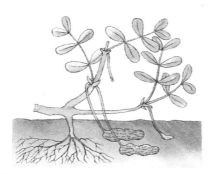

▲ **Figure 4B7b** *Next most important are the* **pulses** *(for instance peanuts). Pulses grow in poor soil because they have nitrogen-fixing root bacteria.*

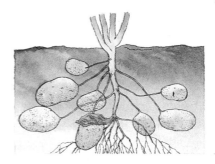

▲ **Figure 4B7c** *Third most important are* **tubers** *(for instance, potatoes).*

Fibres

Almost all plant cells have a tough coating of cellulose; and in many plants, some cells are long and thin but have especially thick cell walls. Such cells form **fibres**, many of which can be spun into threads and then woven into fabrics.

▲ **Figure 4B8a** *Cotton* plants (Gossypium *spp.)* have threads attached to their seeds which act as parachutes during wind dispersal.

▲ **Figure 4B8b** *Kapok,* for stuffing anoraks and sleeping bags, consists of seed fibres from the tropical kapok tree (Ceiba pentandra).

▲ **Figure 4B8c** *Fibres more commonly come from the* **xylem** *vessels. Fibres for* **linen** *come from the flax plant – the same plant as the linseed (*Linum usitatissimum*).*

▲ **Figure 4B8d** *Jute* (Corchorus spp.), *is used for ropes and tough fabrics.*

Timber

In many plants the cellulose walls of the cells in the stem become toughened by **lignin**. Cellulose toughened in this way is called **wood**, referred to commercially as **timber**. Foresters distinguish between **softwoods**, from the trunks of conifers; and **hardwoods**, from flowering trees such as oak. Softwoods are not necessarily soft, nor hardwoods hard. The softest timber of all is balsa: a 'hardwood'!

Timber products

The worldwide production of paper is now about 220 million tonnes per year. It is now mainly made from softwood pulp. The wood is pulped either mechanically, with giant rollers, or chemically, using hot sodium hydroxide (NaOH) or sodium sulphide (Na_2S) to dissolve the lignin and release the cellulose fibres. The pulp is then filtered on to wire mesh to drain, then pressed and rolled. Disposable nappies – with a market value of about £330 million per year in Britain alone – are also made from wood pulp. One pine tree will provide up to 1000 nappies.

Drugs

Plants are the world's chief source of drugs. They provide most of the effective drugs in traditional medicines, as used by 80% of people in the world. Western pharmacology recognizes 7000 plant-based medical compounds, now used in about one in four drugs in western medicine. Yet of the 250 000 flowering plants in the world, only 5000 have been tested for useful drugs in laboratories. Many more wait to be discovered.

▲ **Figure 4B9a** *The first modern oral contraceptives ('the pill') were produced from steroids from a yam, genus Dioscorea.*

▲ **Figure 4B9b** *Aspirin, originally from willow-bark, cures headaches and inhibits blood-clotting, which helps prevent heart attacks.*

▲ **Figure 4B9c** *Digitalis from foxglove regulates heartbeat.*

▲ **Figure 4B9d** *Cocaine and its derivatives from the leaves of the South American coca plant are anaesthetics, though dangerously abused by addicts.*

▲ **Figure 4B9e** *Fruits of the poppy, Papaver somniferum provide opium, again a dangerous drug and the source of heroin, but also of extremely useful pain-killers.*

Pesticides

Plants produce chemicals to ward off attack from pests, some of which are already extracted to form 'natural' pesticides. Some, like nicotine, have long been employed. The most commercially important these days are derivatives of pyrethrin, originally extracted from an African daisy, *Tanacetum cinerariaefolium*.

Improving plant productivity

Old fashioned trial and error and modern scientific investigation have ensured that cultivated plants are given growing conditions which ensure a good yield. But how could their productivity be further increased? One answer is to improve crop varieties by selective breeding, aided nowadays by genetic engineering. To achieve this requires not only a deep understanding of the mechanisms of inheritance but also a careful analysis of what improvements should most usefully be made.

Potatoes for all purposes

In 1993 Britain's farmers grew almost 6 700 000 tonnes of potatoes – more than 100 kg for each man, woman, and child – which sold in the supermarkets for £2.5 billion. Clearly Britain takes potatoes very seriously – and rightly. They provide at least as much fuel energy and protein per hectare as any cereal, and their protein contains many amino acids essential for human protein synthesis (see Figure 4B10). In Britain they are a significant source of vitamin C. Indeed potatoes provide a nearly complete diet (almost on their own they fed populations of poor people in the 19th century). But potatoes can still be improved – in three main areas.

▶ **Figure 4B10** *Nutrient content in potatoes, bread and meat (g 100 g⁻¹).*

	Boiled potatoes	Chips	Crisps	White bread	Lean beef steak grilled
Water	80	48	2.7	39.0	64
Energy (k joules)	335	1212	2228	974	692
Protein	1.4	3.0	6.3	7.8	28.6
Fat	0.1	18.9	35.9	1.7	6.0

Range and cultivation

Producers are always seeking improvements: for instance, better shape, greater uniformity and smoother skins. A particular need at present is to develop potatoes for the lowland tropics. Potatoes originated from the cool Andes mountains of South America and grow best in temperate climates – but they are much more nutritious than most tropical root crops.

Pest resistance

The catalogue of potato pests worldwide includes 128 insects, 68 nematodes, 38 fungi, 23 viruses, and 6 bacteria. Many do only minor damage but some are extremely destructive.

■ **Potato leaf-roll virus** (PLRV) and **potato virus Y** are troublesome in Britain. Potato viruses in general are carried by aphids – so virus control is largely a matter of aphid control.

■ The fungus *Phytophthora infestans*, known as '**potato blight**', destroyed virtually the entire potato crop of Ireland and western Scotland in 1845 – a time when poor people lived almost entirely upon potatoes. Many thousands died in this 'Potato Famine' and many others emigrated to America. British farmers may still spray potato crops up to ten times per year to protect against blight. More resistance is always needed.

- In Britain the nematodes – 'eelworms' – known as **potato cyst nematode**, or *Globodera*, almost stopped potato cultivation in East Anglia in the 1950s. Varieties like **Maris Piper** now have partial resistance but more resistant varieties are still being looked for.

Quality

Cooks need floury potatoes for baking, waxy ones for salads, and firm ones for boiling. No-one likes potatoes that blacken on cooking: a character which must be bred out of cultivated varieties. Crisp manufacturers want potatoes that take up only a little fat – much less than the 30 to 40% by weight which many varieties do. But they do not want them to turn brown when fried – which they do if they contain free reducing sugars.

Breeding better potatoes

Breeding programmes are divided into two phases.

- First the breeders try to produce a good, new variety by crossing, back-crossing and so on (see page 218).
- Then they must **multiply** the new 'improved' plant to produce enough seed for farmers to sow. This **multiplication** takes several years, and can be complicated because many crops do not **breed true** (see page 218) and so desirable new characters can be lost.

Potatoes reproduce **sexually** to produce seeds (in tomato-like fruits) and so can be crossed with other varieties as with any other crop. But they are also multiplied **asexually**. Potatoes are not roots, like turnips. They are **stem tubers** – the swollen tips of underground stems or **rhizomes**. When planted these tubers produce a whole new plant that is genetically identical to the parent: the parent and all its descendants form a **clone**. Potatoes can thus be multiplied asexually without losing desirable characters. Confusingly, potato tubers for planting are called 'seed potatoes'.

New genes from wild relatives

All European potatoes are varieties of a single species, *Solanum tuberosum*. But South America harbours 154 different species – and many of them contain genes that could help to improve *S. tuberosum* if only the cultivated species can be crossed with them. For example, the wild *S. berthaultii* has hairy, sticky leaves, which aphids find difficult to walk on.

More subtly, the leaves produce a chemical called (E)-beta-farnesene, which is extremely similar to an 'alarm pheromone' produced by the aphids themselves. 'Alarm pheromones' are chemical signals which some animals produce to warn their relatives of danger. So aphids are 'frightened' to land on *S. berthaultii*! Cross-breeding *S. tuberosum* with *S. berthaultii* is now producing hairy-leaved varieties that are more aphid-resistant.

Some wild relatives that contain useful genes cannot be crossed with *S. tuberosum* by sexual means but can be crossed using tissue culture. Thus *S. brevidens* contains genes that confer resistance to potato leaf-roll virus. Cultured cells of *S. tuberosum* have been fused artificially with *S. brevidens* cells to produce **somatic hybrids**. These can be grown into whole plants which retain the resistance to PLRV. Potatoes are also the first arable crops to be improved commercially by genetic engineering. For example, a 'promoter' gene has been introduced which enhances the genes that produce proteins.

Genes and heredity

The mechanisms of heredity – how it is that offspring resemble their parents, but are not exactly the same – have puzzled people for thousands of years. But no-one understood how it worked until an Austrian monk, working in a monastery in what is now the Czech Republic, began to provide the answer. The monk was Gregor Mendel (1822–1884). The foundations which he provided are outlined below.

The monohybrid cross

Mendel experimented with garden peas (*Pisum sativum*). He crossed plants with round seeds with plants that had wrinkled seeds, and showed that the resulting offspring (the first filial or F_1 generation) all had round seeds. He then crossed members of the F_1 generation together and found that their offspring (the F_2 generation) included some individuals with round seeds and some with wrinkled seeds. In the F_2 generation, the round-seeded offspring outnumbered the wrinkled-seed offspring in a ratio of 3:1 (Figure 4B11).

▼ **Figure 4B11** *The monohybrid cross.*

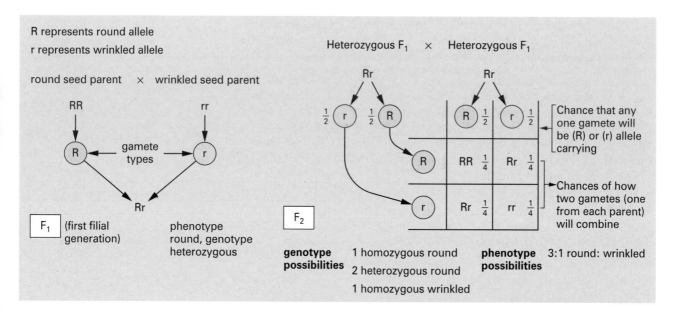

Mendel concluded that each expression of the seed coat character was determined (or controlled) by a discrete 'factor' which we now call a **gene**. He also concluded that every individual carries *two copies* of each gene; one inherited from the mother, and one from the father. However, he said, the gametes (eggs or sperm or pollen) must carry only *one* copy of each gene. Then, when the gametes fuse at conception, the resulting **zygote** again has two copies of each gene.

Mendel saw that genes for a character such as seed coat must exist in more than one alternative form which today are called **alleles**. It was clear, too, that some alleles are **dominant** over others; and ones that are dominated are called **recessive**. In peas, the round-seed allele is dominant over the wrinkled-seed allele – so the F_1 offspring of round and wrinkled parents all have round seeds, even though each of those offspring contains both a round and a wrinkled allele.

The allele for round seeds is represented by a capital **R**, and the allele for wrinkled seeds by **r**. (The lower case **r** shows that it is only a variant on the other form of the gene, **R**, but is recessive.)

For any one character each offspring may inherit the same allele from each parent, and it is then said to be **homozygous** for that character. Or it may inherit a different allele from each parent for a given character, and is then **heterozygous** for that character. An individual that is heterozygous in one character is said to be a **monohybrid**.

What the plant actually looks like is its **phenotype**. Its genetic make-up is its **genotype**. Clearly, plants with the round seed phenotype may have one of two different genotypes: either **RR**, or **Rr**. But only one genotype, **rr**, will produce a wrinkled phenotype.

These observations led Mendel to frame his First Law – the **Principle of Segregation**. This states that the two alleles in a gene pair separate when gametes are formed. Half the gametes carry one allele, and the other half carry the other. Mendel did similar experiments for another character in peas: green cotyledons versus yellow cotyledons. Again he found that there was a single allele for each expression of character, with yellow dominant over green.

The dihybrid cross

Mendel then set out to see what happened when homozygous peas with round yellow seeds were crossed with homozygous peas with wrinkled green seeds. Clearly, the resulting F_1 offspring are heterozygous both for seed coat and for seed colour; and so they are called **dihybrids**. The resulting F_1 offspring all have seeds that are both round and yellow: **R** dominates **r**, and **Y** dominates **y** (Figure 4B12).

But what happens when the F_1 offspring of the initial dihybrid cross are mated? The figure below gives the answer. Phenotypically, 9/16 of the individuals of the F_2 generation have round yellow seeds; 3/16 have round green seeds; 3/16 have wrinkled yellow seeds; and 1/16 – the 'double recessive' – have wrinkled green seeds. This is the famous 9:3:3:1 ratio.

Such studies led Mendel to his Second Law – the **Principle of Independent Assortment**. This states that 'genes for different characters are passed independently into the gametes, and inherited independently'.

▼ **Figure 4B12** *The dihybrid cross.*

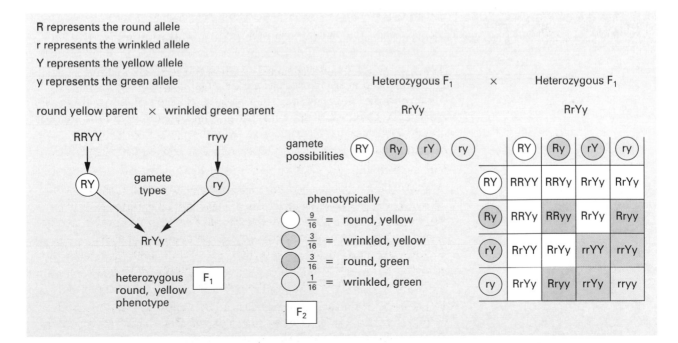

Making better crops

In principle it seems easy to improve crops; that is, to produce plants that grow faster, look or taste better or are more resistant to stress and disease – in fact to do whatever farmers, wholesalers, or consumers desire. First breeders select the best individual plants. Secondly they cross-breed individuals containing at least some of the characters thought desirable, hoping to produce offspring that combine these characters.

Problems with cross-breeding for better crops

What is 'best'?

Farmers obviously want crops that give a reliably high yield in the conditions they are able to provide and that are resistant to pests. But different people want different things and no one plant can combine all desirable characters. For example, barley plants use more energy to produce a gram of protein than a gram of starch. But the total grain yield is strongly related to the total starch content. So if a breeder tries to maximize protein content yield may be reduced. Breeding, in short, involves compromise.

Many crops are already excellent

Crop plants may lack just a few characters that can be found in their wild relatives. Wheat, for example, has many wild relatives (various grasses), which contain genes that give resistance to fungus diseases. So breeders cross the wheat with the wild grass to obtain the gene, but also acquire many undesirable features of the wild grass at the same time (such as low yield). So they take the first generation (F_1) cross between wheat and grass and cross-breed that with the original wheat – saving only those individuals in the F_2 generation which contain the resistance gene. By such repeated **back-crossing** breeders gradually dilute the contribution of the wild grass until only the desired fungal resistance character is left.

Crop plants do not always breed true

Some crops, like wheat and garden peas, are **inbreeders**; seed is produced from pollen and ova from the same plant. Such plants **breed true**: the offspring are very like the parents. But many other plants – like maize and most brassicas (including cabbages and turnips) – are **outbreeders**. The plants are only healthy and the yields high if the two parents are genetically different. Outbreeding species therefore produce highly heterozygous offspring. They all differ somewhat from the parents, so the breeder cannot quite be sure what they will be like.

One way around this problem is to **multiply** the crop by asexual means. Potatoes do not breed true if the flowers are crossed to produce seed. But in practice potatoes are multiplied by increasing the output of **tubers**, which are genetically all the same (see pages 214–15).

Another solution to the problem is to produce **F_1 hybrids**. The male and female parents are genetically uniform. But the males and females are different from each other. So the F_1 offspring are both heterozygous and uniform. But seed collected and grown from these will not be uniform.

Traditional breeding generally operates only within species

If breeders want to improve, say, tomatoes, they can do so only by crossing with other tomatoes. Genes that might be useful, for example, for pest resistance, that happened to occur only in peppers (capsicums) could not be introduced even though peppers and tomatoes are related.

New techniques

Nowadays, the techniques of **genetic engineering** enable breeders to introduce genes from any plant – or indeed from any other organism – into any plant. In practice, genetic engineering in plants combines two sets of techniques: **tissue culture** and **genetic engineering**.

Tissue culture

Individual slices of plant tissue – or even individual cells – can be kept alive in culture. The culture supplies everything – amino acids, sugars, oxygen, growth factors – which the cell would normally receive within the living plant. Some specialist plant tissues are now cultured to manufacture valuable materials – like cells of the *Cinchona* tree which produce the anti-malarial drug **quinine**.

In addition, many plant cells retain the quality of **totipotency**. That is, a single cell from stem or leaf can be multiplied to give rise to an entire new plant. In this respect, plants are quite different from animals. You cannot multiply a muscle or a skin cell to produce an entire animal.

Because plant cells are so often totipotent, tissue culture can be used as a rapid method of asexual reproduction, producing huge **clones** of offspring that are genetically identical to the adults. This is the basis of **plant micropropagation** and is especially useful in crops such as coconut which do not normally produce suckers or tubers and cannot be multiplied asexually by conventional means. Cultured cells can be subjected to genetic engineering more easily than can whole plants.

Genetic engineering

In principle, the basic techniques for genetic engineering in plants are the same as in bacteria (see page 200). Desired genes – stretches of DNA – are snipped out of the parent (donor) organism with the aid of restriction enzymes, introduced into **vectors** and then put into the new host (in this case cultured plant tissue).

There are three main problems.

- **To identify genes that really are worth transferring** into a host. It is not easy to find out precisely which piece of DNA produces which desirable character.
- **To find good ways of introducing the new gene into the host**. Vectors are often organisms which normally cause disease, and operate by integrating themselves into the host's genome. Key examples are the bacterium *Agrobacterium tumefaciens*, which causes tumours in plants, and various viruses. These disease organisms are modified so that they will introduce new DNA, but will **not** cause disease (see page 201).
- **To control the gene once it is in the new host**. For example, a gene intended to produce protein in the seed should not start producing that protein in the roots.

Breeding animals

Livestock are improved in the same ways as crops. Breeders begin by selecting individuals that have at least some of the characters they want, then they cross different individuals with different desirable characters, hoping to produce offspring that combine the good characters. In this way, each species becomes divided into breeds, each suited to a particular task. Breeds are the animal equivalent of plant varieties. But each species of livestock presents the breeder with its own particular problems.

Cattle

In Britain and the United States cattle are raised only for milk or beef (while some calves are raised for veal). Dairy cattle are intended to direct most of the energy they receive from food into milk production, and traditionally they were bred with skinny bodies and big udders. Ayrshires and Jerseys are examples.

Beef cattle by contrast were bred with big, round muscles, like Aberdeen Angus and Hereford. But the commonest breed by far these days is the Friesian or Holstein, which is 'dual-purpose'. Friesians produce enormous amounts of milk but they also produce calves big enough to be worth raising for beef (see pages 222–5).

In much of Africa and Asia cattle are vital work animals, pulling carts and ploughs. Traditionally oxen – castrated males – did the work and cows merely provided more oxen. But today scientists aim to provide multi-purpose animals that can pull a plough *and* also produce reasonable amounts of milk and meat.

Sheep

Sheep traditionally are kept for meat, milk, and wool. Nowadays in Britain meat (sold as 'lamb') is the chief output but in the past wool was more important. Traditional breeds produce just one or two lambs, once a year in spring, but breeders now employ three main methods to increase output. First they cross small-bodied ewes (which do not eat much) with a big-bodied ram to produce big-bodied, fast-growing lambs. In the second they cross-breed with varieties such as Dorset Horn which are able to breed all year round – to produce two litters per year, or at least three in two years. The third procedure is to cross with breeds such as Finnish Landrace which can produce up to five lambs at a time.

Pigs

Sheep and cattle mainly eat grass, which means they can be raised on food that human beings cannot eat. Wild pigs are omnivores, and their domestic descendants need a much richer diet. Traditionally they are fed largely on household scraps and other wastes – as they still are in China – but in western countries they feed mainly on grain. Thus modern pigs are raised on food that human beings could eat.

Pigs also differ radically from sheep and cattle in their reproduction. While wild sheep and cattle produce one calf or lamb each per year, wild pigs produce four to six offspring. But in modern intensive farms pigs commonly produce two litters per year and begin a third pregnancy, averaging at least 20 and up to 30 offspring per year. Partly because the output is so high, breeders have plenty to select from and modern pig-breeding has become extremely precise, with growth-rates and body shape (conformation) exactly geared to requirements.

New technologies

Animal breeding is being accelerated by new technologies of which five are outstanding.

- In **artificial insemination** or '**AI**', sperm from outstanding or 'elite' stud males is used to inseminate many different females. The technique is of most use in cattle in which (a) bulls are expensive to keep, (b) individual cows produce only one calf and (c) the sperm can be stored frozen (this has not so far been the case for pigs). In fact, AI technology is most advanced in cattle and human beings although conservation biologists make some use of it in zoos.

- *In vitro* **fertilization** or 'IVF'. Ova (eggs) are fertilized in a Petri dish by sperm obtained by AI to produce an embryo. Among farm livestock, the technique is again of most use in cattle. One great advantage is that outstanding (elite) females can be stimulated by hormone injections to produce several ova at a time, and to produce several batches of ova in a season. So a cow can give rise to a dozen or more calves in a year instead of only one. But the embryos cannot be raised to maturity in a Petri dish. IVF must be followed by embryo transfer.

- **Embryo transfer**. Here, the young embryo is introduced into the uterus of a 'foster' cow who is first given hormone injections to make her womb receptive. In this way, foster mothers who are not themselves outstanding genetically can give birth to the calves of elite dams (mothers) and sires (bulls). IVF is also now widely used in human medicine. Usually (but not always) the embryo is put back into the womb of the woman who first produced the egg.

- **Genetic engineering** is also now being employed in farm livestock – to some extent in cattle but especially in poultry. In mammals (like cattle) the new DNA is introduced to young embryos produced by IVF. In practice animals have been engineered (or **transformed**) for two main purposes. First, transformed animals may produce materials that are useful in human medicine. Thus sheep have been given genes for human blood clotting factors, which they then produce in their milk. These factors can then be used to treat haemophiliacs. Secondly, animals have been given special genes to make them more productive. Thus cattle given extra genes for growth hormone may produce more milk.

- **Cloning** may soon become economically worthwhile. Young elite embryos produced by IVF can be divided, and each individual cell may develop into a complete embryo. Already up to five sheep embryos have been produced from a single eight-cell embryo.

All techniques of animal husbandry and breeding, both the new and the traditional, raise many kinds of question – political, economic, and ethical, as well as scientific. For example, are they worthwhile? Are they humane? Are they good for the consumer? Can they be practised in the Third World, as well as in rich countries? Some of these issues are raised in Chapter 4C.

Biological production in context

Science in the world of human values

Chapters 4A and 4B were concerned with the scientific principles of growing organisms and harvesting useful products from them. Once scientific concepts are applied in the wider world outside the laboratory, human values must also be considered. In the case of biological production there are additional questions raised by the fact that living systems are involved and because biological production sprawls across much of our countryside. These issues are explored in this chapter.

The roast beef of old England?

Meat in one form or another is a common element in the diet of the developed world. Since World War II British farmers have been encouraged to produce more meat so that most of us eat it at least once a day. In order to obtain an ever increasing yield of meat from a static or decreasing amount of land, many animals are now reared intensively. Large numbers of animals are raised on a relatively small area of land. This means that they cannot rely solely on their natural food, grass, because there simply isn't enough to go round. The animals are fed concentrated food with high levels of the nutrients necessary for growth. The high cost of such feedstuffs is offset by not investing capital in the large area of farmland which would otherwise be necessary to grow all the food that the animals need.

John Durrant, an animal nutritionist, describes the way in which a typical beef animal is reared. 'To a large extent the beef industry is a by-product of the dairy industry,' he says. 'Dairy cows produce as many male calves as female and these bull calves are obviously of no use on a dairy farm. Dairy farmers either have a small part of their farm devoted to rearing calves for beef, or they sell them on at about ten days old for somebody else to do the rearing.' Much of the art of profitable beef breeding is to grow cattle to the size at which they are slaughtered for meat as quickly as possible at the lowest cost.

▶ **Figure 4C1** *An average weight gain of around 0.6–0.8 kg a day produces these 600 kg beasts from the 50 kg calf born almost 2 years ago.*

The male calves weigh around 50 kg at birth and are allowed to suckle at the cow for a few days to gain natural immunity from the colostrum in milk. They are then separated from the cows and moved in small groups into calf units where they are fed on reconstituted milk for about 6–7 weeks. At the same time they gradually eat increasing quantities of calf pellets. John explains that growing calves need a high proportion of protein and other nutrient sources for metabolism in their diet because they are laying down large amounts of new tissue such as brain, skeleton and muscle. Calf pellets provide these nutrients. They are made from a wide variety of materials including cereals, sugar beet pulp and molasses from the sugar industry, peas, beans and the by-products from the oil-seed industry. By the end of this 6–7 week period each calf will have consumed around 25 kg of milk powder and 20–30 kg of calf pellets!

During their first winter the calves stay inside eating silage (about half a tonne each) and between a quarter and a half tonne of pellets, of a different grade containing less protein. By the spring, the animals weigh around 200 kg and towards the end of April they are turned out onto pasture for the first time. They are brought in again in October for the second winter when they are fed up to slaughter weight – most beef animals are slaughtered at between fifteen and twenty-four months of age. By the time of slaughter they weigh around 500–600 kg. As John points out, the system can produce quite astonishing daily weight gains – the more intensively reared bulls may gain up to 1.5 kg a day.

◄ **Figure 4C2** *Farmers need to buy large quantities of calf pellets to feed their calves. Farmers can discuss the type of pellet required with their supplier.*

Intensive farming has developed to meet the demand for large quantities of economically produced meat of uniform quality and appearance. It sometimes receives a bad press, but most farmers care very deeply about their livestock and make conditions as comfortable and clean for their animals as possible.

Once the animals leave the farm, considerable effort is made to reduce the time it takes for their meat to reach the market. The carcasses are passed on to the supermarket or butcher and sold quickly, generally without the hanging and preparation which would once have been needed to produce a tender joint of meat. Proteolytic (protein digesting) enzymes may be injected into the carcass, or electric shocks applied to try and mimic the tenderizing effect of old-fashioned hanging.

A different way of doing things

▲ **Figure 4C3** *Carol and Philip Hockey in their farm butcher's shop.*

Carol and Philip Hockey believe that intensive farming is not the only way to produce meat economically. Over the last 24 years they have built up a farm and a farm butcher's shop from almost nothing. Their animals are all reared in a traditional way on foods grown on the farm. Their meat is additive free and sold at no more than the equivalent in the supermarket partly because they avoid the distribution costs necessary to bring meat from the farm to a wide range of retail shops.

Carol and Philip enjoy a very comfortable standard of living. As Carol says, 'We would like to see our farm as a model for the future. But for other people to want to follow that model, it's no good being well meaning, hard-working and hard up – you have to show that you are a commercial success. We started with a third of an acre and reared dairy calves for other farmers, using traditional methods – I didn't even realize there was another way of doing things until at the first farm show we attended someone came up and said, "so you're the funny farmers from Verwood!".'

For 'funny farmers' it must be said that Philip and Carol have done well. They are people of strong principles who work hard and feel deeply that other farmers could follow where they have led. As public concern over the production of meat increases and the demand for meat falls, Carol thinks that their farm could be valuable in demonstrating to the world in general, and other farmers in particular, that there is a viable alternative to intensive farming.

How is beef produced at the Hockeys' farm? Unlike many beef producers Carol and Philip do not buy up unwanted bull calves from dairy farmers. They decided to set up their own breeding lines, choosing pure-bred Charolais cattle for their large carcasses and meat with virtually no hidden fat, responding to the consumer demand for leaner meat which has been growing over the last decade or more. They have five Charolais bulls and these are crossed either with Charolais cows or with pure bred Welsh Black cows which produce good milk for suckling their calves and are a very hardy breed. The calves which result from these crosses weigh about 50 kg at birth.

The calves stay suckling from their mothers for six months, weaning themselves naturally. The group of calves which have been born at around the same time are kept together as they grow, for cattle form attachments to each other and the Hockeys feel that staying with the same group reduces the stress of separation from their mothers. The cattle graze freely in meadows throughout the spring and summer until in November they are brought, still in their association groups, into open barns where they decide their own sleeping and feeding areas.

In the barns they are fed a combination of hay and silage both cut from the Hockeys' own meadows. The combination of straw and droppings which is regularly removed from the barns during the winter is rested for two years and then spread onto the pasture lands as manure. Carol explains, 'Both the cattle and soil are regularly tested for any mineral deficiencies and the cattle provided with mineral licks during the winter. Any deficiencies in the pastures must be made good through the animals' feed to prevent the problem being perpetuated. We may be traditional but we are scientific. In the spring the animals are returned to the pastures until they are around eighteen months of age, weighing 650 kg, when they are sent for slaughter.'

▼ **Figure 4C4** *It is important for Carol and Philip to be sure they get their own animals back from the slaughterhouse. They have special dispensation from the Ministry of Agriculture for an ear to be left on their animals with their identity tag attached.*

On return to the farm the carcasses are hung in the traditional way for ten days to mature and tenderize the meat. At this point the carcasses are butchered (cut into joints for sale), again on the farm itself. The Hockeys not only sell beef but also make their own additive- and colouring-free beefburgers and sausages, which can be bought at the farm shop. Carol says that in their system the meat yield per animal is the same or greater than animals reared more intensively. They believe that the stress-free life maximizes the growing potential of the animals.

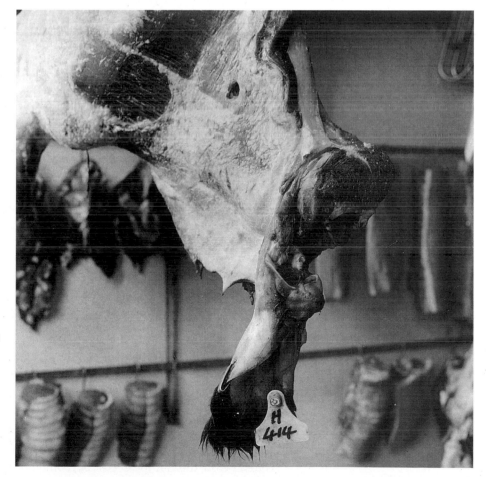

Market restrictions on agricultural products

If food production were left solely to the free market, supplies would fluctuate widely from year to year because of weather and disease and, as a result, prices would also vary widely. These fluctuations could destabilize economies. Therefore many governments interfere in the market for agricultural produce to try and guarantee stable food supplies at reasonable prices.

Agricultural support in the United Kingdom (UK)

In most sectors of agriculture in the UK there are controls over production. Blockades on shipping during World War II showed how dependent this country was on imported agricultural produce. Since the war, all governments have pursued a policy of increasing food production at home, aiming towards farming **self-sufficiency**. Subsidies were paid to farmers to encourage them to produce more crops and materials.

The farming industry has been very successful at increasing production. In 1955, less than 50% of all food and animal feed was home produced, but now home produced food and feed represents almost 60% of consumption. In 1970, the UK imported 6.16 million tonnes of wheat and barley, but in 1990 the UK exported more than 6 million tonnes of cereals.

Agricultural support in the European Union (EU)

The UK has, for many years, been a member of a much larger trading organization, the European Union (EU). Europe as a whole operates a system of agricultural support, known as the **Common Agricultural Policy** (**CAP**). In the past the Policy dictated that the more food produced, the more support was paid out. If too much was produced and free market prices were pushed down as a result, the EU would step in as a buyer, pay a higher guaranteed price, and put the surplus into store or sell it at a discount price. This led to overproduction of some commodities on a Europe-wide basis, especially in milk and cereals. Measures have been taken to restrict output. These measures apply across the EU, penalizing all countries, whether they are overproducing or not.

For example, when European **quotas** were introduced to limit milk production in 1984, the UK was not self-sufficient in liquid milk. Since the quotas nevertheless forced farmers to cut milk production here, this country remains less than self-sufficient in liquid milk. Over Europe as a whole in 1994, dairy farmers only produced 85% of the volume of milk they produced in 1983. Dairy farmers have been allowed to buy and sell their production quota entitlement, thus allowing them to expand or contract their farms. Because it is effectively a licence to produce milk, the quota is worth a lot of money.

These restrictions on production have arisen for two main reasons. First, there is a heavy **economic cost** of supporting surplus production. Farmers are guaranteed prices for their produce, which may be much higher than the world market price. Storing or selling the excess produce incurs further costs. The surplus can be kept as a strategic reserve, but this needs expensive storage facilities. Alternatively, it can be sold onto the world market, but only at discounted prices (often below the European cost of production).

The second reason is **political**. There have been significant international moves towards freer world trade, in which subsidies, quotas and export guarantees are discouraged. The legal device for organizing world trade is **GATT** (**General Agreement on Tariffs and Trade**). The 1993 agreement demands that less support is given to the export of surplus production and that markets across the world should open up to more imported products.

At present, **export subsidies** help the EU and other nations sell their surplus grain onto the world market cheaply. The taxpayer meets the cost of the difference between the high cost of production and the low selling price. These same countries limit access to their own markets by **import restrictions**. These take the form either of limits on how much of a product can be imported (quotas again), or of a tax on imports to increase their price and protect more expensive home produced goods.

Even before these pressures on production and sale from the GATT agreement, the EU was already reforming CAP because of the huge cost of subsidized production. Within the EU there has been a 35% cut in grain support prices and cuts in both milk and beef support prices. The Union oilseed trade has now moved to world price levels.

Since 1993, nearly all farmers have been required to **set aside** a minimum of 15% of their cropped land to qualify for subsidies from the remaining 85% of the area. They also receive a payment per hectare for their set aside land in partial compensation for loss of income from that land. Any grower who chooses not to comply with this system receives no support.

Agricultural subsidy as a social support

If it were not for subsidies from both EU and national sources, much of the UK's hills and uplands would not be farmed. The maintenance of farming families here means that familiar landscapes are preserved, many of them designated **Areas of Outstanding Natural Beauty** or **National Parks**.

Without the combination of restrictions and support, some areas of the country would be farmed very intensively, while others would be left to revert to scrub. Even with the current system in place, rural depopulation is a growing concern in most EU member states. Because farming incomes are poor in comparison with those in many other industrial sectors, many people are tempted away from the industry by declining incomes and job prospects.

In addition to the EU-wide approach to agricultural support, there are voluntary initiatives from national governments, which often have an environmental benefit. Among the most successful of these are the UK's **Environmentally Sensitive Areas** schemes, which pay farmers to change their farming system or practices for environmental benefit.

But there are also some national policies which restrict the ability of UK farmers to compete with their counterparts in other EU countries. For example, the UK is phasing out certain types of sow housing on welfare grounds, and has acted on its own in this area. This means that while there may be valid animal welfare reasons for adopting this policy, it puts UK pig producers at a disadvantage, because their costs of production are higher.

Farm animal welfare

Consumers want cheap but high quality animal products. Most people also want farm animals to be kept well. However, they seem unwilling to accept that good welfare costs money and that this extra cost must be borne by the consumer. Farmers are under pressure to produce animal products cheaply and therefore animal welfare may be put at risk. What are the laws and regulations that govern the well-being of animals and how effective and useful are they?

The main legal framework

Most people in western societies accept that farm animals can be used for human purposes as long as they have a good life and a quick and humane death when they have to be killed. The term generally used in this context is **animal welfare**. It is useful to replace it with the longer description **physical health and emotional well-being**. These words have strong positive implications that health is more than the absence of disease and well-being is more than the absence of distress and discomfort.

The principal piece of UK legislation which applies specifically to the welfare of farm animals is the **Agriculture** (**Miscellaneous Provisions**) **Act 1968**. This Act, among other things, makes it an offence, punishable by fine or imprisonment, to cause unnecessary pain or distress to livestock being kept for farming purposes on agricultural land.

But proving, in a court of law, that an animal was suffering from unnecessary pain or distress can be difficult. It is accepted that an obviously diseased or injured animal must be in pain or distress – especially if a veterinary surgeon testifies that in his/her professional opinion the animal has indeed suffered.

The suffering may be considered unnecessary, for example, if the owner had not taken steps to have it relieved in some way, by having the animal humanely killed, for instance. The beating of an animal, especially if there are signs of bruising, is usually taken as an obvious cause of pain. Animals also show recognizable and obvious signs of fear. In such extreme cases, suffering is relatively easy to prove. The real problems come in less blatant situations.

Many people believe (with some scientific evidence to support them), that as well as physiological needs for food, water, shelter and so on, animals have behavioural needs. They are genetically programmed to carry out certain behaviour patterns and may suffer if they are not allowed to fulfil these needs.

For instance, hens in battery cages cannot dust bath or scratch the ground, as they do when free in farmyards. Are they suffering when so deprived? Pregnant sows, confined to sow stalls with solid floors, cannot root in the ground as they would if kept outside in fields. It has been suggested that so-called **bar-gnawing** (shown by some confined sows by champing or biting on their stall fittings, especially the horizontal metal bars set in front to stop them moving forward) is a sign of frustration. Many feel this frustration is a form of emotional distress, but it has proved difficult to have these behavioural signs taken seriously in court.

Other codes and welfare regulations

A somewhat different approach to suffering has been through the **Codes of Recommendation for the Welfare of Livestock** made under the Agriculture (Miscellaneous Provisions) Act 1968. These codes are only advisory and failure to adopt them is not necessarily an offence under the Act.

However, they do have legal standing; a stock-keeper cannot claim ignorance of them and he/she disregards their advice at his/her own risk. If the stock-keeper should be prosecuted under the 1968 Act for causing unnecessary pain or distress, failure to observe provisions in the Code may be used in evidence against him/her.

A farmer who adopts the recommendations in the Codes is unlikely to cause animals to suffer. However, the **Preface** to the Codes states that nearly all livestock management systems impose restrictions on stock and that some of these can cause unacceptable degrees of discomfort or distress by preventing animals from fulfilling their basic needs. But the detailed recommendations in the Codes – if adopted – should ensure animals' general comfort, health and welfare.

More recently the principles behind the Codes have been expressed by the **Farm Animal Welfare Council** – the official advisory body to Agriculture Ministers – as the so-called **FAWC Five Freedoms**. A good animal management system should provide:

- **freedom** from hunger and thirst – by ready access to fresh water and a diet to maintain full health and vigour
- **freedom** from discomfort – by providing an appropriate environment, including shelter and a comfortable resting area
- **freedom** from pain, injury or disease – by prevention or rapid diagnosis and treatment
- **freedom** to express normal behaviour – by providing sufficient space, proper facilities and company of the animal's own kind
- **freedom** from fear and distress – by ensuring conditions and treatment which avoid mental suffering.

Once animals are moved off the farm to market or slaughterhouse, their welfare is covered by the old but effective **Protection of Animals Act 1911** (1912 in Scotland). These Acts make it an offence to cause unnecessary pain, suffering or distress to any captive or domesticated animal.

Statutory Orders have been made under the **Animal Health Act 1981** to safeguard the welfare of animals in markets and while being transported within the UK. The **Slaughterhouse Act 1974** and **Regulations** made under it specify who can kill animals at a slaughterhouse and how it should be done.

There is much good legislation for farm animal welfare and serious efforts are made by the majority of animal owners to fulfil the requirements of the law. But there are problems. Market forces encourage the development of large intensive units, there is continual pressure to increase efficiency, with more animals looked after by smaller numbers of stock-keepers. It can be difficult to give animals individual attention. Nevertheless it remains essential to seek a balance between the needs of society and the needs of the animals which society uses.

Engineered excellence – or scientific nightmare?

Biting into a ripe tomato expecting sweet-flavoured flesh but getting a mouthful of tasteless mush happens to us all. Fruit and vegetables get over-ripe, tired and 'past it' very quickly. Because they are picked long before they are ripe to be transported and stored in supermarkets they often have surprisingly little taste. The prospect of flavoursome, ripe tomatoes, strawberries, sweetcorn and mushrooms, all with a long storage life, is a dream for farmers, shopkeepers and shoppers alike. Genetic engineering is promising to make the dream come true.

▲ Figure 4C5

Genetic engineering promises more

Around the world about one third of all the food produced is destroyed by pests – animals, plants and fungi. People in the developed world object to finding caterpillars in their cabbages. Fruit and vegetables should be pest-free, and farmers spray regularly with chemicals designed to kill off the animals and fungi which might damage the crop. In developing countries the appearance of the food is less important than the amount. Sprays are used to ensure acceptable crop yields. Biological pest control (see page 232) will solve some of the problems – but wouldn't it be wonderful if crop plants could be persuaded to make their own pesticides? There would be no need to spray chemicals on crops any more, and no worries about the effect of pesticides on people and the environment.

In fact all of these things and more are now possible – and some of them are already happening – through genetic engineering (see page 200). Genetically engineered yeasts, which use sugars more efficiently than natural yeasts, are now used regularly in bread production in the UK. Human genes have been engineered into sheep cells so that the sheep produce human proteins in their milk. One of these proteins is used by haemophiliacs to make their blood clot, instead of relying on the same protein extracted from human blood, which can expose them to the risk of contracting AIDS and hepatitis. Genetically engineered plants and animals promise an exciting new world, where diseases can be controlled and crops can be designed to grow in the desert, taste of what we choose and bring about their own pest control – but there are concerns as well.

More and more evidence shows that it is better for human babies to be fed human breast milk than to be fed modified cow's milk (formula) from a bottle. Babies would certainly be better served by breast milk. Wouldn't it be marvellous if by using genetic engineering cows could be made to produce milk more similar to human milk? All babies could have the benefits of breast milk.

Problems with the application of genetic engineering

The 'Flav Savr' tomato is a genetically engineered tomato soon to arrive on our supermarket shelves. It has had an **antisense gene** inserted which switches off the synthesis of the gene coding for the enzyme **polygalacturonase**, which causes the softening of tomatoes as they ripen. Because such genetically engineered tomatoes are less likely to be damaged when they are harvested and will last longer on the supermarket shelves, they can be left to ripen naturally on the plant much longer than their non-engineered relations. This should mean that they have a much better flavour. So far, so good – but some questions need to be addressed.

Will the public be happy at eating engineered produce – indeed, will they be given a chance to decide? In 1994 a group of ordinary people, who were not scientists, were brought together to look at these issues (a 'consensus conference'). They felt that all genetically engineered products should be labelled as such, but the industry itself is not happy with this. They would prefer not to draw attention to the origins of novel foodstuffs.

If genetically engineered plants and animals cross-breed with wild populations of plants or animals, this could seriously damage the balance of the environment. In some cases this risk can be overcome by making most of the individuals infertile. The possibility of plants producing their own pesticides is an ecologically sound step which will reduce the need for chemical spraying and so reduce poisons in the food chain, but there are two main worries. One is that if pests gradually become resistant to the effects even more powerful chemical sprays will be needed in the future. The other is that if the pesticidal chemicals are present within the tissue of fruit and vegetables rather than sprayed on the outside, they can't be washed off – and so may actually increase the intake of toxins. These are concerns which need answering.

Despite these concerns, it is important to keep an open mind. It is also important that scientists and food technologists explain clearly the possible risks as well as the benefits of their work. Lack of information can lead to fear of the unknown. The very least that agricultural scientists can do is to inform people of the facts about their work so that the public in general have a chance to assess the advantages and the dangers. The debate will continue.

Pest control

In 1970 the flood plain of the Sepik River in Papua New Guinea was a vast expanse of water which supported 80 000 people. Their food was fish (for protein) and the wild sago palm (for carbohydrate), and they travelled everywhere by canoe. Ten years later in 1980, the whole region was covered with a thick, choking mat of *Salvinia* plants, which spread over 250 km² and weighed 2 million tonnes. Villages were deserted and a way of life was on the verge of destruction. This is a dramatic example of how destructive plant pests can be.

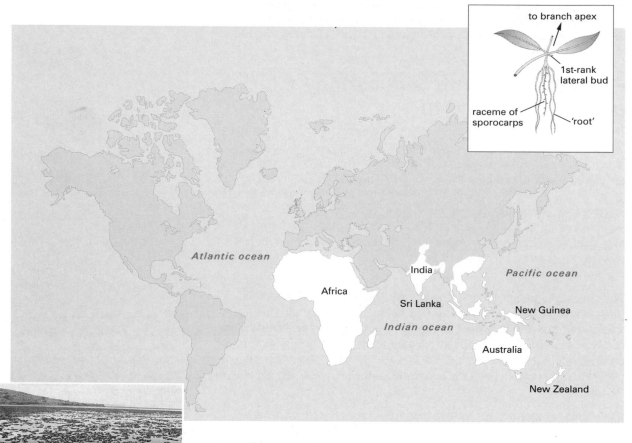

▲ **Figure 4C6** *By the 1980s* Salvinia *had spread to Africa, India, Southeast Asia and Australasia, destroying the ecology of huge areas of water.*

Papua New Guinea was not the only country affected by this plague. The floating fern *Salvinia* is native to some of the countries of South America where as part of a balanced, stable ecosystem it causes no problems. But people introduced it first to Sri Lanka and then to other areas without realizing the damage which would result.

Why did the weed spread so rapidly?

Salvinia only reproduces asexually, making new plants at the end of rhizomes very rapidly when the temperature and the nitrogen levels in the water are right. Because there were no natural pests of the weed in its new homes, it could grow unchecked. Bits would break off and get carried along the natural waterways from one lake to another, and so more choking weed mats would form.

Controlling the weed proved to be almost impossible. In small bodies of water it could be cleared using machines, pesticides or by hand but these options are almost always too expensive and unworkable. Biological control was the only remaining possibility.

Using one pest to destroy another

For many years the main weapons against animals or plants which become pests have been chemical sprays. A great deal of modern food production is due to the success of this chemical warfare. But people are becoming increasingly concerned at both the environmental effect of chemical sprays and the effect of buying expensive pesticides on the fragile economies of developing countries. **Biological pest control** involves using one living organism to control the activities of another. Employing the natural enemies of a pest species can be just as effective at control as expensive chemical sprays, without necessarily causing harmful environmental effects. Biological control, and **integrated pest management**, where biological control is combined with very limited chemical intervention, are seen by many as the way forward.

If an animal introduced to control a weed actually preferred to feed on food crops it would be a disaster and so great care must be taken with biological pest control. There have been very few mistakes – but when things do go wrong the consequences are severe. In 1967 giant African land snails were introduced to Tahiti for food. Some escaped, bred rapidly and became pests. A carnivorous snail, *Euglandina*, was introduced without proper research as a biological control to destroy these giant snails. It had no effect on them – but wiped out hundreds of other snail species which were found only on Tahiti and the surrounding islands! No-one yet knows the long-term effects of a mass extinction like this, but the balance of life on the island can never be the same again. With genetically engineered microbes being lined up as a major new form of biological pest management, controls will need to be stricter than ever.

Does anything eat *Salvinia*?

To control the spread of *Salvinia*, scientists needed to know as much as possible about the plant and where it came from. It took some time to get the information needed, but after several years of work three possible 'biological controllers' had been found, all feeding on *Salvinia* – a weevil, the larvae of a moth and a grasshopper. In 1980 a few thousand weevils were released at Lake Moondarra in Australia. The weevil population increased to over 100 million and destroyed 30 000 tonnes of *Salvinia* in less than a year! The moth and the grasshopper made no real difference to the *Salvinia* situation.

The benefits of biological control of *Salvinia* by weevils have been enormous. In Sri Lanka it has been estimated that the benefit:cost ratios for the weevil compared to other control efforts are 53:1 in cash terms, and 1673:1 in terms of hours of human labour. In Papua New Guinea the economic benefits have not been accounted specifically – but the villages by the side of the Sepik River are full of people again, their traditional way of life restored to them by a weevil.

▼ **Figure 4C7** *The wonder weevil! Introducing* Cyrtobagous salviniae *to a lake choked with* Salvinia *means that within a year the weed will have been reduced by 99% and the area will have become a real lake again.*

Monoculture – good or bad?

Chapter 4B showed how few species of crop plant are cultivated on a wide scale. World agriculture is tending to produce an even narrower range of crop varieties, bred to tighter and tighter specifications. The resulting monocultures, uniform 'stands' of the same variety grown over large areas, have advantages – but also raise problems.

Pressures towards uniformity

To some extent this trend is inevitable. Some crops are simply more productive, tastier, and convenient than others – and farmers grow them where they can.

Monoculture has advantages. Farmers like uniform crops because then they know how the plants respond to particular treatments – for example, whether they yield more useful, saleable components with extra nitrogen fertilizer, or simply produce more bulk of parts which have no commercial value. And consumers like to know what they are getting.

But monoculture also has dangers. A completely uniform crop can be wiped out by a single pest or disease – as the 'lumper' potatoes grown in Ireland in the 19th century were laid waste by the fungus *Phytophthora infestans* in 1844 (see page 214).

In the long term, breeders need to retain genetic variation to be able to breed new varieties for the future. Changing markets demand new varieties. So too do changing environments. Climatic variation, such as the possible 'Greenhouse Effect', may demand crops that grow in warm climates, but must also thrive in the changing daylengths of temperate latitudes. Most tropical crops, adapted to the more constant day lengths found in the tropics, do not grow well at higher latitudes.

Breeders everywhere must strive to conserve ancient varieties of all the main crops, with their increasingly rare genes; and also wild plants, especially those related to crop species, from which useful genes might be transferred.

Genes in store

In theory there are several ways to conserve plants which contain rare genes. They can be maintained in **reserves** in the wild, or on special farms that serve as 'reserves' of traditional crops. Many are grown in botanical **gardens**, like the Royal Botanic Garden at Kew. Others may be sold through the horticultural trade, to be grown by amateurs in their own gardens. But most are simply stored as seeds in **seed** or **gene banks**.

Varieties of the world's major crops are held in international gene banks established by the Consultative Group on International Agricultural Research (**CGIAR**) founded in 1971 by the Food and Agriculture Organization of the United Nations (**FAO**) and the **World Bank**. For example, the International Potato Center (**CIP**) in Peru stores 12 000 different '**landraces**' (traditional varieties) of potato.

In this country Kew holds 5000 wild species as seeds, relatives of valuable crop plants. Commercial seed companies hold their own collections and the Henry Doubleday Research Organization at Coventry preserves rare vegetables – particularly valuable now that the EU is reducing the kinds grown commercially.

The problems with gene banks

The principles of gene banks seem easy: collect seed and keep it clean, cool and dry until it is needed. But there are three big problems.

Collection

Each species or variety in store must be represented by different seed samples known as **accessions**. Between them the accessions should contain all the alleles (see page 216) present in the original species (or variety). But it is not easy to gather the right accessions. If collectors simply focused on the commonest types, they would miss out the unusual varieties which may contain the rarest and possibly most valuable alleles. If they focus on these unusual varieties, then samples will not be representative of the whole.

Rare plants are often found only in difficult country or on remote farms. Many traditional crop varieties ripen over a long interval (one of the snags of non-uniformity!) and tropical plants in general may be non-seasonal (perhaps tending to flower and set seed intermittently and at random), so timing the collection of seeds is not easy.

Storage

Many seeds can be stored satisfactorily by drying. Thus, every 1% reduction in water content below 14% generally doubles the life of a seed. Onion seed with a 4% water content is said to last at least 1000 times longer than with 14%. Below 4%, however, the seed may be damaged as fats begin to oxidize. Keeping the seed cool also helps: commonly between +4°C and −20°C. These days seed is often stored in liquid nitrogen at −196°C; but recovery from such low temperatures is not always easy.

Drying does not always help preservation. In particular, many tropical seeds are **recalcitrant** – which means they are damaged by drying. Valuable species with recalcitrant seeds include coffee, cacao (cocoa), citrus, rubber, and many palms like coconut and oil palm. One possible solution is to store them as germinated embryos.

Germination

Many seeds germinate as soon as they are warmed and moistened, but others enter a state of **dormancy** and need particular conditions to 'reawaken' them. Spring-sown cereal seeds generally need a period of cold to imitate winter.

Genetic engineering to save the day?

Nowadays any gene from any organism can in theory be introduced into crop plants by genetic engineering (see page 200). Future crops might have a basic genome with extra genes from scores of other species. Perhaps the ideal variety of any species would be uniform in the genes for productivity (for example, yield or shape) but contain a huge variety of alleles for disease resistance. But these options cannot be realized unless breeders have access to the greatest possible variety of genes!

The movement for gene banks raises huge political issues which inhibit progress. For example, should seeds from remote areas belong to the people who own the land – or to the companies or agencies who collect that seed and save it from extinction?

Fertilizers. The role of the big N

Plants draw nutrients from the soil. They need nitrogen (N) in the largest amount. Farmers must be sure to apply the right amount of nitrogen fertilizer at the right time. If the soil contains more soluble nitrogen than plants can use, it disappears into the water or atmosphere to become a serious pollutant. With too little nitrogen, plants become pale and spindly; with too much they become lush, cereals grow too tall and fall over (lodge). A well-grown cereal crop takes up about 200 kg of N ha^{-1} year^{-1}.

Nitrogen is always cycling

Nitrogen is constantly circulating between the soil, the atmosphere, water in all its forms, and organisms, live and dead (see Figure 4C8).

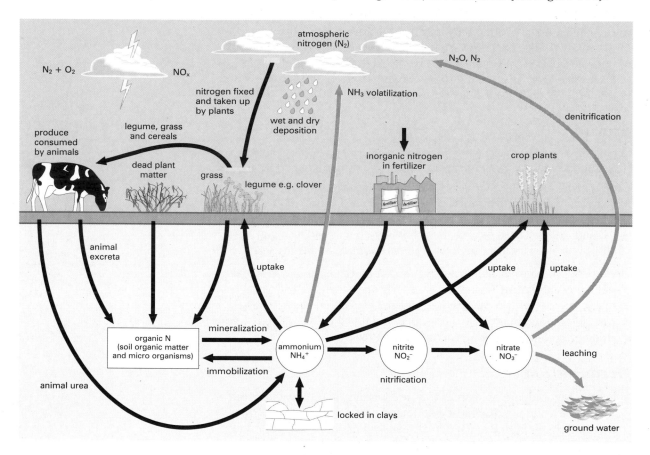

▲ **Figure 4C8** *The nitrogen cycle.*

Nearly 80% of the air is N_2, and it also contains ammonia (NH_3), and oxides such as N_2O and NO_2. In part these compounds are produced naturally (for example, ammonia from urine) but nowadays they arise as pollution from heavily fertilized fields and from traffic fumes. Ammonia and oxides of nitrogen in the atmosphere may be washed into the soil by rain – and provide 50–60 kg of nitrogen per hectare per year, about 25% of the annual needs of a cereal crop! But these airborne materials are damaging. They form nitric acid – a source of **acid rain**.

But the main natural route from atmosphere to soil is by nitrogen fixation. This process occurs in all environments, including the ocean. Various bacteria (including **Cyanobacteria**, once known as 'blue-green algae') are able to trap N_2 in the soil (or ocean surface) and convert it to ammonium ions NH_4^+ (a reduction process).

More significant for western growers are the nitrogen-fixing bacteria that live **symbiotically** in the roots of plants. Most important are the *Rhizobium* bacteria which live in the root nodules of **leguminous** plants such as peas and beans (pulses) and of green 'forage legumes' such as clover and vetches. Pulses can grow without added nitrogen fertilizer, and grass needs far less fertilizer if it is grown together with clover in a 'mixed sward'. But *Rhizobium* bacteria are choosy – each kind grows on only a few host species, so breeders and genetic engineers now look for more versatile and tolerant strains.

The accumulation of dead organic matter in the soil (**humus**) commonly contains thousands of kg of nitrogen ha^{-1}. This nitrogen is in 'organic' form. Plants cannot use it until soil bacteria break down the organic materials and release it as NO_3^- or NH_4^+.

Farmers also provide extra nitrogen in the form of fertilizer. **Inorganic** fertilizers are almost all 'artificial', generally salts of ammonium, such as ammonium nitrate. There are also organic fertilizers such as **manure** (animal excrement mixed with straw), **slurry**, which is excrement in water (washings from the animal houses), **compost**, which is rotten organic material of any type, and **green crops** such as clover, which can be ploughed in.

From fertility to pollution

There are forces at work in the soil tending to remove the nitrogen which the farmer adds. The crop's intended nutrient is turned into a pollutant of air and waterways.

NH_4^+ can volatilize straight into the atmosphere as ammonia gas (NH_3). **Nitrifying** bacteria turn the NH_4^+ to nitrate and **denitrifying** bacteria convert this NO_3^- to nitrogen and oxides of nitrogen, which also float off into the air. These are the most important reasons for soil loss of nitrogen during summer.

If the soil is too cold for crops to absorb nitrogen – or the crops are harvested and the soil is bare – surplus NO_3^- is **leached** out of the soil by rain, and **runs off** into the waterways. It may accumulate in groundwater – and in high concentrations can be dangerous. It converts to nitrite, NO_2^-, which in humans can combine with the haemoglobin in the blood. This inhibits oxygen uptake and in babies may lead to **methaemoglobinaemia** or 'blue baby syndrome'. More commonly, excess nitrogen running into ponds or lakes leads to **algal blooms** – excess of algae, which die and then rob the waterway of oxygen, so that everything may die. Run-off of nitrogen occurs mainly in winter.

This run-off can be caused by both excess artificial fertilizer and organic manures applied at the wrong time: slurry on bare autumn fields is among the worst culprits. Recent research at the Rothamsted Experimental Station in Hertfordshire has shown that the main source of run-off in the 1980s was grassland that was ploughed up during World War II to make way for arable food crops. The nitrogen from the rotting grass has taken more than 40 years to work its way down to the groundwater.

Biological production and the British landscape

The principles which govern the productivity of farming and forestry are the same as those underlying the healthy survival of natural communities of plants and animals. Nevertheless, the demands of farming and the needs of wildlife are often thought to conflict. It is essential to produce food and other products efficiently. Is it inevitable that economically viable farming can only occur at the expense of the country's wildlife?

The origins of the countryside

It has been difficult for a long time to draw sharp boundaries between natural and man-made environments. Much of the countryside of England and Wales, which many people find so attractive, is highly artificial; largely the result of decisions taken by farmers and other users of the countryside in the 18th century about what they wanted the land to provide. Even the 'wildest' parts of Britain's landscape have been heavily influenced by human activity. The task today remains what it has probably always been, to create a countryside to meet a variety of human needs which includes provision for wildlife.

Until recent centuries most of Britain was covered in deciduous oak forest. That is Britain's 'natural' environment. Now only scraps remain, for example, in parts of the New Forest. The 'open' country that dominates today was originally created by cutting down the woods (**deforestation**) – mostly for timber, and to make way for farming. Even the 'wild' heather moors of the Scottish Highlands are 'man-made' – and maintained as heather for the sake of the grouse. Most forests in Britain today are commercial 'softwoods' (see page 213).

In theory society can produce any kind of landscape thought desirable – but only if people agree on the basic principles. Unfortunately, they don't. At one extreme, some people would sweep away all wild creatures that are mildly inconvenient (like the otter) while at the other there are those who want to restore the original post-Ice Age fauna: the bear (last seen in Britain in the Middle Ages); the beaver (last recorded in Loch Ness in the 16th century); and the wolf (extinct in England from the 17th century, and in Scotland by the 18th). That would mean restoring much of the original deciduous forest.

A reasonable compromise can probably be achieved between these two positions. Thus, most people would endorse present attempts to reintroduce the white-tailed eagle to west Scotland. This was Britain's commonest large bird of prey until the 19th century, when it was shot and poisoned in the false belief that it killed lambs. Yet most people probably feel that Britain is not yet ready for bears. But there are perpetual battles over particular areas of land. After all, any one space might be a wildwood, a motorway, a farm, or a hypermarket. In an island of 60 million people compromise is essential, but how can it be achieved?

▲ **Figure 4C9** *The European wolf.*

How Britain might be designed

Policies for farming and forestry are of most significance as these activities occupy most of the space. The Government, consumers, and the EU between them decide how much of each farmed commodity is produced. The task is to arrange the necessary farms and commercial forests to meet all the needs of people and accommodate wildlife.

To achieve this the different habitats with their specialist species – for instance, salt-marshes, raised bog and chalk downland – have to be identified. Parts of these can then be conserved as refugia (refuges for particular species) or as **Sites of Special Scientific Interest**, **SSSIs**, which are especially interesting habitats. Such patches may then be protected by law as **nature reserves**.

But isolated patches are extremely vulnerable. They suffer **edge effects** – encroachment by the surroundings. Farmland weeds invade isolated woodland refugia. Ancient ponds once surrounded by pasture or woodland may now be encircled by arable fields and starved of nourishing autumn leaves. The water-table of wetlands may fall if the surrounding region is drained for farming. It has not proved possible to maintain the Large Copper Butterfly on the Fens of Cambridgeshire, as drainage has changed the vegetation. Over time, the range of species in isolated reserves usually diminishes which is known as **species relaxation**.

A key issue is that populations of animal species generally need to be big if they are to be viable in the long term. Countries that still have large animals already feel this. Yellowstone National Park in the US is huge – yet it is not big enough to hold viable numbers of grizzly bears. In Britain, many bat populations may be too isolated to survive.

This difficulty can be countered in part by **wildlife corridors** between habitats, which link different small populations into one big one. Thus many species of woodland bats are unwilling to fly across open fields, but they will follow a hedge. So a well-placed hedge can link bats from different woods that otherwise would be isolated.

Landscapes are mosaics: successions of patches that each serve different purposes and yet support and complement each other. The habitats of all animals are mosaics. They may sleep in one place (like a hole in a tree), feed in another, and perhaps migrate to different areas in winter and summer. The animal's habitat includes all the different places – and the conservationist must understand their importance and maintain them all.

The entire countryside could be thought of as a mosaic. Some might be **intensive farmland**, growing the maximum amount of product in the minimum space. The less land needed for food, the more would be left for other purposes, which could include areas of wilderness, for instance deciduous forest, wetland, and heath.

Some land might be managed for **extensive farming**, which can be both productive and wildlife-friendly. An example is traditional dairy pastureland, rich in plants such as cowslip, which is now a rare species in Britain since there are so few such traditional pastures left. The chalk downland of the south of England used to be grazed by sheep which prevented shrubs and trees from growing. A wide variety of herbaceous plant species continued to grow on the grazed areas, while at the same time farmers could make a living from the meat and wool which was produced.

In the end, economic factors will control what happens. The appearance of our countryside, in all its diversity, is the historical consequence of people organizing the land to make a living from it. How the landscape looks in the future will depend on how people can make a living from it in the 21st century.

Thoughts and actions

1 Distinguish between biotechnology and industrial microbiology.

2 What are the differences between eukaryotes and prokaryotes?

3 Write a list of the main differences between mitosis and meiosis.

4 Describe the relationship between molecular DNA, chromatids and chromosomes.

5 What are the features of DNA which make it suitable as genetic material?

6 a Write a narrative containing the terms:
   - codon
   - transcription
   - base-pairing
   - translation
   - pyrimidines
   - nucleotide
   - mRNA
   - replication
   - uracil
   - ribosome
   - gene
   - alkaptonuria
   - purines
   - amino acid
   - DNA.

   b Rewrite your account for a popular science book. You must explain the ideas about genes and how they control cell behaviour and allow cells and organisms to resemble their parents without using jargon or technical terms.

7 Distinguish, quoting examples, between primary and secondary metabolites.

8 What is exponential microbial cell growth and why does it occur?

9 What differences in culture conditions might there be between a system for producing acetone from the bacterium *Clostridium acetobutyrium* and the antibiotic cephalosporin from a filamentous fungus?

10 Chapter 4B began with the story of the plant products used to produce and maintain cricket bats. What are the materials and their specific plant sources which go into the manufacture of:
   a newsprint
   b a hammock
   c a sailing boat built of traditional materials and
   d a ready-made vegetarian pasta dish and its packaging?

11 The new technology of genetic engineering raises many questions. A group of interested people are forming a committee to discuss the issues, but they are not scientists. Produce a short explanation to help them understand the technology using the following terms:
   - DNA ligase
   - plasmid
   - palindromic sequence
   - retrovirus
   - transformation
   - restriction endonuclease
   - recombinant DNA
   - protoplast
   - vector
   - DNA cloning
   - gene therapy.

12 Distinguish clearly between physical and biological containment of genetically engineered organisms.

13 Human clotting factor 8, which is used to prevent bleeding in haemophiliacs who lack the gene for producing this factor themselves, has been produced by genetic engineering since 1991. What might be the advantages of this engineered factor 8 compared with the natural product purified from donated human blood?

14 Draw up lists of the external variables which govern the growth of **a** microbial cultures and **b** green plants. Explain the similarities and differences.

15 Consider three widely grown food crops; wheat, peas and potatoes. Using information from tables in Chapter 4B, the Reference section and elsewhere, work out which crop provides the best yield of fuel energy and protein for human consumption, with the most economical use of fertilizer.

16 Green pods are dominant to yellow pods in pea plants. Pure breeding green-podded peas are crossed with pure-breeding yellow-podded peas. What will be the genotypes and phenotypes of the F_1 and F_2 generations of plants produced from these pure-breeding parents?

17 Pea pods can either be full or constricted. Full is dominant to constricted. What phenotype and genotype ratios will be obtained from F_1 and F_2 generations of pea plants bred from pure-breeding full, green podded and pure-breeding constricted, yellow-podded parents?

18 Mendel obtained F_1 plants from crossing tall- and short-stemmed parents. If these F_1 plants were crossed with short-stemmed plants, what would be the genotypic and phenotypic results?

19 Ripe tomatoes can be either yellow or red. Plants with these two phenotypes were crossed as follows.

Parental phenotype	Phenotype of offspring
red x red	54 red
red x red	41 red, 14 yellow
red x yellow	65 red
yellow x yellow	59 yellow
red x yellow	29 red, 26 yellow

a What phenotype is dominant?
b What are the genotypes of the parents and offspring in each cross?

20 In chickens, there are two, independently assorting genes which control the shape of the comb on the head. They are designated R and P genes, each with a dominant and recessive allelic alternative (R and r; P and p). Any genotype containing at least one dominant R and one dominant P (R-P-) will give a **walnut** comb, the genotype R-pp produces **rose** comb, rrP – **pea** comb and rrpp **single** comb.
a How many different genotypes will produce the rose phenotype? What are these genotypes?
b If you obtain offspring numbers of 31 walnut, 28 rose, 10 pea and 9 single from crosses between walnut and rose parents, what are the genotypes of the parents?

21 In humans, the main colour of the eye is controlled by a single gene, with a dominant allele for brown and a recessive allele for blue.
a Joan is brown-eyed and pregnant. Her mother had brown eyes, her father had blue. Joan's partner, Martin, also has brown eyes. Both his parents were brown eyed. What is the probability that Joan and Martin's baby will have blue eyes?
b David and Mary Smith both have blue eyes. Could any of their children have brown eyes?
c Peter and Margaret are both brown eyed. They have four children of whom two, Jane and Michael, have blue eyes. What are Peter and Margaret's eye colour genotypes?

22 Gardeners can buy packets of F_1 hybrid vegetable seeds. These are usually more expensive than seed for standard varieties of vegetable. Why is this? Can you draw up a list of the advantages which plants grown from such F_1 hybrid seed might have over ordinary varieties?

23 A great deal of effort in plant biotechnology has been devoted to engineering resistance of crop plant species and varieties to herbicides.
a Outline the principles of one technique for engineering such resistance.
b Explain why achieving this objective is seen as desirable.
c What disadvantages might there be in widespread cultivation of crops resistant to herbicides?

24 The first genetically engineered (transgenic) food plant to be made available in shops and supermarkets was the 'Flav Savr' tomato. This seemed good news for the consumer enabling supermarkets to sell much tastier fruit. Conventional tomato varieties are picked green so that they are firm to handle and then ripened artificially with ethylene gas. To try and avoid them going squashy they do not undergo the long flavour developing process – so they are firm but tasteless! The 'Flav Savr' ripens naturally without going soft.

However, a large number of objections are being raised to the introduction of the 'Flav Savr' tomato. Through discussion and investigation, compile a list of these objections. How would you counter these objections? What is your own opinion about the introduction and sale of 'Flav Savr' tomatoes?

25 New technology is being applied to the breeding of both plant and animal species. List the techniques used for plants and animals separately. Explain the differences in terms of the physiological differences between plants and animals.

26 You have a plot of land $25\,m^2$. What vegetable would you plant on this land if you wanted to maximize the yield of **a** carbohydrates, **b** protein and **c** fat from this plot? What approximate yield of each of these three crops would you expect to get?

27 Refer to Figures R34.1 and R34.2 in the Reference section, which list some of the common pesticide residues left in food, together with the LD50 toxicity values of herbicides and other common ingested food and drug substances. The numbers suggest that pesticide intake is generally low and that herbicides are not so toxic as common food and drug substances.

a Do you think that most people believe that herbicides and pesticides are as harmless as these figures seem to suggest?

b Can they be taken at face value? How would you criticize these figures and how they are presented?

c Public understanding of science issues is often strongly influenced by images presented in the media. Take the information in this question and use it to produce two pamphlets to be handed out at a big agricultural show. One is for the National Farmers Union (NFU) and the other for an environmental group like Friends of the Earth.

28 A summary of the overall objectives of the Common Agricultural Policy of the European Union lists the following key themes:

- to increase agricultural productivity
- to guarantee security of supplies
- to stabilize markets
- to provide stable prices for consumers and
- to protect the living standards of farmers.

Is the policy achieving its aims? What are its disadvantages? Do its benefits outweigh the problems?

29 Compare the main features of the legal frameworks for health and safety of human workers in laboratories, of farm animals, of the food and medicines which we buy in shops and pharmacies, and those governing genetically engineered organisms. What ethical principles are involved in each case ? How do these differ in the different frameworks?

30 Nitrogen is the element which plants need to draw from the soil in the greatest quantity in order to grow.

a From data in the figures in the Reference section, calculate how many kilograms of nitrogen are applied each year to

- the wheat crop and
- the barley crop in England and Wales.

b If no nitrogen fertilizer were applied, by about how much would grain yields fall in the first year?

c Estimate the amount (in kg) of nitrogen which flows into lakes and rivers every year from the fertilizer applied to wheat and barley combined.

d Nitrogen on the fields is beneficial, increasing crop yields and helping in the production of cheaper food. But nitrogen in rivers and lakes causes many environmental problems. What are they and how might they be prevented?

31 If wheat yields 7 tonnes of grain per hectare and potatoes about 35 tonnes of tubers per hectare, calculate the protein yield of the two crops per hectare. Are you surprised by the result?

32 Boiled potatoes contain about 10 mg of vitamin C per 100 g. Oranges give about 50 mg per 100 g. Are potatoes or oranges the most important source of vitamin C in Great Britain?

33 An average man needs about 10 000 kJ of fuel energy per day. If he lived solely off potatoes (and this is not so ridiculous, people have survived on diets composed almost entirely of potatoes for quite a long time) he would need 3.4 kg of potatoes to provide 10 000 kJ.

a How many kg of potatoes would be required per year to meet his needs?

b Given that the average annual yield of potatoes is 36 tonnes per hectare, how many square metres of land would be needed to provide the year's total dietary supply of potatoes?

c There are about 5.6 million hectares of arable land in Britain. If all this was devoted to growing potatoes, how many people (surviving by eating only potatoes) could this land support? How does this number relate to the present population of Great Britain?

UNIT 5

Controlling movement and energy

Movement control

On the skids

Speed kills, and there is no one who knows that better than the traffic police who have to investigate the causes of road traffic accidents. Sometimes, the only evidence they have to go on is a thin black trace of rubber on the road, the sign of a fast-moving vehicle's sudden braking. Some straightforward physics helps to determine just how fast the vehicle was travelling at the moment it braked.

▶ **Figure 5A1** *Traffic police record details of the positions of vehicles involved in an accident. Accurate measurements allow them to deduce the sequence of events leading up to the crash.*

Black marks

A red saloon car speeds along a straight stretch of open road. Suddenly, the driver puts her foot hard down on the brakes. The car skids to a halt, leaving a trail of black skid marks on the tarmacadam road surface, and the driver gets out. Two police officers step out from the verge and congratulate the driver on her handling of the car.

This is part of a police investigation of a road traffic accident. The red car has been involved in an accident on this stretch of road, and the police are carrying out tests to find out how fast it was travelling at the time. The owner has claimed that he was travelling below the speed limit; the only objective evidence the police have to go on is the length of the skid marks and the nature of the road surface.

To find the car's speed, the police need to know two things: over what distance was the car slowing down (equal to the length of the skid marks), and what was its **deceleration**? Deceleration is the rate at which its speed was decreasing; it is a negative **acceleration**. There are two ways to find the car's deceleration. One is to measure the time the car takes to come to rest from a known speed in the skid test.

$$\text{Deceleration} = \frac{\text{decrease in speed}}{\text{time taken}}$$

The alternative method for determining deceleration involves investigating the friction between tyres and road surface. When a car brakes so that its wheels lock, the tyres skid over the surface of the road. The deceleration is determined by how smooth the road is; this can be measured using a sled test. Sections of car tyre are fixed to the underside of a board or sled, and this is dragged along the road. The force needed to drag a weighted sled gives a measure of the drag factor of the road surface, and this can be used to calculate the deceleration of the car. Figure 5A2 shows the deceleration possible on different road surfaces.

$$\text{Drag factor} = \frac{\text{force to drag sled}}{\text{weight of sled}}$$

then: deceleration = drag factor $\times g$

Once the car's deceleration has been determined, this information is combined with the stopping distance measured from the skid marks to deduce the speed at which it was travelling when the driver started to brake.

$$\text{Speed}^2 = 2 \times \text{deceleration} \times \text{distance travelled}$$

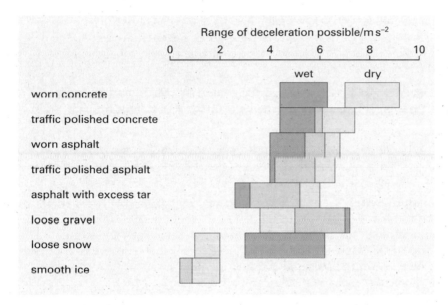

◀ **Figure 5A2** *The deceleration of a car depends on the state of the road surface. It is generally harder to stop on wet roads.*

More evidence

Other information about vehicle speeds comes from the amount of damage done to the vehicles involved, and from the positions of bits of debris thrown into the air by the impact. Again, careful measurements are essential to determine the positions of fragments; from the distances they have travelled, it is possible to deduce their initial speeds.

Heavy goods vehicles have a tachometer built into their speedometer. This 'spy in the cab' keeps a continuous record of the speed of the lorry, which can prove invaluable to the prosecution or the defence in circumstances where it is necessary to establish the truth of a driver's claims about speed of travel just before an accident. Perhaps one day all vehicles will be fitted with a device which can store as much information about distance, speed and acceleration as the black-box flight recorder fitted in most passenger aircraft. Until then, the officers who carry out these investigations will have to carry on with their painstaking measurements and calculations to establish a reliable picture of just what happened to make those black marks on the tarmacadam highway.

Measuring movement

In studying something which moves, there are four important quantities which need to be measured in order to describe its motion: distance, speed, acceleration and time. There are a variety of techniques used to measure these quantities. Sometimes, a quantity is measured directly; at other times, its value may be deduced from other measurements. In order to process measurements electronically, for example with a computer, it is desirable to have sensing devices which give an electrical output.

Position and distance

Camera rangefinders use **ultrasound pulses** to determine the position of the object being photographed. These high frequency (40 kHz) sounds reflect back from the target; a timing circuit measures the time taken for the return trip, and from this *time-of-flight* method, the distance can be found.

A robot arm in a factory may include several position sensors. **Micro-switches** detect when the arm reaches the limit of its working range, and automatically prevent the device from swinging into a zone where it might collide with other equipment. As one segment of the arm moves, it turns a **variable resistor** or **potentiometer**. As the resistance changes, this provides a changing voltage which indicates the position of the arm.

A **reed switch** is a magnetically operated switch; it has a springy metal strip which closes a circuit when a permanent magnet is brought close.

Another electromagnetic method is used to detect the arrival of a car at traffic lights. A wire **induction loop** is buried in the road; when a car passes over, the metal body changes the strength of the magnetic field around the coil, and this is registered by the traffic light controls.

An **optoswitch** has two parts: a light emitting diode (LED), together with a photodiode or phototransistor to detect the light. In one arrangement, the shaft of a motor has alternating black and white stripes. The white stripes reflect the light, and so the detector produces a series of voltage pulses as the shaft rotates. In this way, the precise position of the shaft and its rate of rotation can be found.

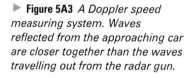 **Figure 5A3** *A Doppler speed measuring system. Waves reflected from the approaching car are closer together than the waves travelling out from the radar gun.*

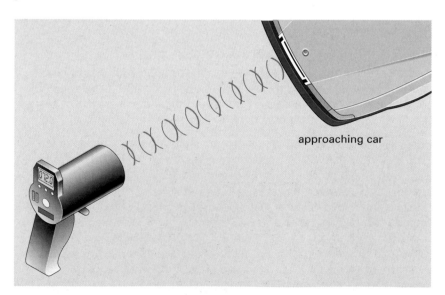

approaching car

Speed

Police speed traps use two different approaches to measure the speed of a moving vehicle. The more old-fashioned **radar** approach is a time-of-flight method like the camera rangefinder. The instrument transmits pulses of radiowaves and calculates the distance from the time taken for the waves to reflect off the target and return to a sensor. Further calculation gives the rate of change of distance, i.e. the speed.

A more direct method uses the **Doppler effect**. As radio waves reflect from a moving target, their frequency changes. It increases for a vehicle approaching the speed patrol, and decreases for a vehicle moving away. This comes about because an approaching car intercepts an increased number of radio waves, and so the number of waves reflected each second is greater.

Light gates are similar to optoswitches. A timing circuit measures the time interval when a moving object interrupts a light beam. Provided the length of the object is known, the speed can be calculated (Figure 5A4a).

Acceleration

An **accelerometer** is any device used to determine the acceleration (rate of change of speed) of a moving object. A number of different principles are used: for example, a pendulum in an accelerating vehicle hangs at an angle to the vertical, and the angle can be used to determine the acceleration. Alternatively, a heavy weight is placed on a pressure measuring device. As the vehicle accelerates, the pressure increases.

Light gates can also be used to determine acceleration. Since the measurement requires *changes* of speed to be found, the object which interrupts the light beam must be more complex (Figure 5A4b). Alternatively, two or more light gates may be used.

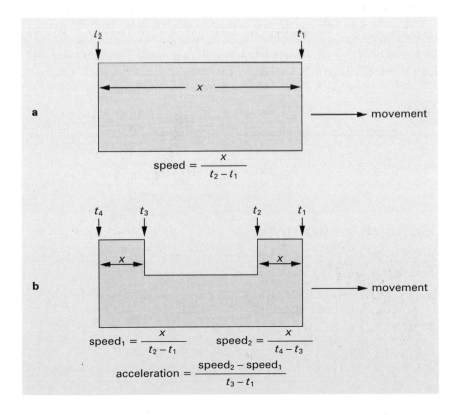

◀ **Figure 5A4** *Cards designed to interrupt a light beam for measuring **a** speed, and **b** acceleration.*

$$speed = \frac{x}{t_2 - t_1}$$

$$speed_1 = \frac{x}{t_2 - t_1}$$

$$speed_2 = \frac{x}{t_4 - t_3}$$

$$acceleration = \frac{speed_2 - speed_1}{t_3 - t_1}$$

Equations of motion

A car accelerates away from traffic lights. Friction slows a moving conveyor belt. A computer disc drive spins into action. All of these examples of motion involve changing positions, speeds and accelerations. In order to describe motion, it is necessary to start with some simpler situations. The equations of motion (kinematic equations) describe motion with constant acceleration.

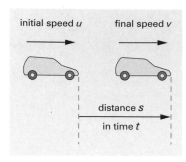

▲ **Figure 5A5** *Defining quantities during steady acceleration.*

Defining quantities

An object is accelerating if its speed is changing. Its **acceleration** is the rate of change of its speed. The **equations of motion** discussed here apply to an object moving with constant acceleration in a straight line. They are a *description* of the object's motion. The *explanation* of its motion, in terms of forces, is dealt with on page 255.

The speed of an object increases from an **initial speed u** to a **final speed v** in **time t**. In this time, it travels a **distance s**. It has **acceleration a**. These are the five quantities which are related to one another by the equations of motion.

Quantity	Symbol	SI unit
Initial speed	u	$\mathrm{m\,s^{-1}}$
Final speed	v	$\mathrm{m\,s^{-1}}$
Time	t	s
Distance	s	m
Acceleration	a	$\mathrm{m\,s^{-2}}$

The equations of motion

Equation	Comment
1 $v = u + at$	Comes from definition of acceleration: $$a = \frac{\text{change in speed}}{\text{time taken}} = \frac{(v - u)}{t}$$
2 $s = ut + \frac{1}{2}at^2$	When acceleration $a = 0$, simplifies to $s = ut$, i.e. distance = speed × time
3 $s = \frac{(u + v)}{2} \times t$	i.e. distance = average speed × time
4 $v^2 = u^2 + 2as$	An equation which does not involve time t

Solving problems

In using the equations of motion to solve problems, it is helpful to follow a straightforward procedure.

Step 1 List the quantities which are known, together with the quantity or quantities to be found.

Step 2 Select the appropriate equation connecting these quantities.

Step 3 Substitute values in the equation.

Step 4 Solve the equation.

Note that, because the equations are all related to one another (they are not independent), there may be more than one which can be used in any particular situation.

In the examples which follow, the quantities are shown with their units throughout, for correctness. This makes it clear that units are correctly balanced within the equations. For routine calculations, it may be simpler to omit units when substituting in the equations.

Example 1

A car leaves the traffic lights with an acceleration of $2.0\,\mathrm{ms}^{-2}$. How fast will it be moving after $5\,\mathrm{s}$?

(Note that u is zero, because the car starts from rest.)

Substituting in **equation 1**: $v = u + at$

gives $v = 0\,\mathrm{ms}^{-1} + 2\,\mathrm{ms}^{-2} \times 5\,\mathrm{s} = 10\,\mathrm{ms}^{-1}$

Hence the car's speed after $5\,\mathrm{s}$ is $10\,\mathrm{ms}^{-1}$.

$u = 0\,\mathrm{ms}^{-1}$
$a = 2\,\mathrm{ms}^{-2}$
$t = 5\,\mathrm{s}$
$v = ?$

Example 2

How far will the car in Example 1 travel in the 5 s time interval?

Substituting in **equation 2**: $s = ut + \frac{1}{2}at^2$

gives $s = 0\,\mathrm{m} + \frac{1}{2} \times 2\,\mathrm{ms}^{-2} \times (5\,\mathrm{s})^2 = 25\,\mathrm{m}$

Hence the car travels $25\,\mathrm{m}$ in $5\,\mathrm{s}$.

$u = 0\,\mathrm{ms}^{-1}$
$a = 2\,\mathrm{ms}^{-2}$
$t = 5\,\mathrm{s}$
$s = ?$

Example 3

A traffic police officer measures skid marks on the road which extend for a distance of 40 m. From the nature of the road surface, she estimates the deceleration of the lorry involved as $5\,\mathrm{ms}^{-2}$. How fast was the lorry travelling when the driver applied the brakes?

(Note that the acceleration is *negative*, since the lorry is slowing down.)

Substituting in **equation 4**: $v^2 = u^2 + 2as$

gives $0\,\mathrm{m}^2\mathrm{s}^{-2} = u^2 + 2 \times (-5\,\mathrm{ms}^{-2}) \times 40\,\mathrm{m}$

Rearranging gives $u^2 = 400\,\mathrm{m}^2\mathrm{s}^{-2}$

and hence $u = 20\,\mathrm{ms}^{-1}$

Hence the lorry must have been travelling at a speed of $20\,\mathrm{ms}^{-1}$ when the brakes were applied.

$v = 0\,\mathrm{ms}^{-1}$
$s = 40\,\mathrm{m}$
$a = -5\,\mathrm{ms}^{-2}$
$u = ?$

Distance–time graphs

Figure 5A6a shows a distance–time graph for an object moving at a steady speed. The distance moved increases at a steady rate, and this is shown by the fact that the graph is a straight line.

Figure 5A6b shows a distance–time graph for an object whose speed changes. Its speed gradually increases – it might be a car running away down a hill – and this is shown by the graph getting gradually steeper.

It is possible to deduce the speed of the object from its distance-time graph. In the case where speed is constant (Figure 5A6a), the speed is simply given by the gradient (slope) of the straight line graph. This follows from the relationship $\text{speed} = \left(\dfrac{\text{distance}}{\text{time}}\right)$.

Where speed is changing, the gradient of the graph is no longer constant (Figure 5A6b). To find the speed at a particular instant, it is necessary to draw a tangent to the curve at the point of interest, and find the gradient of the tangent.

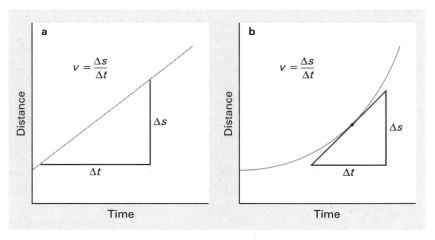

▲ Figure 5A6

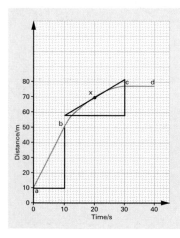

▼ Figure 5A7

Numerical example

Figure 5A7 shows the distance–time graph for a car approaching a junction. Qualitatively, this graph shows an initial straight section (AB) as the car travels at a steady speed. Section BC is curved, indicating decreasing speed as the car slows down. Finally (CD) the line is horizontal, indicating that the car has come to a halt – its speed is zero.

The graph can also be used to give quantitative information.

Section AB:

$$\text{speed} = \text{gradient of line} = \frac{50\,\text{m} - 10\,\text{m}}{10\,\text{s}} = 4\,\text{m s}^{-1}$$

At point X:

$$\text{speed} = \text{gradient of tangent at X} = \frac{(82\,\text{m} - 58\,\text{m})}{(30\,\text{s} - 10\,\text{s})} = \frac{24\,\text{m}}{20\,\text{s}} = 1.2\,\text{m s}^{-1}$$

Speed–time graphs

In the case of speed–time graphs, it is possible to deduce both acceleration and distance travelled.

Figure 5A8a is a straight line speed–time graph. This represents the motion of an object moving at increasing speed; in this case, with constant acceleration. The gradient of the graph gives its acceleration.

Figure 5A8b is a curved graph, indicating that the speed is not changing at a steady rate. The acceleration is changing, and must be deduced from the gradient of the tangent to the graph. Where the graph has positive gradient, the object is speeding up (accelerating). A negative gradient corresponds to slowing down (decelerating).

The distance travelled by the object in any time interval is found from the area under the graph. (This is because the area is a speed multiplied by an interval of time.) For a straight line graph (Figure 5A8a), this calculation is relatively simple, since the area is a combination of rectangles and triangles.

For a curved graph (Figure 5A8b), the area under the graph is harder to calculate. It may be found by a variety of means: counting squares, or cutting out and weighing, or by approximating the curve to a series of straight lines.

Numerical example

Figure 5A9 shows the speed–time graph for an object falling through air into a liquid. Its motion can be described qualitatively.

Section AB: constant acceleration through the air.
Section BC: acceleration decreasing as it approaches terminal velocity in the liquid, because of the liquid's viscosity.
Section CD: falling at a steady speed in the liquid.

The graph can also be used to give quantitative information.

Section AB:

$$\text{acceleration} = \frac{20\,\text{ms}^{-1} - 0\,\text{ms}^{-1}}{2\,\text{s}} = 10\,\text{ms}^{-2}.$$

At point X:

$$\text{acceleration} = \frac{(27.5\,\text{ms}^{-1} - 21\,\text{ms}^{-1})}{(6\,\text{s} - 2\,\text{s})} = 1.6\,\text{ms}^{-2} \text{ approx.}$$

Section AB:
distance travelled = area 1 $= \frac{1}{2} \times 2\,\text{s} \times 10\,\text{ms}^{-1} = 10\,\text{m}$.

Section BD:
distance travelled = area 2 = 146 m approx (by counting squares).

(Note: each square represents $0.2\,\text{s} \times 1\,\text{ms}^{-1} = 0.2\,\text{m}$.)

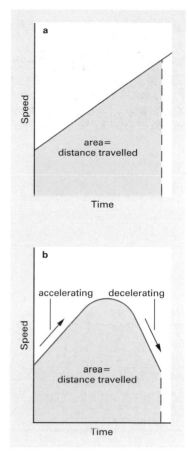

▲ **Figure 5A8**

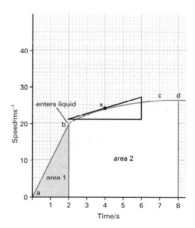

▲ **Figure 5A9**

Creating an impact

A karate chop that breaks a brick in half, a pole-vaulter falling to Earth, and a Formula 1 racing car hitting the safety barrier – three vivid images created by Dr Majid Sadeghi, Director of the Cranfield Impact Centre, illustrate the importance of control during collisions. The Impact Centre studies collisions of real objects so that they can understand how safety can be designed into road and rail vehicles, aircraft and packaging.

Classifying collisions

What links Majid's diverse examples of collisions? They must all be **inelastic**. In an inelastic collision, there is no bounce. As the pole-vaulter lands, she does not want to bounce back into the air or absorb energy through her own body – the landing mat is there to absorb her kinetic energy. Similarly, the karate expert does not want his hand to bounce off the brick, nor endure load for any length of time, which is why he chooses brittle material.

Kinetic energy is the energy that something has when it is moving. In a **perfectly elastic** collision, an object retains its kinetic energy as it bounces off an obstruction at the same speed but in the opposite direction.

Majid describes the Impact Centre's work: 'We study collisions of real objects rather than idealized masses. For economy, we try to use computer studies but we can only make these reflect real behaviour when we have experimental data to use in the calculations. So we also have to do a lot of experimental work, sometimes on components, sometimes – though less often – on full-size vehicles complete with dummy drivers.

'Early in any study we have to decide just what are we trying to keep safe, and what will damage it. The answer is that people are more important than objects. In a car collision, for instance, there's a lot of kinetic energy to be absorbed, and it's better that it should be absorbed by the car than by the passenger.'

> **Kinetic energy** is the energy possessed by any moving object. For a body of mass m moving at speed v,
>
> kinetic energy $E_k = \frac{1}{2}mv^2$

▼ **Figure 5A10** *A racing car on the test rig at Cranfield Impact Centre, ready for a test run – energy-absorbing nose and dummy driver in position.*

A crumpled nose

When a racing car runs into a barrier, it stops in a fraction of a second. Its kinetic energy must be absorbed safely, or the driver may be seriously hurt or killed. Richard Jones, a test engineer with the Centre, is carrying out a full-scale test on a new energy-absorbing nose for the Formula 1 cars of the Pacific Racing Team. The new nose, a composite of aluminium honeycomb and carbon-fibre reinforced epoxy, weighs about 5 kg. It has been designed to absorb all the kinetic energy of the car, driver and a tankful of fuel, driven at $11\,\mathrm{m\,s^{-1}}$. To be a successful design, as this one is, the nose must crumple on impact. The remainder of the car should be undamaged and the driver not trapped, so that, if it had been a real car, it could probably have raced on once the nose has been replaced. What's more, the nose must not stop the car so suddenly that the fuel tank is damaged. That is checked by seeing whether the tank's contents leak during the test.

Designing for collapse

The absorption of energy during an impact must be managed to minimize the amount transferred to the passengers or goods being transported. This involves investigating the energy used to deform the various components within the vehicle structure. If they are bent, broken or crushed by the impact, the kinetic energy is converted into heat (and a little noise). If they simply absorb energy and remain elastic, that energy is converted back into kinetic energy, and the object bounces back. In most collisions, it is desirable to avoid this possibility, as a bouncing object such as a racing car can create uncontrolled vehicle kinematics and damage.

Test measurements

During the test, the dummy representing the driver must not be subjected to forces that would injure a real driver. Fastened in place by a genuine safety harness, its chest contains an accelerometer connected to a datalogger that measures the acceleration 20 000 times each second during the impact. Computer software calculates the acceleration over intervals of 3 milliseconds (ms). This is related to the possible level of injury to the vehicle's occupant.

A driver can survive average accelerations up to $20g$ for a time of 3 ms. (Accelerations are often quoted as multiples of g, the acceleration caused by gravity. This is the acceleration of a freely falling object near the Earth's surface; $g \sim 9.8\,\mathrm{m\,s^{-2}}$.)

Instrumentation

At the Impact Centre, they use accelerometers based on the piezoelectric effect. Squeezing a piezoelectric crystal changes its electrical properties. A stress sets up a voltage difference across the crystal.

The car's speed immediately before impact is measured by arranging for it to interrupt a **light beam** connected to an **electronic timer**.

It is possible to study the details of how a car's nose-cone collapses, using **high-speed photography**. The Impact Centre's 1000 frames per second camera provides a sequence of about 80 pictures during each test.

Test results

Technicians test the racing car's energy-absorbing nose by bolting the car body on to a trolley supported by four air bearings. They add extra mass to compensate for the wheels and engine, which have been removed. It is pulled up an 11° slope, at the same time stretching six bungee ropes to provide most of the energy.

Measurements
Mass of car: 780 kg
Speed on collision: $11.18\,\mathrm{m\,s^{-1}}$
Rebound speed: $0.25\,\mathrm{m\,s^{-1}}$
Stopping distance = length of nose destroyed: 0.445 m

Deductions
Kinetic energy before collision: 48.7 kJ
Kinetic energy after collision: 24 J
Fraction of kinetic energy absorbed: 99.95%
(from $s = \dfrac{(v + u)}{2} \times t$) duration of impact: 0.079 s
(from $v^2 = u^2 + 2as$) deceleration: $141\,\mathrm{m\,s^{-2}} = 14.4g$

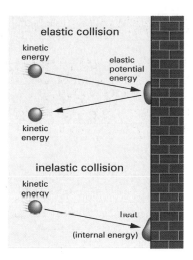

▲ Figure 5A11 *Energy changes during elastic and inelastic collisions.*

Interpreting the data

High speed alone doesn't kill. A passenger can be equally comfortable in a train at 125 mph, a holiday plane at 500 mph or Concorde at Mach 2. It is speeding up and slowing down – acceleration and deceleration – that can cause discomfort and damage.

But even high acceleration or deceleration may not kill, so long as they last for a very short time. Astronauts or jet fighter pilots will be able to withstand a few *g* for a few seconds – most fit people can do that.

▲ **Figure 5A12** *Majid Sadeghi and Richard Jones prepare the rig to test a sample of energy absorbing material.*

In a collision, even a 'low-speed' collision, the deceleration may be much higher, because the car stops within a very short distance. To prevent the driver being injured, the area intended to absorb the energy has to be designed to do so in a controlled way. Designers use results from the work of the Cranfield Impact Centre to make sure that a collision of a given energy takes as long as possible, and that they are as inelastic as possible.

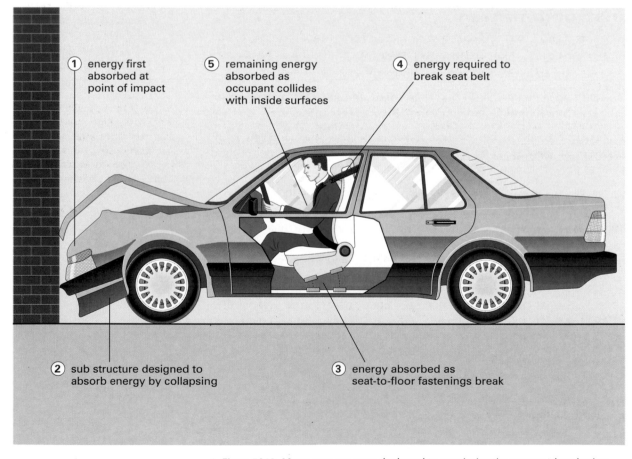

① energy first absorbed at point of impact

⑤ remaining energy absorbed as occupant collides with inside surfaces

④ energy required to break seat belt

② sub structure designed to absorb energy by collapsing

③ energy absorbed as seat-to-floor fastenings break

▲ **Figure 5A13** *Many cars are now designed to maximize the energy absorbed on collision without harming the driver and passengers.*

Making sense of collisions

The death rate on British roads has declined markedly in recent years. This is partly due to better driving and better designed roads. But it is also due to improvements in the design of cars. Understanding what happens in collisions, in terms of energy and momentum, and how to cope with the energy involved, have made for cars with many new safety features such as crumple zones, safety cages and air bags.

Making predictions

In any collision, there are three quantities that are conserved: mass, energy and momentum. In this context, the idea of conservation has a special meaning. Conservation of mass, for example, means that the total mass of the objects colliding is the same after the collision as it was before. Mass is not destroyed in a collision, nor is it created.

Knowing that these quantities are conserved, scientists can predict the behaviour of colliding objects. Understanding the behaviour of colliding objects is the first step to designing safer transport systems. On this page, ideas about the conservation of energy are discussed. The conservation of momentum is discussed on page 257.

Creating acceleration

If a car is travelling at a steady speed, the forces on it are balanced. In particular, the driving force of the engine is balanced by the drag force of air resistance (Figure 5A14a). If the driver presses harder on the accelerator, the forward force increases. The horizontal forces are now unbalanced, and the car accelerates forward (Figure 5A14b). Similarly, braking adds an extra force backwards, and the car decelerates (Figure 5A14c).

So an *unbalanced* or *resultant force* F produces an acceleration a in the same direction as the force. The size of the acceleration depends on the size of the force, and on the mass m of the car. According to **Newton's second law of motion**, these quantities are related by

$$F = ma$$
force (in newtons, N) = mass (in kg) × acceleration (in ms^{-2})

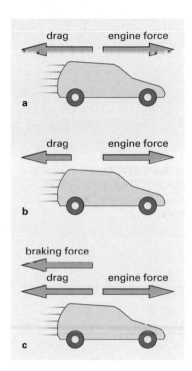

▲ **Figure 5A14** *A car will accelerate or decelerate when there is an unbalanced force acting on it.*
a Balanced forces at steady speed.
b Acceleration – unbalanced forces.
c Deceleration – unbalanced forces.

Doing work

As the unbalanced force pushes the car forward, making it accelerate, it increases the car's **kinetic energy**. Kinetic energy E_k is the energy of any moving object. ($E_k = \frac{1}{2}mv^2$ – see page 252.) The force is said to have done work in order to increase the car's kinetic energy. The amount of **work done** depends on the force F and the distance s through which it moves.

$$W = Fs$$
work done (in J) = force (in N) × distance moved (in m)

In this case, the amount of work done on the car is equal to the car's increase in kinetic energy.

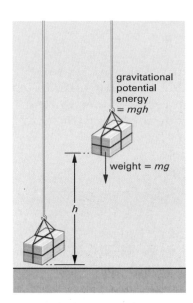

▲ **Figure 5A15** *Any object lifted against the force of gravity is given gravitational potential energy.*

More energy

Work is also done when a force is used to lift an object – it is given **gravitational potential energy** E_p – see Figure 5A15.

$$E_p = mgh$$

gravitational potential energy (in J) = mass (in kg) × acceleration due to gravity (in ms^{-2}) × height (in m)

Rubber bands and springs are elastic. Forces deform them, but they spring back to their original shape when the force is removed. Stretching or squashing an elastic object increases its **elastic potential energy**. In any collision, there are transfers of energy among these three forms. The fact that energy is conserved means that the total energy (found by adding all forms) is constant.

Power

Power measures the rate at which energy is transferred. This definition applies to any method of energy transfer – by doing work (i.e. by a force moving), by heating, by electrical transfer and so on.

$$P = \frac{W}{t}$$

power (in watts, W) = $\dfrac{\text{energy transferred (in J)}}{\text{time taken (in s)}}$

Lifting power

A crane lifts a load of 2500 kg to a height of 30 m in 1 minute. The load gains gravitational potential energy.

Gain in energy = mgh = 2500 kg × 9.8 ms^{-2} × 30 m = 735 kJ

Power = $\dfrac{\text{energy}}{\text{time}} = \dfrac{735\,\text{kJ}}{60\,\text{s}} = 12.25\,\text{kW}$

Absorbing kinetic energy

Packaging materials protect objects by absorbing energy when the package is accidentally dropped or hit. The material deforms and absorbs the kinetic energy of the moving object; work is done in deforming the packaging, and the kinetic energy becomes **internal energy** within the material – it becomes hotter.

A carton of mass 20 kg contains eggs. It falls from a counter 1 m high on to a hard concrete floor. The corner of the carton is pushed in a distance of 4 cm – none of the eggs breaks! From this information, it is possible to calculate the carton's speed as it reaches the floor, the average force on the carton on impact, and its deceleration as it hits the floor.

Gravitational potential energy of carton on counter = mgh = 20 kg × 9.8 ms^{-2} × 1 m = 196 J

This is equal to the carton's kinetic energy when it reaches the floor. Hence we can calculate its speed:

$$(\text{speed})^2 = 2 \times \frac{E_k}{m} = 2 \times \frac{196\,\text{J}}{20\,\text{kg}}$$

so speed $v = \sqrt{19.6} = 4.4\,ms^{-1}$

The force of impact must do 196 J of work to absorb this energy; it does this in a distance of 4 cm. Hence:

$$\text{force } F = \frac{\text{work done}}{\text{distance}} = \frac{W}{s} = \frac{196\,\text{J}}{0.04\,\text{m}} = 4900\,\text{N}$$

$$\text{and acceleration } a = \frac{F}{m} = \frac{4900\,\text{N}}{20\,\text{kg}} = 245\,\text{ms}^{-2}$$

Seat belt safety

A passenger whose mass is 60 kg is in a car travelling at $10\,\text{ms}^{-1}$ when it is involved in a collision. The passenger is restrained by a seat belt, which provides an average force of 10 kN to prevent her from hitting the windscreen. From this information, it is possible to calculate how far forward the passenger will be thrown in the collision.

$$\text{Kinetic energy of passenger} = \tfrac{1}{2}\,mv^2 = \tfrac{1}{2} \times 60\,\text{kg} \times (10\,\text{ms}^{-1})^2 = 3000\,\text{J}$$

The seat belt has to change this amount of kinetic energy into elastic potential energy; in other words, the force of 10 kN must do 3000 J of work.

$$\text{Distance moved } s = \frac{W}{F} = \frac{3000\,\text{J}}{10 \times 10^3\,\text{N}} = 0.30\,\text{m}$$

So the passenger is thrown forward by an average distance of 30 cm, and hopefully would not hit the windscreen.

Momentum changes

Another important quantity to calculate in a collision is **momentum**, because this is related to the force that acts during the collision. To calculate the momentum of an object, it is necessary to know its **velocity** v – its speed *in a particular direction*.

$$\text{Momentum } p = mv \quad \text{momentum (in kg m s}^{-1})$$
$$= \text{mass (in kg)} \times \text{velocity (in m s}^{-1})$$

In an inelastic collision an object's momentum is destroyed – it is transferred to the ground in the situation shown in Figure 5A17. In an elastic collision, its velocity is reversed and its momentum is changed from $+mv$ to $-mv$.

The change in momentum of an object in a collision is related to the force F acting on it and the time t for which it acts.

$$Ft = mv - mu$$
$$\text{force} \times \text{time} = \text{change in momentum}$$

Direct hit

A bat strikes a ball of mass 300 g with an average force of 100 N for 0.2 s. To calculate the speed of the ball after it has been hit,

$$\text{momentum of ball} = Ft = 100\,\text{N} \times 0.2\,\text{s} = 20\,\text{kg m s}^{-1}$$

$$\text{speed of ball} = \frac{\text{momentum}}{\text{mass}} = \frac{20\,\text{kg m s}^{-1}}{0.3\,\text{kg}} = 67\,\text{ms}^{-1}$$

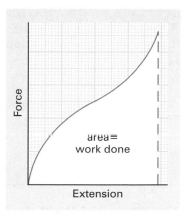

▲ **Figure 5A16** *In practice, the restraining force provided by the seat belt is not constant. It increases as it is stretched, as shown by this graph. The work done by the force must be found by determining the area under the force-extension graph.*

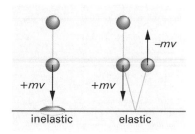

▲ **Figure 5A17** *Momentum changes during a collision.*

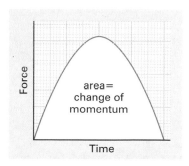

▲ **Figure 5A18** *In practice, the force of the bat on the ball is not constant. It increases to a maximum, and then decreases to zero as the ball flies off. The change in momentum of the ball must be found by determining the area under the force-time graph.*

Greater safety

In Britain, every individual has a 1% chance that they will die in a road accident. The chance of being seriously injured at some time is considerably higher. Understanding the science of motion has led to the development of a range of safety measures that can improve the chances of getting through life unscathed.

Only one head

A fall of only 60 cm on to a hard surface may be enough to fracture a skull. And the skull needs protecting because it protects the brain.

That's what a helmet is for – a good one will cushion the effect of a fall by reducing the head's deceleration when it hits the road or the edge of a kerbstone.

There is a British Standard for cycle helmets. BS 6863 says that a cycle helmet will 'normally consist of a shell, not necessarily of hard material, either containing or providing the necessary means of absorbing impact energy, and either fitted with or providing means for retaining the helmet on the head in an accident.'

▼ **Figure 5A19** *Apparatus used for testing shock absorption by a cycle helmet.*

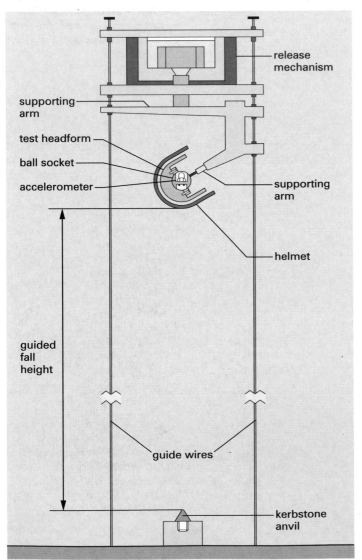

So the helmet must absorb the kinetic energy of the head as it hits the ground – the impact must be inelastic. There must be an energy-absorbing material – usually expanded polystyrene, in either a hard or soft shell construction.

Each design of helmet is tested in an impact test described in BS 6863, to find out whether it really reduces the deceleration of the head. The helmet is fitted to an artificial head containing an accelerometer. It is then dropped 1 m. If the accelerometer shows the deceleration of the head to be less than $330g$, a real head would be well protected.

Tyre standards

Pneumatic tyres are composite materials. Whether for cars, bikes or lorries, they are sophisticated constructions of rubber, steel and fabric. They must retain the air pressure, and they must provide the frictional force with the road surface without which the vehicle would slip or skid. Good tread is vital to ensuring good frictional contact. The present law requires that there should be at least 1.6 mm of tread throughout a continuous band around the central three-quarters of the tyre – Figure 5A20a. The tread is designed to provide good road holding even on wet roads.

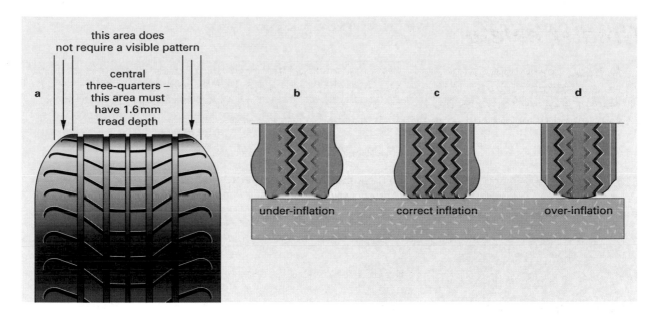

this area does not require a visible pattern

central three-quarters – this area must have 1.6mm tread depth

a

b under-inflation

c correct inflation

d over-inflation

The only area of contact with the road surface is the small 'footprint' where the round tyre is flattened by the weight of the vehicle. Put the wrong air pressure in the tyre (Figure 5A20b–d) and the footprint's size and shape are altered. This changes the behaviour of the car, so that the driver finds it hard to predict its acceleration, cornering and braking.

Traffic police know how the footprint changes during sudden braking. The weight of the car is thrown forwards on to the front tyres, so that they deform as in Figure 5A20b. They leave a twin-track skid mark on the road. The rear tyres have reduced weight on them, so they deform as in Figure 5A20d, leaving a narrow, single skid mark.

▲ **Figure 5A20** *a The tread on a tyre must be at least 1.6mm deep over the central region. **b–d** The correct pressure is needed to give good contact between the tyre and the road surface.*

Better brakes

When the driver's foot goes down on the brake pedal, the car slows down. The car's kinetic energy decreases, and it is the job of the brakes to convert it to heat. In a **disc brake** (Figure 5A21), brake pads press against a spinning disc fixed to each wheel. The frictional force between disc and pad does work, and the disc and pad become hot. The heat is transferred to the surrounding air.

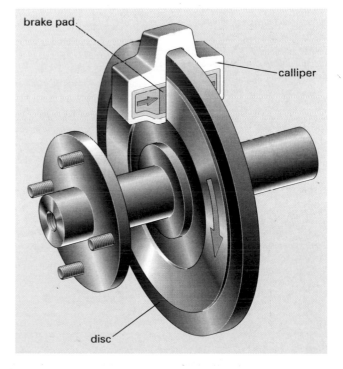

brake pad

calliper

disc

▶ **Figure 5A21** *Hydraulic pressure from the brake system pushes the brake pads against the spinning disc.*

Developing the world's best engines

Ten thousand people work at the Rolls-Royce Aerospace factories in Derby. They take an engine through its entire life cycle: designing, developing, producing, selling and supporting the product in service. A sizeable proportion of the workforce is involved with development and testing of the engines. The aim is to make engines that are the world's best, which are better than those of their chief competitors on both performance and price. John Merrey is a graduate technologist working on the test programmes.

▲ **Figure 5A22** *Though qualified as an electronic engineer, John Merrey (right) now works in the mechanical test department. He moved from Swansea, after gaining his degree at Southampton University.*

Measuring the effects of spin

John Merrey works in the Spinning Section of the Mechanical Test Engineering Department where he tests engine components, such as front fan, compressor and turbine sections. These sections are put into large pits and spun at speeds as high as 20 000 rpm in a partial vacuum.

The test rig is checked for unwanted vibrations caused by resonance effects which could cause the test component to break or damage the test rig. The spinning section performs cyclic fatigue testing. This is to establish a safe working life for an engine component, sometimes measuring stresses at different parts of a component, and finding out what happens following damage to a fan blade, which might be caused, for example, by a bird striking the engine.

In the event of a blade or part of a blade flying off during the test, the important thing is that it shouldn't damage the engine or scatter debris. A blade that is at one moment rotating at approximately 4000 rpm and then flies off from the fan, changes instantly from rotational motion to high-speed linear motion. The engine casing is wrapped with Kevlar, the material that is used to make bullet proof vests. It must withstand and contain the impact of a loosened blade which flies off during the test, to prove that it can do so in service.

In the testing area large motors driven by currents of up to 600 A provide the rotation. The speed of rotation can be measured using a **capacitance probe** – a potential difference between the probe and a spinning toothed wheel, called a phonic wheel, mounted at the top of the shaft driving the test component, means that as the distance between the teeth on the phonic wheel varies as it spins, so the capacitance of the system varies with the result that a current flows in the circuit. The frequency of the current gives a direct measurement of the rate of rotation of the shaft driving the test component.

Capacitance probes are sometimes mounted around the rim of a test component to measure the gap distance which will decrease as the speed of rotation increases, strain increases and the component grows in diameter.

Trainees

Rolls-Royce has a highly skilled workforce. They join with the appropriate qualifications and then receive on the job training. They don't just need to know about engineering; they must also learn about safety, production, sales, and how the business works.

Tajinderpal Dahele is a third-year technical apprentice. He's already achieved NVQ level 2, and when he qualifies he will have reached NVQ level 3. Then he may have opportunities for further part-time study, possibly to degree standard. In the meantime he's gaining experience of the work of various departments, such as Project Engineering. His job there is to co-ordinate small projects for other departments. For example, one department requested modifications to a large 'foot' for mounting an engine during tests. Tajinderpal looked after the job, dealing with designers, organizing estimates of cost, providing schedules and ordering materials. This took him into different Rolls-Royce factories, so he has to be aware of safety issues, and of the rules that come under the heading of Codes of Safe Working Practices. One of the requirements of his training programme is that he should make a note of safety issues on every single page of his training log book.

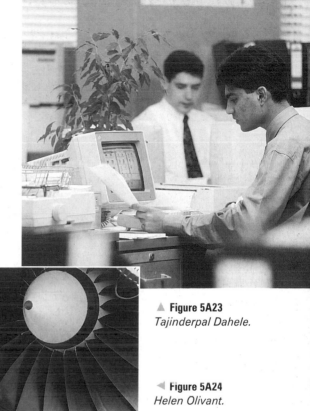

▲ Figure 5A23
Tajinderpal Dahele.

◀ Figure 5A24
Helen Olivant.

▼ Figure 5A25
Richard Wheeldon.

Helen Olivant is an engineering trainee in the final year of her four-year apprenticeship. When she qualifies she will join a department where she will receive specialist training. In the meantime she's learning drafting skills, working some of the time at drawing boards but most of the time with CAD (computer aided design). Working in a drawing office appeals to her – there are the benefits of being part of a team, of needing to keep up to date with techniques in CAD, including the probable future use of virtual reality, and of being at the heart of the technical business of building jet engines.

Apprentice engine fitter **Richard Wheeldon** is gaining experience of setting up engines and running them in the experimental test bed facility – large cells where engines can be tested around the clock seven days a week without causing a nuisance to the community. Testing often involves running the engine non stop for 150 hours, or accelerating and decelerating between low and high speed (power) 3000 times to simulate the arduous conditions of take off and landing. For safety reasons, no one is allowed in the test bed when engines are running, so the engines are controlled from an adjacent room using instrument panels and screens of information similar to that displayed for a pilot. Just as on the aircraft, a throttle provides the only control of engine speed, supplying more or less fuel to the burners that provide energy for the turbines which in turn drive the fan and compressors. The master control switches, without which an engine cannot run, can be fitted with padlocks. Any team working on the test bed must fit its own padlock on to the switch to prevent accidental start-up. Switches can have several padlocks hanging from them when an engine is being rigged or derigged to ensure complete safety.

The Governor's story

It was invented in the 18th century to control the speed of the steam engines that powered the Industrial Revolution. Nowadays, it is fitted to motorcycles ridden by sixteen-year-olds, and to coaches cruising down the motorway at a steady 70 miles per hour. It is the 'Whirling Regulator' or governor, an automatic control device with two centuries of history.

Steam control

In 1982 the steam engine at the Queen Street Mill at Harle Skye near Burnley ceased to drive the looms. It was the last rotative steam engine in the Lancashire cotton industry. Many industries – steel rolling, water and sewage pumping, mine haulage and railways – had relied on steam power, but it was the textile mills whose requirements were the most demanding.

For spinning cotton, it was essential that the speed of the steam engine should be constant, otherwise the yarn would be thicker in some parts than in others. Speed regulation was vital, day and night, as spinning machines were brought in and out of operation. The governor was the device which made automatic speed control possible.

A governor controls the flow of steam. In the version shown in Figure 5A26, the two massive balls E are spun round as the engine shaft rotates. If the engine speeds up, the balls fly outwards and upwards; the system of levers pulls down on the arm F, which has the effect of closing the butterfly valve Z. This reduces the flow of steam to the engine, and it slows down. If the engine speed drops too far, the balls drop and the valve opens wider. It is an example of a **negative feedback system** – see page 289.

Matthew Boulton and James Watt, leading designers and manufacturers of steam engines, described the value of the governor: 'The only new invention of any consequence we have lately added to the Engine is the regulator or Governor ... it certainly, when kept in order itself, gives greater steadiness and regularity especially in the cases of taking off and putting on work as it will not permit 2 strokes per minute of increase of velocity though all the work were taken away at once.'

▼ **Figure 5A26** *An early drawing of the 'Whirling Regulator' developed for steam engines.*

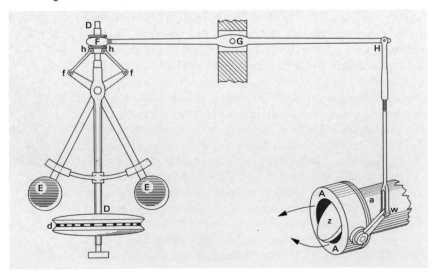

▲ **Figure 5A27** *This governor controls the speed of a steam engine used to pump water at the British Engineerium at Hove.*

Automatic transmission

From the early days of steam engines, governors went on to be fitted to many different rotating power sources. Even the clockwork motors of early gramophones had governors to ensure that the record was played at a steady speed. Motorcycles and coach engines may be fitted with governors to restrict their speed for reasons of safety.

Another type of governor is used in cars with automatic transmissions (automatic gear change) – see Figure 5A28. The drive shaft that turns the wheels also turns a governor. As the speed of rotation increases, the weighted valves move outwards, allowing oil to be pumped through to the pistons which engage a higher gear. When the speed drops, the valves move back inwards, and the oil flows back to engage low gear.

▼ **Figure 5A28** *The spinning governor in an automatic transmission controls the flow of oil to the gear-changing pistons.*

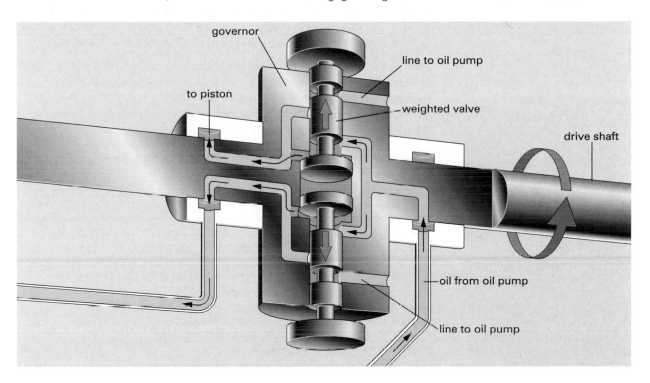

Forces in rotation

When an object is rotating or following a circular path, it needs an unbalanced force to maintain this motion. This force must be directed towards the centre of the circle; the object is being constantly pulled towards the centre. The force is described as a **centripetal force**. If the force is insufficient, the object will fly off at a tangent to the circle.

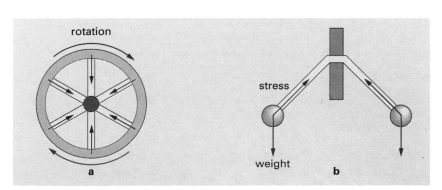

◄ **Figure 5A29** *Centripetal forces: a In a rotating wheel, the rim is pulled inwards by the tension in the spokes. b In a governor, the centripetal force on the ball is provided by the unbalanced horizontal component of the stress in the supporting arm.*

Flow control

Sailboard speedo

Windsurfing is an exciting sport, and speed surfing is a growth activity. Experts can reach speeds in excess of 20 knots. But how do they know just how fast are they travelling across the surface of the water? Michael Lord looked for a sailboard speedometer in the shops, but drew a blank. So he invented one for himself.

Michael Lord is a keen windsurfer. He invented his speedo while still at school. What motivated him?

'This invention arose from my own frustration at not being able to purchase a sailboard speedometer, as no reliable product was available. I could not estimate my speed and it is not practical for me to enter expensive professional standard speed trials, which are held over 500 m measured courses. Indeed, many recreational sailors will actually have difficulty in completing such long and demanding courses at speed in strong winds. Moreover, with speed runs in excess of 20 knots now being achieved by experts, the average sailor is actively discouraged for safety considerations.'

Every sailboard has a fin or 'skeg', attached to the underside of the board. The skeg gives the board directional stability, as well as contributing to the lift which keeps the board planing across the water. Michael decided to design a speedo which would fit inside the skeg. It had to be in a position where it would be permanently in the water without adding to the drag.

Dynamic pressure

At the heart of the speedometer is a **pitot tube**. This is a fine tube, pointing forwards in the direction of travel. As water is forced into the tube, the pressure inside increases. The greater the speed, the greater the rise in pressure. (This increase is known as the **dynamic pressure**.) At the rear of the speedo is a second pressure tube, the **static tube**, which sits sideways on to the direction of travel. In this orientation, the static tube does not experience any increase in pressure, and so there is a pressure difference between the two tubes which increases as the speed increases.

Between the pitot tube and the static tube is a **pressure transducer**, which responds to the pressure difference by producing a corresponding voltage. From this voltage, electronic circuitry produces a digital read-out of the sailboard's speed.

Dynamic future

Michael has high hopes for his sailboard speedo. 'Research amongst the retail trade has shown that there is a definite market to be filled by an effective speedo. There are tens of thousands of windsurfers throughout the world and no suitable speed device is available. I believe that my device is unique – the search by the Patent Office has not revealed any similar products. It will allow everyone from the novice to the expert to assess his/her speed and the effects of sail trimming.

'With further development to the display, it will be possible to include a maximum speed and average speed readout. The principle of the invention is not confined to windsurfing and, as it contains no moving parts, I am confident that it could be fitted into dinghies, or any craft where drag is a consideration.'

▲ **Figure 5B1** *Michael Lord with the speedometer display on his sailboard.*

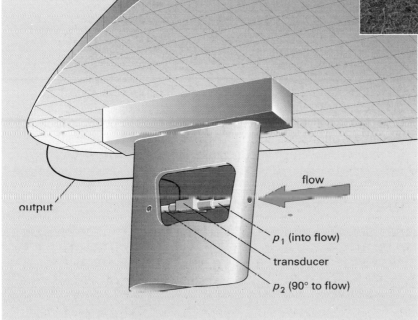

flow

output

p_1 (into flow)

transducer

p_2 (90° to flow)

◀ **Figure 5B2** *The speedometer fitted into the sailboard skeg.*

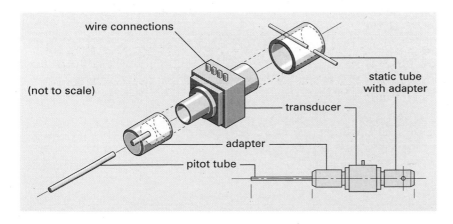

wire connections

(not to scale)

static tube with adapter

transducer

adapter

pitot tube

◀ **Figure 5B3** *The pitot tube and the static tube are fitted on either side of a pressure sensitive comparator which incorporates a force-sensing transducer.*

Fluid flow

Gases and liquids are fluids. A fluid is anything which can flow. The air that everyone breathes, the blood pulsing through veins and arteries, the milk poured on to a bowl of cereal for breakfast – these are all fluids on the move. So what are the characteristics of fluid flow?

Seeing fluid flow

Air is a fluid. It is transparent and colourless, and so it is difficult to detect the details of how it is moving. A **wind tunnel** can be used to show up the pattern of air flow. Streamers of smoke are injected into the moving air, and they show up regions of turbulence. The smoke shows up the paths of air molecules; these lines are known as **streamlines**. In a liquid, a coloured substance such as potassium permanganate may be injected to show up the streamlines.

- Cars are designed to be streamlined, to reduce air resistance. This can give improved fuel consumption figures and increased top speeds. Advertisements may quote the **drag coefficient**, which gives an indication of how well streamlined the car body is. Wind tunnels are used in the design process, to identify features which may give rise to air resistance.
- Athletes such as cyclists and skiers have used wind tunnels to test new designs of equipment, clothing and helmets. They seek to minimize turbulence and friction to give them a winning edge over their competitors.
- Aircraft use pitot-static tubes, similar to the sailboard speedo on page 265, to determine their speed through the air. The tube, and other instrumentation such as aerials, must stick out of the body of the aircraft into the cold air outside. To check that they are functioning correctly, they may be tested in a wind tunnel.
- Architects use wind tunnel tests on models of buildings to help them to predict localized air flow (e.g. in shopping arcades) and the pressures the wind creates (e.g. in very tall buildings).

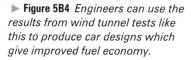
▶ **Figure 5B4** *Engineers can use the results from wind tunnel tests like this to produce car designs which give improved fuel economy.*

Steady and turbulent flow

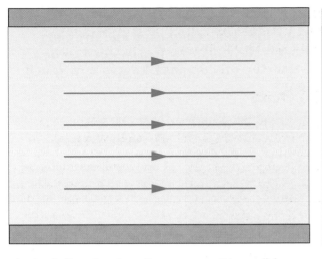

a In steady flow, the streamlines run smoothly parallel to one another.

b When a fluid flows steadily along a pipe, frictional drag at the walls means that the flow is fastest at the centre.

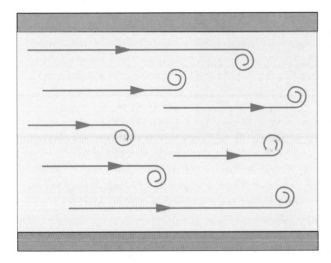

c When the speed of flow increases, turbulence may set in, destroying steady flow and increasing drag.

d A streamlined design can restore steady flow, and allow faster movement of the fluid.

▲ **Figure 5B5** *Fluid flow.*

Turbulence can have several detrimental effects on fluid flow. It causes increased drag so that, for example, a vehicle moving through air is slowed down. An aircraft which sets up turbulence gives its passengers a bumpy ride. For a liquid flowing through a pipe, turbulence introduces irregularity into the rate of flow, and makes the flow much harder to control.

Bernoulli's principle

The pressure in a fluid depends on its speed. In regions where it is moving fast, the pressure is lower than in regions where it is moving more slowly. This principle, which is called after the 18th-century Swiss mathematician Daniel Bernoulli, is made use of in several devices that are used to measure the rate of fluid flow – for example, the venturi meter shown on page 269.

Measuring fluid flow

Oil is a valuable liquid. It flows from oil wells; it may then flow hundreds or even thousands of kilometres along pipelines; it flows into tanks and cans and drums. As it flows, it is vital to keep track of how much is flowing. Any losses need to be accounted for; precise measurements ensure that the oil company knows how much oil it has to sell, and how much tax it has to pay.

▲ **Figure 5B6** *Turbine flowmeters like these are widely used for monitoring flow rates – for example, for the fuelling of ships and the filling of beer barrels at the brewery.*

Turbine flowmeters

This type of flowmeter is built into a pipeline. The turbine rotor is mounted on a spindle, centrally within the pipe. The pressure of the oil on the vanes spins the turbine round at a rate which increases with the rate of flow.

A series of magnets are mounted in the rim of the turbine (see Figure 5B7). As each one passes a detector coil mounted on the outside of the pipe, a brief voltage pulse is induced in the coil. The coil is connected to an electronic counting circuit which detects the pulses. The counter has been calibrated so that it gives a direct reading of the rate of flow of the oil. A turbine flowmeter can measure flow rates as low as $5\,\mathrm{cm\,s^{-1}}$.

In a related type of flowmeter, the turbine has small studs of iron embedded in its rim. The detector coil is wound around a permanent magnet. Again, as the turbine spins, a series of voltage pulses is induced in the coil, and these are electronically counted to give a measure of the rate of flow.

▶ **Figure 5B7** *The construction of a turbine flowmeter.*

Electromagnetic induction

Whenever the magnetic field near a coil of wire *changes*, a voltage is induced (generated) in the coil. This can happen if a magnet is moved near the coil, or if the coil moves past a magnet. The voltage induced depends on: the strength of the magnetic field, the size of the coil and speed of movement.

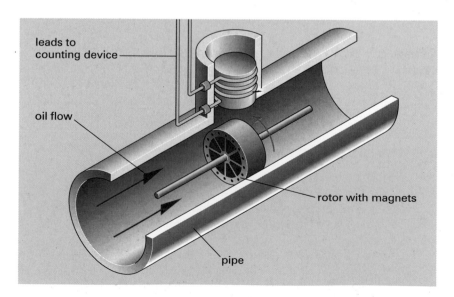

leads to counting device

oil flow

rotor with magnets

pipe

Venturi meters

A venturi tube is a constriction in a pipe along which a fluid is flowing. Since the same volume of fluid passes through the wide and narrow sections of the pipe each second, the fluid must travel faster in the narrow region of the pipe. If its speed is greater, its pressure is lower – a consequence of the Bernoulli effect (page 267). One way to think of this is that the pressure difference is needed to provide the force which accelerates the fluid through the constriction. Alternatively, the fluid has lost pressure energy and gained kinetic energy.

In a **venturi meter**, two pipes lead off from the main pipe, one from the constriction and the other before the constriction, where the fluid has its normal pressure. There is therefore a pressure difference between these two pipes, which depends on the speed of flow. Pressure gauges on the two pipes will show different readings. A better way to deduce the speed of flow is to connect a manometer between the pipes, or to connect a differential pressure sensor between them.

An **orifice plate** is a simpler design. The plate has a narrow hole which the fluid must be forced through. There is therefore a pressure drop across the plate, and this can again be measured and interpreted to give the rate of flow.

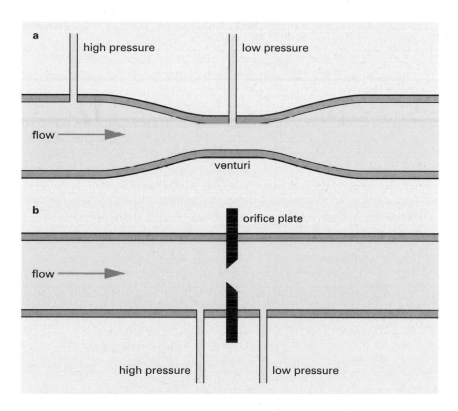

◄ **Figure 5B8** *The construction of a* a venturi meter, and *b* an orifice plate.

Vortex meters

When streamlined flow breaks down and becomes turbulent, eddies (or vortices) appear in the moving fluid. This is made use of in **vortex meters**. A non-streamlined object is positioned in a section of the pipe in order to produce eddies in the flow (Figure 5B9). The steel ball is pushed up and down by the pressure differences caused by these eddies. The rate at which it moves increases with the speed of flow, and this is detected by measuring the voltage pulses induced in the detector coil.

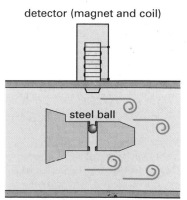

▲ **Figure 5B9** *The construction of a vortex meter.*

A steady flow of work

Eating, drinking, moving and thinking can seriously damage your health. Drugs and alcohol disrupt the internal stability of the body. Salts upset the balance of ions and water in cells and fluids. The cells themselves produce a continuous flow of ammonia, converted to urea in the liver. The kidneys are the centre of the process by which harmful dissolved substances are removed from the blood supply. If the kidneys fail, death may follow within days.

Kidney dialysis

In societies with generous health care provision, death from kidney failure is increasingly rare. Kidneys are one type of organ whose action we have learnt to copy. Blood and water can flow almost together, either side of a selectively permeable membrane, which allows small particles like molecules of water and urea, but not the blood cells, to pass through it. The blood loses its unwanted hitchhikers, and the water carries them away. That is what happens not only in kidneys but also in the dialysers in kidney machines.

Paul Harbuz knows about kidney machines. He is a technician working in the dialysis unit of the City Hospital in Nottingham. With new tubes to carry the blood for each patient, and new membranes in the dialyser, each machine he looks after keeps several people alive.

The machines apply electronic control to the gentle flow of fluids in two systems. One system contains a patient's blood, which is pumped from the patient's body, through the dialysis machine and back to the patient. The blood must not come into contact with parts such as the inside of a pump, since that would introduce the very significant danger of infection passing from one person to another. So each patient's clean new plastic pipeline is clipped into the machine, and wrapped in a semicircle around a peristaltic pump. That has two rollers on a rotating arm, and the rollers simply squeeze the pipe to push the blood around. A magnet mounted on the arm generates an electrical pulse every time it rotates past a Hall effect probe (a semiconductor detector of magnetic fields) mounted on the machine.

The second fluid system carries water, with added 'Renalyte', which provides the right concentration of ions such as Na^+, Ca^{2+}, K^+, Mg^{2+}, Cl^-, and organic compounds like acetate and glucose. These concentrations will determine the flow of ions and dissolved organic compounds through the selectively permeable membrane in the dialyser itself.

The solution must be at the right temperature so that it does not significantly heat or cool the blood before it returns to the patient's body. A temperature sensor in the heater unit provides information to the machine's computer to control the current in the heating element. Another temperature sensor, closer to the patient, is linked to a visual display and to the computer, which will shut down the system if the temperature is not within the right range.

Pumps in the circuit act as hydraulic 'batteries'. It is the batteries in an electrical circuit that supply energy to maintain a flow. Batteries provide potential difference, and pumps provide pressure difference, with the fluids flowing from places where pressure is high to where it is low. A throttle acts rather like a resistor does in an electrical circuit. A resistor reduces the flow and the result is that there is a potential difference, or voltage, between its ends. The throttle results in a pressure difference –

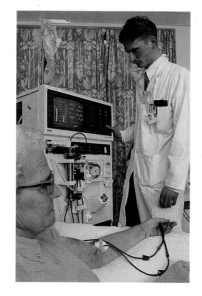

▲ **Figure 5B10** *Paul Harbuz started work in the City Hospital's Medical Equipment Servicing Unit pretty much straight from school. Now after studying at Nottingham Trent University he's an expert in practical aspects of fluid flow and electronic control. With his two colleagues he looks after the Hospital's 75 machines, which provide a steady flow of work.*

it creates a pressure drop to control the rate at which 'Renalyte' flows in from a bottle. Varying the size of the throttle or the pressure across it will alter the flow.

A conductivity sensor consists of two metal electrodes sticking into the tube. The higher the concentration of ions, the more current flows. If the ion concentration isn't right then the computer can shut the system down.

Before the solution enters the dialyser it passes through a V-slot flowmeter (see page 276). That is a transparent vertical tube holding a weight with a magnet – the faster the flow the higher the weight is lifted, and static Hall probes detect the magnet, thereby detecting the flow of fluid. The rate of flow of the solution can be adjusted between 250 and 600 ml min^{-1}, compared with a rate of flow of blood through the machine of about 350 ml min^{-1} for an adult and 150 ml min^{-1} for a child.

An infra-red device detects any blood in the liquid that flows away from the dialyser. That could mean that part of the selectively permeable membrane has punctured and the solution and blood are mixing. The computer uses the signal to shut the machine down if necessary.

▼ **Figure 5B11** *A kidney dialysis machine is a complex system of fluid measurement and control.*

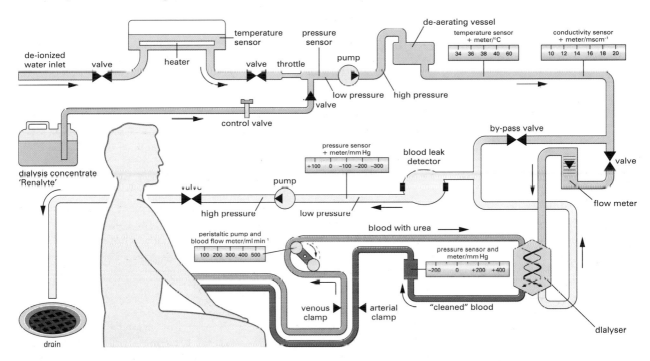

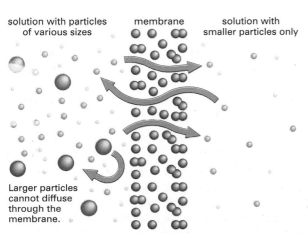

◀ **Figure 5B12** *A selectively permeable membrane is at the heart of every kidney dialysis machine.*

solution with particles of various sizes

membrane

solution with smaller particles only

Larger particles cannot diffuse through the membrane.

Diffusion takes place through the membrane in both directions. If there is a higher concentration of one type of particle on one side, then there is a net flow of those particles through to the side of lower concentration.

Down the drain

Most communities in the developed world have some means of disposing of their sewage and their storm water – rain and melting snow. Drains carry the water and its contents, usually by gravity in sloping sewers, to a point where it can be cleaned up and pumped into a river or the sea. While the daily flow of sewage can be very predictable, storm water flow can vary greatly. This presents major problems for the engineers who design the systems which people have come to rely on.

Predictability ...

In the UK, the average volume of water used by each person at home is about 150 to 200 litres per day. All of the water from washing machines, baths, showers, WCs and so on is eventually discharged into the drains as domestic sewage.

Industries also discharge effluent into the drainage system. Recent regulations mean that many companies now pre-treat their effluent to reduce its effect on the performance of the main sewage treatment plants.

▶ **Figure 5B13** *The flow of sewage to a plant varies throughout the day, and it depends where the treatment plant is situated.*
Q is the rate of flow; Q = 1 is the average rate for the whole day.

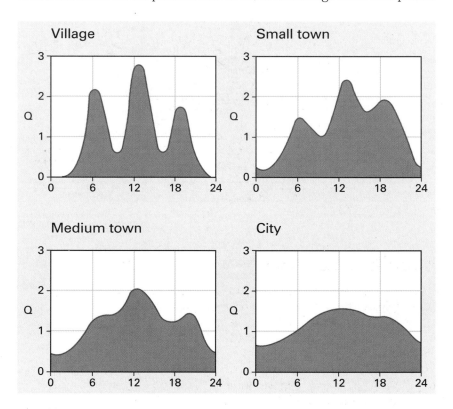

... and unpredictability

Storm water is unpredictable both in frequency and in volume. There may be periods of steady rain, or weeks of drought followed by a cloudburst in which 50 mm of rain falls in an hour. Drainage engineers must optimize any system to handle the predictable daily flow of sewage while being able to cope with the worst possible storms of the next century.

Six thousand people might live in one square kilometre of town, producing about one million litres of sewage every day. A 50 mm downpour on this area would deliver 50 million litres of rainwater, a large proportion of which ends up in the drains.

Practical sewage systems make use of gravity to bring sewage to a pumping station. The sewers may be buried 10m deep or more. Then pumps in the station lift the sewage and pressurize it so that it can be discharged into pressure pipes or mains which can follow the lie of the land, even uphill. The pumps have two main functions. First they must lift the effluent from the low-level sump in the station to the level of the pressure main (the static head). Second, they must overcome the friction between the effluent and the inner surface of the pipe (the friction head).

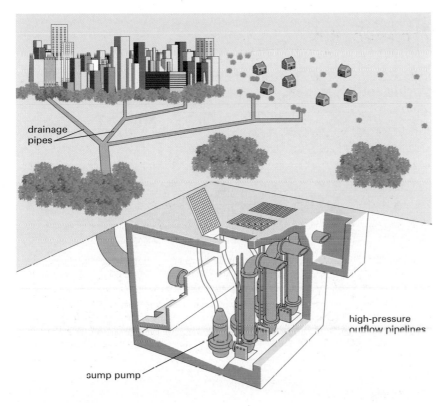

◀ **Figure 5B14** *Electrically powered pumps in a sump force sewage upwards into the pressure main.*

drainage pipes

high-pressure outflow pipelines

sump pump

Avoiding suction

Pumps can be used to create 'negative pressure' to suck water up to a height of 10m. Atmospheric pressure is sufficient to force water up to this height. In practice, a height of 5m is more realistic because of problems with friction, but even this has its problems. The water in the pump is under reduced pressure, and vapour bubbles are likely to appear. These collapse suddenly, producing very high forces on the internal surfaces of the pump. This effect is known as **cavitation**, and it can lead to rapid erosion of the cast iron inside of the pump, perhaps within a couple of months.

To overcome this, it is now common practice to eliminate suction by using submersible pumps which operate beneath the water surface. The versatility of these pumps has led to their use in an increasing range of applications around the world – draining mines and quarries, circulating the water in fish and shrimp farms, flood control, irrigation and providing river water for treatment. There are probably more pumps in the world today than any other type of industrial machine.

▼ **Figure 5B15** *A modern submersible pump has an electric motor which is capable of operating underwater. The spinning impeller of a centrifugal flow pump can cope with raw sewage which may be contaminated with rags and other fibrous waste.*

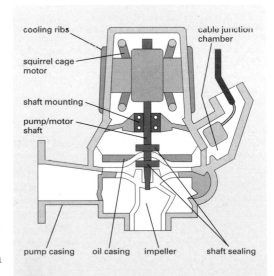

cooling ribs

cable junction chamber

squirrel cage motor

shaft mounting

pump/motor shaft

pump casing   oil casing   impeller   shaft sealing

Fluids under control

Whether it is the flow of petrol from tank to carburettor, water from well to reservoir, or gas from storage tank to user, pumps and valves are the essential elements in the controlled flow of fluids in pipes.

Pick of the pumps

A pump has to create a pressure difference in a fluid. That pressure difference can then be used to make the fluid flow.

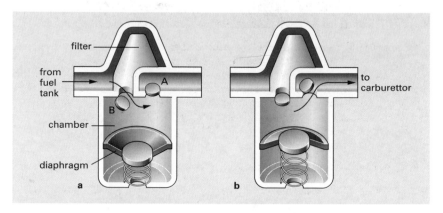

▲ **Figure 5B16** A **diaphragm pump** can be used to pump petrol from the fuel tank of a car to the carburettor. It is driven by a rotating cam from an electric motor. **a** The lever pulls the diaphragm downwards, creating low pressure in the chamber so that fuel flows in. **b** The lever pushes the diaphragm upwards, increasing the pressure and forcing the fuel through to the carburettor. Note how the flap valves A and B open and close automatically as the pressure in the chamber changes.

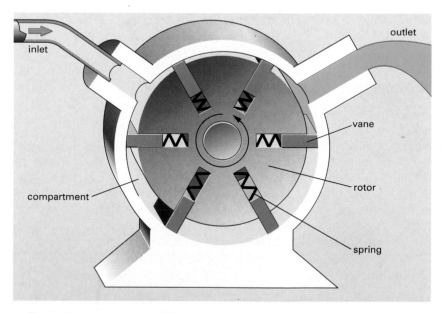

▲ **Figure 5B17** A **rotary vane pump** is often used in petrol pumps at filling stations. They can also be used to create vacuums with pressures down to approximately 10^{-5} atmospheres. The chamber of the pump has a rotor which is mounted slightly off-centre. Vanes project outwards from the rotor; they are spring-loaded so that they maintain contact with the sides of the chamber. As the rotor turns, the compartments between the vanes get smaller, and the fluid is squeezed into a shrinking space. It squirts out of the chamber at high pressure.

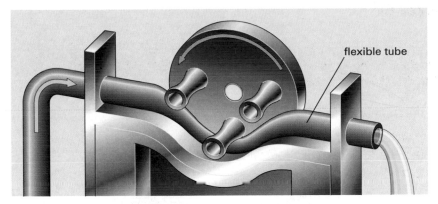

▲ **Figure 5B18** *A **peristaltic pump**, like the one used in the kidney dialysis machine on page 271, has the advantage that the fluid being pumped does not come into contact with any moving parts of the pump. Hence the fluid is less likely to become contaminated, and the pump does not get clogged up with a fluid like blood. The moving rollers gently squeeze the tubing, forcing the fluid along. It imitates the action of peristalsis, the way in which food is moved through the gut by contractions of the gut wall.*

Varieties of valves

Valves open and close to allow or prevent the flow of a fluid. They may be adjustable, to control the rate of flow; they may be electrically or pneumatically operated, so that they can be incorporated into an automatic system. A simple tap is a type of valve, and can be motorized for electrical control.

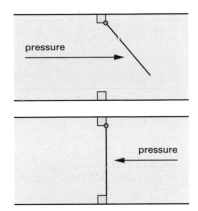

▲ **Figure 5B19** *In a simple **one-way valve**, the pressure of the fluid itself forces the valve shut when the fluid tries to flow the wrong way.*

◀ **Figure 5B20** *In this **pneumatic regulator valve**, a type of **diaphragm valve**, the shaft is moved up and down according to the position of the diaphragm. The diaphragm is controlled by pneumatic pressure, as air is forced into the chamber at the top of the valve.*

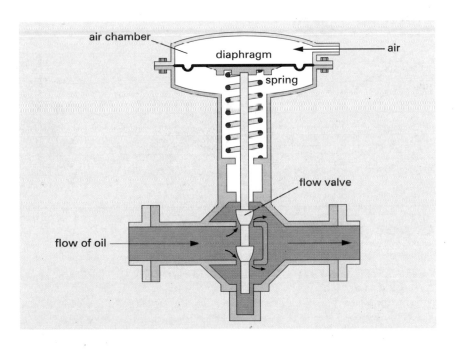

▶ **Figure 5B21** *A **differential pressure valve** is used in automatic gas water heaters. When the tap is turned on, the gas ignites to heat the water. Its operation is based on the difference in pressure created by a venturi tube. The water flows through a narrow section of pipe, and the low pressure in this section is fed through to the chamber above the diaphragm. The higher pressure of the water in the wide tube pushes the diaphragm upwards, opening the gas inlet valve. When the water is turned off, the pressures on either side of the diaphragm are equal, and the spring closes the gas valve.*

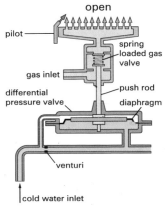

Gas flow

Gases are less dense than liquids. They are also readily compressible, unlike liquids, so their density may change significantly as they flow. This makes for new problems in the technology of flow measurement and control.

Anemometers

Wind speed is measured using an anemometer. A **rotating cup anemometer** spins at a rate which depends on the wind speed. The rate of rotation of the spindle may be detected electromagnetically – the spindle turns a small generator – or by a stroboscopic technique, in which the spindle is marked with a series of black and white stripes. As the spindle rotates, these flash past an optical detector which gives a readout of wind speed. A **rotating vane anemometer** works in a similar way.

In a **hot-wire anemometer**, a fine nickel wire is heated by an electric current passed through it. The air flow cools the wire, and its resistance decreases. The greater the wind speed, the more the cooling and so the lower the resistance. A meter detects the changing resistance; it is calibrated to give direct readings of wind speed.

▼ **Figure 5B22** *Three types of anemometer: **a** rotating cup, **b** rotating vane, and **c** hot wire.*

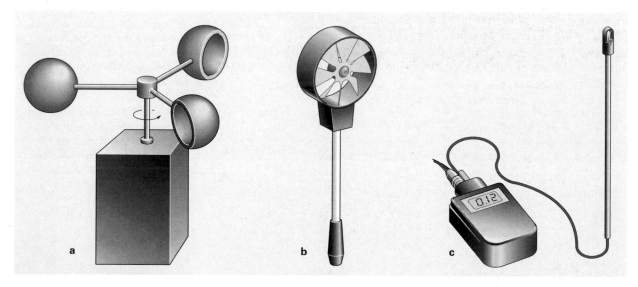

V-slot meters

This type of meter is useful for measuring the rate of flow of a gas in a pipe. It is also useful for some liquids. A **rotameter** has a tube of increasing diameter. As the gas flows up the tube, it pushes a conical weight upwards. The greater the flow rate, the farther the weight will rise. The scale can be read to give a direct reading of the flow rate. Alternatively, the weight can be magnetic, and its position can then be detected by a Hall probe or other magnetic detector.

Gas metering

Natural gas is an important fuel, and it costs money. A reliable metering system is essential. A modern ultrasonic meter can be connected to electronic systems into which it can feed digital signals, making for highly automated billing.

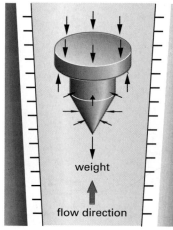

weight

flow direction

▲ **Figure 5B23** *The construction of a V-slot meter.*

In an ultrasonic meter, pulses of ultrasound are passed across the flow of gas. It travels faster in one direction than the other, as it is carried along by the gas. The difference in transit times gives a measure of the speed of flow of the gas.

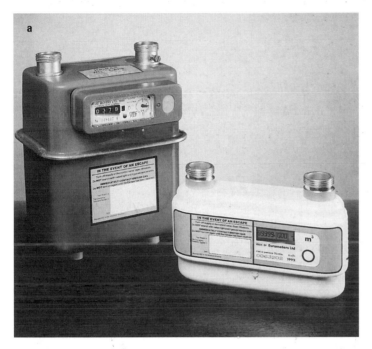

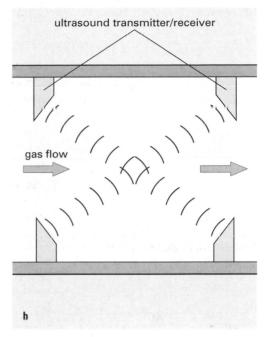

▲ **Figure 5B24** *a An ultrasonic gas meter (right), half the size of a traditional domestic meter. b Ultrasound pulses travel alternately with and against the flow of gas.*

Units of flow

There are three different ways of describing the rate of flow of a fluid.

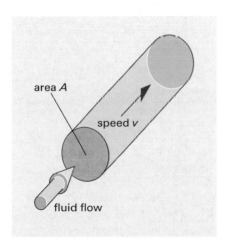

◄ **Figure 5B25** *A fluid of density ρ is flowing at speed v along a pipe of cross-sectional area A.*

Quantity	Formula	Units	Alternative units
Speed	v	$m\,s^{-1}$	$km\,h^{-1}$, mph, knots
Volume rate of flow	vA	$m^3\,s^{-1}$	$l\,s^{-1}$, $m^3\,h^{-1}$
Mass rate of flow	ρvA	$kg\,s^{-1}$	tonne h^{-1}

Energy control

Modelling thermal energy transfer

There are over 20 million homes in the UK. Of these, 75% were built before 1965, the year when the first requirement was made to include additional insulation within the building fabric. The housing stock is therefore very poorly insulated. Energy – and money – are going to waste. In Bristol, a large-scale project is aimed at assessing the extent of the problem and taking steps to make savings.

Energy flows at home

Figure 5C1 shows the energy flows through a typical house. Energy comes in from the fuel supply, from the occupants, and from solar gain – direct heating from sunlight. Some of the energy supplied is used for such purposes as cooking, lighting and operating electrical devices. Ultimately, most of this energy contributes to space heating – keeping the house warm enough for the comfort of the occupants.

The diagram also shows how energy leaves the house – through the walls, floors and roof, and in flue losses from gas or oil-fired boilers. To reduce the energy demand of the house, it is necessary to cut down on these losses. It is also desirable to try to increase the solar gain – the Sun's radiation comes free!

Energy loss is not just an expensive business. It also wastes valuable reserves of non-renewable fossil fuels. And it also means that more carbon dioxide, which is linked to global warming, is released to the atmosphere. Domestic energy control is therefore an important problem to deal with. But how to decide on priorities? Just what can be done about it?

▶ **Figure 5C1** *Energy flows in a typical home. The thickness of the line indicates roughly the relative contributions of the different components. The diagram suggests different ways in which improved fuel economy can be achieved.*

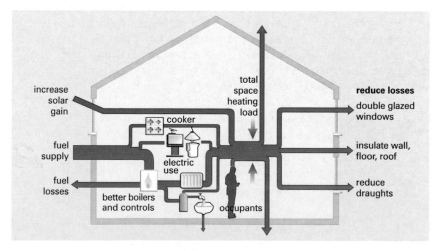

Computer modelling

Jon Walker is an energy consultant. He is the Technical Director of the Bristol Energy Centre, and he works with clients to help them identify what might be the most cost effective measures for improving the energy efficiency of their homes.

Jon uses a computer model which simulates the energy flows in the home. It is called BREDEM (Building Research Establishment Domestic Energy Model) and is based primarily around a series of calculations to assess thermal energy transfer within the property. Other calculations are carried out to assess the energy demand for water heating, lighting and other uses. The computer can also calculate the annual carbon dioxide emissions produced by the home. These calculations are backed up by comprehensive databases of fuel and material costs.

◀ **Figure 5C2** *Jon Walker at work, using the BREDEM program to assess a house in Bristol with the householder.*

▼ **Figure 5C3** *The NHER scale.*

energy rating	
10	very energy efficient house
9	
8	
7	new house built to 1990 building regulations
6	
5	
4	
3	
2	
1	
0	very energy inefficient house

Not only is it important to gather information on the building – types of wall, floor, roof, insulation, heating system and so on – but it is also essential to understand how people use the building. For example, if the householder is in all day and requires heat during that time, the energy consumption will be much higher than if the householder is out for most of the day. The level of heating required is also important. Internal temperatures might vary between 18 °C and 21 °C, depending on what people regard as comfortable. A difference of 1 °C from 21 °C to 20 °C might cut the fuel bill by up to 10%. Lifestyles and people's expectations have to be considered as an important part of the assessment.

'We've monitored identical homes that have a factor of ten difference in energy demand. This is due solely to the impact of the householders' lifestyle,' says Jon.

The results of Jon's survey give the home a score on the National Home Energy Rating (NHER) scale of 0 to 10. This scale is based on predicted annual running costs. The program will also tell the client what measures will improve the rating to what level, and what the capital costs and expected savings might be.

As Jon says, 'I hope that this type of home rating will become as widely recognized as "miles per gallon" is for cars.'

Predicting improvements

The results of a home survey, when fed into the computer, give a clear indication of the cost of possible improvements and the savings to be made. Jon Walker says 'I try to "fine tune" the running costs calculated by the computer program to match the actual fuel bills. Then, when we consider the options for improvement, we can give a more accurate idea of the benefits that can be gained from any investment.'

▶ **Figure 5C4** *A typical screen dump shows the computer assessment of space heating costs.*

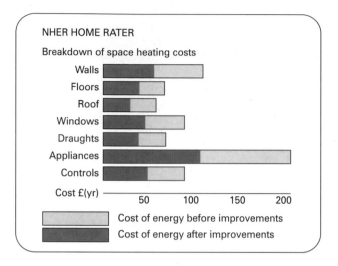

The client can obtain a certificate like that shown in Figure 5C5. This provides documentary evidence of the analysis. Although the service currently costs between £50 and £100 depending on the level of detail required, the hope is that new developments will bring down the costs substantially.

Taking stock

Many houses in the UK belong to Local Authorities. For a long time, councils have found it difficult to identify the priorities for expenditure on improving energy efficiency because of a lack of information on the energy efficiency of their housing stock. Unable to visit all their properties to carry out detailed surveys, they may use a simplified version of the NHER program to produce a stock profile of their housing.

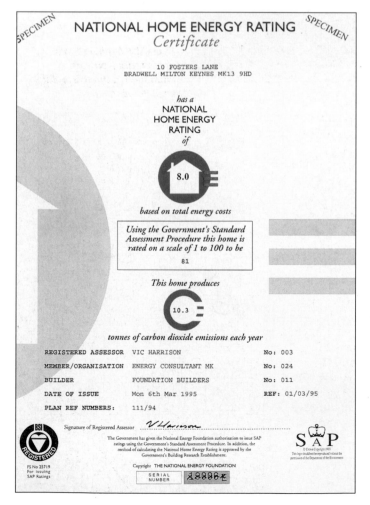

◀ **Figure 5C5**. *The NHER certificate shows the house's rating on the NHER scale, together with the level of CO_2 production.*

Bristol City Council, in the south west of England, has carried out a survey to produce a stock profile of their housing. It shows that the great bulk of their housing scores 3, 4 or 5 on the NHER scale – see Figure 5C3. This stock profile can then be used as the basis for formulating policy, setting targets for refurbishment and monitoring progress, and identifying priority estates or house types for more detailed analysis.

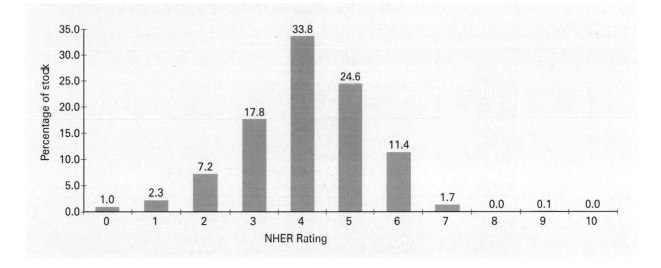

Figure 5C6 *The energy rating profile for Bristol City Council's housing stock, based on 1242 houses out of a total stock of 36 000.*

Managing energy

Graham Sims is an Area Services Manager with the responsibility of running a local housing office within Bristol. He also has the policy brief for energy and green issues within the housing directorate, and therefore the job of trying to coordinate the energy efficiency policy for all housing within the city.

Figure 5C7 *Graham Sims works to reduce energy consumption in the Bristol City Council housing stock.*

He says, 'The sample survey that has been done has already been used as the basis for formulating energy policy. We are trying to build up a comprehensive database of energy information about our housing stock throughout Bristol. This stock profile is an invaluable aid to achieving this goal. In the longer term, because it helps us to target our investment on our least energy efficient housing, the stock profile will help us towards our main aim of increasing the average rating of all the housing in Bristol.'

These computer models, based on the science of thermal energy transfer, can therefore be powerful tools within the world of energy management. They allow the user to model energy flow within the building, and then predict how the energy efficiency of the building might be improved and what impact improvements might have on energy demand. This allows effective decisions to be made on investment in energy efficiency, an important step in meeting national targets for the reduction of carbon dioxide emissions, not to mention the individual target of reducing fuel bills.

Improving insulation

Building standards are regularly improved. The Building Regulations suggest, among other things, the desirable properties of building materials and the permitted area of the windows and doors. This means that the fuel bills for a modern house are much lower than for an older, unimproved house. Modern insulating materials have been designed to give effective performance, based on a scientific understanding of the principles of thermal energy transfer.

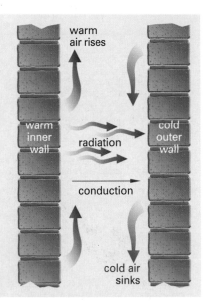

▲ **Figure 5C8** *Mechanisms of thermal energy transfer through a brick cavity wall.*

Heat escaping

Energy moves out from a warm house towards the colder outside world. When energy is lost to the outside air through a cavity wall, it first passes by conduction through the inner brick layer to the cavity. Then there are three possible mechanisms by which it may travel further.

- Most of the energy is transmitted by **radiation**. The inner surface of the cavity is warmer than the outer surface, and radiates infra-red waves across the gap. Infra-red waves are a form of electromagnetic radiation, less energetic than visible light.
- A small proportion of the energy escapes by **convection**. The air next to the inner wall becomes warmer; it expands and becomes less dense than the surrounding air, and so it floats upwards. A convection current is established within the cavity. Warm air arriving at the top of the cavity can escape from the top of the wall.
- Finally, a tiny proportion of the energy escapes by **conduction** through the air in the cavity. Energy is transferred from one air molecule to the next when they collide.

Reducing the flow

Since radiation is the predominant mechanism of thermal energy transfer through a cavity wall, it seems desirable to reduce this, perhaps by filling the gap with a solid material that will prevent the passage of infra-red radiation. But then, a solid material is likely to conduct much better than air. So good insulating materials try to combine the best aspects of solids and gases.

Figure 5C9 gives values of the **thermal conductivity** for several common building materials. (Thermal conductivity k is explained on page 85.) Not every piece of a particular type of material has the same conductivity – the composition may vary slightly – but these figures are quoted in the Building Regulations as being suitable values for use by building designers.

▶ **Figure 5C9** *Thermal conductivities of some common building materials.*

Insulation material	Thermal conductivity /$W m^{-1} K^{-1}$	Other building material	Thermal conductivity /$W m^{-1} K^{-1}$
Beaded polystyrene	0.035	Brickwork	0.84
Glass–fibre quilt	0.040	Cast concrete	1.40
Mineral fibre slab	0.035	Plaster	0.16
Polyurethane boards	0.025	Timber	0.14
Cavity foam (urea formaldehyde)	0.040	Glass	0.9
		Steel	50

In Figure 5C9, all those listed as 'insulation materials' are actually composites of a solid material and a gas. The solid accounts for only about 1% to 3% of the total volume, so these materials have very low densities. Although the properties of the solids vary a great deal, because so little of each insulant *is* solid, thermal conductivity is largely dependent on the gas. In the first four cases, the gas is air which has a conductivity $k = 0.024\,\mathrm{W\,m^{-1}\,K^{-1}}$. The conductivity of the composite is higher because some energy is conducted through the solid material and some is also radiated across the air spaces.

In the case of rigid polyurethane foam, a gas is used as the blowing agent to make the foam (see page 113). A gas with a lower thermal conductivity than air is chosen to improve the thermal conductivity over air-filled structures.

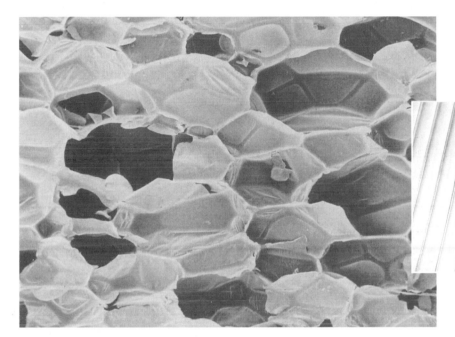

◀ **Figure 5C10** *This photomicrograph shows the microstructure of a rigid polyurethane foam. The gas-filled pockets contribute greatly to its thermal resistance.*

▲ **Figure 5C11** *The rate of flow of energy through a wall can be measured directly, using a* **thermal flow meter**. *This sensor has hundreds of tiny thermocouples on each surface to measure the temperature difference across its thickness. The sensor is connected to a meter which is calibrated to give a readout in $\mathrm{W\,m^{-2}}$.*

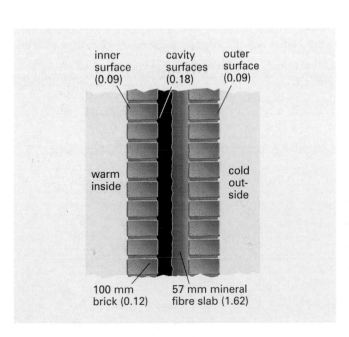

inner surface (0.09)   cavity surfaces (0.18)   outer surface (0.09)

warm inside

cold out-side

100 mm brick (0.12)   57 mm mineral fibre slab (1.62)

◀ **Figure 5C12** *The U-value (see page 84) of a wall, as required by the Building Regulations is $0.45\,\mathrm{W\,m^{-2}\,K^{-1}}$. Its thermal resistance is given by $1/U = 2.22\,\mathrm{m^2\,K\,W^{-1}}$. This is made up of several contributions, as shown here. The mineral fibre slab, 57 mm thick, contributes the bulk of the wall's resistance. An extra 1.4 m of brickwork would be needed to give an equivalent effect.*

An architect's sums

A detailed survey of a house or other building can provide the measurements needed to determine the building's energy requirements. These depend on the dimensions and building materials. It is also important to assess the way in which the building will be used, and to take into account the likely variation in outside temperatures.

Fabric loss

An architect is designing a new warehouse, which is to be built on the Isle of Wight; it will be used as a do-it-yourself store. How much are the annual heating bills likely to be?

▶ **Figure 5C13** *The warehouse design.*

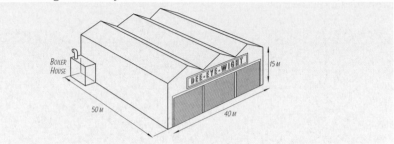

The first step in this calculation is to use the U-values of the different parts of the warehouse to determine how fast energy will be lost through the floors, walls, windows and roof. (U-value is defined on page 84.)

Area of floor = $50\,\text{m} \times 40\,\text{m} = 2000\,\text{m}^2$
U-value of flooring material = $0.35\,\text{W}\,\text{m}^{-2}\,\text{K}^{-1}$
Loss through floor = U-value × area = $0.35\,\text{W}\,\text{m}^{-2}\,\text{K}^{-1} \times 2000\,\text{m}^2 = 700\,\text{W}\,\text{K}^{-1}$

Thus the floor will lose $700\,\text{W}$ (or $700\,\text{J}\,\text{s}^{-1}$) for every 1 degree difference in temperature between the inside and outside. Adding up this quantity for each element of the building gives the fabric loss of the building.

Ventilation loss

For comfort, it is important to change the air in a building. This comes about partly through draughts, through doors being opened, and through ventilation and air conditioning systems. The air coming in is colder than the air going out, and so this constitutes another source of heat loss.

Typically, the air in a building is likely to be changed four times each day. To calculate the energy lost, it is necessary to use the density and the specific heat capacity of air (see page 83).

Volume of air = $50\,\text{m} \times 40\,\text{m} \times 15\,\text{m} = 30\,000\,\text{m}^3$

Mass of air changed each hour = $30\,000\,\text{m}^3 \times 1.29\,\text{kg}\,\text{m}^{-3} = 38\,700\,\text{kg}$

Energy lost every six hours per kelvin temperature difference
$$= 38\,700\,\text{kg} \times 993\,\text{J}\,\text{kg}^{-1}\,\text{K}^{-1} = 38.4\,\text{MJ}\,\text{K}^{-1}$$

$$\text{Rate of energy loss} = \frac{38.4\,\text{MJ}\,\text{K}^{-1}}{21\,600\,\text{s}} = 1780\,\text{W}\,\text{K}^{-1}$$

This is known as the ventilation loss. When added to the fabric loss, this gives the specific loss, the rate of energy loss from the building for each degree difference in temperature between the inside and the outside. For the warehouse, the total fabric loss might be about $3000\,\text{W}\,\text{K}^{-1}$, giving:

specific loss = ventilation loss + fabric loss = $(3000 + 1780)\,\text{W}\,\text{K}^{-1}$
$$= 4780\,\text{W}\,\text{K}^{-1}$$

Degree days

The amount of heating required varies throughout the day, and from day to day. It varies from place to place and it depends on the temperature required. To simplify calculations, the degree day system has been devised.

This system assumes that heating is only necessary when the outside temperature drops below $15.5\,°C$. (The inside temperature will be a few degrees higher than this, because of the contribution of people and machines to the heating.) If the temperature drops to, say, $14.5\,°C$ for a day, then this will contribute one degree day to the annual total. The map (Figure 5C14) shows the distribution of degree days across the country. This shows that, for example, in the Isle of Wight, about 1650 degree days of heating will be needed in one year.

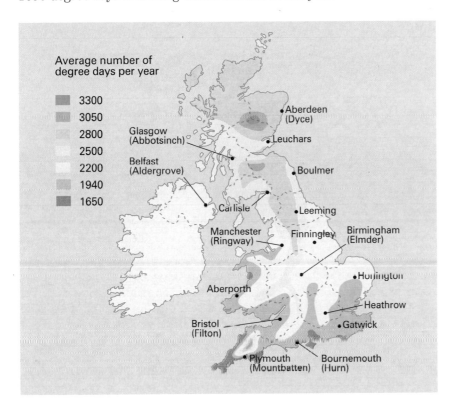

Average number of degree days per year

- 3300
- 3050
- 2800
- 2500
- 2200
- 1940
- 1650

Aberdeen (Dyce)
Glasgow (Abbotsinch)
Leuchars
Belfast (Aldergrove)
Boulmer
Carlisle
Leeming
Manchester (Ringway)
Finningley
Birmingham (Elmder)
Honington
Aberporth
Heathrow
Bristol (Filton)
Gatwick
Plymouth (Mountbatten)
Bournemouth (Hurn)

◀ **Figure 5C14** *Degree day map of the UK.*

The warehouse is to be built on the Isle of Wight; its annual energy requirement can now be found.

Energy required per degree day = specific loss per day
$$= 4780\,\mathrm{JK}^{-1} \times 60 \times 60 \times 24 = 4.1 \times 10^{8}\,\mathrm{JK}^{-1}$$

Energy required per year = specific loss per day $\times$ degree days
$$= 4.1 \times 10^{8}\,\mathrm{J} \times 1650 \text{ degree days} = 680\,\mathrm{GJ} \text{ per year}$$

The bottom line

The warehouse is to be heated by a gas-fired system which is 80% efficient. The price of gas is about £4.20 GJ^{-1}. Now the architect can produce an estimate of the annual gas bill:

$$\text{Energy required} = \frac{680\,\mathrm{GJ}}{0.80} = 850\,\mathrm{GJ}$$

$$\text{Cost} = 850\,\mathrm{GJ} \times £4.20\,\mathrm{GJ}^{-1} = £3570$$

Fuel and money

Most homes in the UK rely on fossil fuels to provide the bulk of their space heating. If coal, oil or gas are not being burnt on the premises, then the householder is probably relying on electricity generated as fuels are burned at the power station. Fuel costs money, so increases in energy efficiency are of benefit to a great many people.

Money for fuel

Figure 5C15 compares the cost of different fuels, and electricity, for domestic consumers. These figures are all shown as the cost for one **kilowatt hour** (1 kWh) – the amount of energy transferred when a 1 kW appliance is used for 1 hour. (1 kWh = 3.6 MJ.) The relatively high cost of electricity reflects the fact that power stations are typically only 40% efficient in their use of fuel.

Fossil fuels are **primary energy sources**. Electricity, which is usually generated from fossil fuels, is a **secondary energy source**.

▶ **Figure 5C15** *Comparing fuel costs; typical prices for domestic consumers, 1995.*

Fuel	Cost per kWh	Appliance	Efficiency	Cost per useful kWh
Gas	1.5p	Boiler	75%	2.0p
		Gas fire	60%	2.5p
Oil	1.4p	Boiler	70%	2.0p
Coal	2.4p	Boiler	70%	3.4p
Electricity	7.2p	Electric heater	100%	7.2p

In comparing the costs of different heating systems, their efficiencies must also be taken into account. A gas boiler, for example, wastes energy by releasing hot flue gases to the outside atmosphere. An electric heating system can be 100% efficient; all of the electrical energy supplied contributes to heating up the building.

$$\text{Efficiency} = \frac{\text{energy usefully transferred}}{\text{energy supplied in fuel}} \times 100\%$$

Improving efficiency

Gas fires and boilers are inefficient because of the hot flue gases, including CO_2 and CO, which are lost. They can also be dangerous because the flue gases are poisonous. Engineers have produced significant improvements in safety and efficiency over the years.

Figure 5C16a shows the principle of a balanced flue gas heater. Air, needed for the fuel to burn, is drawn in to the boiler. It flows past the flue gases, and so is partially heated before it reaches the flames. A separate flow of air is heated through a metal heat exchanger, and it is this air which warms the room. The flue gases do not enter the room, and so there is minimal danger to the user.

Figure 5C16b shows a modern gas condensing boiler. It has a large surface area for transferring energy to the water. It extracts additional energy from the flue gases by cooling them sufficiently to allow some to condense within the boiler. The condensed gases must be able to drain from the system. A condensing boiler is expensive, but the extra capital cost can be recovered in two to four years because it is likely to be 80–85% efficient.

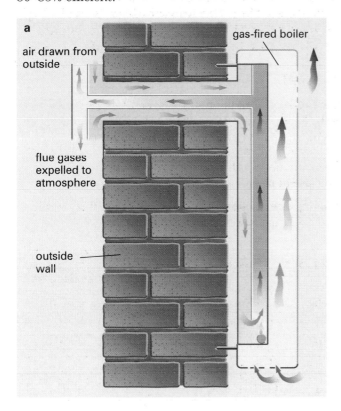

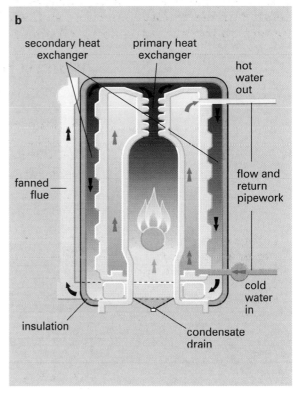

▲ **Figure 5C16** *The construction of* ***a*** *a balanced flue gas wall heater, and* ***b*** *a gas condensing boiler.*

Efficient polluters?

Burning fuels produces carbon dioxide and water vapour. Carbon dioxide contributes to the greenhouse effect and hence to global warming. Because fossil fuels are generally impure hydrocarbons, they can produce other polluting gases when they burn. Sulphur is present in coal and oil; nitrogen from the air is also oxidized when fuels burn, so the flue gases from power stations and smaller-scale boilers and fires produce sulphur and nitrogen oxides.

Some power stations are fitted with equipment to remove some of these pollutants. However, this is an expensive process, and the overall efficiency of the power station is reduced by 2 or 3%. The most modern combined-cycle gas-fired power stations are up to 50% efficient. The gas is first burned, and the hot gases produced turn one set of turbines; the gases are then used to heat water to generate steam, as in a conventional power station, and the steam turns a second set of turbines.

◄ **Figure 5C17** *Fuel consumption and production of pollutants for a typical house (annual energy consumption 30 GJ).*

Fuel	Annual consumption /kg	CO_2 production /kg	SO_2 production /kg
Oil	960	2800	5.8
Gas	1030	2600	0
Coal	1300	3200	13.0
Electricity*	—	9200	30.0
*electricity generated from a mixture of fossil fuels			

Loop the loop

Flick the switch to turn off the heater. Turn the dial to warm up the oven. Energy transfer systems, whether they are in homes, factories, cars, or the human body, need to be controlled. Users decide on targets – just what is the desired temperature? – and an automatic system uses feedback to ensure the target is reached.

In hot water

Most showers have a temperature control (Figure 5C18a). The water temperature can be changed by setting the control to a higher or lower position. This is a simple system with an **input** (hot and cold water), a control mechanism, and an **output** (warm water).

To ensure the water is at the correct temperature, the user checks the temperature of the water, and adjusts the control appropriately (Figure 5C18b). The user provides a **feedback path** between the output and the input.

With the presence of the feedback path, the system is known as a **closed loop** system. (Without the feedback, it is an open loop system – a contradiction in terms.) Information about the output (the temperature of the water, sensed by the person's hand) allows the user to decide whether the output matches the desired output. This information is fed back to the input, and the input control is changed correspondingly.

▶ **Figure 5C18** *Getting the water temperature right.*

Some advantages of automatic feedback systems ...
Operator released for other tasks
Cheaper to run
More sensitive control
More efficient operation
Long-term stability
... and some disadvantages
Can be complex to set up
Potentially unstable under fault conditions

In this example, a person has taken the role of several components of the system: the temperature **sensor**; the **comparator**, which compares the output temperature with the desired value; the nerves which provide the **feedback path**; and the mechanical input to the **controller**. It is often much better to have a fully automatic system which can perform all of these tasks.

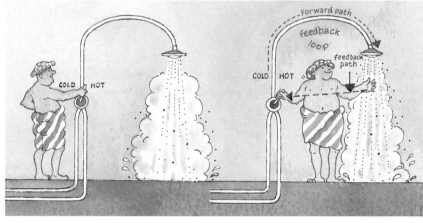

▶ **Figure 5C19** *The components of an automatic feedback system. The user sets the goal – the desired outcome; feedback can ensure that the goal is achieved and maintained.*

Feedback control in heating

Many houses have heating systems with automatic temperature control. A **thermostat**, usually mounted on a convenient wall, measures the room temperature. When the temperature falls below the set value, the heating system is switched on, and the temperature gradually rises again.

This type of feedback is known as **negative feedback**; as the temperature *decreases*, the heat input into the system *increases*.

In a system like this, the thermostat has several functions: it allows the user to set the desired temperature; it detects the temperature; it compares the set and actual temperatures; and it controls the heater.

The heater is switched on as the temperature drops below the set level, and off again as the set level is achieved. The thermostat must be designed to ensure that the system does not switch off and on too frequently.

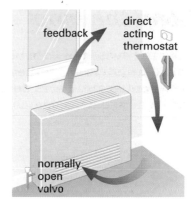

▲ **Figure 5C20** *A central heating system with thermostatic control.*

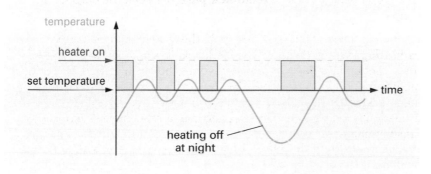

◀ **Figure 5C21** *Temperature fluctuations of a closed loop heating system.*

Thermostats are usually fitted to hot water cylinders so that the temperature of the domestic hot water is controlled separately from the room temperature. It is also possible to fit thermostatic radiator valves, so that individual radiators are separately controlled. Different rooms in a house can then be heated to different temperatures.

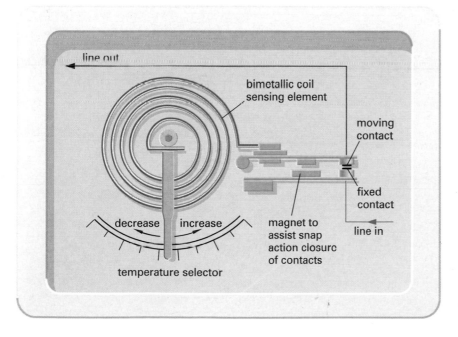

◀ **Figure 5C22** *A room thermostat based on a bimetallic coil. As the temperature drops, the coil gradually winds up. Eventually, the contacts snap together at a point set by the position of the temperature selector.*

Heat where it's needed

Electricity is useful. It is a clean and convenient way of transporting energy to the place where it is required. It is available at the flick of a switch. In industry, several different heating techniques make use of electric current to supply energy just where and when it is needed.

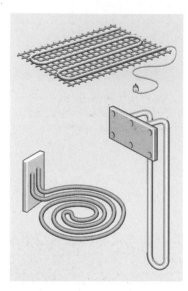

▲ **Figure 5C23** *Some resistance heating elements. Elements like these are used in domestic immersion heaters, cookers and electric kettles.*

▶ **Figure 5C24** *Using direct resistance heating in the production of metal springs for heavy vehicles at the West Bromwich Spring Company.*

Resistance heating

Indirect resistance heating is used in many industrial applications – in ovens and furnaces, in water boilers and for heating printing press platens. Some typical resistance heating elements are shown in Figure 5C23. A coil of resistance wire, surrounded by insulating material, is mounted inside a protective metal sheath. As the electric current flows through the wire, energy is transferred from the current to the wire (because of its resistance) and the wire gets hot. Energy is then transferred outwards by conduction.

A related approach is used in **direct resistance heating**. Here, the current is passed through the item to be heated. For example, in metal cutting, a metal rod (the electrode) is placed in contact with the metal which is to be welded or cut. A high current is passed through the electrode into the metal; the resistance at the point of contact means that energy is transferred rapidly from the current, and the metal glows white hot and melts.

This is also used in heating metal billets or rods. A high current is passed through a steel rod until it glows brightly at a temperature of 1000 °C; this is sufficient to soften the steel so that the rod can be rolled, stretched or coiled into a desired shape such as the springs used in the suspensions of lorries. The advantage of direct resistance heating is that the energy is supplied directly to the component that is to be heated. Although some heat necessarily radiates away, the process is much more efficient than the use of a furnace where a lot of energy is wasted in heating the furnace itself.

Energy from resistance

When an electric current I flows through a resistance R, energy is transferred at a rate P given by

$$P = I^2R$$

power (in W) = rate of energy transfer

$$= [\text{current (in A)}]^2 \times \text{resistance (in }\Omega)$$

In the circuit shown in Figure 5C25, the current I is measured by an ammeter (connected in series, so that the current flows through the meter). The voltmeter is measuring the voltage (or potential difference) V across the resistance element R.

The resistance, voltage and current are related by

$$V = I \times R \quad \text{voltage (in V)} = \text{current (in A)} \times \text{resistance (in }\Omega)$$

The power may also be calculated using $P = IV = \dfrac{V^2}{R}$.

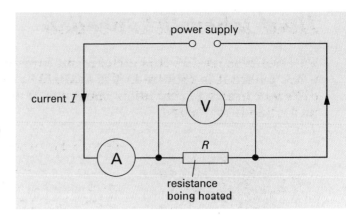

▲ **Figure 5C25** *A circuit for measuring the power delivered during resistance heating.*

More electroheat

Resistance heating is not the only way in which electricity is used in heating. The following are also ways of heating using electricity.

Microwave heating

Used in the food industry for drying products, for cooking meat, fish and potato crisps, and for sterilization. In a microwave oven, microwaves are generated using a magnetron (a type of electronic valve). Microwaves are electromagnetic radiation with wavelengths of the order of a few millimetres or centimetres. These penetrate the food and are absorbed by water molecules. The energy of the microwaves is thus directly absorbed by the food; the containers and the oven itself stay relatively cool.

Microwave heating is also used in other industries, for example, to melt an adhesive without overheating the materials being joined.

Infra-red heating

Used in 'stoving' (baking) paint on car bodies to give a more durable finish, for drying printing inks on plastic containers, sterilizing medicines and instruments. Since infra-red radiation is a form of electromagnetic radiation similar to visible light, it has the advantage that it can be focused on to a point where it is required, with little waste to the surroundings.

Induction heating

Used in large furnaces to melt metals. Also used for other processes such as tempering and annealing (see page 102). A large alternating current in a coil sets up a varying magnetic field. This makes current flow in a piece of metal which is to be melted, and the metal's resistance results in a rapid transfer of energy.

Advantages of electrical heating:
- high efficiency (approaching 100%)
- no fuel storage
- instant availability
- no pollution at point of use
- versatile.

Cold when it's needed

The frozen food industry has an enormous turnover. Food technologists devise new frozen products daily. If properly packed and frozen, food can have a greatly extended life, with more of its food value preserved than is the case with drying, canning and other techniques. Fridges and freezers remove energy from food so that the chemical reactions of decay are brought nearly to a halt.

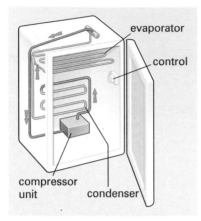

▲ **Figure 5C26** *A freezer makes use of the energy changes involved in evaporation and condensation.*

Extracting energy

A freezer has to remove energy from food in order to freeze it. There is also a constant slow leakage of energy into the freezer, because the insulation cannot provide a perfect barrier to the flow of heat, so the freezer must remove this energy, too.

Figure 5C26 shows the construction of a freezer. Heat is extracted from the food by the evaporator; the refrigerant fluid is pumped round the circuit by the compressor, and the extracted heat escapes from the condenser into the surroundings.

The refrigerant is a fluid that is pumped in a continuous cycle around the freezer. It is a liquid as it enters the evaporator. Here, the pressure is low, and the liquid evaporates rapidly. As it does so, its temperature drops. It cools the surrounding metal container, and the food is cooled by the metal. The gas leaving the evaporator is pumped by the compressor into the pipes of the condenser. Here it is under higher pressure, and it condenses, giving energy to the metal of the condenser. Energy then leaves the condenser by radiation and convection. The liquid refrigerant now continues round to the expansion valve, and the cyclical process continues.

A freezer or refrigerator has a thermostat so that the final temperature reached can be set by the user. For a domestic freezer, this is usually about −18°C, but commercial and industrial freezers and cold stores may be as cold as −40°C.

Latent heat

When a solid melts or a liquid evaporates or boils, energy must be put into the system. This is because energy is required to break the bonds between neighbouring molecules of the substance. So when the refrigerant is allowed to expand rapidly in the evaporator, its molecules break free from one another and the temperature of the fluid drops. The cold gas can then absorb energy from its surroundings before it is pumped round to the condenser.

Similarly, in order to condense a gas or freeze a liquid, energy must be extracted. It is this energy which is released from the condenser of the freezer when the refrigerant condenses.

The energy involved in a change of a state is known as **latent heat**. In order to calculate the energy involved when a substance changes state, it is necessary to know its **specific latent heat** (of melting or boiling). This is the amount of energy required to melt or boil 1 kg of the substance.

Melting (ice ⟶ water)	$L = 330\,\mathrm{kJ\,kg^{-1}}$
Boiling (water ⟶ steam)	$L = 2260\,\mathrm{kJ\,kg^{-1}}$
These figures show the energy that must be supplied to change ice to water, or water to steam. The same amount of energy must be removed to reverse the change.	

Thus to freeze 0.5 kg of water at 0°C, the amount of energy which must be extracted is given by

$$\text{energy} = mL = 0.5\,\mathrm{kg} \times 330\,\mathrm{kJ\,kg^{-1}} = 165\,\mathrm{kJ}$$

Typically, food is frozen from a temperature above 0°C to a temperature below 0°C, so more energy than this must be extracted; this can be calculated knowing the specific heat capacity of the food.

Electronic control

The thermostat in a fridge or freezer senses the temperature in the freezing compartment, and switches the compressor on if the temperature rises above the set level. Usually, the sensing circuit of the thermostat operates an electrical relay to switch on the compressor. Figure 5C28 shows a circuit for doing this.

The **thermistor** is a resistor whose resistance changes rapidly with temperature (see page 81). The operational amplifier (op amp) acts as a **comparator** to compare the voltages at its inputs. One voltage comes from the thermistor, and the other from the **variable resistor**. When the thermistor resistance falls as the temperature rises, the voltage across it drops and the comparator switches on the **transistor**. A current flows through the **relay coil**, activating it and closing the **switch**. The compressor starts up.

Adjusting the **variable resistor** allows the user to set the temperature at which the compressor comes on. Moving the contact upwards increases the voltage at the negative (−) input to the op amp.

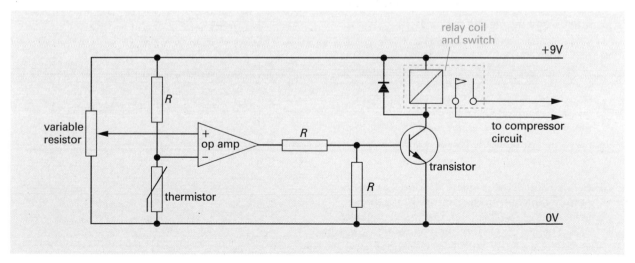

▲ **Figure 5C28** *An automatic temperature control circuit. In this example, the relay is used to switch on a freezer's compressor when the temperature rises; it could be simply adapted to switch on a heater when the temperature in a room drops.*

Thoughts and actions

1 Write a paragraph in non-technical language, outlining road safety precautions, addressed to a teenage cyclist. (You will find relevant information in Chapter 5A.)

Write a second paragraph dealing with the same ideas, but using scientific terminology. You should include the following terms, among others:
- energy (kinetic, elastic etc.)
- momentum
- force
- work done.

2 When traffic police are interpreting the skid marks of a car, they use two equations (pages 244–5) which are derived from the kinematic equations. Explain how equations 1 and 4 on page 248 are modified to give the equations used by the police.

In a police investigation, a car is found to have skidded to a halt in a distance of 40 m. The drag factor of the road is measured to be 0.4. Calculate the car's deceleration, and its speed when it started to skid.

3 Measurements taken during the impact test described on pages 252–3 can be used to calculate a variety of quantities. Use the results given at the foot of page 253 to check the values given for kinetic energy, duration of impact and deceleration.

4 Design an impact test similar to that described on pages 252–3 which you could carry out in your college or school laboratory to investigate the energy-absorbing characteristics of egg boxes. Your plan should state the measurements you would make, together with how you would make them, and what you would expect to deduce from them.

5 Feedback is used in many systems as a method of providing automatic control. The general principles of feedback are discussed on page 288. The governor described on page 262 is an example of a mechanical negative feedback system.
a Why is it called a *feedback* system?
b Why is the feedback described as *negative*?
c Why is it called a *mechanical* system?
d Why is the control it provides described as *automatic*?

6 The principle of **electromagnetic induction** is as follows: If an electrical conductor (such as a wire or a coil of wire) moves through a magnetic field, a voltage difference is induced across its ends. Alternatively, the conductor may be stationary, and the magnetic field may change.

Many sensors and measuring devices use the principle of electromagnetic induction, because the voltage difference induced can be readily detected. Scan the pages of Unit 5 to find as many such devices as possible. Classify them according to whether they use a moving conductor or a changing magnetic field.

7 In an impact test on a crash helmet (page 258), the force on the helmet is measured using force transducers which give a continuous record of the force on the helmet during the impact. The graph below shows how the force on a helmet (with dummy head) of mass 4.0 kg varied during one test. Use the graph to deduce:
a the greatest force on the helmet
b its greatest deceleration (in $m\,s^{-2}$, and in g)
c the change in momentum of the helmet during the impact
d its speed at the instant of impact.

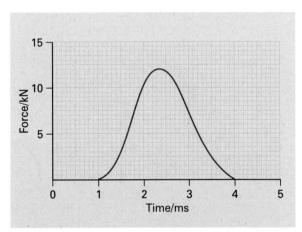

▲ Figure 5T1

8 Sketch a speed–time graph to represent the motion of a car which is travelling at a steady speed until the driver notices a brick wall ahead. She brakes, but the car does not stop before it hits the wall. Indicate on the graph:
a the point where the car's speed is greatest
b the point where its deceleration is greatest.

9 The graph shown in Figure 5A2 shows that the police cannot be entirely sure about the deceleration of a car on a particular road surface. There is a range of possible drag factors for each condition. How will this affect the certainty with which they can treat their evidence? (You will find ideas about the reliability of data in Chapter 8A.)

How is this problem reduced by the use of a drag sled?

Imagine that you were the defence lawyer in a court case in which your client is accused of exceeding the speed limit, based on evidence gathered in the ways described on pages 244–5. In what ways would you attempt to cast doubt on the police case?

10 In their promotional literature, car manufacturers make a variety of claims for the different models they produce – acceleration and speed, fuel consumption, safety etc. Study some advertising leaflets, and identify the technical information they provide.

If consumers are to make sensible comparisons between different models, they require reliable information presented in a standard way. Draw up a specification for the technical data which you think would be useful to consumers in making their choice between different but similar models.

11 When Michael Lord designed his sailboard speedo (page 264), he found that no equivalent meter was available. He thinks there is a good market for his design, if he can sell it to sailboard manufacturers. Draw up a statement which Michael might send to a prospective manufacturer of his speedo. You will need to give a clear technical description of the speedo, together with an assessment of its value to sailboarders.

12 When Chris Boardman became an Olympic cycling champion, both he and his bicycle had been extensively tested in a wind tunnel like the one shown on page 266, to improve the aerodynamic design of his cycle, helmet etc. Lotus, who helped to develop his cycle, put a great deal of resources into ensuring his success. Is it fair that one cyclist should have this degree of help in becoming a champion? Who won the race, Chris Boardman, the cycle, or the whole team who worked to help him win?

13 There are probably more pumps in the world today than any other type of industrial machine. Several different types of pump are described on pages 270–7.
   a Describe the operation of a peristaltic pump, such as is used in a kidney dialysis machine. Why is it appropriate for this task?
   b Copy and complete the table in Figure 5T2. Include as many types of pump and their uses as you can find.

Type of pump	Uses
	aerating a tropical fish tank
diaphragm pump	
	evacuating a vacuum flask
	pumping sewage

▲ Figure 5T2

14 Oil of density $800 \, \text{kg m}^{-3}$ is flowing along a pipe of diameter 0.25 m. In a measurement of the mass rate of flow, 300 kg is collected in 10 s. Calculate:
   a the mass rate of flow in kg s^{-1}
   b the volume rate of flow in $\text{m}^3 \text{s}^{-1}$
   c the speed of flow in m s^{-1}.

15 Water treatment engineers have the problem of dealing with all the water which comes down the drains to the treatment plant. The amount of water can vary dramatically, as is shown by the graphs in Figure 5B13 (page 272). Explain why the volume of water in the drains may vary:
   a with a regular daily pattern
   b with the seasons
   c over a long period of time, for example, when new housing estates are built.
Why is this a problem for the water treatment companies?

16 Nowadays, anyone who installs a pipe which carries water to a garden tap must include a non-return valve, to prevent water from the garden flowing back down the pipe and contaminating the domestic supply. Draw a design for a simple non-return valve which automatically prevents water from flowing the wrong way.

17 Any gas boiler has an efficiency which is less than 100%. Explain what is meant by the term *efficiency* in this context.

Why is the efficiency of a balanced flue gas heater greater than that of a conventional gas fire? What further improvements are made in a gas condensing boiler?

An electric heater is likely to be almost 100% efficient, but the cost of the energy which it supplies is much greater than for a gas fire. Why is this?

18 Study the table given in Figure 5C17 (page 287). Write a paragraph comparing the environmental impacts of different fuel supplies used in a typical house.

19 Some domestic hot water tanks are fitted with two electrical immersion heaters, one at the bottom and one half way up. In normal use, the upper heater provides sufficient hot water. Use the idea of convection to explain why the upper heater does not heat the water in the lower half of the tank. Why is this a useful way of saving energy?

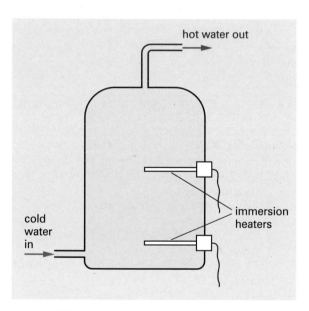

hot water out

cold
water
in

immersion
heaters

▲ **Figure 5T3**

20 Study Figure 5C1 on page 278. This shows the energy flows in a typical home.
  a List the different sources of energy which contribute to space heating in the home.
  b List the different ways in which energy is lost from the home.
  c Suggest ways in which the amount of energy lost could be reduced.
  d Consider your own home. In what ways might you reduce its energy demand without reducing the comfort of its occupants?

21 a How much energy must be supplied to boil 100 g of water at 100 °C?
  b How much ice at 0 °C could be melted with this amount of energy?

22 Cavity foam is an effective form of insulation for houses. The structure of materials such as polyurethane foam is described in Chapter 2B. Explain the different ways in which this material can help to reduce heat loss through walls.

23 a In measurements on a new composite building material, it is found that the rate of heat flow through 5 m^2 of the material is 30 W, when a temperature difference of 18 °C is maintained across it. Calculate the *U*-value of the material. Would this material be suitable for use in building the walls of houses?
  b How would you set about measuring the rate of heat flow in a test like this?

24 In studying the energy demand of different homes, staff from the Bristol Energy Centre have found great variations between similar homes – see page 279. These variations arise from differences in lifestyle between the occupants; energy demand can differ by as much as a factor of ten. Suggest some differences in lifestyle which might give rise to such big differences.

25 Premature babies often have to spend some time in an incubator. Their surroundings must be maintained at a constant temperature.
  a Draw a block diagram to represent a system for maintaining an incubator at 39 °C.
  b How would you measure the temperature of the incubator?
  c How does negative feedback play a part in your system?
  d Are there any disadvantages in using an automatic system in this situation?

26 Why should we have Building Regulations which specify the maximum permitted *U*-values for building materials?

27 No freezer is perfectly insulated. Energy is always leaking in from the surroundings, and must be pumped out. Some people suggest that a freezer should be kept well-filled to maximize the efficiency of its use. It has even been suggested that empty space in a freezer should be filled with old newspapers. What do you think?

UNIT 6

Controlling reactions

How far? Chemical equilibria

Photography

Photography demonstrates in an often beautiful way how the results of chemical reactions are affected by temperature, timing, and the concentrations of materials.

▲ **Figure 6A1** *Silver halide crystals in a photographic film. The larger crystals are about 3 μm in size.*

Light sensitive chemicals

The film used for black and white photography is coated with an emulsion made of grains of silver halide trapped in gelatine. An image can be captured on this film because light causes the silver halide to react. The camera shutter opens for an instant exposing the silver halide to light and the light energy triggers a transfer of electrons from the halide ions to the silver ions, reducing them to metallic silver.

Developing the film

The image produced on the film is the 'negative' of the scene that was photographed. In the areas of film exposed to the brightest light, the most dark metallic silver is produced. This image is not visible, however, because the brief exposure to light only reduces a tiny proportion of each grain of silver halide to silver. The film is said to contain a hidden or 'latent' image which will appear when the film is developed. This is done by placing the film in a 'developer', which is an alkaline solution of a mild reducing agent.

If film is left in the developer too long all the silver ions in the emulsion are reduced to silver. The trick is to keep it in the developer for exactly the right amount of time. The first silver ions to be reduced by the chemicals in the developer are those which are next to the atoms of metallic silver produced by the reaction with light. The developer, therefore, carries on the reduction of silver ions that the light started and intensifies the image.

When an image of exactly the right intensity has been produced, the reaction has to be stopped, immediately. The chemistry of developing film was designed with these quick stops in mind. The developer only reduces the silver ions in alkaline conditions. To stop the process, the film is transferred to a 'stop bath' containing a solution of dilute ethanoic acid. Once the alkalinity is neutralized, the reduction stops.

▼ **Figure 6A2** *Stages in developing a black and white film.*

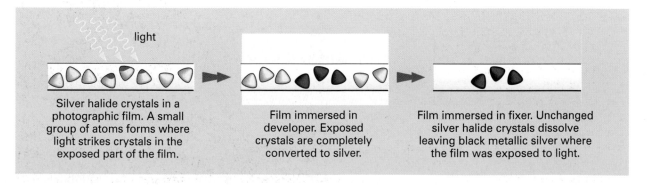

light

Silver halide crystals in a photographic film. A small group of atoms forms where light strikes crystals in the exposed part of the film.

Film immersed in developer. Exposed crystals are completely converted to silver.

Film immersed in fixer. Unchanged silver halide crystals dissolve leaving black metallic silver where the film was exposed to light.

Fixing the image

All this chemistry has to take place in the dark. Exposing the emulsion to light would cause silver ions all over the film to be reduced and the image would be obliterated. Before the developed film can be taken out of the darkroom, the silver halide has to be removed in a reaction that will leave behind the dark silver grains. This is done by placing the film in a 'fixer'. This is a solution of sodium or ammonium thiosulphate which reacts with the silver halides to give a water-soluble complex of thiosulphate ions with silver ions, $[Ag(S_2O_3)_2]^{3-}$.

After this reaction and several washes, the negative is allowed to dry and then used to make a print. The photograph is printed on paper which, like the film, is coated with an emulsion containing silver halide. Light is shone through the negative onto the paper to give the emulsion a brief exposure to the image. Then the paper is developed by the same process as the negative.

Controlling the processes

The temperature of the baths of chemicals used in the processing of film is critical to the quality of the final photograph. Liverpool-based professional photographer Geoff Roberts explains. 'If the temperature is too high, the developing reaction occurs too quickly and the picture looks grainy because the particles of silver produced are too large. The chemical solutions are designed to be used at 68°C and at this temperature the time for development is usually exactly as recommended by the manufacturers.

Ignoring the instructions to save time can lead to problems. 'There are occasions when a photographer will want to develop photos quickly' says Geoff. 'A picture may be needed to go with a late-breaking newspaper story, for example. One short cut is to wash the developer or fixer off by holding the film under the cold-water tap rather than wash it in a series of water baths at 68°C. One problem with this is that tap water is too cold. The rapid temperature change between warm developer and the cold water can cause cracks to form in the photographic emulsion and ruin the picture.'

'If the fixer solution is too concentrated or the film isn't well washed, silver halide is left behind and years later the negative will go brown as it slowly turns to metallic silver. If the fixer is too cool or not concentrated enough, the negative image appears washed out with not enough contrast between lights and shades.'

Even so, there is, according to Geoff, room for a bit of art as well as science in the development of film. 'Most photographers who do their own developing, keep the developing in mind as they take their pictures. Photos taken on a sunny day have strong blacks and whites and these usually require a little less time in the developing solution.'

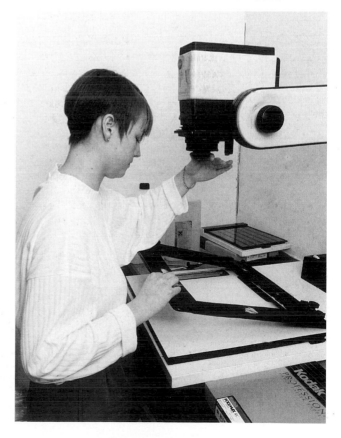

▼ **Figure 6A3** *Photographer at work in Geoff's darkroom.*

Manufacturing an anaesthetic

Controlling chemical changes is also important in industry which manufactures drugs and other essential products on a large scale. During an operation, there's a good chance that nitrous oxide (N_2O) will be one of the anaesthetic gases given to the patient. After an accident, an injured person needing quick pain relief may be offered a mask connected to a cylinder of Entonox, a fifty-fifty mixture of nitrous oxide and oxygen. Entonox is also used for pain relief by women in labour.

Laughing gas

Many modern drugs are complex molecules produced by expensive multi-step syntheses, yet one of the most widely used and enduring anaesthetics is a small inorganic molecule that can be manufactured in a one-step continuous process.

Nitrous oxide, N_2O, was first prepared and recognized as a distinct gas by Joseph Priestley in 1772 and the possibility that it could be used to relieve pain during surgical operations was first raised in 1799 by Humphry Davy. Before it received much serious attention, however, it was adopted as a recreational drug and given the name 'laughing gas'. In the first part of the 19th century, breathing nitrous oxide livened up many of the more exclusive scientific and medical parties in Europe and America. It was an American dentist who first demonstrated its usefulness as an anaesthetic in 1845.

Small amounts of nitrous oxide can be produced in the laboratory by allowing iron to react with nitric acid. Nitric oxide (NO) is first produced, but an excess of iron reduces this further to nitrous oxide.

$$2NO(g) + Fe(s) \longrightarrow FeO(s) + N_2O(g)$$

Commercially, however, the best way to produce it is by the thermal decomposition of ammonium nitrate:

$$NH_4NO_3(l) \xrightarrow{250\,°C} N_2O(g) + 2H_2O(g)$$

▼ **Figure 6A4** *Mike Sherwin in the control room of the BOC plant.*

The manufacturing process

Obtaining the raw material for the manufacture of nitrous oxide is easy and cheap. Each year in Britain millions of tonnes of ammonium nitrate are produced for use as a fertilizer. Given that ammonium nitrate is also an explosive, however, it may seem an unlikely chemical to use in a continuous process which involves high temperature. In practice this reaction is remarkably easy to control and development of the right plant and procedures have made it safe. The gas has been successfully manufactured by this method for several decades in plants all over the world.

BOC's plant in Worsley near Manchester (see pages 4–5) makes all the nitrous oxide used in Britain. The starting material is a 90–92% solution by weight of ammonium nitrate which is kept in heated storage tanks (see pages 4–5 to find out how analysts check the purity of this starting material). A compressed air pump transfers it at a constant rate into a second tank, known as 'the melter' where it is heated further. Compressed air is again used to keep a continuous flow of warmer liquid into the reaction vessel. Ammonium dihydrogenphosphate is also added as a catalyst.

The plant runs 24 hours a day, 5 days a week. Over the weekend, the reaction vessel is kept at 180 °C. On Monday morning electric heating coils in the walls of the vessel are used to heat it to 250 °C and the reaction begins. In fact, two reactions take place in these conditions:

$$NH_4NO_3(l) \longrightarrow N_2O(g) + 2H_2O(g)$$
and $$NH_4NO_3(l) \longrightarrow NH_3(g) + HNO_3(g)$$

The presence of the catalyst (ammonium dihydrogenphosphate) encourages the reaction that produces nitrous oxide but the side reaction is important too because it controls the temperature in the reaction vessel.

The process is particularly elegant because the reactions themselves keep the vessel at the reaction temperature, 250 °C. Once the reaction begins, the heating coils can be turned off because the decomposition of ammonium nitrate to nitrous oxide and water is exothermic. The reaction produces enough heat to keep the reaction vessel at 250 °C. The temperature doesn't rise above this, however, because of the second reaction and the fact that it is reversible. Much of the ammonia and nitric acid that is produced react to form ammonium nitrate again in an endothermic reaction. This relatively cool liquid ammonium nitrate drips back down into the reaction vessel.

$$NH_3(g) + HNO_3(g) \longrightarrow NH_4NO_3(l)$$

Meanwhile, the gaseous nitrous oxide and water vapour are drawn upward through pipe work to a condenser which removes most of the water. Then, the nitrous oxide gas bubbles through four columns of liquid, called scrubbers, to remove impurities:

- column 1 – contains water and it just removes particles
- column 2 – contains a solution of 10% sodium hydroxide and 2% manganate(VII) to neutralize and dissolve nitric acid and any other acid in the gas
- column 3 – contains acid to neutralize and dissolve the alkalis in the gas
- column 4 – contains water to give the gas a final clean.

The nitrous oxide is then compressed to force most of the water remaining in the gas to condense. The rest of the water is removed by passing the gas through a bed of silica gel and activated alumina.

At this point, the nitrous oxide is tested for impurities prior to being compressed in the plant's storage tank. From this tank and after further tests, the gas is transferred to cylinders for storage, distribution and sale.

Energy changes and chemical reactions

Understanding energy changes helps chemists to control reactions. During the manufacture of nitrous oxide, energy from the decomposition of ammonium nitrate keeps the chemicals hot so that the reaction keeps going fast enough. This is one of many examples which show that it is important to measure and monitor energy changes.

Exothermic or endothermic?

Reactions that take energy in from the surroundings are **endothermic**.

Reactions that give out energy to the surroundings are **exothermic**.

During a chemical change, there is an exchange of energy between the reaction and the surroundings. The decomposition of limestone requires a constant input of energy, not only to start it off but to keep it going. On the other hand, the decomposition of ammonium nitrate only needs a little energy to start it, after which the energy from the exothermic reaction is enough to keep it going.

A familiar example of an exothermic reaction is the flame produced by burning natural gas, methane, in air. Here, the energy given out warms buildings and cooks food. But the combination of methane gas and oxygen that produces the flame needs to be coaxed into reacting. Without a match or an electric spark the reaction will not get going. At room temperature methane and oxygen could quite happily coexist without ever reacting. This is because, in all reactions, regardless of whether they are exothermic or endothermic, some of the chemical bonds in the reactants have to be broken before the new chemical bonds of the products can be formed. Only then will the reaction continue.

So what decides whether chemical reactions take in or give out energy to the surroundings? To answer this question it helps to think of chemical bonds as tiny springs. In order to get methane to react with oxygen, those tiny springs joining all the atoms in the methane and oxygen molecules have first to be stretched and broken. And, as anybody who has ever used a chest expander knows, this requires an input of energy.

▶ **Figure 6A5** *Bond breaking and bond forming when methane burns in oxygen.*

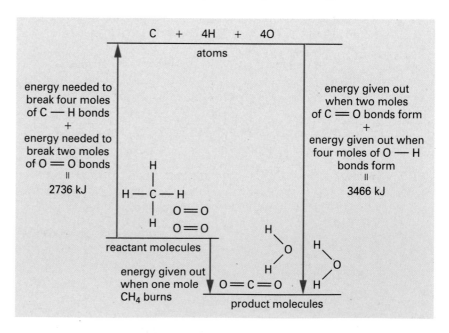

Then new bonds have to be formed by oxygen atoms with the carbon or hydrogen atoms. Bond formation always releases energy to the surroundings – just like a relaxing spring. Consequently what determines whether a chemical reaction is endothermic or exothermic is the overall difference between the energy taken in to break the bonds of the reactants, compared to the energy given out in forming the bonds of the products. This difference is called the **enthalpy change** of the reaction, and is represented by the sign ΔH.

An example of an exothermic reaction

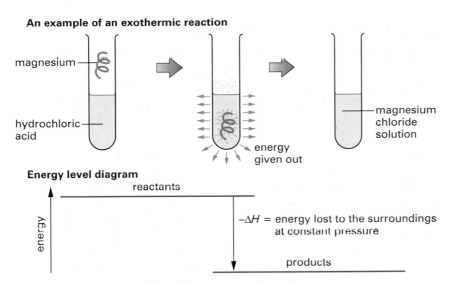

◀ **Figure 6A6** *Energy changes in an exothermic reaction.*

In the case of burning methane, there is more energy given out by forming the new bonds in the products than is needed to break the old bonds in the reactants. The reaction is exothermic and the enthalpy change is given a negative value, $-\Delta H$. For endothermic reactions, more energy is taken up in breaking the old bonds in the reactants than is given out in product formation. The enthalpy change for endothermic reactions is given a positive value, $+\Delta H$.

An example of an endothermic reaction

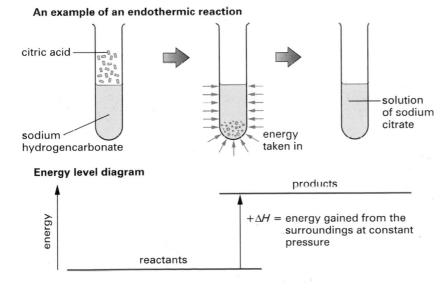

◀ **Figure 6A7** *Energy changes in an endothermic reaction.*

▼ **Figure 6A8** *The activation energy of a reaction.*

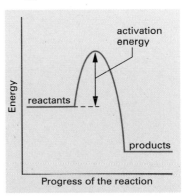

The energy required to initiate a reaction is called the **activation energy**. It is like an energy hill where the reactants have to climb before a reaction will occur: the higher the hill, the more difficult it is to get the reaction started.

How far? Chemical equilibria **303**

Reversible changes

Some changes go only in one direction. The changes that happen to a raw egg in boiling water cannot be reversed by cooling it down. To produce a soft boiled egg a cook has to check that it stays in the water for just the right amount of time. Other processes in the kitchen are easily reversed such as a table jelly setting as it cools but becoming a liquid again on warming. Chemists, like cooks, have to understand how to control conditions to get reactions to go far enough and in the right direction.

Burning methane in air is an example of an **irreversible** change. The gas burns to form carbon dioxide and water, then it is virtually impossible to turn the products back into methane and oxygen. Like a raw egg, the methane in natural gas used for cooking was produced by complex biological processes – but a very long time ago.

In contrast, melting and evaporating are familiar reversible processes. Heating turns water into steam but water reforms as steam condenses on cooling.

$$H_2O(l) \xrightarrow{\text{heat}} H_2O(g)$$

$$H_2O(g) \xrightarrow{\text{cool}} H_2O(l)$$

Combining the two equations gives:

$$H_2O(l) \overset{\text{heat}}{\underset{\text{cool}}{\rightleftarrows}} H_2O(g)$$

Many chemical reactions are also reversible. When blue copper(II) sulphate crystals are heated, for example, they decompose to give a white powder of anhydrous copper(II) sulphate and water vapour.

$$CuSO_4.5H_2O(s) \xrightarrow{\text{heat}} CuSO_4(s) + 5H_2O(g)$$

Add water and the white powder turns blue as it changes back into the hydrated form of copper sulphate, and it gets very hot.

$$CuSO_4(s) + 5H_2O(l) \xrightarrow{\text{cool}} CuSO_4.5H_2O(l)$$

Combining the two processes in one equation gives:

$$\underset{\text{reactants}}{CuSO_4.5H_2O(s)} \overset{\text{heat}}{\underset{\text{cool}}{\rightleftarrows}} \underset{\text{products}}{CuSO_4(s) + 5H_2O(l)}$$

Reversible reactions can go both ways. The change from left to right in the equation is the **forward** reaction (from reactants to products). The change from right to left is the **backward** reaction (from products to reactants).

A reversible process can go forwards or backwards depending on the conditions. The direction of change may vary with the temperature, the pressure or the concentrations of the chemicals.

Equilibrium

Reversible changes often reach a state of balance, or equilibrium. Melting ice and water, for example, are in equilibrium at 0 °C. The equilibrium state is a mixture of both sides of the reversible change.

A mixture of two solutions of iodine helps to explain what happens when a reversible change reaches a state of equilibrium. Iodine is slightly soluble in water but much more soluble in aqueous potassium iodide solution. The solution is yellow-brown. Iodine is also soluble in hydrocarbons such as hexane in which it forms a violet solution.

Potassium iodide solution and hexane do not mix. Figure 6A9 shows what happens on shaking iodine with the two solvents.

▼ Figure 6A9

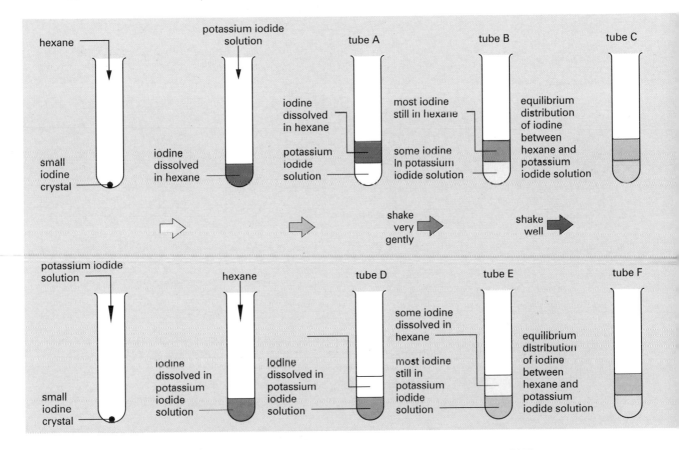

The graphs in Figure 6A10 show how the iodine concentrations in the two layers change with shaking. In tube C, the iodine is distributed between the hydrocarbon and aqueous layers and there is no more change. In this tube there is an **equilibrium**.

$$I_2(hexane) \rightleftharpoons I_2(aq)$$

Tube F looks just like tube C. The equilibrium mixtures in the two tubes are the same.

This demonstration with iodine solution illustrates two important features of equilibrium processes:

■ at equilibrium, the concentration of reactants and products does not change
■ an equilibrium can be approached from either the 'reactant side' or the 'product side' of a reaction.

▼ Figure 6A10

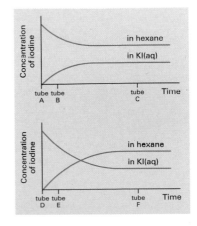

How far? Chemical equilibria **305**

Dynamic equilibrium

Figure 6A11 gives a picture of what happens to the iodine molecules on shaking a solution of iodine in hexane with aqueous potassium iodide.

$$I_2(\text{in hexane}) \rightleftharpoons I_2(\text{aq})$$

All the iodine molecules start in the hydrocarbon layer. At first, on shaking, movement is in one direction (the forward reaction) as some molecules move into the aqueous layer. There is nothing to stop some of these molecules moving back into the hexane but this backward reaction starts slowly because the concentration in the aqueous layer is small. So to begin with, iodine transfers from the hexane to the aqueous layer because the forward reaction is faster than the backward reaction.

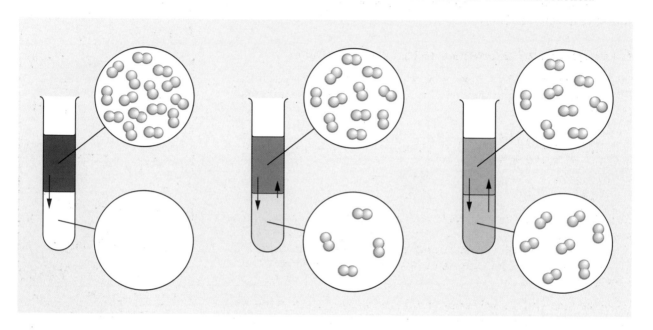

▲ **Figure 6A11** *Iodine molecules reaching dynamic equilibrium between two solvents.*

As the concentration in the aqueous layer rises, the backward rate increases until, at equilibrium, the two rates are equal. At equilibrium, the movement from one layer to the other continues, but there is no overall change. This is because each layer is gaining and losing iodine molecules at the same rate. This is **dynamic equilibrium**.

Decomposing ammonium chloride

Here is an example of how the idea of dynamic equilibrium applies to chemical changes. At room temperature and open to the atmosphere, ammonia gas and gaseous hydrogen chloride react to form a white smoke of ammonium chloride particles.

$$NH_3(g) + HCl(g) \longrightarrow NH_4Cl(s)$$

Heat solid ammonium chloride in a tube open to the atmosphere and it decomposes back into gaseous ammonia and hydrogen chloride.

$$NH_4Cl(s) \longrightarrow NH_3(g) + HCl(g)$$

But on heating ammonium chloride in a **sealed container**, it does not decompose completely. The reactants and products reach a state of **equilibrium**. At this stage, it appears as if the reaction has stopped.

What has actually happened is that the decomposition of ammonium chloride to gaseous ammonia and hydrogen chloride (the forward reaction), and the combination of the two gases to form ammonium chloride (the backward reaction) are both proceeding at the same **rate**. The equilibrium is not static, it is **dynamic**.

Shifting the position of equilibrium

Chemists have discovered that they can control reactions to change the proportions of reactants and product at equilibrium. To do so they apply one of the fundamental principles about chemical equilibria, first noticed by the French chemist Le Châtelier, that 'when a chemical system which is in equilibrium is subjected to a change, the system will alter in such a way as to lessen the change'.

Changing the pressure and temperature

The decomposition of ammonium chloride illustrates the way in which the temperature and pressure within a container affect an equilibrium mixture.

$$NH_4Cl(s) \underset{\text{higher pressure}}{\overset{\text{lower pressure}}{\rightleftharpoons}} NH_3(g) + HCl(g)$$

low volume   large volume
of solid   of gas

Le Châtelier's principle predicts that increasing the pressure will cause the equilibrium to shift to the left. Turning gas molecules into a solid reduces the volume of the system and so tends to lower the pressure. The effect of increasing the pressure is to increase the amount of ammonium chloride.

Raise the temperature by heating and the equilibrium shifts in the direction which takes in energy. The formation of ammonium chloride is exothermic while the decomposition of the solid is endothermic. So that if the sealed container is heated, this favours the decomposition reaction to gaseous ammonia and hydrogen chloride which takes in energy.

$$NH_4Cl(s) \underset{\text{lower temperature}}{\overset{\text{higher temperature}}{\rightleftharpoons}} NH_3(g) + HCl(g)$$

Changing the concentration

Figure 6A13, on the next page, shows how Le Châtelier's principle applies to aqueous bromine. Bromine in water is an equilibrium mixture:

$$\underset{\text{orange}}{Br_2(aq)} + H_2O(l) \rightleftharpoons \underset{\text{all colourless}}{\underbrace{OBr^-(aq) + Br^-(aq) + 2H^+(aq)}} \tag{1}$$

The solution is yellow-orange because of the dissolved bromine molecules some of which do not react with water. All the ions on the right-hand side of the equation are colourless.

Heterogeneous
The equilibrium of ammonium chloride with the gases ammonia and hydrogen chloride involves two phases: solid and gaseous. It is an example of a heterogeneous equilibrium.

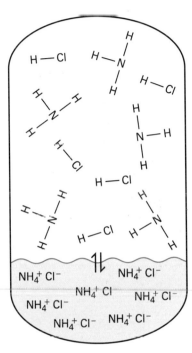

▲ **Figure 6A12** *Heating ammonium chloride in a sealed container.*

Disturbance	How does the equilibrium mixture respond?	The result
Concentration of Br_2 increases.	It moves to the right. Some water is used up by reaction with bromine.	More products form.
Concentration of hydrogen ions decreases (by adding alkali).	It moves to the right to make up for the lost hydrogen ions.	More of the bromine reacts turning into products. The solution turns colourless.
Concentration of hydrogen ions increases (by adding acid).	It moves to the left to get rid of added hydrogen ions.	$OBr^-(aq)$ and $Br^-(aq)$ react with hydrogen ions to turn back into bromine and water. The mixture turns orange.

▲ **Figure 6A13**

Adding alkali turns the solution almost colourless. Hydroxide ions in the alkali react with hydrogen ions removing them from the equilibrium mixture.

$$H^+(aq) + OH^-(aq) \longrightarrow H_2O(l) \tag{2}$$

As the hydrogen ion concentration falls, the reaction (equation 1) moves to the right to counteract the change as predicted by Le Châtelier's principle. This happens because lowering the hydrogen concentration slows down the backwards reaction while the forward reaction still goes on as before. The position of equilibrium shifts until the concentrations again are such that forward and backward reactions carry on at the same rate.

Homogeneous
The equilibrium formed in solution when bromine reacts with water is all in the one aqueous phase. It is an example of a homogeneous equilibrium.

Adding acid puts back lots of hydrogen ions and restores the yellow colour (see Figure 6A14) as the equilibrium shifts back to the left to reduce the hydrogen ion concentration again.

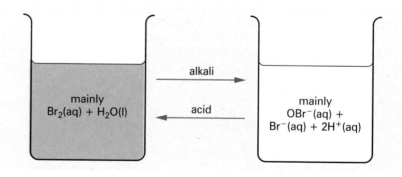

▶ **Figure 6A14** *Shifting the equilibrium position in aqueous bromine by adding acid or alkali.*

Equilibrium concentrations

In the 1860s, two French chemists, Marcellin Berthelot and Péan de St Gilles, established some of the main ideas about chemical equilibrium by studying the reversible reaction which forms ethyl ethanoate. This ester is an important industrial solvent, used in lacquers, adhesives, the manufacture of plastics, and as a food flavouring.

When ethanol and ethanoic acid are mixed they form ethyl ethanoate and water. However, the reaction is reversible; if ethyl ethanoate is left in contact with water, it hydrolyses to form ethanoic acid and ethanol.

$$CH_3CO_2H(l) + C_2H_5OH(l) \rightleftharpoons CH_3CO_2C_2H_5(l) + H_2O(l)$$

ethanoic acid   ethanol   ethyl ethanoate   water

Both the forward and backward reactions are very slow at room temperature, but adding a catalyst and heating increase the rates. Acids and alkalis catalyse the reactions.

Adding sulphuric acid to a mixture of the ethanol and ethanoic acid gets the forward reaction going. As this reaction proceeds, the concentrations of the reactants decrease and slow down the rate of the forward reaction. Meanwhile, the concentrations of ethyl ethanoate and water increase so that the rate of the backward reaction builds up from zero turning ethyl ethanoate back to ethanoic acid and ethanol. There comes a point where the rates of the forward and backward reactions are equal, the composition of the mixture remains the same and the mixture is at equilibrium.

Concentration at equilibrium at 20°C /mol dm^{-3}					
Equilibrium mixture	Ethanoic acid	Ethanol	Ethyl ethanoate	Water	K
1	0.345	0.345	0.660	0.660	3.66
2	0.114	0.114	0.090	0.531	3.68
3	0.105	0.105	0.151	0.261	3.57
4	0.082	0.082	0.204	0.118	3.58

The table shows the concentrations of acid, alcohol, ester and water in four different equilibrium mixtures. From experimental data such as these, chemists have derived a law which makes it possible to predict the composition of this system at equilibrium. The rule here is that the concentrations of the products multiplied together, divided by the concentrations of the reactants, also multiplied together, is a constant at a given temperature.

The convention is to represent concentrations of substances by putting square brackets around their formulas. So, $[CH_3CO_2H]_{eq}$ stands for the equilibrium concentration of ethanoic acid. This makes it possible to write the equilibrium law as a formula.

$$\frac{[\text{ethyl ethanoate}]_{eq}[\text{water}]_{eq}}{[\text{ethanoic acid}]_{eq}[\text{ethanol}]_{eq}} = \text{equilibrium constant, } K$$

The **value** of K is independent of the starting concentrations of reactants.

The equilibrium law

For any reaction where one mole of A reacts with one mole of B to give one mole of C and one mole of D:

$$A + B \rightleftharpoons C + D$$

the rule is that:

$$\frac{[C]_{eq}[D]_{eq}}{[A]_{eq}[B]_{eq}} = K_c$$

The rule is to put the concentrations of the reactants from the right-hand side of the equation on the top of the fraction. The concentrations of the products from the left-hand side of the equation appear on the bottom.

The subscript 'c' indicates that the equilibrium constant is calculated using concentrations (in moles per litre).

Not all reactions follow this simple pattern. Consider, for example, the reaction of methane with water vapour at 1500°C, which can be a commercial source of hydrogen:

$$CH_4(g) + H_2O(g) \rightleftharpoons CO(g) + 3H_2(g)$$

Studies of this reaction show that the equilibrium law takes this form:

$$\frac{[CO]_{eq}[H_2]_{eq}^3}{[CH_4]_{eq}[H_2O]_{eq}} = K_c$$

Notice in this relationship, that the concentration of hydrogen is raised to the power 3, reflecting the number of moles in the equation. K_c for this reaction has the units $\text{mol}^2\,\text{dm}^{-6}$.

This leads to a general form of the **equilibrium law**. For a reaction which takes this form:

$$mA + nB \rightleftharpoons pC + qD$$

the equilibrium law formula becomes:

$$\frac{[C]_{eq}^p[D]_{eq}^q}{[A]_{eq}^m[B]_{eq}^n} = K_c$$

Some important conclusions follow from the equilibrium law:

- where K_c is large (≈ 100), the equilibrium mixture contains a high proportion of products,
- where K_c is very large ($>10^{10}$) the reaction effectively goes to completion,
- where K_c is small (≈ 0.01), the reaction does not go very far and concentration of products is low at equilibrium,
- where K_c is very small ($<10^{-10}$) the reaction 'does not go',
- the value of K_c is not affected by adding more reactants or more products to an equilibrium mixture.

The equilibrium constant, K_c, is a constant for a particular temperature. Raising or lowering the temperature generally alters the value of the constant.

$K_c = 0.01$

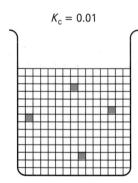

reactants predominate

$K_c = 100$

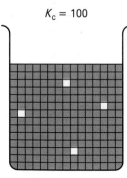

products predominate

◀ **Figure 6A16** *The proportions of reactants (yellow) and products (orange) for two values of K_c.*

How equilibria respond to changes in conditions

There are many industrial processes which are reversible reactions. Chemists and engineers control these reactions by manipulating the conditions of temperature, pressure, and the concentration of reactants and products to shift the equilibrium in the right direction.

Concentration changes

Le Châtelier's principle predicts that adding water to an equilibrium mixture of ethanol, ethanoic acid and ethyl ethanoate will make the position of equilibrium shift to the left.

$$CH_3CO_2H(l) \; + \; C_2H_5OH(l) \; \rightleftharpoons \; CH_3CO_2C_2H_5(l) \; + \; H_2O(l)$$

    acid   alcohol   ester   water

A chemist can make a quantitative prediction with the help of the equilibrium law:

$$\frac{[CH_3CO_2C_2H_5]_{eq}[H_2O]_{eq}}{[CH_3CO_2H]_{eq}[C_2H_5OH]_{eq}} = K_c = 3.6 \text{ at } 20\,°C$$

Adding some water increases $[H_2O]$ so the mixture is not at equilibrium. Immediately after adding water the expression no longer equals K_c. As a result the equilibrium position shifts: the ester concentration falls and the acid and alcohol concentrations rise until once again the system is at equilibrium with concentrations which, when entered in the equilibrium law expression, give a value equal to K_c. This is what Le Châtelier's principle expects but with the equilibrium law a chemist can calculate how far the equilibrium will shift given the amount of water added and the value of K_c.

Pressure changes

Pressure changes generally only affect gas reactions because gases are so much more compressible than solids and liquids. This is easy to demonstrate with a syringe of nitrogen dioxide, NO_2 (see Figure 6A17).

▼ **Figure 6A17** *The effect of compressing a sample of nitrogen dioxide gas.*

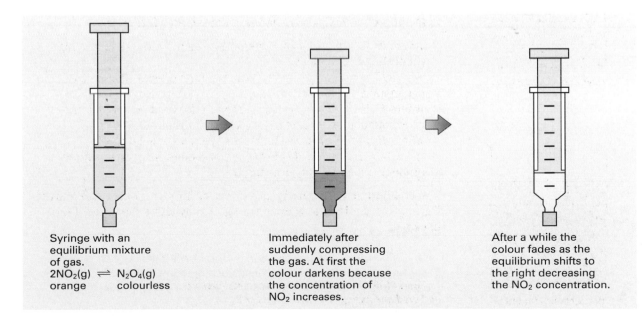

Syringe with an equilibrium mixture of gas.
$2NO_2(g) \rightleftharpoons N_2O_4(g)$
orange   colourless

Immediately after suddenly compressing the gas. At first the colour darkens because the concentration of NO_2 increases.

After a while the colour fades as the equilibrium shifts to the right decreasing the NO_2 concentration.

At room temperature and pressure a syringe full of nitrogen dioxide contains an equilibrium mixture because molecules tend to join up in pairs as N_2O_4 molecules.

$$2NO_2(g) \; \rightleftharpoons \; N_2O_4(g) \qquad \Delta H = -57.2\,\text{kJ mol}^{-1}$$
brown   colourless

Le Châtelier's principle predicts that raising the pressure will make the equilibrium shift in the direction which tends to minimize the change by reducing the number of gas molecules. Raising the pressure favours the formation of N_2O_4.

The equilibrium law explains the prediction:

$$\frac{[N_2O_4]_{eq}}{[NO_2]^2_{eq}} = K_c$$

K_c does not change when the pressure changes. The concentrations of the two gases adjust to values which give the same value for the constant when substituted in the relationship. Suddenly doubling the pressure doubles all the concentrations (a factor of 2) so at that instant the value of $[N_2O_4] \div [NO_2]^2$ decreases by a factor of two. The position of equilibrium shifts to increase $[N_2O_4]$ and decrease $[NO_2]$ until the value equals K_c again.

Temperature changes

Equilibrium constants do vary with temperature. Changing the temperature of an equilibrium mixture brings about changes in concentrations as they adjust to match the new value of the equilibrium constant.

The formation of N_2O_4 from NO_2 is exothermic. Le Châtelier's principle predicts that an equilibrium mixture of NO_2 and N_2O_4 will shift to the left as the temperature rises – in the direction which takes in energy. This is confirmed by the values for the equilibrium constant which show that the value of K_c decreases as the temperature rises (see Figure 6A18).

$T\,/^\circ$C	$K_c\,/\text{mol}^{-1}\text{dm}^3$
200	3.2×10^2
400	5.9×10^{-6}
600	1.4×10^{-8}

▲ **Figure 6A18**

▶ **Figure 6A19** *The effect of heating a sample of nitrogen dioxide gas.*

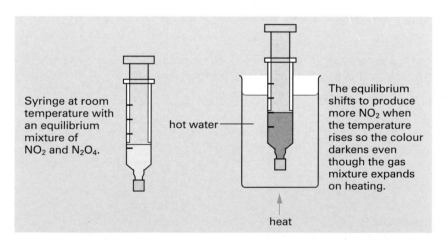

Syringe at room temperature with an equilibrium mixture of NO_2 and N_2O_4.

hot water

The equilibrium shifts to produce more NO_2 when the temperature rises so the colour darkens even though the gas mixture expands on heating.

heat

Endothermic reaction: a rise in temperature favours the products (K_c increases).

Exothermic reaction: a rise in temperature favours reactants (K_c decreases).

Adding a catalyst

Catalysts do *not* affect the position of equilibrium because they speed up both the forward and backward reactions. Catalysts are used because they shorten the time it takes for a reaction mixture to reach equilibrium.

Strong and weak acids and bases

The equilibrium law can account for the ways in which acids and bases affect the pH of solutions. With the help of this law, chemists design systems to control pH in medicines for the human body, in cosmetics and in swimming pools. They can also apply the law to design and control industrial processes for manufacturing chemical and biochemical products.

Theories of acidity have come a long way since Robert Boyle (1661) gave the name acid to chemicals with a sharp taste and explained their properties by imagining spikes on the atoms. In 1816 Humphry Davy suggested that acids all behave in the same way because they contain hydrogen. In the same century Svante Arrhenius took this a step further by thinking of acids as compounds which form hydrogen ions when they dissolve in water.

Today, many chemists find it useful to think of acids in the way that Thomas Lowry and Johannes Brønsted suggested in 1923.

Acids

The Arrhenius theory is still a useful working definition as shown by the description of acids on page 8. Acids do produce hydrogen ions when they dissolve in water.

$$HCl(aq) \longrightarrow H^+(aq) + Cl^-(aq)$$

The Lowry–Brønsted theory takes the idea further by suggesting that every acid–base reaction involves a transfer of hydrogen ions (protons) from an acid to a base. Hydrogen ion transfer starts when acids dissolve in water.

Acids do not simply dissolve in water; they react with it. In water, the hydrogen ions from an acid do not float around freely; instead they attach themselves to water molecules forming **oxonium ions**. So the hydrogen ions jump from the acid molecules to water molecules.

$$HCl(aq) + H_2O(l) \rightleftharpoons H_3O^+(aq) + Cl^-(aq)$$

hydrogen chloride molecules   aqueous oxonium ions   aqueous chloride ions

Note that water accepts a hydrogen ion from the acid, so according to the Lowry–Brønsted definition, it is acting as a base.

Chemists writing about acids and bases use the terms protons, hydrogen ions, $H^+(aq)$ and oxonium ions, $H_3O^+(aq)$ freely and interchangeably.

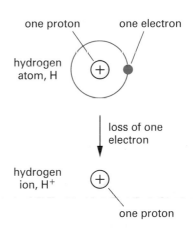

▲ **Figure 6A20** *A hydrogen atom consists of just a proton and an electron. Removing an electron forms a positive hydrogen ion, H^+, which is just a proton. So hydrogen ion transfer is the same as proton transfer.*

▲ **Figure 6A22** *Proton transfer from a hydrogen chloride molecule to a water molecule. The left-hand 'curly arrow' shows that a 'lone pair' of electrons on the oxygen atom forms a new covalent bond with the proton transferring. The second 'curly arrow' shows that the chlorine atom retains both electrons from the bond with hydrogen. The chlorine atom thus gains an electron from hydrogen and turns into a negative chloride ion.*

$$H_2O + H^+ \longrightarrow H_3O^+$$

▲ **Figure 6A21** *The structure of an oxonium ion. Electrons from hydrogen atoms, ●. Electrons in the outer shell of the oxygen atom, x.*

Strong and weak acids

Hydrogen ion transfer is reversible, so in solution there is an equilibrium. Some acids, such as hydrochloric and sulphuric acids, are strong acids – they give away their hydrogen ions to water molecules readily. Almost all the acid molecules react with water and turn into ions – the equilibrium is well over to the right.

Other acids, such as citric and ethanoic acids, are weak acids. Weak acids are reluctant to give away hydrogen ions, so that in water only a very small proportion of the acid molecules ionize – the equilibrium is well over to the left.

$$CH_3CO_2H(aq) \ + \ H_2O(l) \ \rightleftharpoons \ CH_3CO_2^-(aq) \ + \ H_3O^+(aq)$$

ethanoic acid   water   ethanoate ion   oxonium ion

Bases

When a base dissolves it takes hydrogen ions from water molecules to produce hydroxide ions, making the solution alkaline.

$$NH_3(aq) \ + \ H_2O(l) \ \rightleftharpoons \ NH_4^+(aq) \ + \ OH^-(aq)$$

ammonia   water   ammonium ion   hydroxide ion

Here water is acting as an acid, giving hydrogen ions to the base.

Just as there are strong and weak acids, so there are strong and weak bases. Methylamine, CH_3NH_2, for example, has a greater tendency to take hydrogen ions from water molecules than ammonia, so it is a stronger base than ammonia.

Acid and base strength

The equilibrium law provides a way of measuring the strength of acids and bases. For the ionization of ethanoic acid the equilibrium constant is:

$$K_c = \frac{[CH_3CO_2^-]_{eq}[H_3O^+]_{eq}}{[CH_3CO_2H]_{eq}[H_2O]_{eq}}$$

In dilute solutions, there is so much water that the concentration of water is effectively unchanged by the dissolved molecules and ions. So chemists rewrite the equilibrium law equation to include the water term in the constant which is now written as K_a:

$$K_a = \frac{[CH_3CO_2^-]_{eq}[H_3O^+]_{eq}}{[CH_3CO_2H]_{eq}}$$

K_a is called the ionization constant for ethanoic acid. Figure R26.1 in the Reference section shows K_a values for a number of acids.

In a similar way, chemists define K_b for bases. Ammonia is about as strong a base as ethanoic acid is an acid (see Reference section, R27).

The pH scale

The pH scale was devised in 1909 by a Danish chemist working in a brewery. S. P. L. Sørensen was trying to improve quality control of beer making. He needed a convenient scale to measure the acidity or alkalinity of solutions.

The concentrations of $[H_3O^+]$ ions in water can range over many orders of magnitude, typically in the range $10^{-1}\,\text{mol}\,\text{dm}^{-3}$ to $10^{-14}\,\text{mol}\,\text{dm}^{-3}$. Taking logs is a useful way of coping with a wide range of values. Sørensen chose to take logs and then to put in a negative sign to produce a scale of positive numbers running from 1 to 14.

$$pH = -\lg\{[H_3O^+]/\text{mol dm}^{-3}\}$$

◀ **Figure 6A23** *The pH scale.*

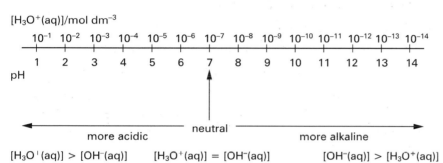

According to the Lowry–Brønsted theory, water can act both as a base accepting hydrogen ions from acids and as an acid giving away hydrogen ions when reacting with bases (see pages 313 and 314). This helps to account for the discovery that there are oxonium ions even in the purest water. To a very slight extent, water molecules react with one another to form ions:

$$H_2O(l) + H_2O(l) \rightleftharpoons H_3O^+(aq) + OH^-(aq)$$

In pure water the concentration of H_3O^+ ions is $1.0 \times 10^{-7}\,\text{mol}\,\text{dm}^{-3}$.

The pH of pure water $= -\lg 10^{-7}$
$= 7$

Buffers

Many reactions only work well at a fixed pH. For example, the pH of blood is closely controlled by the body within the narrow range 7.38 to 7.42. If illness allows the pH to stray outside this range, lower (to 7.00) or higher (to 8.00), the patient usually dies. All living things have evolved a highly efficient way of maintaining the pH of body fluids within closely defined limits.

The secret of biological pH control lies in the mixtures of molecules and ions which 'buffer' changes of pH against the addition of acids and alkalis.

Chemists also use buffer solutions when they wish to study a chemical reaction at a fixed pH. Buffers are equilibrium systems illustrating the practical importance of Le Châtelier's principle.

A typical buffer mixture consists of a solution containing a weak acid and one of its salts, for example, a mixture of ethanoic acid and sodium ethanoate.

$$CH_3CO_2H(aq) \; + \; H_2O(l) \; \rightleftharpoons \; CH_3CO_2^-(aq) \; + \; H_3O^+(aq)$$

acid molecules $\qquad\qquad\qquad$ ethanoate ions from $\quad$ oxonium
$\qquad\qquad\qquad\qquad\qquad\qquad$ sodium ethanoate $\qquad$ ions

Add extra oxonium ions to the buffer mixture and, by Le Châtelier's principle, the equilibrium must move to the left. The added oxonium ions from the acid combine with some of the buffer mixture's ethanoate ions to form ethanoic acid.

Similarly, if extra hydroxide ions, OH^- are added, they react with the buffer mixture's ethanoic acid to produce ethanoate ions and water, thus shifting the equilibrium to the right.

It is as if the ethanoic acid and the ethanoate ion act as a team – one member of the team neutralizes any strong acid that might be added to the solution, while the other member neutralizes any strong base.

Making up a buffer mixture with acid molecules means that there is a reservoir that can provide more hydrogen ions if the system is disturbed by adding an alkali.

Including sodium ethanoate means that there are plenty of ethanoate ions to 'soak up' extra hydrogen ions if the system is disturbed by adding acid.

It is possible to prepare buffer mixtures to work at any pH value throughout the pH scale (see Reference section, R29). It requires choosing the right weak acid and its salt and having the correct mole ratio between them. However, whatever buffer mixture is chosen, it will not protect the pH of a solution against a large addition of acid or base. The amount of strong acid or base that a buffer system can absorb before a significant change in pH occurs, is called the **capacity** of the buffer.

In blood, the body uses dissolved carbon dioxide ('carbonic acid') and hydrogencarbonate ions, HCO_3^-, as a buffer mixture – called the carbonate buffer. Because H^+ ions are very important early on in the biochemical mechanisms of respiration, small changes in pH can have deadly consequences.

When haemoglobin (which is an acid) picks up oxygen, hydrogen ions are released. These are buffered by hydrogencarbonate. So both the following equilibria shift to the right in the lungs where the blood takes up oxygen and releases carbon dioxide to the air.

$$HHb(aq) + O_2(aq) \rightleftharpoons H^+(aq) + HbO_2^-(aq) \qquad (1)$$
haemoglobin   oxyhaemoglobin

$$HCO_3^-(aq) + H^+(aq) \rightleftharpoons H_2O + CO_2(aq) \qquad (2)$$

The equilibria shift to the left where the blood circulates between metabolizing cells releasing oxygen and taking up carbon dioxide.

In some medical conditions, such as uncontrolled diabetes, there may be a large flow of hydrogen ions into the blood. The buffer system of equation 2 responds by shifting to the right converting HCO_3^- to CO_2. If the CO_2 concentration rises the buffer action ceases so that the pH falls drastically leading to coma and possibly death. The body's response is to begin to breathe rapidly and deeply, thus losing the excess CO_2 from the lungs and allowing more hydrogencarbonate ions to react with hydrogen ions. So a healthy body quickly responds to a lowering of blood pH by increasing the rate of breathing. Notice, though, that it takes both mechanisms, buffering and deep breathing, to protect the body.

Mountaineers suffer from the opposite problem. At high altitude there is less oxygen and so they tend to breathe at a higher rate. If they have not acclimatized properly, they can over breathe and they lose too much CO_2, shifting equilibrium 2 to the right and lowering the hydrogen ion concentration. In other words, the pH of the blood begins to increase. This removal of protons stops the haemoglobin/oxyhaemoglobin equilibrium in equation 1 moving to the left as it should when releasing oxygen to cells. Result: the cells become starved of oxygen. The best way to overcome this problem is to give oxygen or to get off the mountain as quickly as possible.

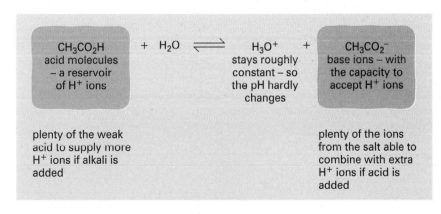

◄ **Figure 6A24** *The action of a buffer solution.*

CHAPTER 6B

How fast? Rates of chemical change

Fireworks

Every entertainer knows that getting the timing right is an essential part of a high-quality performance. Every fifth of November, when Britain's children are entertained by fireworks, the quality of their performance depends on the firework designer's understanding of the chemical reactions that go on inside a firework and how to control their speed.

▶ Figure 6B1

You start the chain of chemical reactions in a firework in the same way as you start the chemical reactions of the bonfire. You set light to it. In both the bonfire and the firework a fuel is oxidized. The difference is that, for the bonfire, oxygen in the air is the oxidizing agent while fireworks contain an oxidizing agent mixed with the fuel. That makes it possible to gain greater control of the rate of the combustion.

'When someone lights a fuse on a firework, it has to burn reliably even on a wet and windy night', explains Ron Rapley, technical director of the Huddersfield company, Standard Fireworks. 'When designing a category 3 firework, the kind that can be sold to the public in ordinary shops, we give it a fuse which burns for between 5 and 15 seconds between it being lit and the firework going off. The Health and Safety Executive has judged that a delay of at least 5 seconds is necessary to allow the person who lit the firework to get clear, but the wait must be no longer than 15 seconds or the person might be tempted to go back to investigate why nothing has happened.'

The 'blue touch paper' firework fuse is paper impregnated with the oxidizing agent potassium nitrate. This ensures that the paper will burn even when damp and that it can't be blown out. The higher the potassium nitrate content of the paper, the faster it burns. Another type of fuse known as a Chinese fuse is rolled up tissue paper containing a thin thread of gunpowder.

Gunpowder is the main active ingredient in fireworks. It is a mixture of powdered charcoal, sulphur and potassium nitrate. Charcoal and sulphur are the fuel and, because they are in close contact with the oxidizing agent, potassium nitrate, they can burn very quickly when the mixture is ignited. The speed of burning can be varied, however, depending on how the gunpowder is formulated.

'If the aim is just to produce a bang, we confine granules of gunpowder in a small tube made of stiff card', Rapley explains. 'When it's ignited, almost all the granules burn at once and in a split second, the gunpowder, with a volume of one cubic centimetre, becomes about 300 cubic centimetres of gas. The cardboard tube contains it just enough so that when it does escape a shock wave is produced and that is the bang you hear.'

'In a rocket, the gunpowder has to burn more slowly. We achieve this by compressing the gunpowder to form a cylinder and placing it in the propelling chamber, which has a hole at the bottom. When a rocket is lit, only the base of the gunpowder cylinder ignites and it slowly burns upward. The gases produced escape from the hole and these propel the rocket upward. The longer the cylinder, the higher the rocket goes.'

'In the nose of the rocket is the display chamber. This contains the rapid burning granules of gunpowder and several hundred tiny balls made up of inorganic salts with a coating of compressed gunpowder. As the rocket motor portion completes its burn, it ignites the display chamber. The gunpowder burns quickly, heating and releasing the inorganic salts to make a star burst. We choose the salts to achieve the colour we want and on heating they produce the same colours as they do when heated in a Bunsen burner flame. Sodium salts give a yellow star, potassium is violet, copper is blue-green, strontium is red and aluminium is white.'

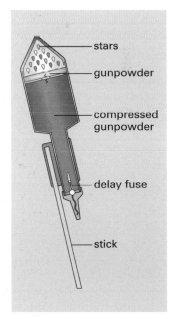

▼ **Figure 6B2** *The inside of a firework rocket.*

- stars
- gunpowder
- compressed gunpowder
- delay fuse
- stick

Measuring reaction rates

In chemical reactions, amounts or concentrations of substances change. Reactants disappear and products form. The rates at which these changes take place give a measure of the 'rate of reaction'.

To monitor the rate of reaction of magnesium with hydrochloric acid:

$$Mg(s) + 2HCl(aq) \longrightarrow MgCl_2(aq) + H_2(g)$$

an observer can measure:

- the rate of loss of magnesium, or
- the rate of loss of hydrochloric acid
- the rate of formation of magnesium chloride
- the rate of formation of hydrogen.

There is no meter for measuring reaction rates directly. Instead chemists measure a property which changes with the amount or concentration of a reactant or product and calculate the rate. For the reaction of magnesium with acid it is probably easiest to follow the formation of hydrogen by collecting the gas with a measuring cylinder (over water) or a syringe and recording the volume at regular intervals.

$$\text{Rate} = \frac{\text{change in any property}}{\text{time for the change}}$$

Rates may be measured in a variety of practical units such as cm^3 per second, but then be converted to the useful unit – moles per second $(mol\ s^{-1})$.

▶ **Figure 6B3** *Two ways of collecting and measuring a gas produced by a reaction.*

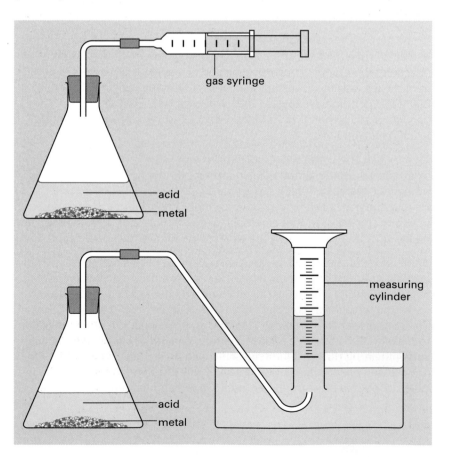

gas syringe

acid
metal

measuring cylinder

acid
metal

Example

What is the average rate of formation of hydrogen when $48\,cm^3$ of the gas forms in $10\,s$ from magnesium and hydrochloric acid at room temperature and pressure? What are the rates of formation of magnesium chloride and the rate of disappearance of acid?

Answer

The volume of one mole of any gas at room temperature and pressure $= 24\,000\,cm^3$ (see Reference section, R12).

So the amount of hydrogen, H_2, formed in the first $10\,s = \dfrac{48\,cm^3}{24\,000\,cm^3\,mol^{-1}}$

$$= 0.002\,mol$$

So the average rate of formation of hydrogen $= \dfrac{0.002\,mol}{10\,s}$

$$= 0.0002\,mol\,s^{-1}$$

The equation (see page 320) shows that while the reaction produces one mole of hydrogen gas two moles of acid disappear and one mole of magnesium chloride forms.

So the rate of formation of magnesium chloride $= 0.0002\,mol\,s^{-1}$

The rate of disappearance of hydrochloric acid $= 0.0004\,mol\,s^{-1}$

Figure 6B4 shows how the volume of hydrogen varies with time. At each point the gradient of the curve is a measure of the rate of reaction. The graph is steepest at the start where the reactants are most concentrated and the reaction is at its fastest. As the reaction continues, it slows down until it eventually stops when one or other of the reactants has all gone.

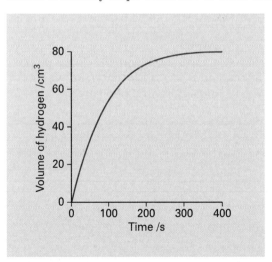

◀ **Figure 6B4** *The volume of hydrogen plotted against time for the reaction of magnesium with hydrochloric acid.*

In drag racing, the officials time cars over a fixed, quarter-mile distance. The fastest car covers the distance in the shortest time. Similarly, chemists can compare the initial rates of chemical reactions by finding the time to produce a certain amount of one of the reactants.

In Figure 6B5, line A shows the formation of a product under one set of conditions. It takes t_A seconds to form x mol of the product. Line B shows what happens under new conditions when the reaction is slower. Now it takes t_B seconds to produce x mol of product.

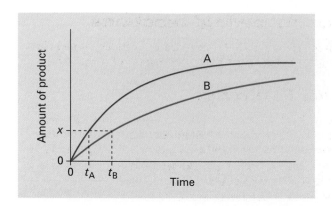

Average initial rate of formation of product on line A $= \dfrac{x}{t_A} \text{mol s}^{-1}$

Average initial rate of formation of product on line B $= \dfrac{x}{t_B} \text{mol s}^{-1}$

t_B is greater than t_A so the initial rate for line B works out to be less than for line A. By setting up the investigation so that the value of x is always the same, it is possible to use $1/t$ as a measure of the initial rate.

Example

The data in the table (Figure 6B6) come from an investigation of the effect of concentration on the rate of reaction of powdered calcium carbonate (0.5 g samples) with dilute hydrochloric acid. The investigator recorded the time taken to collect a certain volume (x cm^3) of carbon dioxide for three different concentrations of acid.

Calculate $1/t$ as a measure of the initial rate for each set of results and plot a graph to show how the rate varies with concentration.

Acid concentration /mol dm^{-3}	Time, t, to collect x cm^3 gas /s
2.0	8
1.0	16
0.5	32

▲ **Figure 6B6** *Table of results.*

Answer

The table (Figure 6B7) shows the values of $1/t$. Figure 6B8 is the graph of $1/t$ against concentration. As the graph shows, the initial rate of this reaction is proportional to the acid concentration. Doubling the concentration doubles the rate.

[HCl] stands for the concentration of hydrochloric acid in moles per litre, so:

rate of reaction $\propto$ [HCl]

Acid concentration /mol dm^{-3}	Initial rate $1/t$ s^{-1}
2.0	0.125
1.0	0.062
0.5	0.031

▲ **Figure 6B7** *Table calculated to show values of $1/t$.*

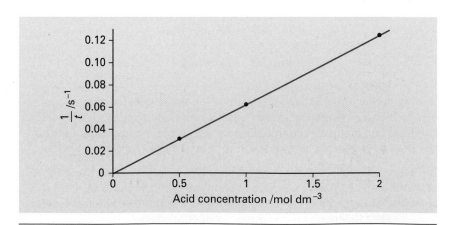

▶ **Figure 6B8** *Graph to show how the rate varies with concentration.*

Methods for 'following' reactions

Collecting a gas in a measuring cylinder over water or in a syringe is just one of many methods for keeping track of the progress of reactions.

Measuring rates by titration

The procedure is to withdraw samples from the reaction mixture at regular time intervals. The investigator 'quenches' the reaction in the samples to stop further change, perhaps by rapidly cooling the samples in ice or by removing a catalyst. Once the reaction has been quenched, the investigator can analyse the samples by titration to find the concentration of one of the reactants or products.

The titration procedure is suitable for studying the reaction between iodine and the ketone, propanone. The reaction is catalysed by acid. Taking samples and running them into excess alkali stops the reaction. Titrating with sodium thiosulphate measures the concentration of iodine.

$$CH_3COCH_3(aq) + I_2(aq) \longrightarrow CH_3COCH_2I(aq) + H^+(aq) + I^-(aq)$$

Measuring rates with a colorimeter

Another way to monitor the reaction of iodine with propanone is to put the reaction mixture in a colorimeter. Iodine is the only coloured species present. At first the solution is orangey-brown but the mixture becomes yellow, then colourless, as the iodine reacts and turns into colourless molecules and ions. Reading the colorimeter at regular intervals shows how the iodine concentration varies with time.

Measuring rates with a conductivity meter

The number and nature of the ions present in a solution affect its conductivity. Dipping two inert platinum electrodes into a reaction mixture and connecting them to a suitable meter makes it possible to take conductivity readings at regular intervals and thus follow the course of a reaction in the solution.

This technique is suitable as a way to investigate the rate of reaction of bromoethane with hydroxide ions in alkaline solution.

$$CH_3CH_2Br(l) + OH^-(aq) \longrightarrow CH_3CH_2OH(l) + Br^-(aq)$$

Bromide ions are large and slow moving in water compared to hydroxide ions, which are very mobile. So as the reaction proceeds the conductivity of the solution falls.

> **Species**
> Chemists use the term 'species' to cover a variety of atoms, molecules and ions. When iodine reacts with propanone the chemical species present include: iodine and propanone molecules, iodopropanone molecules, hydrogen ions and iodide ions.

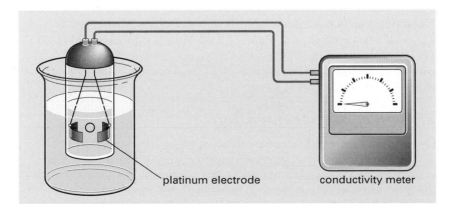

◀ **Figure 6B9** *Using a meter to measure the conductivity of a solution.*

platinum electrode   conductivity meter

What affects the rate of a reaction?

A sliced loaf of bread goes stale faster than an unsliced loaf. Milk standing in a warm kitchen goes sour more quickly than milk kept in a refrigerator. Changing the conditions alters the rates of these processes and many others.

Factors which affect the rate of chemical reactions are:

- the **concentration** of reactants in solution – the higher the concentration, the faster the reaction (see Figure 6B8 on page 322)
- the **pressure** of gaseous reactants – high pressure compresses gases and increases the concentration of reactants
- the **surface area** of solids – powdering a solid increases the surface area in contact with a liquid or gaseous reagent
- the **temperature** – typically a 10°C rise in temperature roughly doubles the rate of reaction
- **catalysts** – this includes not only industrial catalysts but also the many enzymes which speed up and control biochemical reactions
- **radiation** – photosynthesis depends on sunlight; alkanes react at room temperature with chlorine or bromine in UV light.

The factors in action

Figure 6B10 illustrates the effect of changing conditions on the reaction of zinc metal with dilute sulphuric acid.

$$Zn(s) + H_2SO_4(aq) \longrightarrow ZnSO_4(aq) + H_2(g)$$

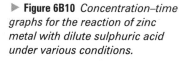

▶ **Figure 6B10** *Concentration–time graphs for the reaction of zinc metal with dilute sulphuric acid under various conditions.*

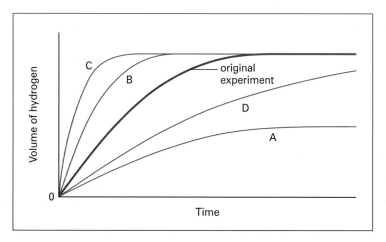

The original conditions

The red line plots the volume of hydrogen gas against time using an excess of zinc turnings and $50\,cm^3$ of $2.0\,mol\,dm^{-3}$ sulphuric acid at 20°C. The reaction gradually slows down and stops because the acid concentration falls to zero. There is more than enough metal to react with all the acid (an excess).

The effect of concentration

Line A shows the result of using $50\,cm^3$ of $1.0\,mol\,dm^{-3}$ sulphuric acid but leaving all the other conditions unchanged. Halving the acid concentration lowers the initial rate. The reaction slows down because the concentration falls as the acid reacts with the metal. The final volume of hydrogen gas is cut by half because there was only half the amount of acid (in moles) at the start.

The effect of temperature

Line B shows the result of carrying out the reaction at 30 °C while leaving the other conditions the same. This speeds up the reaction and more or less doubles the initial rate. The chemical amounts are not changed so the final volume of gas, collected at room temperature, is the same as for the original set-up.

The effect of surface area

Line D shows the result of keeping to all the original conditions but using the same excess of zinc metal in larger pieces. Fewer larger bits of metal have a smaller surface area so the reaction starts more slowly. The amount of acid is unchanged and the metal is still in excess so that the final volume of hydrogen is the same.

The effect of a catalyst

Repeating the investigation as carried out originally but with a few drops of copper(II) sulphate, produces line C. Copper(II) sulphate catalyses the reaction so the reaction starts more quickly and the graph is steeper. Catalysts do not affect the theoretical yield of products and so the final volume of gas is the same as before.

Calculating the rate

Plotting concentration against time gives a picture of the change in rate as the reaction progresses. The gradient at any point measures the rate of reaction, as shown in Figure 6B11.

▼ **Figure 6B11** *The gradient of a concentration–time graph measures the rate of reaction at that point.*

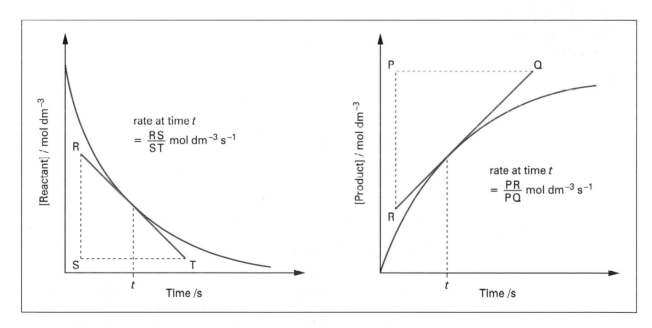

Rate equations

A chemical engineer designing a reactor to make a new product needs to know exactly how the rate of the synthesis varies with the concentrations of the reactants. This knowledge, based on experiment, is summed up by the rate equation for the reaction. This information is especially useful in the chemical industry because it tells chemists what the concentrations of reactants and products will be at any time after the reaction has started. Knowing that, chemists can then determine the best time to collect the products or re-stock the reaction vessel with reactants.

> The square brackets denote 'concentrations in moles per litre'. k is a constant called the rate constant. The value of k varies with temperature.

> Rate equations cannot be deduced from chemical equations. They can only be discovered, along with the numerical values of the rate constants, by experiment.

Consider the reaction between hydrogen peroxide and hydriodic acid in aqueous solution:

$$H_2O_2(aq) + 2HI(aq) \longrightarrow 2H_2O(l) + I_2(aq)$$

The rate equation for this change is:

$$rate = k[H_2O_2(aq)][HI(aq)] \tag{1}$$

At first sight the form of the rate equation is unexpected because there are two molecules of hydrogen iodide for each molecule of hydrogen peroxide in the balanced chemical equation. Another example, the decomposition of gaseous ethanal into a mixture of carbon monoxide and methane, also shows that it is not possible to predict the form of the rate equation from the balanced equation.

$$CH_3CHO(g) \longrightarrow CH_4(g) + CO(g)$$

The rate equation is again unexpected and takes this form:

$$rate = k[CH_3CHO(g)]^2 \tag{2}$$

Reaction orders

Rate equation (1) shows that the rate of reaction of hydrogen peroxide with hydriodic acid is proportional to the hydrogen peroxide concentration (rate $\propto k[H_2O_2]^1$). The reaction is **first order** with respect to the hydrogen peroxide concentration. What this means is that doubling the hydrogen peroxide concentration doubles the rate.

Rate equation (2) shows that the rate of decomposition of ethanal varies with the square of the ethanal concentration (rate $\propto [CH_3CHO]^2$). The reaction is **second order** with respect to the ethanal concentration. Doubling the ethanal concentration quadruples the rate.

In general, for a reaction of the type:

$$xA + yB \longrightarrow products$$

the rate equation takes the form:

$$rate = k[A]^p[B]^q[C]^r$$

Chemists describe the indices p, q and r as the reaction orders. In this example the reaction is order p with respect to reactant A and order q with respect to reactant B.

Notice the appearance of C in the general rate equation, despite the fact that it is not included as a reactant in the balanced equation for the reaction. C might be a catalyst. The reaction of iodine with propanone is catalysed by acid and the concentration of hydrogen ions appears in the rate equation.

$$CH_3COCH_3(aq) + I_2(aq) \longrightarrow CH_3COCH_2I(aq) + H^+(aq) + I^-(aq)$$

Experiments show that the reaction is first order with respect to propanone and hydrogen ions but zero order with respect to iodine molecules. This means that changing the iodine concentration has no effect on the rate. The rate equation is:

$$\text{rate} = k[CH_3COCH_3]^1[I_2]^0[H^+]^1$$

which simplifies to:

$$\text{rate} = k[CH_3COCH_3][H^+]$$

because $[I_2]^0 = 1$.

Finding the order of a reaction

Chemists have developed a range of methods to determine reaction orders. In simple cases the order can be deduced from the concentration–time graph. Consider the decomposition of hydrogen peroxide solution:

$$2H_2O_2(aq) \longrightarrow 2H_2O(l) + O_2(g)$$

The practical problem is to find the value of n in the rate equation:

$$\text{rate} = k[H_2O_2]^n$$

The concentration of hydrogen peroxide can be monitored with time by titration and plotted on a graph against time.

The question is: 'What is the order of the reaction, n?'

Consider three possibilities.

- If $n = 0$ (zero order) the graph will be a straight line because rate $= k[H_2O_2]^0$ is the same as rate $= k$
- If $n = 1$ (first order) the graph will curve such that the time it takes for the concentration to halve (the half-life) is constant, whatever the starting point on the curve
- If $n = 2$ (second order) the graph will be an even steeper curve; the half-life is not a constant but increases as the reaction proceeds.

Studies of the decomposition of hydrogen peroxide show that it is in fact a first order reaction. So the rate equation is:

$$\text{rate} = k[H_2O_2]^1$$

> **Units**
> Reaction rates are measured in $mol\,dm^{-3}\,s^{-1}$.
> The units of a rate constant depend on the form of the rate equation.
> For a first order reaction, such as the decomposition of hydrogen peroxide, the units of k are s^{-1}.

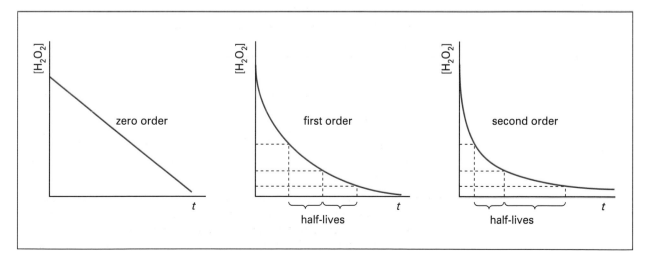

▲ **Figure 6B12** *Concentration–time graphs for zero, first and second order reactions.*

A collision model to explain reaction rates

In gases and liquids, molecules are in constant motion. Millions upon millions of collisions occur every second. Imagining molecules colliding with each other leads to a theory which can account for the effects of concentration, temperature and catalysts on reaction rates.

One step or more?

It has to be remembered that the equation for any chemical reaction simply shows the net overall change. For example, octane (one of the main constituents of petrol) burns with oxygen according to this equation:

$$2C_8H_{18}(l) + 25O_2(g) \longrightarrow 16CO_2(g) + 18H_2O(g)$$

This does not mean that in a single simultaneous event, 2 molecules of octane collide with 25 molecules of oxygen and are converted to 16 molecules of carbon dioxide and 18 molecules of water. Snooker players know that the chances of three balls colliding simultaneously in two dimensions are pretty slim. The likelihood of 27 molecules colliding together at the same time in three-dimensional space are vanishingly small.

Clearly then, the equation for a reaction cannot (except in very simple cases) refer to the way by which the reaction occurs. In most cases, a reaction consists of a series of steps involving collisions between a small number of molecules. This is where the study of rates can provide a lot of information to help chemists understand how reactions go, that is the mechanisms of reactions.

Collision theory and the effect of concentration

The fundamental idea is that a chemical reaction occurs when molecules of the reactants collide with each other, leading to the breaking of some chemical bonds and the formation of new bonds.

Do all molecular collisions lead to a reaction?

Looking at the example of octane burning, the answer has to be only sometimes, because collisions between octane molecules do not normally lead to a reaction. Only collisions between octane and oxygen molecules seem likely to lead to a reaction.

Are there enough molecules of reactants in the system for enough effective collisions to occur?

Too few reactant molecules and collisions which lead to change are rare. The reaction is then very slow. This can be overcome by ensuring that, in solution, the concentration of reactants is high enough. In the gas phase, high concentrations of reactants are achieved by adjusting the pressures and volumes of the reacting gases. However, too high a concentration of reactants can lead to the reaction proceeding too quickly and spiralling out of control into an explosion.

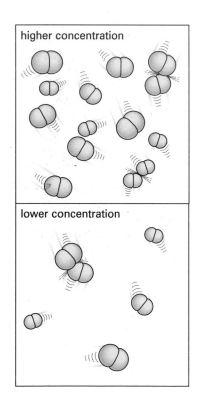

higher concentration

lower concentration

▲ **Figure 6B13** *In solutions of higher concentration and in gases at higher pressure, particles are closer together. They have a greater chance of colliding. There are more collisions and reactions are faster.*

Are the molecules in the right physical state to lead to effective collisions?

Liquid petrol (which contains octane) burns rapidly in air. However, if the petrol is first vaporized (as it is inside a car engine) the reaction with air is explosive. Ensuring that the petrol and the air are both gaseous means that the reactant molecules can rapidly intermingle, leading to many favourable collisions and a rapid reaction. This is a homogeneous reaction.

When metals react with acid (see page 324) one reactant is a solid while the other is a liquid – they are heterogeneous reactions. The reactant molecules are only able to meet at the interface between the two different phases. So the area of contact between the phases is crucial in determining the rate of the reaction.

Similarly, in the case of a reaction between one reactant in the gas phase and the other in the solid phase, it is the size of the solid particles that determines the area of contact: the larger that area, the faster the rate of the reaction. Try lighting a campfire by setting alight a log with a match. Then do the same with wood shavings, which have a much greater surface area for the same mass of wood. If the particle size of the solid phase is very small, the reaction can be so fast as to lead to an explosion. Grain elevators (used for storing harvested cereal crops) sometimes explode with devastating results, as a result of a chance spark igniting fine grain-dust particles.

Does the alignment of molecules matter when they collide?

What is clear is that molecules have to be in the correct orientation for a reaction to take place. Careful investigations have shown that this is definitely important when it comes to a reaction like one of the steps in the decomposition of nitryl chloride, NO_2Cl (see page 332). This involves collisions between nitryl chloride molecules and chlorine atoms. Nitryl chloride is an unsymmetrical triangular molecule, with two oxygen atoms and a chlorine atom at the three corners of the triangle with the nitrogen atom sitting at the centre.

◀ **Figure 6B15** *A triangular nitryl chloride molecule.*

If a chlorine atom collides with the molecule where the nitrogen atoms or oxygen atoms are sited, then no reaction takes place. If, however, the chlorine atom strikes the nitryl chloride molecule at the site of the chlorine atom, then a reaction occurs.

◀ **Figure 6B16** *Collision of chlorine atoms with nitryl chloride molecules.*

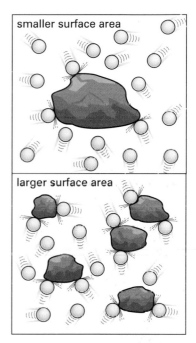

▲ **Figure 6B14** *With a greater surface area of solid, effective collisions are more frequent so the reaction rate is greater.*

Collision theory and the effect of temperature

It is not enough for the molecules to collide frequently and in the right orientation. In soft collisions, the molecules simply bounce off one another. It is like trying to play snooker using eggs for balls. Only if the collisions between the eggs are strong enough will they break. The factor that determines the energy of collisions between molecules is how fast they are moving. And that is determined by the temperature of the system. The higher the temperature, the faster the molecules move, and the greater the energy of molecular collisions.

If all molecular collisions led to a reaction then reactions would be over virtually instantaneously (and explosively). Clearly, only a small number of collisions do lead to a reaction. Only pairs of molecules which collide with enough energy to stretch and break chemical bonds can lead to new products.

The decomposition of nitryl chloride goes through an in-between, transition stage. A bond starts to form between the free chlorine atom and the chlorine atom attached to the nitryl chloride molecule, while the bond between that chlorine atom and the nitrogen atom is breaking.

$$O_2N—Cl + Cl \longrightarrow [O_2N\cdots Cl\cdots Cl] \longrightarrow O_2N + Cl_2$$

The point where the old bond hasn't quite broken and the new bond hasn't quite formed is the position of maximum energy and represents the transition state at the top of an energy barrier between reactants and products (Figure 6B17).

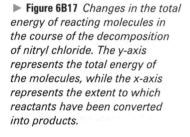

► **Figure 6B17** *Changes in the total energy of reacting molecules in the course of the decomposition of nitryl chloride. The y-axis represents the total energy of the molecules, while the x-axis represents the extent to which reactants have been converted into products.*

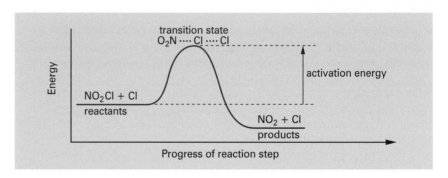

It is as if the reactant molecules have to climb an energy hill before a reaction can take place.

The difference in energy between the reactants and the transition state is the activation energy, E_a. The greater the activation energy the more difficult it is to form the transition state. Therefore, the less likely it is that collisions will be energetic enough to climb the activation energy hill and then go to products. So the rate of the reaction is slower. On the other hand, the lower the activation energy, the easier it is for the reaction to go and the faster the rate of the reaction to form products.

Raising the temperature increases the kinetic energy of the reactant molecules and so increases the number of collisions likely to form the transition state and therefore lead to products. Figure 6B18 shows the distribution of energies in a gas at two temperatures. The whole area under each curve represents the total number of molecules. Raising the temperature means that there are more molecules with higher energies so the curve shifts to the right.

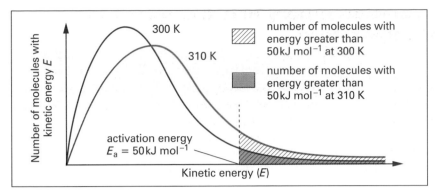

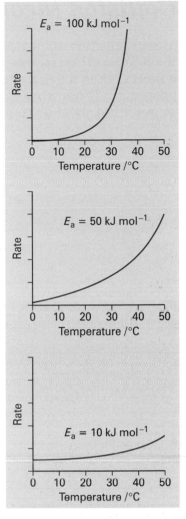

▲ **Figure 6B18** *The distribution of molecular kinetic energies of molecules at 27°C and 37°C. The shaded areas represent the numbers of molecules with energy greater than the activation energy where $E_a = 50\,kJ\,mol^{-1}$.*

A typical value for the activation energy of a reaction is $50\,kJ\,mol^{-1}$. Figure 6B18 shows that only a small proportion of the molecules (represented by the shaded areas) have energies greater than $50\,kJ\,mol^{-1}$.

Raising the temperature by only 10°C roughly doubles the number of molecules with energies greater than the activation energy. So for a gas reaction with an activation energy of $50\,kJ\,mol^{-1}$, the rate constant in the rate equation roughly doubles for a 10°C rise in temperature from 30°C to 40°C (Figure 6B19).

Collision theory and the effect of catalysts

Catalysts are probably the most important method for altering the rate of a chemical reaction. These are substances that speed up or slow down the rate of a reaction but remain themselves chemically unchanged or used up. The catalyst can be in the same phase as the reactants, in which case it is called a **homogeneous catalyst**, or it can be in a different phase, in which case it is known as a **heterogeneous catalyst**.

Catalysts speed up reactions by providing an alternative pathway for the reaction involving a different transition state. The energy barrier with a catalyst is lower so more molecular collisions have the energy needed for the bond breaking which leads to atoms rearranging to form new products.

▲ **Figure 6B19** *How the rate of reaction varies with temperature for three different values of E_a.*

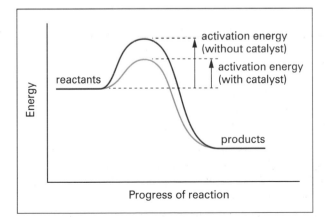

▲ **Figure 6B20** *The activation energy with a catalyst is lower.*

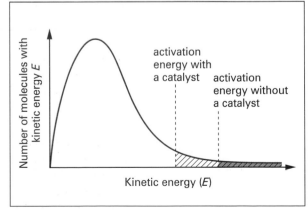

▲ **Figure 6B21** *Lowering the activation energy increases the number of molecules with enough energy to react.*

Collision theory and reaction mechanisms

Most reactions do not occur in one step but in a series of steps. It is like getting a meal at a cafeteria: first picking up a tray, then collecting a hot meal, followed by a sweet, then a drink, next paying and finally taking cutlery. It is frustrating for customers if one step in this process is much slower than the others so that queuing to get a hot meal or to pay becomes much the slowest step.

Canteen supervisors monitor customers as they buy their meals to make sure that they understand the process, can regulate the flow of people and avoid queues. Chemists cannot simply observe the individual steps in a reaction so their problem is to work out what they are.

This is where a study of rates and a knowledge of rate laws can be all important. Also useful is the idea that there may be a slowest, **rate-determining step** which limits the overall rate. The species involved in the rate-determining step are likely to show up in the rate equation.

The decomposition of nitryl chloride shows how the rate equation can offer clues leading to the discovery of the **mechanism** of a reaction.

$$2NO_2Cl(g) \longrightarrow 2NO_2(g) + Cl_2(g)$$

Practical investigations show that this is a first order reaction:

$$\text{rate} = k[NO_2Cl] \quad \textit{experimental}$$

This is rather strange because it means that the slowest step involves only a single nitryl chloride molecule. One possible explanation is that nitryl chloride molecules first split into NO_2 and chlorine atoms in a rate-determining step, followed by a fast reaction of the chlorine atoms with nitryl chloride molecules:

$$NO_2Cl \longrightarrow NO_2 + Cl\bullet \quad \text{(slow)}$$
$$NO_2Cl + Cl\bullet \longrightarrow NO_2 + Cl_2 \quad \text{(fast)}$$

The rate-determining step in the reaction only involves nitryl chloride molecules and so the predicted rate equation is:

$$\text{rate} = k[NO_2Cl] \quad \textit{theoretical}$$

The experimentally determined rate law and the theoretically derived one are the same. This is strong evidence (but not conclusive proof) in favour of the proposed mechanism.

This mechanism involves short-lived species with unpaired electrons – so-called **free radicals**. When the covalent bond between chlorine and nitrogen breaks in the first step of the reaction, each atom takes one of the shared-pair of electrons making up the bond.

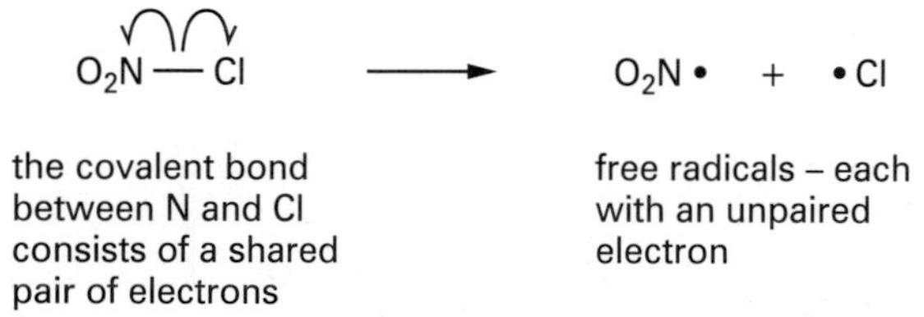

> **Reaction mechanism**
> The mechanism of a reaction is the sequence of bond breaking and bond forming steps which result in the overall change described by the balanced chemical equation for the reaction.

> **The rate-determining step**
> The whole reaction goes at the rate of the slowest step in the mechanism. The slowest step is the rate-determining step.

$$O_2N \overgroup{—} Cl \longrightarrow O_2N\bullet \; + \; \bullet Cl$$

the covalent bond between N and Cl consists of a shared pair of electrons

free radicals – each with an unpaired electron

▶ **Figure 6B22** *Bond breaking to form free radicals.*

Enzymes

A living cell's ability to package and control complex chemical reactions is awe inspiring. Cells use large, intricately-folded protein molecules called enzymes to catalyse chemical processes between molecules that under normal circumstances would not react, or would only react very slowly.

Enzymes can recognize (from amongst millions of others) the molecules whose reactions they catalyse, do the reaction and release the products, and be ready to start again in less than one ten-millionth of a second. In contrast, laboratory reactions are slow and comparatively haphazard.

Studying the rate of enzyme catalysed reactions has helped biochemists to develop theories which explain how enzymes work. This has proved important in the design of medicines to prevent or cure disease by inhibiting enzymes which can be harmful to health.

Figure 6B23 illustrates a theory to explain the action of an enzyme which splits up large molecules. An example is lysozyme which helps to destroy bacteria by breaking down sugars in the cell walls of some bacteria. The enzyme is a coiled protein molecule with an active site. Sugar molecules are the **substrate** on which the enzyme acts.

In simple terms, the reaction involves converting substrate molecules (S) into products (P). The enzyme (E) is a catalyst so it speeds up the process but does not show up in the overall equation for the reaction.

$$S \longrightarrow P$$

substrate   products

If the substrate concentration is low: rate $= k[E][S]$.

If the substrate concentration is high: rate $= k[E]$.

Biochemists interpret these findings in terms of this mechanism:

$$E \ + \ S \ \xrightarrow{\text{step 1}} \ ES \ \xrightarrow{\text{step 2}} \ EP \ \xrightarrow{\text{step 3}} \ E \ + \ P$$

enzyme   substrate   substrate in   products in   enzyme   products
                        active site   active site

Step 1 is the rate-determining step when the substrate concentration is low. The rate at which enzyme and substrate come together to form a complex determines the overall rate. So both the enzyme and substrate appear in the rate equation.

When the substrate concentration is high, however, all the active sites of the enzyme molecules are occupied. The enzyme is present as the complex ES and the overall rate is governed by the rate at which it releases products by steps 2 and 3. Now only the enzyme concentration determines the overall rate since $[ES] \approx [E]$.

▼ **Figure 6B23** *A model illustrating a possible mechanism for the breakdown of a substrate molecule into two smaller molecules.*

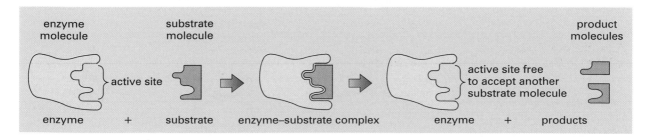

New tricks with old reactions

It seems strange to think that these could be the last days of the internal combustion engine, which has dominated personal transportation for the second half of the 20th century. Much as it has contributed to extraordinary mobility for many people, the internal combustion engine has polluted the air, forced many industrialized countries to rely heavily on oil from politically unstable regions, and intensified the long-term threat of global warming.

▲ **Figure 6B24** *The Ballard 30 kW Fuel Cell power plant, completed in 1994, provides power to an industrial plant.*

It now seems possible that sometime in the next decade, auto-manufacturers will be ready to market new, super energy-efficient cars powered by fuel cells that drive powerful, high-torque electric motors. Such vehicles will produce virtually no polluting gases such as carbon dioxide, which contributes to the greenhouse effect, or oxides of nitrogen or sulphur that are the main causes of acid rain. They can be fuelled by hydrogen from a variety of secure energy sources.

The development of fuel cells depends on a detailed understanding of one of the simplest chemical reactions: the burning of hydrogen to make water.

$$2H_2(g) + O_2(g) \longrightarrow 2H_2O(l)$$

The reaction is highly exothermic and the equilibrium constant, of the order of 10^{80}, is most definitely on the side of reactants going to products (see page 310). However, a gas jar containing two volumes of hydrogen and one volume of oxygen at room temperature, though potentially highly explosive, could exist in this state forever.

This is because at room temperature, the collisions between hydrogen and oxygen molecules are just not of the right type, or energetic enough, or of the right frequency to ensure that they react. The activation energy is too high for the reaction to go at a measurable rate at room temperature. But place a glowing splint in the jar and the explosion can shatter the glass.

What happens is that the hot glowing splint excites some molecules of hydrogen and oxygen to such an extent that their collisions are now energetic enough to overcome the activation energy and cause the reaction. Then, the energy given out is so great that it excites more hydrogen and oxygen molecules into reacting. More energy is given out and in a fraction of a second the reaction spirals out of control and becomes an explosion.

There is another way to induce this reaction. Throwing a pinch of palladium on charcoal into the gas jar has the same effect as the glowing splint. The palladium on charcoal acts as a catalyst. The surface of the palladium catalyst has sites where reactant molecules can attach themselves. Reactant molecules adsorbed onto these sites can find themselves close enough together to react and in the right orientation. Bond breaking and formation occur much more easily when the reactant molecules are aligned in the right manner, so the catalyst lowers the activation energy of the reaction (see page 330).

▶ **Figure 6B25** *Palladium on charcoal acts as a catalyst for the reaction of hydrogen with oxygen.*

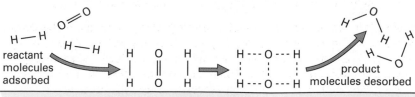

A heterogeneous catalyst, such as palladium, is effectively a 'dating agency' bringing together with ease those molecules that by themselves have difficulty meeting productively. Catalysts like this are now set to produce a revolution in the way that we use fuels.

Producing usable energy by burning fuels is a highly inefficient process. Petrol and diesel engines are never more than about 25–30% efficient. The rest of the energy produced during the burning of these fuels merely goes to heat up the surroundings.

In a fuel cell, with the help of a catalyst, it is feasible to combine hydrogen and oxygen in such a way that, instead of the energy of the reaction heating up the surroundings, it produces electricity.

A hydrogen–oxygen fuel cell has two porous electrodes and hot concentrated potassium hydroxide solution as the electrolyte. Hydrogen gas circulates under pressure around one electrode where it is oxidized to water, while oxygen gas is pumped round the other electrode where it is reduced to hydroxide ions:

$$O_2(g) + 2H_2O(l) + 4e^- \longrightarrow 4OH^-(aq) \quad \text{(at the positive electrode)}$$

$$2H_2(g) + 4OH^-(aq) \longrightarrow 4H_2O(l) + 4e^- \quad \text{(at the negative electrode)}$$

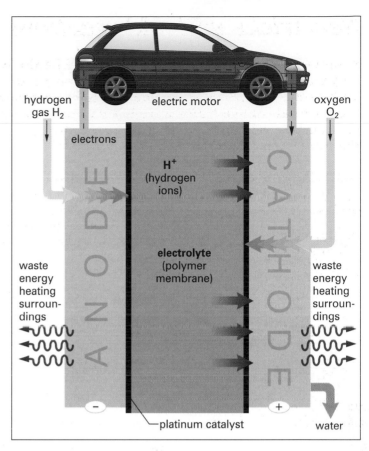

▲ **Figure 6B26** *How a car runs on a fuel cell.*

The efficiencies of these cells can be as high as 75% and they were used in the early American Gemini spacecraft where they also provided the astronauts with drinking water.

Until quite recently, fuel cells were expensive and cumbersome pieces of equipment. But fuel-cell technology has moved on since the space-race days of the 1960s. The new fuel cells, produced by Ballard Power Systems in Vancouver, Canada, are highly compact pieces of equipment. They are based on a design pioneered for the space programme, but Ballard have made significant improvements to the design, so that the electrodes consist of thin sheets of a porous carbon-based conducting material coated with a small amount of platinum catalyst. These sandwich the electrolyte which is an ultrathin conducting membrane.

The first vehicles powered by fuel cells include a bus cruising the Vancouver streets, and commercial vehicles on test at Daimler-Benz's research headquarters near Ulm in Germany. They use stacks of 24 of the fuel cell units, weighing a total of about 50 kilos. In the case of the Vancouver bus, this amounts to the delivery of 125 horse-power to the bus's powerful electric motor, and gives a range of about 100 miles.

Fuel cells score better than vehicles running off conventional rechargeable batteries. No matter how efficiently these batteries can be made to run, ultimately they depend on non-renewable, polluting forms of electricity generation. Instead of pollution coming from the vehicle, the use of conventional batteries merely shifts those emissions back to the power-stations which generate the electricity to recharge the batteries.

'We need fuel cells with the power-to-weight ratio of an internal combustion engine', says Paul Howard, Ballard Power Systems vice-president.

Firoz Rasul, Ballard's president, is optimistic. 'Sure we need to get costs down, but I reckon that in less than 10 years, fuel cells installed in vehicles for the private customer will be commercially competitive with cars powered by internal combustion engine.'

Controlling chemical change

Problem solvers at Plymouth

Controlling reactions can be tricky even on a laboratory scale. A procedure which works well on one occasion may cause problems on another. Even tried and tested synthetic methods may not work because of slight changes to the starting materials or reagents.

Day by day

Ten years ago, when Andrew Tonkin and Andy Arnold decided to work for the University of Plymouth, they did not know what a job as a university lab technician would be like, but they had not been offered any other jobs so they decided to give it a try.

'We have to do so many different things, I can't really tell what a typical day is like,' says Andy. 'Basically we're here to give technical support to the students at the university who are studying chemistry. There are a lot of different students and they're studying many different things.'

'The students doing undergraduate courses have to do three to four hour practicals,' says Andrew. 'The department has nine teaching labs and runs four or five practical sessions of about 20 students each day. Some of the practicals the lecturers set are quite simple and the students can do almost everything themselves in the time available. Then we only have to set out the equipment and reagents they will need. When the practical is more time consuming we have to do some of it for them. We make up solutions and, to economize, we sometimes recover the starting materials that have already been used by a group of students.'

Cracking a dimer

'In one of the practicals the students have to use cyclopentadiene,' Andy explains. 'You can't buy this reagent because, unless you keep it very cold, it dimerizes in a few hours. You can only get it by cracking dicyclopentadiene. This involves refluxing it for about an hour and then separating the monomer from the dimer. Since the boiling point of the monomer, cyclopentadiene is about 100°C lower than that of the dimer, this isn't hard. We just rearrange the apparatus and distil off the cyclopentadiene. The students could easily make it themselves but it takes a lot of time so we have to get into work at 7 am to get it ready for a 9 am practical class.'

'To be fair, we only have to do this a couple of times in the year,' Andrew adds. 'And a lot of the work is more challenging than this.'

Problems with zinc

'A couple of years ago, one of the lecturers decided to get the students to do a Reformatsky reaction, which involves an intermediate with zinc atoms in an organic molecule. The reaction seemed quite simple so the lecturer didn't bother to try it out before giving it to the first group of students to do. None of the students could get it to work at all so we had to drop everything to try to find out what had gone wrong and to put things right before the next group of students were scheduled to do that preparation.

'We immediately suspected the zinc. We had given the students zinc dust, which had been sitting on a shelf for some time. It was possible that a layer of zinc oxide on the surface might be stopping the reaction. I looked up a method of dissolving the oxide in Vogel's *Practical Organic Chemistry* and tried it out. It made no difference. The lecturer thought that there might be something wrong with the cyclohexanone they were using, so we redistilled it to be on the safe side.'

'Meanwhile we decided to melt down the zinc dust to make a bar of metal and then mill some fresh zinc turnings, which we knew would have a clean surface. The next time we tried the reaction, it worked and it worked for the students as well.'

'That's what's so good about this job,' says Andy. 'When you start work each morning, you have no idea what will be thrown at you. The final year students, the PhD students, and the post docs – they all have projects or research to do and they all come to us with problems or just to ask advice.'

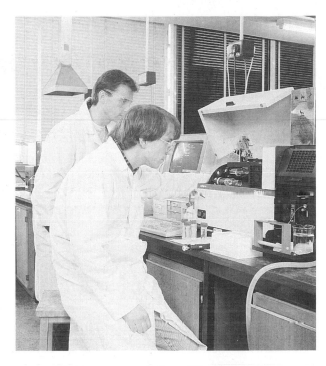

▲ **Figure 6C1** *Andy and Paul, a research student, using an atomic absorption spectrophotometer.*

Demonstrating

Andy and Andrew are agreed on what they like doing best: demonstrating the analytical instruments to students and researchers who are unfamiliar with them. Says Andy, 'Each of us has a group of instruments that we have to be really familiar with. It's our job to make sure that people who need to use an instrument are directed to the ones that will give them the results they need. We also have to make sure that they use them properly.'

'And if the instrument isn't working we have to try to work out what is wrong and what has to be done to fix it,' adds Andrew.

Paperwork

Like many jobs, the work of a university lab technician involves spending increasing amounts of time doing paperwork. 'We have to do a COSHH assessment for each practical the students do,' says Andy, 'and make sure that each student gets a copy.'

Qualifications

Andy and Andrew both started at the university after passing two A-levels, but then they did a Higher National Certificate in Chemistry followed by a Royal Society of Chemistry Certificate in Applied Chemistry as day-release students. 'With the experience I have I might be able to get a better paid job in industry,' says Andy, 'but I honestly don't want to leave here. I don't know anywhere else I could have the variety of work, deal with so many interesting people or have the responsibility I get here.'

Thinking on their feet

Moving from a college or university laboratory to industry can be a shock. 'I mean,' said one young chemical engineer, 'you get no idea whatsoever about the sheer size and impact of working at an oil refinery.' 'Yes,' said another, 'standing amongst the immense pipework and the towers, I couldn't believe I was part of such a dynamic process.'

'A chemical engineer's job in industry is 90% working with people and 10% technical.'

'The kick you get is that you can influence and control those big steel beasts and the products that come out of them,' added a third member of the group, 'even when you talk about scaling-up processes at university, it often tends to be theoretical – you don't realize just how much they are scaled up.'

The three engineers were part of a group of young graduates working for Esso at Fawley near Southampton. The combined refinery and petrochemical plant is an industrial complex covering about 1300 acres with about 40 process units that make up the vast array of pipes and towers. In addition there are workshops, laboratories, administration blocks, computer facilities as well as a health centre.

The group was engaged in an energy conservation exercise covering the whole refinery. They had divided the refinery into areas and then looked at every source of energy for the furnaces, and boilers – steam, electricity and so on. They questioned everything and challenged people: Is this the best way of doing it? Why are we doing it like this? What other ways could we use?

They spent a lot of time looking at the way things work and talking to the people who operate processes. Then they got together as a team back in the office to work out a programme, check it, make calculations and get out drawings; then they went back to the refinery to see if their suggestions were practicable. They had to get everything costed and approved by management; next they had to put it into practice and check that the work was correctly carried out and the new equipment monitored once it had been installed.

◄ **Figure 6C2** *In amongst the pipework of one of the process units.*

One of the recent recruits commented: 'You get no idea, until you arrive here and start, just how much responsibility they'll give you right from the beginning. They let you stand on your own feet and you're exposed to all sorts of men and women: technicians, process operators as well as top management.'

Sometimes action is required quickly. A young manager at Fawley remarked: 'My job is about making decisions and about people. The decisions are not always taken after a week's calculation and several meetings. I might be out there on a rainy Friday afternoon in winter with a problem that's got to be solved to keep a continuous process going. A number of people will be looking to me for a decision. You have to make the right choice with safety being a paramount factor.'

▲ **Figure 6C3** *Working as a team reviewing energy conservation for the refinery.*

Specialization and research

Some specialist teams at Fawley work exclusively on particular processes such as the catalytic cracker – the machine that cracks crude oil fractions using a catalyst. Over many years the team builds up knowledge and expertise about the equipment, its performance and possible modifications. Team members are in touch with other cat-cracker experts in Europe and the United States; by working closely with them they are able to contribute to a highly specialized pool of knowledge.

Environmental impacts

Many people in industry, especially the oil industry, have a highly developed feel for the extent to which the results of their work affect other industries, the public and the environment. 'I was very aware that I was entering an industry that, frankly, has some potentially unpleasant pollution factors built into it. At university the current of opinion was temporarily away from technology, what with the publicity given to global warming, industrial accidents and oil spills. But to be objective – the world relies on technology and oil and will do for years to come. And since I've joined the industry I've found that the people here share the same concerns as I do: but the great thing is we're in a position to improve things and this we are doing. Instead of standing on the touch-lines yelling, I'm actually doing something about safety, about conservation, about maintaining environmental standards. I think this is the realistic approach.'

'I was sitting in the control room at about two in the morning, it was the first time I'd been on duty at night and I sat there watching the dials and so on … and thinking, "So this is what it's like…" when an operator came in and said the refinery equivalent of "There's trouble at t'mill!". I looked round but he was talking to me. That's when you begin to find out about yourself.'

Perfecting the manufacture of 5504

The continuing story of ICIA5504 (see pages 158–63) illustrates some of the challenges faced by people at the forefront of developing new processes and products. Once Zeneca began building the chemical plant for manufacturing their new fungicide, the company was seeing the culmination of more than six years' work by several teams of chemists and chemical engineers. Patrick McNeilly was a member of one of the teams.

'The manufacturing process for 5504 that my colleagues and I have developed is a company secret so I can't reveal any details about it but I can set out in principle what we did.

'First of all, I probably should explain why it has to be secret. Zeneca has patented ICIA5504. This means that for a certain number of years we own the rights to the chemical. We have the right to stop other companies selling it, or we can choose to license other companies to sell it in return for a royalty payment. After our patent runs out, though, other chemical companies will also be free to make and sell it without a licence from us.

'The molecular structure of 5504 is not a secret. Nor are the synthetic routes that our research chemists used to make it. That information has to be made public when a chemical is patented. But there is a world of difference between knowing this information about 5504 and knowing how to manufacture it cheaply enough to make it a product that we can sell to farmers. It took Zeneca over six years to develop the process and that research cost a lot of money. If we can keep the details secret, we will still have the edge on our competitors when our patent on 5504 runs out.

'Developing a viable manufacturing route is quite different from working out a laboratory process for small scale synthesis. Our manufacturing process has several steps and each step has its own team of process chemists and chemical engineers. For more than a year the team I'm on has been working to perfect the conditions for one step of the process.

When we took on the project, another team had got our reaction working reasonably well. The yield of the product was good but there was a problem. Our reaction took 24 hours to complete. When you have a multi-step process, it is simply not cost effective to tie up a chemical plant on one reaction for 24 hours, so we had to speed up the reaction.

'Before we could do anything, we had to understand what was really going on in the reaction. We found that a side reaction was competing with the desired reaction and producing unwanted by-products.

'We had to do something about this side reaction too because it decreased the amount of product produced for each kilogram of reagent used. The more improvement we made, the less reagent would be wasted and the less effluent would have to be treated.'

'The first thing we had to look at was how the temperature would affect the efficiency of the reaction. Increasing the temperature generally speeds up chemical reactions, but that means it speeds up side reactions as well as the desired reaction. We were pleased to find that on raising the temperature, the desired reaction proceeded faster than the side reaction and this increased efficiency as well as speed. There was one problem though. One of the reactants is volatile and boiled off as we raised the temperature above a certain level. We got around this by using fractional distillation to separate the volatile reactant from the vapours rising from the reaction vessel and then added it back.

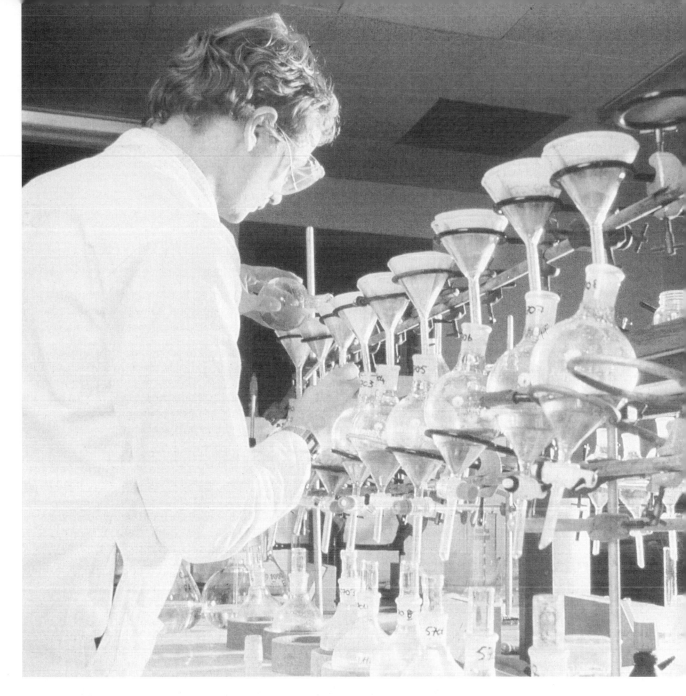

'The concentration of the various reagents in the reaction mixture also affects the rate of reactions so we did a series of experiments to find the optimum rate of addition of each reagent and the optimum temperature. As a result of this work we were able to increase an already acceptable yield and reduce the reaction time from twenty-four hours to five.'

▲ **Figure 6C4** *Perfecting the chemical reactions which make up a chemical manufacturing process involves carrying out the reactions many times making slight variations to the reaction conditions. The results must then be analysed to see what effect the changes had on the speed of the reaction and the concentrations of products and by-products produced.*

Making sulphuric acid in Derbyshire

Even established chemical processes need constant monitoring and development to ensure that they run efficiently, safely and with minimal impacts on the environment. Over the years there have been many changes at a chemicals complex at Staveley near Chesterfield in Derbyshire in response to varying economic, technical and social conditions.

Industrial beginnings

There has been heavy industry in Staveley for many centuries. The earliest industrial activity in the area was the smelting of locally mined iron ore using charcoal, and later, coal and coke from nearby deposits. Records show that local ironmaking was taking place as long ago as 1300.

Chemical manufacture at Staveley began in 1912 when the company began to extract hydrocarbons such as benzene, toluene and naphtha from the coke ovens. The first sulphuric acid plant was installed a year later, in an effort to make a valuable product from the unpleasant smelling hydrogen sulphide in the coke gas.

With the closure of the ironworks in 1965, the site was taken over by a new company called Staveley Chemicals. Since then, the site has changed ownership twice and a number of new chemical units have been built. One of these was a sulphuric acid plant built in 1972.

Today, there are three principal manufacturing units occupying the 75 hectare site at Staveley: the sulphuric acid plant, the benzole refinery and the chlor-alkali plant. A French company, Rhône-Poulenc, has owned the chemical plant since 1989. The company employs 350 people compared with a peak of around 7000 at the turn of the century when blast furnaces produced 10 000 tonnes of iron each year.

▼ **Figure 6C5** *Plant manager Colin Andrews wearing a hard hat and safety glasses which are mandatory in the sulphuric acid plant.*

Bringing in the sulphur

Traditionally, sulphur was imported from France, Mexico and Poland, but most of the sulphur now used at Staveley comes as a by-product from the refining of crude oil at places such as Milford Haven and Coryton.

The liquid sulphur arrives in 25 tonne loads by road tanker. It is transported quite safely at a temperature of 125–140°C inside the lorries.

A burning issue

At the beginning of the Contact Process, pumps supply a controlled feed of molten sulphur from the main storage tank to the sulphur furnace where it burns in dry air. The air supply comes from a drying tower where a current of air is circulated upwards through a stream of 96% sulphuric acid. 'There is intimate contact between the moist air and the acid. The acid is a very hygroscopic material and so absorbs the moisture,' says Colin Andrews.

Why does the air have to be so dry? 'If you've got moisture around, it can instantly form acid which will corrode our downstream pipework.'

Burning sulphur in the furnace produces a gas stream which contains about 10% sulphur dioxide at a temperature of 1000°C. The remainder of the gas stream consists of about 11% unreacted oxygen and 79% nitrogen from the feed of dry air.

$$S(l) \quad + \quad O_2(g) \quad \longrightarrow \quad SO_2(g) \qquad \Delta H = -297\,kJ\,mol^{-1}$$

sulphur   oxygen   sulphur dioxide

A one metre thick refractory lining of heat-resistant bricks protects the inside of the furnace. The reaction is highly exothermic so the hot gases from the furnace pass through a heat exchanger which acts as a boiler to produce steam for use throughout the works.

A successful conversion

After the gas stream has been cooled in the boiler and mixed with more dry air, its temperature is down to around 420°C. It then flows into the top of the converter, a large cylinder which converts the sulphur dioxide in the gas stream into sulphur trioxide. In the converter, the gases pass through four separate beds of catalyst, composed of pellets of vanadium(V) oxide. These pellets are ribbed to increase the surface area on which the reaction can take place.

According to Colin Andrews, the life of the catalyst pellets is very variable. 'It depends on the rate at which you run the plant. The pellets can break down and form fine dust, and this together with the ash in sulphur tend to block the catalyst bed, so the air flow through the plant tends to drop off. At that point, you have to remove the catalyst, sieve it, get rid of the fine particles and replace the pellets with a top up of fresh ones. We especially have to sieve the top two beds because most of the conversion takes place here and they have the highest temperatures.' This clear-out is normally undertaken at shutdowns once every two years. 'We hope we don't have to do it more frequently,' adds Colin with a wry smile.

Hygroscopic
Hygroscopic substances tend to absorb water from the air.

PROPERTY OF
TOWER HAMLETS COLLEGE

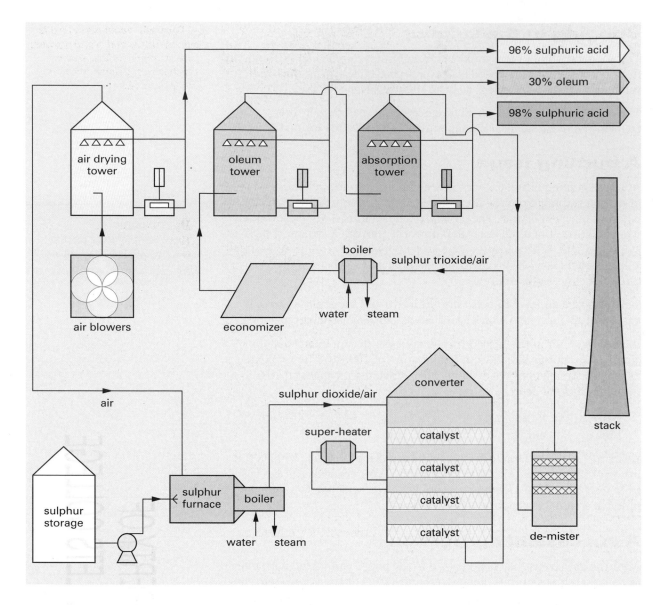

▲ **Figure 6C6** *The Staveley sulphuric acid plant. A plant diagram showing main units, inputs and outputs.*

The catalytic reaction in the converter is exothermic.

$$2SO_2(g) \quad + \quad O_2(g) \quad \rightleftharpoons \quad 2SO_3(g) \qquad \Delta H = -98 \, \text{kJ mol}^{-1}$$

sulphur dioxide   oxygen   sulphur trioxide

Unfortunately, this is a reversible reaction. As the temperature rises, the position of equilibrium shifts to the left, lowering the yield of sulphur trioxide and increasing the proportion of unchanged sulphur dioxide and oxygen. As a result, only about 60% of the sulphur dioxide is converted into sulphur trioxide by the first bed of catalyst.

The temperature rise across the top bed is typically around 180°C, so the gas exits from it at about 600°C. Adding cold, dry 'quench' air reduces the temperature to approximately 450°C before the gas stream enters the second bed. More of the sulphur dioxide reacts with oxygen, resulting in an 82% conversion to sulphur trioxide as the gas temperature is raised once more to approximately 550°C.

In order not to waste the energy, the gases are piped out of the converter and through another heat exchanger, called a superheater, where steam is heated from 250°C to 350°C before being used to generate electricity.

The cooled gases are led back into the third catalyst bed at about 440°C. This time, since most of the reaction has already been completed, the temperature rise is only about 20°C. By now, about 98% of the sulphur dioxide has been converted, but this is still not good enough. More quench air is added before it enters the fourth and final bed at 420°C. Here, the temperature rise is only about 5°C as the conversion level of sulphur dioxide to sulphur trioxide reaches 98%.

Gas pressure in the converter is only just above normal atmospheric pressure. Although a more complete conversion of the sulphur dioxide could be achieved at higher pressure, the economics of doing this would not be worthwhile since only 2% is lost under the existing conditions.

As the gas leaves the converter, more heat is extracted in another boiler and then another heat exchanger known as an economizer. This lowers the temperature of the gas to around 200°C, cool enough to begin absorbing the sulphur trioxide.

Sulphur trioxide and oleum

The next stage is to convert the sulphur trioxide gas into sulphuric acid and oleum by passing it through two absorbers. This lengthy process is necessary because sulphur trioxide and water react very violently when mixed to form acid.

'The absorption train at Staveley is rather special,' says Colin Andrews. 'We operate what's called a full-flow oleum tower. We absorb sulphur trioxide first into oleum in the oleum tower and then into 98% sulphuric acid in an absorption tower.' The strengths of the liquids in both towers are maintained by constant withdrawal of the circulating streams and the addition of weaker acid and water.

The first step is to pass the gas up a tower which has 30% oleum circulating around it. This is a counter-current process with the gas and liquid flowing in opposite directions. About 20–25% of the sulphur trioxide dissolves in the oleum. 'It very much depends on the temperature at which the tower is run,' explains Colin, 'the hotter the tower, the less gas is absorbed.'

The liquid leaving the oleum tower can be drawn off and heated to distil off some of the sulphur trioxide, leaving 20 or 25% oleum. The sulphur trioxide vapour is then cooled and condensed for sale as a liquid. More concentrated (65%) oleum can also be obtained at this stage by mixing 30% oleum with sulphur trioxide.

The remaining sulphur trioxide in the gas flow moves on into the absorption tower which has concentrated (98%) sulphuric acid trickling down over closely packed ceramic saddles. The sulphuric acid concentration rises to about 98.5% as sulphur trioxide reacts with water. This is another exothermic process, as the equation shows.

$$H_2O(l) + SO_3(g) \longrightarrow H_2SO_4(l) \quad \Delta H = -130\,kJ\,mol^{-1}$$

water   sulphur   sulphuric acid
         trioxide

As the acid flows out at the bottom of the tower, its concentration is returned to 98% by adding water.

The hot acid is then cooled with cold water in plate heat exchangers before being diverted into large storage tanks.

Cleaning up

Any sulphur dioxide or sulphur trioxide escaping from the plant can cause air pollution. Sulphur dioxide is poisonous, and even in small quantities can cause people to cough and choke. Sulphur dioxide is also one of the gases which produces acid rain.

'If the plant is operating efficiently, there should be minimal slippage of sulphur trioxide past the absorption tower,' says Colin. However, a very small amount of unreacted sulphur dioxide passes through as it does not dissolve appreciably in oleum or sulphuric acid.

◀ **Figure 6C8** *The 85 metre high stack is so tall because it is designed to allow winds to disperse the residual gas to prevent harmful effects at ground level. A spiral fin provides wind deflection.*

A demister vessel removes acid mist from the waste gas before it passes up the main chimney stack, but the emission still contains the unchanged sulphur dioxide. 'We have continuous on-line monitoring of the sulphur dioxide concentration going up the stack – a typical value is about 0.15% by volume,' says Colin Andrews. At present, the upper limit on the amount of sulphur dioxide emitted equates to no more than 2% of the sulphur burnt.

The stack is 85 metres high and is designed to disperse the emissions over a wide area. 'The system ensures that there will be no harmful effects at ground level,' comments Colin.

However, new environmental legislation will soon have a big impact on the way the acid plant operates. Colin Andrews explains: 'New emission limits have been imposed on us by HMIP (Her Majesty's Inspectorate of Pollution). Early in 1994, we applied for and obtained an authorization to run the plant under the Environmental Protection Act of 1990. We now have a strict limit on the amount of sulphur dioxide we are allowed to discharge. There is also a planned improvement programme to bring our plant up to somewhere like the standard of a new plant within a certain time.'

One of the most likely changes will probably be an upgrading from the current single absorption design to a double absorption process. Modern plants typically obtain a sulphur dioxide conversion rate of around 99.7%.

The main difference lies in the layout of the converter. The gas stream is diverted midway through the conversion process into an absorption tower before being sent back into the converter for further passage through the beds of catalyst. 'Because you've absorbed some of the sulphur trioxide, you are able to shift the equilibrium to the sulphur trioxide side of the equation and you get more conversion compared to normal,' explains Colin.

There is another way to reduce emissions. 'The other option we're looking at is a tail-gas scrubbing technique. The demister is followed by a tower containing a scrubbing liquid. You can then convert the sulphur dioxide into something else.'

Chemical hazards

Sulphur trioxide and oleum are very dangerous substances. Both of these liquids are carried in road tankers made of mild or stainless steel.

During spillages, they remain in liquid form but give off dense, white fumes of sulphuric acid mist, when in contact with moist air. However, when sulphur trioxide comes into contact with water, an explosive reaction produces a thick mist of sulphuric acid. The best way to deal with such a spillage is to use dry sand or earth to soak it up. Fire brigades have available a special absorbent material, rather like cat litter.

Plans are in place in case of a road traffic accident involving a sulphuric acid tanker. If the spillage is small, the Fire Brigade simply dilute the acid by hosing it away with large quantities of water. A large spill may be neutralized by pouring fine-ground calcium carbonate (limestone or chalk) onto it.

Figure 6C9 *The Hazchem label on a sulphuric acid tanker.*

Figure 6C10 *Diagram showing layout of the effluent treatment plant. Liquid wastes are mixed in the balancing tank, then transferred to the aeration basin where they are broken down by bacteria. The contents of the aeration basin slowly overflow into the clarifier where the sludge settles out and is recycled to the aeration basin for further treatment. Treated effluent is discharged to the River Rother.*

Cleaning up the effluent

Staveley has a biological effluent treatment plant, dating from the late 1960s, to treat waste from each of the manufacturing units.

Most of the treatment takes place in three open-topped tanks. The first is a balancing tank, which stores and mixes effluent so that the conditions do not change too much or too quickly. This ensures that conditions remain stable for the bacteria in the second, aeration, tank.

In the second tank, mechanical stirring and bubbles of oxygen keep bacteria in suspension. Bacterial activity is also encouraged by a continual supply of nutrients (mainly nitrogen and phosphorus), a near-neutral pH and a moderate temperature. The bacteria use oxygen dissolved in the water to break down the contaminants, turning the carbon in organic compounds into carbon dioxide.

Bacteria are added regularly to the aeration basin to maintain stability in the process. They include nitrification bacteria which convert ammonia into nitric acid. The company succeeds in removing 99% of the ammonia from its waste by this method.

The contents of the aeration basin slowly overflow into a third tank, the clarifier. Here the bacterial sludge settles and is recycled to the aeration basin. The treated effluent overflows to the river.

Generally this treatment system is highly efficient in removing contaminants, although it is vulnerable to sudden changes in effluent conditions.

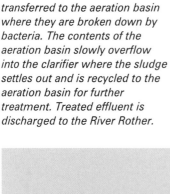

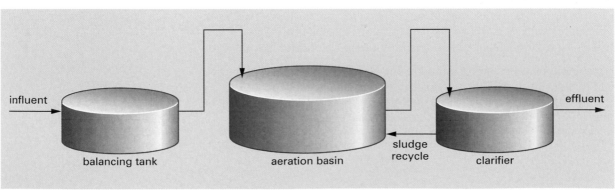

Economics

The manufacture of sulphuric acid is a capital-intensive rather than a labour-intensive industry. Large sums are invested in building, maintaining and upgrading the plant. This will be particularly true when the new pollution regulations come into force at Staveley.

Labour costs are not very high as most of the Contact Process is automated. There are three shifts every 24 hours, with one shift supervisor, one operator and two fillers plus twelve maintenance staff, giving a total of sixteen staff during the day shifts. The older pneumatic controls are gradually being replaced by electronic controls.

The plant is operated continuously apart from the biennial shutdowns. Colin Andrews explains what this involves: 'We have to blow the plant cold, which can take 36–48 hours, before we can break into the converter. Then we have to carry out the sieving, which is very labour intensive. The sieving of the catalyst can take 3 to 4 days. Then there is the problem of starting up and getting the temperature up before you reach the strike temperature of the catalyst. We have to heat up the furnace and blow hot gases through the converter to warm up the catalyst beds. They have to be above 400 °C before you can start burning sulphur, otherwise there is a very inefficient conversion.'

Not surprisingly, unscheduled shutdowns are avoided unless absolutely necessary. This is one reason why most pumps and valves are reproduced in duplicate.

In 1994 the Staveley plant was working virtually flat out. 'We had a sister plant at Avonmouth which shut down in July 1993,' explains Colin. 'Prior to that, Staveley would typically run at loads of 50–70%. Since then, we have been running at loads of 80–100%. It is the first time in the history of the plant that we've run that close to maximum load for a fair proportion of the time. This really was the acid test!' he says with a smile. 'So far, so good.'

The market for acid products is very volatile. Some variations are predictable, such as seasonal fluctuations in demand. 'There are peak periods when we have to burn as much sulphur as possible,' says Colin. One of these coincides with the late summer potato harvest when farmers start buying 77% sulphuric acid to spray their crop. This kills off the potato tops and makes harvesting easier.

There has been a considerable fall in the UK's manufacturing capacity for sulphuric acid because of the economic recession and competition from other sources. One major competitor has been imported smelter acid (which is sulphuric acid produced as a by-product of the smelting of metal ores) from the Continent.

'We are told that at present there is a shortage of sulphuric acid, principally because some plants have been taken off line or decommissioned, and there isn't enough smelter acid available,' says Colin. 'So this plant at Staveley is profitable at the moment.'

Prices of raw materials can swing quite violently. In August 1994, the cost of sulphur was about £40 a tonne, but its price was expected to rise rapidly in the near future. Income from the acid products also varies with market conditions. In the summer of 1994, 98% sulphuric acid was selling for £26 a tonne, while 30% oleum sold for £50 a tonne.

Smelter acid is cheaper, but contains heavy metals, so it is much less pure than acid produced by the Contact Process.

Staveley sells three grades of sulphuric acid: 77%, 96% and 98%. It also produces and sells sulphur trioxide and four grades of oleum, ranging from 20% to 65% concentration. Although about 70% of the acid plant output is in the form of sulphuric acid, the other products are more profitable because the extra processing involved means that they command higher prices.

One other very important source of income is the energy generated during the Contact Process. High-pressure steam from the acid plant generates 4 MW of electricity, which is used on site. This also means that the plant has no fuel bills.

▲ **Figure 6C11** *An operator at work in the control room of the sulphuric acid plant.*

The Solvay process

'The magic of Solvay,' according to Mac Thorpe, 'makes possible a cunning method, devised by Ernest Solvay, for producing sodium carbonate from salt and limestone.' The process invented by this Belgian chemist has operated at Northwich in Cheshire since 1873.

Glass, detergents, bath salts and baking powder are all products made with the help of the Solvay process. Sodium carbonate is used industrially as an alkali in paper-making as well as in the manufacture of soaps and detergents. A growing use of sodium carbonate is to treat waste gases from fossil-fuel power stations to remove the sulphur dioxide that causes acid rain. Brunner Mond and Company Limited produce over one million tonnes per year of sodium carbonate.

Finding a route to sodium carbonate

'Think first of the ideal route to sodium carbonate', said Mac Thorpe, New Business Leader and Laboratory Manager at Brunner Mond.

At first sight it looks simple. Start with two cheap raw materials, mix them and out should pop the products as shown by this equation:

sodium chloride + calcium carbonate → sodium carbonate + calcium chloride
(salt)   (limestone)
$2NaCl$ $+ CaCO_3$ $→ Na_2CO_3$ $+ CaCl_2$

Unfortunately, salt and limestone do not react directly. In fact, the reaction goes the other way. Mixing solutions of sodium carbonate and calcium chloride produces a precipitate of calcium carbonate and a solution of sodium chloride.

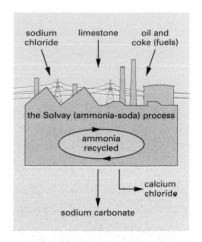

▲ **Figure 6C12** *A summary of the Solvay process.*

▼ **Figure 6C13** *A flow diagram for the Solvay process.*

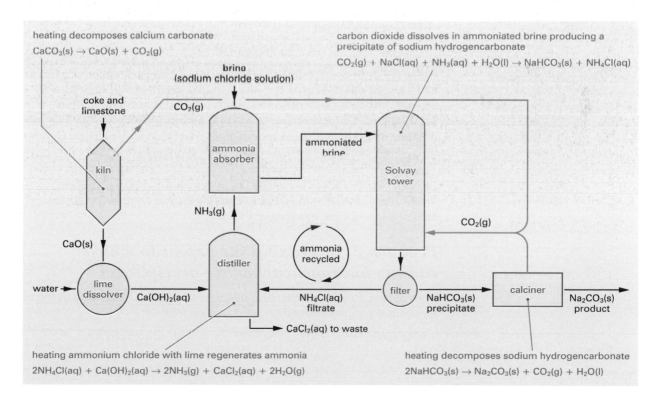

heating decomposes calcium carbonate
$CaCO_3(s) → CaO(s) + CO_2(g)$

carbon dioxide dissolves in ammoniated brine producing a precipitate of sodium hydrogencarbonate
$CO_2(g) + NaCl(aq) + NH_3(aq) + H_2O(l) → NaHCO_3(s) + NH_4Cl(aq)$

heating ammonium chloride with lime regenerates ammonia
$2NH_4Cl(aq) + Ca(OH)_2(aq) → 2NH_3(g) + CaCl_2(aq) + 2H_2O(g)$

heating decomposes sodium hydrogencarbonate
$2NaHCO_3(s) → Na_2CO_3(s) + CO_2(g) + H_2O(l)$

The ingenious Solvay devised an indirect route to the required products by means of a complex sequence of changes with simple chemicals. Figure 6C12 sums up the main inputs and outputs. Figure 6C13 describes the process in more detail.

Controlling reactions

The Solvay process shows that it is possible to apply chemical principles to manage and control reactions. In particular there are three chemical problems to overcome:

- carbon dioxide only ionizes very slightly when it dissolves in water
- sodium hydrogencarbonate is moderately soluble in water
- when sodium hydrogencarbonate does precipitate, the crystals are often very fine, difficult to filter and hard to use.

Problem 1 Producing a high enough concentration of hydrogencarbonate ions

The purpose of the ammonia absorber is to make the sodium chloride solution alkaline. This then means that on carbonation there can be a high enough concentration of hydrogencarbonate ions in the Solvay tower to form a precipitate of sodium hydrogencarbonate.

When carbon dioxide dissolves in water the overall equilibrium is well over to the left:

$$CO_2(g) + H_2O(l) \rightleftharpoons H^+(aq) + HCO_3^-(aq) \tag{1}$$

Something has to be done to shift the position of this equilibrium to the right to raise the concentration of hydrogencarbonate ions. One way is to use a base to remove hydrogen ions.

Ammonia (NH_3) is a base that reacts with water forming ammonium ions (NH_4^+) and hydroxide ions (OH^-).

$$NH_3(g) + H_2O(l) \rightleftharpoons NH_4^+(aq) + OH^-(aq) \tag{2}$$

In the Solvay tower the hydroxide ions from equation 2 react with the hydrogen ions from equation 1, thus driving equation 1 to the right. Overall, carbon dioxide dissolves in the solution containing sodium chloride, ammonium ions and hydroxide ions producing an equilibrium mixture which is well over to the right.

$$CO_2(g) + NH_3(aq) + H_2O(l) \rightleftharpoons NH_4^+(aq) + HCO_3^-(aq) \tag{3}$$

As Tony Woode, science leader at Brunner Mond, puts it: 'Ammonia fixes carbon dioxide and makes the gas react, just as peas, beans and similar plants fix the nitrogen of the air.'

Problem 2 Increasing the extent to which sodium hydrogencarbonate precipitates

The solution to this problem also involves controlling conditions to force an equilibrium process in the required direction.

$$Na^+(aq) + HCO_3^-(aq) \rightleftharpoons NaHCO_3(s) \qquad \Delta H = -20 \, kJ \, mol^{-1}$$

The trick is to contrive the conditions to make the concentrations of sodium ions and hydrogencarbonate ions as high as possible so pushing the equilibrium to the right. Starting with almost saturated sodium chloride solution (brine) makes sure that the sodium ion concentration is as high as possible.

One of the keys to 'the magic of Solvay' is to produce hydrogencarbonate ions without diluting the brine. Dissolving two gases (ammonia and carbon dioxide) in the brine avoids adding any further water while producing as high a hydrogencarbonate ion concentration as possible (see problem 1).

The precipitation reaction is exothermic, so temperature control can affect the position of the equilibrium. Lowering the temperature also helps to shift the equilibrium to the right and increase the amount of sodium hydrogencarbonate which precipitates.

Problem 3 Increasing the particle size of the precipitate

Temperature control can also influence the particle size. The rate of growth of the precipitated crystals is important, as it determines the final particle size.

At lower temperatures, crystals can only grow slowly and do not have time to become large. However the driving force for precipitation is high, and so many separate small crystals form giving a finely divided solid. This is what the people controlling the process want to avoid.

At higher temperatures, individual crystals grow more rapidly forming a precipitate with larger particles. These are easier to filter and handle but the higher temperature reduces the yield.

There are conflicting requirements: on the one hand the optimum amount of precipitate separates at lower temperatures (see problem 2), but for the optimum particle size the temperature has to be higher.

Fortunately, the manufacturers have found a way to get the best of both worlds by allowing the early stages of precipitation to occur from a fairly hot solution and then cooling for the later stages. This happens in the Solvay tower, with the temperature profile shown in Figure 6C14.

▼ **Figure 6C14** *The temperature profile of a Solvay tower.*

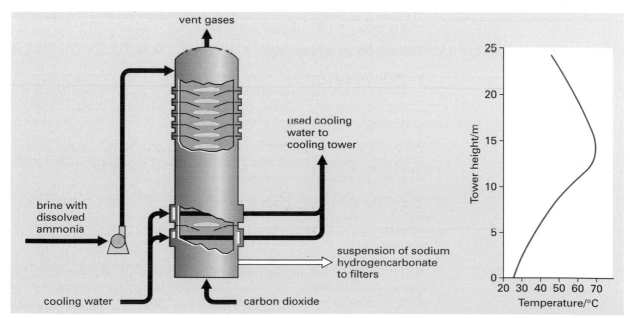

The effective use of material

Part of the 'magic of Solvay' is the economical use of ammonia which is recycled with the help of the calcium oxide from the limestone (see Figure 6C13). The ammonia flows out of the Solvay tower as ammonium chloride solution, $NH_4Cl(aq)$. Adding water to the calcium oxide (CaO) turns it into calcium hydroxide, $Ca(OH)_2$. The beauty of this is that ammonium chloride and calcium hydroxide react together to regenerate ammonia.

As a result the whole Solvay process is highly economic. The raw materials are cheap and plentiful – salt, limestone and coke. The ammonia, and some of the carbon dioxide, are recycled. There are two highly versatile products – sodium carbonate and sodium hydrogencarbonate. The only drawback is that the market for calcium chloride is too small to use all of this by-product formed while regenerating the ammonia.

The effective use of energy

The main sources of energy are:

- burning coke to heat the lime kilns to decompose the limestone
- burning coal, oil and gas to produce high-pressure steam, which generates electricity becoming low-pressure steam for heating.

Steam heating decomposes sodium hydrogencarbonate into sodium carbonate. The whole plant needs so much steam for heating that the power plant generates surplus electricity, which is sold as an additional product.

Some of the energy put into the process is easily recovered, for example, after heating to decompose sodium hydrogencarbonate. Some energy, however, ends up warming the circulating cooling water so that it is not far above atmospheric temperature. This is difficult to recover. New energy recovery schemes are a current topic of study at Brunner Mond. Tony Woode notes that: 'a recent study could only improve by 2% on the accumulated wisdom and expertise of the past 100 years.'

Impacts on the environment

When first developed the Solvay process was dramatically cleaner than earlier methods for making industrial alkalis.

The only liquid effluents are:

- cooling water, much of which is recycled
- dilute calcium chloride solution, from the ammonia distiller. Some of this is converted to useful products. Some is treated and discharged to rivers.

Parts of the modern process are noisy, mainly because of the mechanics of handling solids. These areas are enclosed and soundproofed and staff wear ear protection where necessary.

The site in mid-Cheshire is well placed within a few miles of extensive salt and limestone deposits. Important customers, such as the glass industry, are close at hand. So too is the motorway system, for transport further afield.

Better control of salt mining now limits the subsidence which once caused much damage. The scars of limestone quarries still cause controversy, especially in the Peak National Park.

◀ **Figure 6C15** *A tanker containing sodium carbonate, with the lime kilns in the background, which heat limestone and coke to produce carbon dioxide and calcium oxide, both of which are used in the Solvay process to produce sodium carbonate.*

Economic competition

The ammonia–soda process is technically ingenious, highly economic and has limited impacts on the environment. However, the vital question for its success is whether there is a market for the products, particularly the core product which is sodium carbonate. It has to remain competitive with rival processes.

The rival source of sodium carbonate is a mineral, trona, that is mined extensively, particularly in Western USA. Trona has to be purified, but its treatment is cheaper than the Solvay process. For British users, however, the additional high transport costs outweigh the cheaper cost of production.

There is also a rival chemical to sodium carbonate. As an industrial alkali it competes with sodium hydroxide, as both substances can be used in several industries. Before the 1960s, sodium carbonate was normally cheaper than sodium hydroxide. However, sodium hydroxide is made by electrolysis of brine and one of the co-products is chlorine. Production expanded rapidly in the 1960s, driven by the ever increasing demand for chlorine to manufacture plastics (see pages 156–7) and organic solvents. Cheap sodium hydroxide flooded the market and at one stage the death of the Solvay process was widely predicted.

'Reports of our death were somewhat exaggerated,' says Tony Woode. 'In the 1990s, the demand for chlorine is more static, as some of its uses expand but others decline, for environmental reasons. Demand for sodium hydroxide has increased and is more in line with supply. The price of sodium hydroxide has therefore risen and it is currently less of a threat to the sodium carbonate market.'

'The chemical industry is a complicated network,' said Mac Thorpe, 'with product demand linking to economic cycles. The level of activity in the building trade and the number of new house starts are seen as general economic indicators. The construction industry creates a demand for goods and services, which in one way or another, depend on sodium carbonate. Demand for sodium carbonate is also affected by the balance of trade in the world alkali markets. As aluminium production increases, for example, the demand for sodium hydroxide rises as do prices. This favours the use of sodium carbonate based alkali in some sectors of the paper industry and in phosphate production.'

Thoughts and actions

1 Use examples to explain the difference between:
   a exothermic and endothermic reactions
   b gas phase and liquid phase reactions
   c homogeneous and heterogeneous equilibria
   d batch and continuous processes.

2 a Devise a simple flow diagram to summarize the sequence of steps used to develop a black-and-white film (see pages 298–9).
   b By considering the oxidation numbers of silver, show that a reducing agent is required to convert silver bromide to silver.
   c What are the factors which determine the darkness of the image on a black-and-white negative? How do photographers control these factors to achieve the results they are looking for?
   d Write an equation to show what happens to silver bromide during the fixing of a film with sodium thiosulphate solution. What type of reaction is this?

3 a Explain how a combination of exothermic and endothermic reactions keeps the reactor at a steady temperature during the manufacture of nitrous oxide (see page 301).
   b Why is it vital that nitrous oxide for medical uses is free of nitric oxide, NO? (See page 4.)
   c Consult reference books to find out more about nitric oxide and use the information to explain how the second of the four scrubbers (column 2) makes sure that there is no NO in the nitrous oxide produced.

4 Use the table of bond energies (Figure R31.1) to calculate the overall energy change for the following reactions used in manufacturing processes and state whether they are exothermic or endothermic:
   a one mole of hydrogen gas reacts with chlorine gas to form hydrogen chloride gas
   b one mole of carbon dioxide reacts with hydrogen to form methanol and steam
   c one mole of nitrogen gas reacts with hydrogen gas to form ammonia gas.

   You may find it helpful to use molecular models to decide which bonds break and which bonds form during the reactions.

5 Sketch and label one or more diagrams to show what you picture happening to the molecules as sugar dissolves in water until the solution is saturated.

6 The equation shows the equilibrium system in a solution of chromate(VI) ions which are yellow. Dichromate(VI) ions are orange.
   $$2CrO_4^{2-}(aq) + 2H^+(aq) \rightleftharpoons Cr_2O_7^{2-}(aq) + H_2O(l)$$
   a Predict what you will see if you add acid drop by drop to a solution of sodium chromate(VI).
   b Predict what will happen if you then add sodium hydroxide drop-by-drop to the solution.
   c Explain your predictions.

7 Hydrogen reacts reversibly with iodine vapour to form hydrogen iodide.
   $$H_2(g) + I_2(g) \rightleftharpoons 2HI(g)$$
   The table shows the composition of equilibrium mixtures obtained by heating hydrogen and iodine in sealed tubes.

$[H_2(g)]_{eqm}$ /mol dm^{-3}	$[I_2(g)]_{eqm}$ /mol dm^{-3}	$[2HI(g)]_{eqm}$ /mol dm^{-3}
4.56×10^{-3}	0.74×10^{-3}	13.54×10^{-3}
2.25×10^{-3}	2.34×10^{-3}	16.85×10^{-3}
0.48×10^{-3}	0.48×10^{-3}	3.53×10^{-3}
1.14×10^{-3}	1.14×10^{-3}	8.41×10^{-3}

▲ Figure 6T1

   a Write the expression for the equilibrium constant for the reaction of hydrogen with iodine.
   b Calculate a value of K_c for each of the four equilibrium mixtures in Figure 6T1.
   c Calculate an average value for K_c. Do the results support the equilibrium law.

8 a Calculate the pH of 0.1 mol dm^{-3}, 0.01 mol dm^{-3} and 0.001 mol dm^{-3} solutions of hydrochloric acid.
   b Calculate the pH of a 0.1 mol dm^{-3} solution of sulphuric acid.
   c Why can't you calculate the pH of ethanoic acid in the same way?

9 a What is a buffer solution?
   b Give two examples of the uses of buffer solutions.
   c Use the table in Figure R29.1 in the Reference section to decide how to make up buffer solutions with:
   i pH = 3.0
   ii pH = 12.5.

10 a Write the equilibrium law expression for K_a of methanoic acid.

b Use the table in Figure R26.1 in the Reference section to decide which acid is stronger: methanoic acid or ethanoic acid.

11 A reaction between two gases was monitored by measuring the amount of reactant A and recording how it changed with time.

$A(g) + B(g) \rightleftharpoons C(g) + D(g)$ ΔH, negative

Figure 6T2 shows the results.

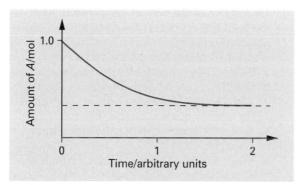

▲ **Figure 6T2**

a From the graph, how long did it take the reaction mixture to reach equilibrium?

b Copy the graph, then sketch three more lines to show what you would expect to happen on repeating the reaction under three different sets of conditions. Take into account the effect of the variables on the position of equilibrium and the rate of reaction. Assume that each time all the conditions remain the same except that the reaction is carried out:

  i   with a catalyst
  ii at a lower pressure
  iii at a higher temperature.

12 Suggest suitable practical techniques for monitoring the reaction of:

a magnesium with dilute hydrochloric acid
b copper(II) ions with ammonia molecules
c ethyl ethanoate with sodium hydroxide.

13 a How is it possible to control conditions to slow down or stop the following changes:
- the reaction of iron with air and water
- a chip-pan fire
- the souring of milk
- the rate of formation of carbon dioxide in the laboratory preparation of the gas.

b How is it possible to control conditions to speed up the following changes:
- the fermentation of sugar to carbon dioxide and alcohol
- the speed at which an epoxy adhesive sets

- the time taken to develop a photographic film
- the conversion of nitrogen oxides in a car exhaust to nitrogen
- the manufacture of ammonia from nitrogen and hydrogen.

14 The results plotted in Figures 6T3, 6T4 and 6T5 come from a study of the rate of reaction of iodine and propanone in acid solution (see page 323). Each graph shows what happened when the starting concentration of one species was varied while the others were kept constant.

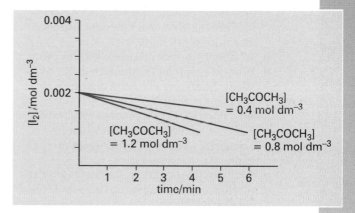

▲ **Figure 6T3**

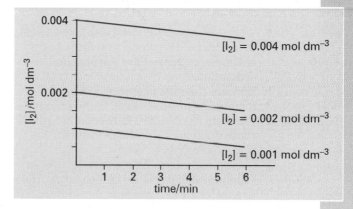

▲ **Figure 6T4**

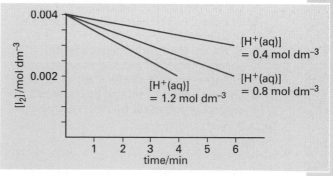

▲ **Figure 6T5**

a How can you find the rate of reaction from a graph of concentration against time?

b Show that the results provide evidence to justify the rate equation on page 327.

15 Compare the experiences of Andy and Andrew at Plymouth University, the work of young engineers on an oil refinery and the development of a manufacturing process by Zeneca. What do these case studies tell you about the differences between controlling reactions on a laboratory scale and on an industrial scale?

16 a What are the main products of the Contact process at Staveley (see pages 342–7)? Identify the chemical reactions used to make these products.

b What are the raw materials for the process?

c How do changing economic conditions affect the supply of raw of materials to the plant in Staveley?

d Why does a Contact process plant have no fuel bills, and why is it able to supply electricity to the other processes on site and to the National Grid?

e What are the conditions for carrying out the reaction to make sulphur trioxide at Staveley? How do equilibrium, rate and economic factors determine the chosen conditions?

f Identify the benefits and risks of the Contact process at Staveley for people who live nearby.

g What steps does the company take to limit the impact of the process on the environment? How effective are the precautions?

h Why are the manufacturers likely to be required to make changes to the process?

i What are the changes in the market which cause fluctuations in the demand for the acid and its price?

j Display the information about the uses of sulphuric acid in Figure 3C1 (on page 164) as a pie chart or bar chart.

17 a Identify the raw materials, required products, co-products and side products of the Solvay process (see pages 351–5).

b Summarize the chemical reactions involved in the process.

c What are the energy sources for the process and what steps are taken to use energy resources as efficiently as possible?

d Give examples to show why temperature control is important in the Solvay process.

e Give an example to show why controlling the concentrations of solutions is crucial to the success of the process.

f How does the Solvay process affect the environment both in the area round the plant and further afield?

g Sodium carbonate is easy to mine in the USA. Why is the Solvay process still economic in Cheshire?

18 The reversible, addition reaction of ethene with steam is used to manufacture ethanol. The reaction takes place in the gas phase at 300 °C in the presence of concentrated phosphoric acid adsorbed on an inert solid. The working pressure is about 70 times atmospheric pressure.

a Write an equation for the reversible reaction.

b Use the table of bond energies in Figure R31.1 in the Reference section to estimate the energy change for the reaction.

c Write the expression for the equilibrium constant.

d What conditions tend to favour a high yield of ethanol at equilibrium?

e Why do you think that the reaction is carried out at 300 °C in the presence of phosphoric acid?

19 Plymouth University needs a new technician for their undergraduate chemistry course (see pages 336–7).

a Draft an advertisement to attract suitable applicants.

b List the main qualities you will be looking for when choosing which person to appoint.

c Prepare a set of questions to ask the applicants at interview.

20 Read the three parts of the extended case study about the new fungicide from Zeneca (see pages 158–63, and 340–41). Write a news story for a local newspaper celebrating the success of bringing this new product to market. Use the outline in Figure 6T6 as a guide.

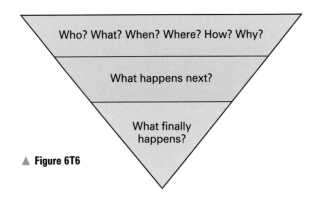

Who? What? When? Where? How? Why?

What happens next?

What finally happens?

▲ **Figure 6T6**

UNIT 7

Human physiology and healthcare management

Cells and organ systems in mammals

Cells in the diagnosis of disease

When a pet becomes ill, it is taken to the vet. A knowledge of cells and organs is essential for understanding how a whole animal works. Simply by examining a dog or cat, a vet will be able to eliminate some diseases or observe symptoms which suggest others. Sometimes X-ray pictures are taken or it is necessary to operate to find out what is wrong. However, there are other tools which help in veterinary diagnosis too.

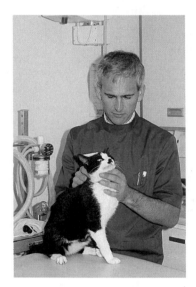

▲ **Figure 7A1** *Paul Coward deals with the problems of a village practice and animals referred to him for his special knowledge in skin diseases.*

A vet's life

Paul Coward is a vet who combines his everyday veterinary work with a specialist interest in animal skin problems. As Paul says, 'One bald, red, itchy dog can look very like another – yet if we can find the cause of the problem we are much more likely to come up with a successful treatment for the animal. Because it is sometimes tricky to decide what the problem is, other vets will refer their persistent cases to me.'

Both dogs and cats are regularly brought in to vets with skin problems, and many of these are treated easily. But in some animals the problem becomes chronic – it just will not go away. These are the cases with which Paul deals.

'I can divide my bald dogs into two main groups,' comments Paul. 'Put at its simplest these are the bald, itchy dogs and the bald happy dogs! About 90% are the bald itchy ones – and in most cases I can make life a lot more pleasant for them. The main causes of the problems are parasites, bacterial infections, yeast infections and allergies. To get to the bottom of the problem I often use **cytology** – which is the study of isolated cells – and **histopathology** – which means the study of diseased tissues. These are techniques for looking at patterns of disease in cells, the basic units from which animals are made. The bald happy dogs are often happy as they are – but their owners are not so contented!

Fortunately these animals too can be helped. When I look at their skin under the microscope the epidermis is usually thin and there are no active hair follicles. This is usually due to hormonal problems which we can treat.'

Case histories

To make a correct diagnosis in skin cases, I rely on three things,' explains Paul. 'First, I spend a lot of time talking to the owners and listening carefully to what they say – in fact, in many cases I am pretty sure what the problem is before I even examine the dog or cat! Then I look at the animal, observing carefully everything I can about its condition. Thirdly I carry out any appropriate tests – these often include taking skin samples (**biopsies**). I can take skin biopsies without a general anaesthetic in about ten minutes, without upsetting the animal. Using the skin test results I can usually come up with the answer – and when the problem is caused by parasites, bacteria, yeast or an allergy we can get some spectacular results.'

The problems behind bald, itchy cats and dogs are not always so straightforward, as the following case shows. Diagnosis is possible by looking for skin cells which look different from normal, healthy ones.

Serious scratching has left this dog (see Figure 7A2) with red, bald, sore patches. Under the microscope lots of inflammatory cells can be seen clustering around small blood vessels in the dermis, and the dermis is thickened. This suggests an allergy, and further tests showed the house dust mite was causing the problem. Steroids will solve the problem fast, but Paul prefers not to use them as they shorten the dog's life. He uses **antihistamines**, which solve the itching so that the fur re-grows, although it can take a while to find the right dose for each animal.

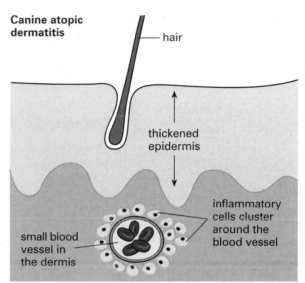

▼ **Figure 7A2** *Diagnosing animal diseases using information from looking at cells and tissues.*

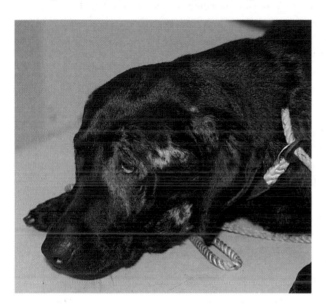

Canine atopic dermatitis

hair

thickened epidermis

small blood vessel in the dermis

inflammatory cells cluster around the blood vessel

Know the cells, know the disease

The way Paul Coward uses histopathology is quite new – many vets only use the veterinary pathology labs to find out if lumps and bumps which they remove from their patients are malignant or not. It is important to know what normal cells look like to be able to recognize the changes that are typical of cancer. Typically cancer cells have abnormal structures, unusually large nuclei, and there are lots of rapidly dividing cells where they are not expected. However, as Paul goes on to explain, some vets also do a bit of cytology for themselves. There are some diseases that can be diagnosed quite straightforwardly in the veterinary surgery using this technique.

Paul relates the story of a cat brought into his surgery with fluid in the chest. 'The cat was elderly and my initial thought was possible heart failure. There shouldn't be any fluid sloshing around in a cat's chest, so you know immediately that something is wrong. This is a condition which can be sorted out very easily with a bit of basic cytology. I inserted a needle into the chest and drew off some of the fluid. I made up a slide, adding stain to show up any cells, and had a look. There are several distinct possibilities and by looking through the microscope I could see immediately that the cat did not have heart failure, but a ruptured **thoracic duct** (the vessel feeding lymphatic fluids back into the blood system). At the moment it seems to be coping with this and is making progress. A combination of the history of the animals and the histology of the disease can usually lead us to diagnosis.'

The structure and function of mammalian cells

A cell is the basic unit of life. A simple model of a mammalian cell is a tiny bag of liquid in which all the chemical reactions of life take place and where all the information needed to make new cells is stored. A closer look shows a complex structure with many parts specialized to carry out particular jobs.

How big are cells?

Most cells cannot be seen with the naked eye – they need to be magnified in some way. The **light microscope** (see Reference section Figure R39) gives us a relatively cheap and easy way of seeing the structure of cells. It can be used to view living cells as well as cells which are dead and have been stained to show up particular features. At best it can magnify a cell about 1500 times. The electron microscope is a far more expensive piece of equipment and only dead material can be used. However, magnifications of many thousands are possible and using a scanning electron microscope 3-D images can be produced.

What do cells do?

Inside the mammal there are many different types of cells doing different jobs. However, most cells have certain functions in common.

- cells carry out cellular respiration (see page 365) although some cells respire more actively than others
- cells contain the genetic material (see page 190) of the organism which carries all the information needed for the replication not only of that particular cell but also of the whole organism to which it belongs
- cells make (**synthesize**) proteins – these may be enzymes which are then active in synthesizing other chemicals or they may form part of the structure of the cell
- cells form secretions and package them for release.

Typical mammalian cells

The structure of a cell seen with the light microscope is too simple to explain how it carries out the complex jobs it has to do. A combination of observation, experiment and the use of the electron microscope over the last 50 years have allowed us to build up a more detailed picture of how cells work.

The living, working cell

Figure 7A3 shows a model of a 'typical' mammal cell. But just as there is no such thing as a 'typical' person, there is no typical cell. Most mammalian cells will contain these features, but the shape, size and arrangement of cells varies widely.

The **cytoplasm** is a jelly-like fluid which contains organelles and many dissolved substances and enzymes. The **nucleus** is the information centre of the cell. It contains the genetic material (DNA) which carries hereditary information. It also contains the **nucleolus** which is involved in the production of RNA. RNA synthesis takes place when the nucleus instructs the cell to produce proteins. The nucleus is enclosed by a special double **nuclear membrane** (see Figure 7A4). This acts as a barrier to the random entry of substances into the nucleus, but the pores allow messenger RNA out to take part in protein synthesis.

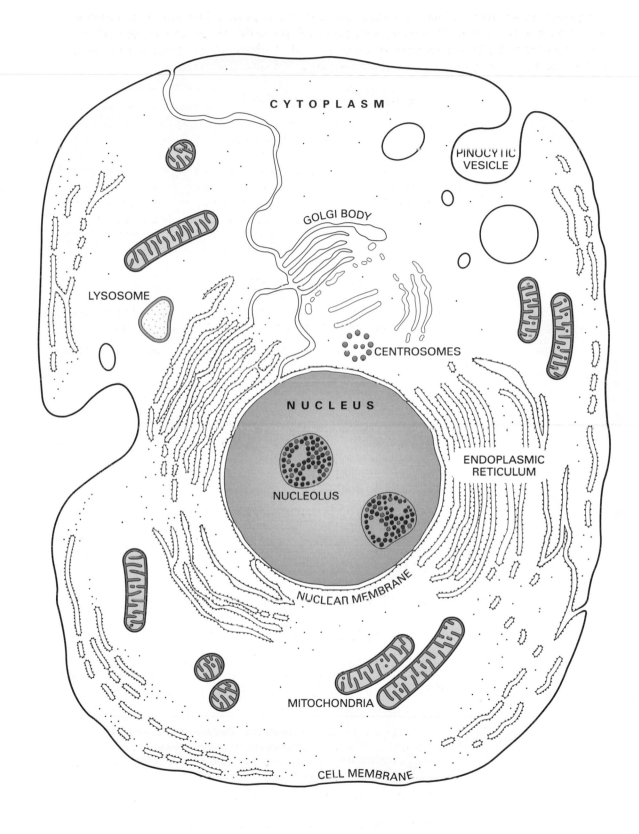

▼ **Figure 7A3** *The electron microscope reveals details of the substructure of a mammalian cell.*

CYTOPLASM

PINOCYTIC VESICLE

GOLGI BODY

LYSOSOME

CENTROSOMES

NUCLEUS

ENDOPLASMIC RETICULUM

NUCLEOLUS

NUCLEAR MEMBRANE

MITOCHONDRIA

CELL MEMBRANE

▼ **Figure 7A4** *Endoplasmic reticulum (ER)* is a 3-D network of tubes and cavities spreading through the cytoplasm. Much of the ER is covered in ribosomes and is known as **rough endoplasmic reticulum** (RER). The part of the network not covered in ribosomes is known as the **smooth endoplasmic reticulum** (SER). **Ribosomes** are the tiny structures responsible for protein synthesis.

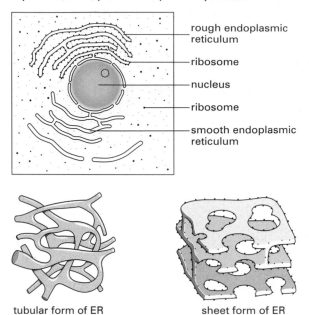

- rough endoplasmic reticulum
- ribosome
- nucleus
- ribosome
- smooth endoplasmic reticulum

tubular form of ER   sheet form of ER

▼ **Figure 7A7** *Lysosomes* are bits pinched off from the rough endoplasmic reticulum. They contain digestive enzymes. One function is defence – they destroy any foreign protein which enters the cell. They also enable the cell to 'self-destruct' as it ages. The lysosome breaks open, releasing the enzymes which then digest the dying cell so that its parts can be put to use elsewhere.

▼ **Figure 7A5** *Golgi apparatus* is made up of stacks of flattened membrane pockets which work closely with the Rough Endoplasmic Reticulum. Its main job is to modify and package materials made by the RER for secretion out of the cell. Cells which secrete large amounts of material, for instance pancreatic exocrine cells, have large amounts of Golgi apparatus.

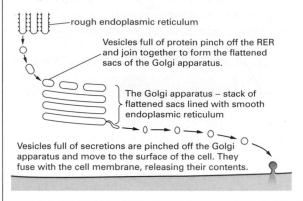

- rough endoplasmic reticulum

Vesicles full of protein pinch off the RER and join together to form the flattened sacs of the Golgi apparatus.

The Golgi apparatus – stack of flattened sacs lined with smooth endoplasmic reticulum

Vesicles full of secretions are pinched off the Golgi apparatus and move to the surface of the cell. They fuse with the cell membrane, releasing their contents.

▼ **Figure 7A6** *Mitochondria* are the sites of cell respiration. Here oxygen-dependent reactions which transfer energy from glucose molecules to molecules of ATP take place.

The outer membrane of the mitochondrion allows small molecules such as glucose to pass through freely, but larger molecules are excluded.

The inner membrane has many folds called **cristae**. These give a much increased surface area for chemical reactions to occur on.

Stalked particles are found on the cristae and are the sites of respiratory ATP synthesis.

The matrix of the mitochondrion contains enzymes to carry out the reactions of respiration, and its own genetic material so that a mitochondrion can reproduce itself.

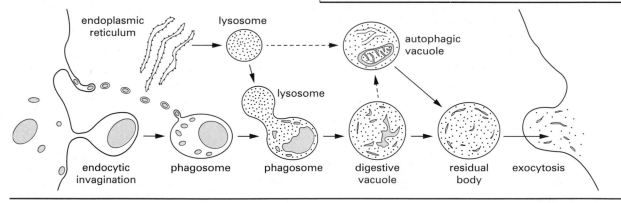

- endoplasmic reticulum
- lysosome
- autophagic vacuole
- lysosome
- endocytic invagination
- phagosome
- phagosome
- digestive vacuole
- residual body
- exocytosis

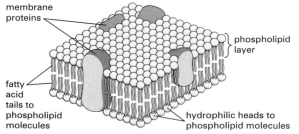

- membrane proteins
- phospholipid layer
- fatty acid tails to phospholipid molecules
- hydrophilic heads to phospholipid molecules

◀ **Figure 7A8** *Cell membrane* is the 'skin' of the cell. It controls all that enters and leaves the cell. It contains pores and transport systems which move substances in and out. It is made up of lipids and proteins and has a fluid structure. The best model we have of the membrane structure is of protein molecules suspended in a dense mass of lipid molecules. It is known as the **fluid mosaic model**, because of its fluid nature and mosaic of lipids, carbohydrates and proteins.

Energy for cells – tissue respiration

The term 'respiration' is sometimes used to mean 'breathing', the exchange of gases between organism and atmosphere. But it has a deeper meaning: the process by which cells in living things break down complex organic molecules to provide themselves with energy. The organic molecules that provide nearly all living things with energy are mostly made in the first place by photosynthesis (see page 206). Respiration reverses the work of photosynthesis.

Animals obtain the molecules which they respire by eating either plants or other animals. The molecules which they obtain in their food in this way are mostly complex – such as **starch**, composed of chains from glucose molecules; **fats**, made up of fatty acids joined by glycerol; and **proteins**, formed from chains of amino acids. These complex molecules cannot be respired directly. First they are digested (see page 376) – broken down into their basic components, such as glucose. These simple molecules are then fed into the cells to be respired.

Processing glucose to release energy

Once in a cell, glucose passes to an organelle in the cytoplasm, the **mitochondrion** (see page 364). This is where respiration takes place. The biochemical mechanism of respiration is the same in virtually all living organisms – plants, animals, fungi, and bacteria. The breakdown of glucose takes place in two stages.

Glucose is split

First, the glucose molecule, which contains six carbon atoms, is broken down to form two molecules of **pyruvate** (or 'pyruvic acid'), each containing three carbon atoms (see Figure 7A9). This process is called **glycolysis**, which means 'sugar splitting'. Glycolysis is an oxidation process but it does not need free oxygen. It can supply some energy and is a form of **anaerobic respiration**.

Once the pyruvate is formed by glycolysis, it suffers one of two fates. In the muscles of animals that need a lot of energy quickly (like an athlete running the 100 metres) it is rapidly converted to a waste product, **lactic acid** (which may build up in the muscles and cause pain if the athlete runs too long). Given more time, the pyruvate is broken down much more thoroughly by a process that does involve oxygen and releases far more energy. This is **aerobic respiration**.

Breaking down pyruvate using oxygen

The breakdown of pyruvate takes place in three stages.

1 First the pyruvate is partially broken down. One of the carbons forms carbon dioxide and the other two go to form an acetyl group in a compound called **acetyl coenzyme A** or 'CoA'.

2 Then follows one of the most important series of reactions in all of biology, one worked out by the Austrian–British biochemist Sir Hans Krebs in the late 1930s. Krebs showed that the two carbons of the **acetyl** group in CoA combine with a molecule of **oxaloacetic acid**, which contains four carbons, and form **citric acid**, which contains six carbons (see Figure 7A10). Then seven more reactions follow in the course of which three things happen:

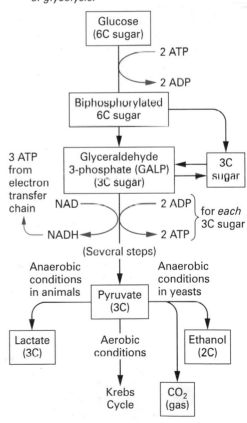

▼ **Figure 7A9** *The key features of glycolysis.*

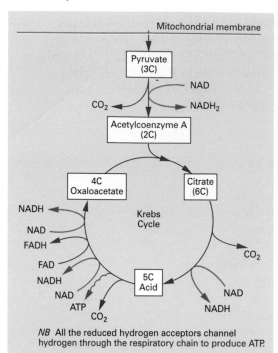

▼ **Figure 7A10** *The core of the Krebs cycle.*

NB All the reduced hydrogen acceptors channel hydrogen through the respiratory chain to produce ATP.

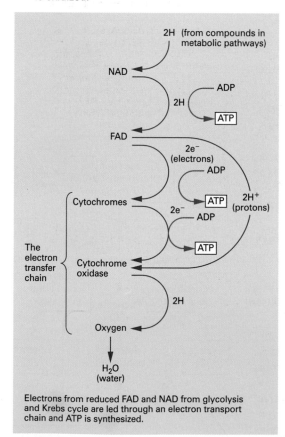

▼ **Figure 7A11** *The electron transfer chain – how NADH is oxidized.*

Electrons from reduced FAD and NAD from glycolysis and Krebs cycle are led through an electron transport chain and ATP is synthesized.

(a) a powerful **reducing agent** is formed, called **NADH**

(b) two carbons are lost to form two molecules of carbon dioxide

(c) oxaloacetic acid – with four carbons – is re-formed.

The re-formed oxaloacetic acid is then able to join with more acetyl from acetyl CoA to begin the whole process again. In other words, this series of reactions forms a **cycle**, known variously as the **tricarboxylic acid cycle**, or the **citric acid cycle** or simply as the **Krebs cycle**.

3 The powerful reducing agent that was formed in the Krebs cycle, NADH, combines with oxygen to produce water – allowing the release of a great deal of energy (see Figure 7A11). So note three main points about the whole process.

■ Some energy can be usefully obtained from glucose by glycolysis without using oxygen.
■ In fact, oxygen is not involved until near the end of the process.
■ But the final oxidation involving oxygen releases about 93% of the energy potentially available from the glucose. In other words, the aerobic stage that involves oxygen is far more efficient than the anaerobic glycolysis, which only allows release of a small fraction of this potential.

ATP – an energy transfer agent

Throughout this account it has been suggested that breaking down sugar (or pyruvate) releases energy. So it does: that is the whole purpose of the process. But if the energy was simply released it would appear in the form of heat and just raise the temperature of the surroundings. Instead, the energy drives a series of chemical changes.

Crucial to the effective use of energy from biochemical respiration is the addition of a phosphate group (P_i) to a molecule known as **adenosine diphosphate**, or **ADP**. In this way ADP is converted into **ATP – adenosine triphosphate**.

ADP is a relatively stable molecule in aqueous solution; it contains all the phosphates it can easily carry. The third phosphate fits rather uncomfortably so the bond holding it to the molecule is relatively weak. When ATP reacts, breaking the weak bond and splitting off the third phosphate, it forms stronger bonds in the products so that overall there is energy released which can bring about chemical change. ATP thus allows controlled energy transfers, exactly when and where a cell needs them.

Note, finally, that the net effect of all these complicated manoeuvres is to oxidize sugar and release energy – the exact opposite of photosynthesis (see page 206–7):

$$C_6H_{12}O_6 + 6O_2 \longrightarrow 6CO_2 + 6H_2O + \text{energy}$$

The interconversions of ADP to ATP and back transfer energy from one chemical system to another.

$$ADP + P_i + \text{reducing energy from respiratory NADH} \longrightarrow ATP$$

Tissues and organs work together

Cells are grouped into tissues and organ systems. The importance of these systems for survival is demonstrated in the case of babies who arrive too soon. In a Special Baby Unit tiny scraps of humanity are fighting for life. Beside one incubator an alarm bleeps. Within seconds a nurse gently strokes a tiny back, talking and encouraging until breathing begins again. Scenes such as this are commonplace as pre-term babies learn to cope with the demands of life outside their mothers' bodies.

Babies who arrive too soon

A normal human pregnancy lasts about 40 weeks (the human **gestation period**). At twelve weeks almost all of the organ systems of an adult body are present. For the rest of the pregnancy these systems grow and mature to a point where they can work properly. During pregnancy the needs of the fetus are taken care of by the mother's body (see Figure 7A12). But when a baby is born early, the systems of the body have to take over and work for themselves. That isn't always as easy as it sounds.

Christine Newsome, the Family Care and Neonatal Nursing Advisor on the Special Baby Unit at the Princess Anne Hospital in Southampton, explains the problems of premature births. 'When birth comes before 23 weeks the baby's organs are simply too immature to cope. The baby may live for a few minutes, but even with the most advanced technology we can't help it to survive. Babies born just a few weeks later do much better – the modern incubators and monitoring systems which we have mean that even babies of only 26 weeks stand a 50:50 chance of survival. We have to monitor everything these babies do to make sure that they are provided with all they need to complete development'.

▼ **Figure 7A12** *Doing things the easy way – a developing baby in a normal pregnancy has all its needs supplied and all waste materials removed – Mum takes the strain.*

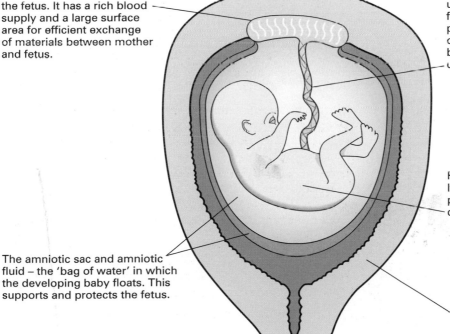

The placenta is made up of tissue from the mother and the fetus. It has a rich blood supply and a large surface area for efficient exchange of materials between mother and fetus.

The umbilical cord joins the fetus to the placenta. It contains two umbilical arteries which carry fetal blood loaded with waste products to the placenta, and one umbilical vein carrying blood rich in oxygen and dissolved food to the fetus.

Fetus – needs food and oxygen. It must also get rid of waste products – mainly carbon dioxide and urea.

The amniotic sac and amniotic fluid – the 'bag of water' in which the developing baby floats. This supports and protects the fetus.

The uterus – the strong bag of muscle in which the fetus develops and which pushes it out at birth.

Blood from the mother flows in the opposite direction to the blood from the fetus – **countercurrent exchange.** This allows the best possible exchange of materials between the two blood systems.

The breath of life

All mammals need a good supply of oxygen to all the tissues. Hand-in-hand with this goes the removal of carbon dioxide which is the waste product of cellular respiration. Before a baby is born its oxygen is supplied and its carbon dioxide removed by the placenta. The lungs are solid for a long time, and up to the moment of birth they are small with very little blood going to them. The alveoli can only be inflated if they are coated with a special, soap-like chemical called **lung surfactant** (a contraction of **surface-active agent**). This begins to be formed in the lungs at around 24 weeks of gestation, and increases as the pregnancy progresses.

'One of the biggest advances in the care of pre-term babies over the last five years has been the development of both artificial and natural surfactants which we can give to our tiny babies,' says Christine Newsome. 'Before surfactant we had to ventilate the lungs artificially for a very long time, and that often led to long-term and permanent damage. Now we can help the babies to breathe on their own much more rapidly.'

Just remembering to breathe is a problem in itself for pre-term babies. Apnoea (failure to breathe) alarms sound off regularly in a premature baby unit, showing that a baby has forgotten to breathe for more than 20 seconds. A baby born at 28 weeks should be breathing between 50 and 60 times a minute, so a 20 second gap is a long time. When the control system fails in a tiny baby there are a variety of things which can be done to help the baby remember to breathe. Sometimes the babies just start again by themselves, or a word or gentle touch is enough. Sometimes they need stimulating more vigorously to get breathing started, and if it is really slow the staff will put a tube directly into the baby's windpipe and use a ventilator to take over the breathing for a while.

▶ **Figure 7A13** *Even when babies are breathing mainly on their own, a continuous positive airways pressure supplied by a machine can make it easier for them to take in air. Christine Newsome and her colleagues are constantly monitoring and adjusting the ventilator for each baby, because changes in the breathing patterns happen from minute to minute rather than hour by hour.*

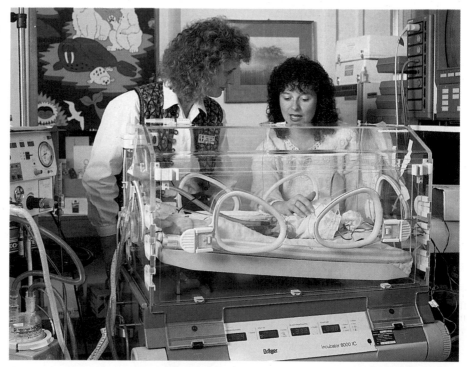

Energy – and materials for growth

Food is needed as a source of energy and provides the materials for growth. Before birth this is supplied by the mother through the placenta. After birth the baby has to take in food for itself. Not only that, the food has to be modified before it can be used. As adults we eat a wide variety of foods, and the main types of compounds in these foods – carbohydrates, proteins and fats – need to be broken down into smaller units before they can be absorbed by the body, carried in the blood and used by the cells. This process is known as **digestion** and it takes place in the **digestive system** or **gut** (see page 377–8).

The choice of food for a premature baby is not easy. Breast milk is the best food, containing the right balance of nutrients for a human infant and providing immunity to disease. Cow's milk is not satisfactory. Babies may develop allergies and they cannot digest the cow's milk proteins properly.

Even in a pre-term baby the gut can usually cope with digestion. It is swallowing the food which is difficult. The sucking, breathing and swallowing reflexes are not co-ordinated and early infants cannot manage their feeding. If a baby attempts to suckle it will probably inhale milk into its lungs. To avoid such problems, pre-term babies are often fed using a naso-gastric tube which goes down from the nose directly into the stomach. Most of the babies will be fed breast milk from their mothers but it can be very hard for a mother to produce and collect the milk which is needed. In the Princess Anne Hospital Special Baby Unit there is a milk bank in operation, so that mothers who make more milk than they need for their full-term babies can donate some to help the very early ones. It is hard enough being born weeks or months too soon without your gut having to cope with a less than perfect diet.

If breast milk cannot be provided, the babies are fed with formula milk or, in the case of the weakest babies, given a mixture of chemicals which is effectively pre-digested food, put straight into the blood. The best indicator that the gut of one of these tiny babies is working is the production of faeces. As Christine put it with a grin 'We're always very pleased when our babies manage a pooh!'

Getting oxygen and digested food into the body of a tiny baby is not the end of the story. Oxygen must be circulated and food moved away from the capillary blood vessels immediately round the gut. The circulatory system has to transport materials around the body. Very tiny babies have several particular problems with this. In a fetus the circulation of the blood to the heart and lungs is very different from that of an adult.

In premature babies the ductus (see Figure 7A14) does not always close off as it should. Treatment with substances called prostaglandin inhibitors may be sufficient to cause the vessel to contract down and close off, but if that doesn't work, surgery is the only answer.

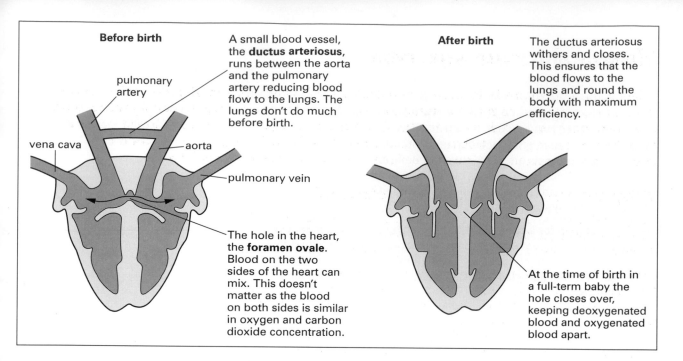

Before birth

pulmonary artery

vena cava

aorta

pulmonary vein

A small blood vessel, the **ductus arteriosus**, runs between the aorta and the pulmonary artery reducing blood flow to the lungs. The lungs don't do much before birth.

The hole in the heart, the **foramen ovale**. Blood on the two sides of the heart can mix. This doesn't matter as the blood on both sides is similar in oxygen and carbon dioxide concentration.

After birth

The ductus arteriosus withers and closes. This ensures that the blood flows to the lungs and round the body with maximum efficiency.

At the time of birth in a full-term baby the hole closes over, keeping deoxygenated blood and oxygenated blood apart.

▲ **Figure 7A14** *Early babies do not always manage the changeover to adult cardio-vascular circulation quite as easily as full-term babies.*

Monitoring the state of a baby's blood can be very useful. Tiny cannulas are introduced into the blood vessels so that samples can be removed easily when needed. $0.5\,cm^3$ is enough blood for normal tests but if a full screen is needed, $1\,cm^3$ is taken. This sounds a very small volume, but tiny babies only have about $80\,cm^3$ blood per kilogram body mass, so they can't spare much and often need tiny transfusions.

The skin of a pre-term baby is very thin, and blood vessels run close to the surface. As a result, heat is lost easily through the skin and babies find temperature control very difficult. Incubators are kept warm to reduce heat loss, and the babies may be swaddled in insulating wraps to keep them warm and prevent them from losing too much water through their very porous skin.

Getting rid of waste

Chemical reactions taking place in the body produce waste products. The reactions which break down amino acids give rise to a chemical compound called **urea**.

Too much urea is dangerous and it is removed from blood by the kidneys. This means that the kidneys of even the most premature babies must work properly as soon as they are born, cleansing the blood of urea and producing urine.

'We have two main ways of monitoring what the kidneys are doing,' explained Christine. 'The "low-tech" way is simply to observe and weigh the nappies. If the babies are producing about $1\,cm^3$ urine per hour for every kg of body weight, then we know that the kidneys are probably working well. We weigh the nappy before putting it under the baby, and then weigh again at intervals, recording the change every time. A more accurate measure of kidney function is obtained whenever we do a blood test. By looking at the levels of urea and creatine in the blood we can get a very accurate measure of kidney function.'

Babies born early teach us the importance of all the systems of the body and that their control and co-ordination are critical. If any system fails to work, the well-being of the whole baby is threatened.

Mammal tissue systems

When a human zygote is formed it contains a fresh combination of genes, with all the information needed to make a human being. From the single zygote cell a multicellular organism develops, with its specialized tissues and organ systems. Different genes are switched on in separate tissues so that the cells of which they are composed can develop a specialized structure and function characteristic of each tissue.

Why do we need tissue systems?

A single-celled animal can obtain oxygen and get rid of carbon dioxide and other waste by simple diffusion. It can digest food within the cell and distribute it by diffusion. Reproduction is a simple matter of splitting in two.

Larger animals have much smaller surface areas in comparison to their total volumes. They need special systems to bring oxygen and food into the body, to transport materials and to get rid of waste products. Even tiny human infants are large enough to need such specialized systems, as the case study on pre-term babies shows (see page 370). Different tissues (groups of specialized cells) have developed to carry out different jobs – some cells carry out digestion, some can transmit electrical signals or contract and relax whilst others are involved in reproduction. Some features of the major tissue types are outlined below.

Epithelial tissues

Epithelial cells are generally simple and unspecialized. They cover all of the outside and internal surfaces of a multicellular organism such as a mammal. There are three main types of epithelium: see Figures 7A15, 7A16 and 7A17.

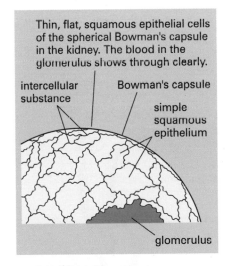

▲ **Figure 7A15** *Squamous epithelium* is made up of thin, flattened square cells with very little cytoplasm. Because they are so thin they are ideal for allowing the diffusion of materials across a lining. They are therefore found in the kidney tubules, the alveoli of the lungs and the blood capillaries.

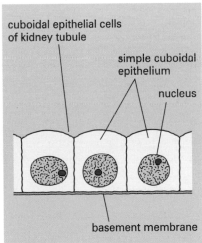

▲ **Figure 7A16** *Cuboidal epithelium* has cube-shaped cells and is often found lining tubes like the pancreatic duct. The cells can be more specialized and produce secretions – they are found doing this job in the salivary, sweat and thyroid glands.

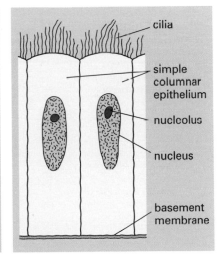

▲ **Figure 7A17** *Columnar epithelium* consists of tall thin cells. They may have microvilli or cilia at one surface. Much of the gut is lined with columnar epithelium, and so is the trachea of the lung. The cilia of lung epithelial cells sweep mucus away, carrying dust and bacteria. Smoking anaesthetizes these cells and prevents cilia from working effectively.

Muscular tissues

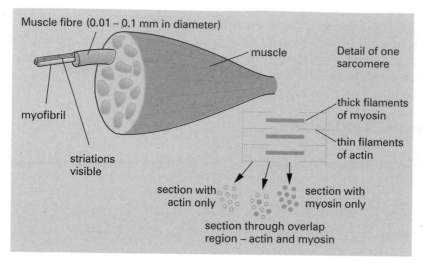

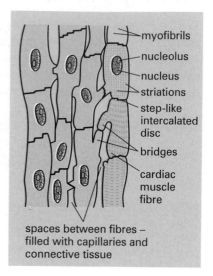

▲ **Figure 7A18** *Striated or voluntary muscle* *is the tissue which moves bones and allows movement. When large numbers of muscle cells contract at the same time they do a large amount of work. Striated muscles contract fast, but also get tired (**fatigue**) rapidly. Muscle cells need energy and there are always many mitochondria present. The diagram shows the typical appearance of this type of muscle – each striped unit is a **sarcomere**. The stripes are caused by the arrangement of thin filaments of two proteins, **actin** and **myosin**. These interact to pull past each other, shortening the muscle fibre as they do so.*

▲ **Figure 7A19** *Cardiac muscle* *is the type found in the heart. The muscle fibres are joined by cross-connections. The big differences between cardiac muscle and normal striated muscle are that cardiac muscle will contract spontaneously, and does not fatigue.*

Connective tissues

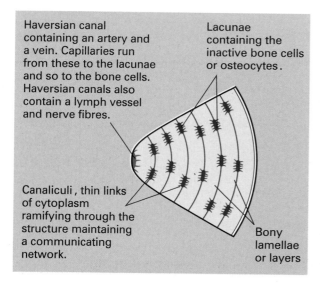

▲ **Figure 7A20** *Bone* *is the tissue of skeletons. It is hard, and provides support for the body and protection for delicate organs such as the brain, heart and lungs. The bone cells (**osteocytes**) are embedded in a mixture of* **collagen fibres** *and* **calcium salts** *which they have secreted. This matrix gives the bone its strength, but the bone cells are kept supplied with food and oxygen. This means that if more bone is needed they can be activated and secrete more matrix.*

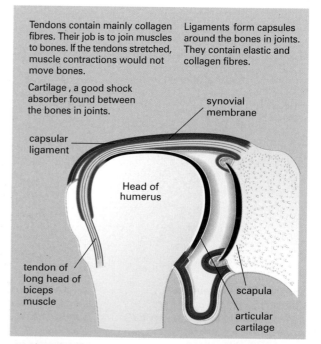

▲ **Figure 7A21** *Fibrous tissue* *contains cells together with varying amounts of* **collagen fibre** *which is strong but not elastic. It sometimes also contains elastic tissue, depending on the job it has to do. Fibrous tissue is important in the skeleton. Examples include the main components of joints in the skeleton: cartilage, ligaments and tendons.*

Taking blood

'People usually say one of three things when they come to see me,' smiles Vanda Henry – '"I'm not very good at this", "I'm afraid I can't look", or "I usually faint!". In fact most people cope really well – although men are more likely to faint than women!'

Vanda is the **phlebotomist** (as someone who takes blood is called) at a busy doctors' practice. The blood samples she takes are used to find out more about people's health. She cheerfully admits that her own dislike of injections and blood tests makes her better at her job, because she is sympathetic to her patients' fears and determined to make the procedure as quick and painless as possible. And it's easier to take blood from a relaxed patient!

Blood is usually drawn from the group of three veins in the crook of the arm. These form an H shape. The linking vein (**median cubical vein**) is the one which is most commonly used for taking blood because it is a good size and can usually be felt, even when a patient is in shock.

'It's very important to use a vein and not an artery,' explains Vanda, 'because it is difficult to stop the bleeding from an artery and a lot of blood can be lost very quickly. When patients are frightened their veins collapse, making it hard to get the blood we need. It is also more difficult with babies and small children because their veins are so tiny,' comments Vanda. 'Very old people have such fragile veins that they often split as soon as you put the needle in. It doesn't hurt, but it leaves a nasty looking bruise.'

What can be learned from a blood sample?

There are about 340 different blood tests for which Vanda can be asked to collect samples. Figure 7A22 gives examples of the information which can be obtained by analysing blood.

▼ **Figure 7A22** *Table of selected blood tests.*

Type of test	Information
Cholesterol	Shows the level of cholesterol in the blood, which is an indicator of risk for heart disease
FBA (full blood count)	All the cells in the blood are counted. It can show up problems from anaemia to blood cancer
AFP (alphafetoprotein)	In pregnant women, this gives an indication of the risk that a baby has Down's syndrome
ESR	A general test for viral infections
Monospot test	This shows glandular fever
HIV	A test for antibodies to the HIV virus which causes AIDS
Urea/Na$^+$/K$^+$	Kidney function tests
Anthony Nolan Trust screening	Tests for bone marrow donors
Hormone titres	Used to detect the menopause and also used in the treatment of fertility problems

Vanda had no medical training before she became a phlebotomist, but had always wanted to do medical work. She saw an advert, applied for the job and after a short training course, set to work! 'The first time I did it I was terrified – but you soon become good at the job and proud of what you can do to make a worrying experience easier for people.'

Blood and the transport system

When the skin is cut, blood appears. This makes the transport system of humans and animals one of the most easily visible of their component parts. The average adult man has about 5 litres of blood and it is vital for life. People who lose more than a litre of blood need to have it replaced to survive. If a sample of blood is left to stand it separates into a straw-yellow liquid with a red cell sediment at the bottom overlain with a thin white layer of white cells (buffy coat layer).

Blood composition

Plasma

Plasma is the main blood component. It contains a protein, **fibrinogen**, which is vital for blood clotting. The scabs formed from clots also prevent the entry of bacteria and protect new growing skin. The clotting mechanism involves several steps to make sure that it only happens when needed. Blood clots forming in the wrong place at the wrong time can be fatal.

Removing fibrinogen from plasma leaves **serum**. This contains dissolved food substances. Waste products are passed into the serum for transport to the excretory organs. Salt (**sodium chloride**) and other ionic compounds (referred to in medical laboratories as **electrolytes**) are kept at a constant level in blood. This helps to maintain the water balance of the whole body (see pages 394–5).

The plasma is also involved in pH balance. It acts as a **buffer** (see pages 316–17), preventing the body fluids becoming too acidic or alkaline. Chemical messages (**hormones**) are carried in blood from where they are made to where they will be effective. Plasma is involved in temperature regulation. It warms up as it passes through heated tissues – such as working muscles – and transfers this energy to areas which are less warm.

Platelets are fragments of very large **megakaryocyte** cells found in the bone marrow. They play an important role in blood clotting. There are about 0.25 million platelets per mm^3 of blood.

▲ **Figure 7A23** *Blood components. If blood clotting is prevented, the blood separates into plasma and cells. The percentage of red cells by volume is known as the* **haematocrit**, *or packed cell volume.*

Red blood cells

Red blood cells or erythrocytes (rbcs) are the most common cells in the blood. The colour comes from the oxygen-carrying red pigment haemoglobin. There are about five million red blood cells in every mm^3 of blood. Red blood cells have a distinctive biconcave disc shape. Formed in the red bone marrow, they lose their nuclei before entering the bloodstream and have only a limited life – each red blood cell lasts around 120 days. The haemoglobin molecule changes shape and colour as it carries oxygen.

White blood cells

White blood cells or leucocytes (wbcs) are larger, nucleated and less common than red cells. They do not contain pigment. There are about 7000 white blood cells per mm^3 of blood. Although they are large they can move in and out of the blood vessels because they can change shape and squeeze through narrow gaps. The main job of white blood cells is to defend against invading bacteria, viruses or foreign cells. They may engulf an enemy cell or produce antibodies to inactivate the invader.

▲ **Figure 7A24** *Red blood cell.*

Transport system

Mammals have a **double circulation** with a closed system of tubes carrying blood to and from all body tissues. The heart acts as a pump. Blood from the body returns to the heart and is pumped to the lungs where it picks up oxygen. This newly oxygenated blood travels back to the heart and is then pumped round the rest of the body again. The tubes of the system vary in structure with the job they have to perform.

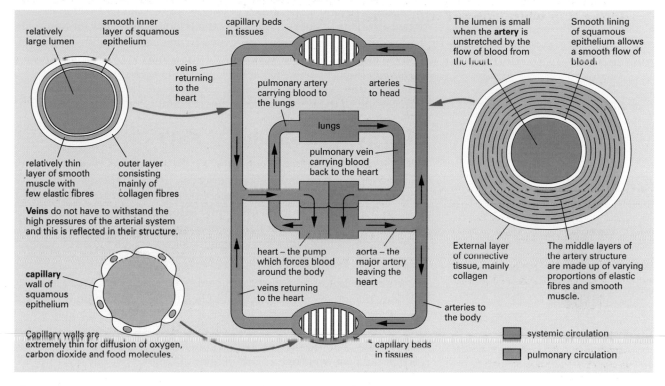

▲ **Figure 7A25** *Mammalian double circulation.*

Arteries

Arteries are the blood vessels which carry blood **away** from the heart. They carry **oxygenated** blood, with the exceptions of the pulmonary artery to the lungs and the umbilical artery in the fetus (see page 367). Arteries which are further away from the heart get smaller and smaller until they form **arterioles**.

Veins

Veins carry blood **towards** the heart, so they carry **deoxygenated** blood which has given up its oxygen to tissues. The exceptions are the pulmonary vein and the umbilical vein. More than half of the total volume of the blood is in the veins at any one time. The larger veins are found between big muscle blocks which squeeze the blood in the veins as they work. One-way valves in the walls of the veins make sure that the blood only moves back towards the heart to be transferred to the lungs.

Capillaries

Capillaries link the arteries and the veins. They are tiny vessels which spread through all the tissues of the body. No cell is far from a capillary. The capillary network is vast, giving an enormous surface area over which food and oxygen can diffuse out of the blood into the cells and through which waste products can diffuse out of the cells into the blood.

Nutrition and digestion

In the developed world food retailers are some of the largest businesses, and magazines are full of exotic recipes and advice on how to lose weight. By contrast, in the developing world there is frequently not enough food to go round; life becomes a constant quest for something to eat. Why is food so important?

Respiration of food is the source of energy for the things a living organism needs to do. Food supplies the building materials for new cells. It provides all of the substances needed to maintain a healthy body. People can manage without food for a surprisingly long time but eventually they become weak and ill and then die. Everyone needs a **balanced diet** – nothing to do with losing weight but everything to do with getting all the things the body needs to function properly.

Energy = Kilojoules = Fat?

Respiration of food supplies energy. Each time the heart beats and every time the lungs inflate, the body's energy resources are being used. The amount of energy which can be obtained when food is respired is measured in **joules** (or more frequently **kilojoules**). The measurements are made by burning food in pure oxygen and measuring how much the energy released heats up a known volume of water. 4.2 joules of heat energy raise the temperature of 1 g of water by 1 °C.

A certain amount of food material must be respired every day to keep the body ticking over. The energy supplied by this respiration is needed even if individuals do nothing all day but lie still being fed through a tube. This is the **basal metabolic rate (BMR)**. Most people use a lot more energy than this as they rush through their lives. Thus an 'average' 18-year-old male will have a BMR of around 7500 kJ per day – yet his actual energy requirement is more likely to be around 12 600 kJ per day. Similarly the 'average' 18-year-old female has a BMR of 5850 kJ per day, but she is more likely to use about 9200 kJ each day.

Around the world the actual food taken in by an individual will vary widely – but the components of that food are the same all over the globe.

Carbohydrates are sugars and starches. Sugars like **glucose** taste sweet. They are **monosaccharides** which join together to form complex carbohydrates like starch (**polysaccharide**). Carbohydrates should provide about half the body fuel needed for respiration.

Proteins provide the building material for the body – they are used to make new cells. They are made up of long chains of **amino acids** joined in different ways to give different types of protein. About 15% of body fuel should be provided by proteins. Adult men need just over 55 g of protein per day. Adult women need 45 g per day.

Fats are needed for cell membranes and some hormones. There can be too much in a fat-rich diet. The excess is stored as body fat. Fats are made up of fatty acids joined to a molecule called glycerol (propane-1,2,3-triol). No more than 35% of body fuel should be provided by fat.

Fibre is indigestible material. It is nevertheless very important in maintaining the action of the muscles of the gut to keep the food moving through the digestive system. Adults should take in about 18 g of fibre per day.

Vitamins and minerals are also needed, but in minute quantities. Although the amount of minerals and vitamins needed in the diet is small, the problems which occur when they are missing are large. Enzymes do not function properly and whole areas of metabolism can fail. Deficiency symptoms are relatively rare in the developed world, but in areas where food is in short supply thousands, if not millions, of people are affected by totally preventable diseases.

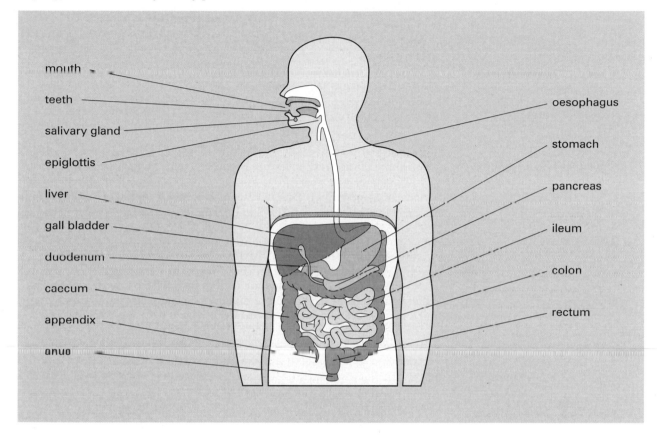

No wonder stomachs rumble!

The **digestive system** (Figure 7A26) takes food into the body and breaks it down into smaller chemical units which can be absorbed and used where needed. In people the main digestive organ is a muscular tube several metres long running from the mouth to the anus. To fit inside the body it is coiled and packed within the abdominal cavity.

Food enters through the **mouth**. The teeth bite off chunks of food and then chew it, breaking it into smaller pieces which can easily be swallowed. These smaller pieces of food have an increased surface area for gut enzymes.

The salivary glands make **saliva**. This coats the food in the mouth, making it easier to swallow. Saliva also contains an enzyme which begins the chemical breakdown of food – it acts on starch, breaking it into the sugar molecules of which it is composed.

The **oesophagus** is the muscular tube which links the mouth with the rest of the gut.

The **stomach** is a strong muscular bag. Cells in the stomach wall produce enzymes which continue the digestion of food, particularly protein. The cells also produce hydrochloric acid – this kills off most of the bacteria which might be eaten with the food and gives enzymes the right conditions

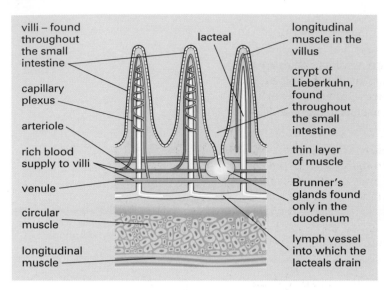

villi – found throughout the small intestine

lacteal

longitudinal muscle in the villus

crypt of Lieberkuhn, found throughout the small intestine

capillary plexus

arteriole

thin layer of muscle

rich blood supply to villi

Brunner's glands found only in the duodenum

venule

circular muscle

lymph vessel into which the lacteals drain

longitudinal muscle

▲ **Figure 7A27** *The small intestine.*

in which to work. Other cells in the stomach secrete a lot of mucus to protect the stomach walls from enzymes and acid. By vigorous contractions the muscular wall of the stomach continues the physical breakdown of the food, squeezing and mixing it into a thick paste called **chyme**.

The **small intestine** is a long coiled tube about 5–6 metres long with a rich supply of blood and lymph vessels. The digestion of food is completed with enzymes produced in the pancreas and the duodenum. The digested food molecules – glucose, amino acids, fatty acids and glycerol – are absorbed into the blood supply as they pass along the intestines.

The lining of the small intestine is covered with finger-like **villi** (Figure 7A27), which give a very large surface area through which the digested food can be absorbed. There is a very rich blood supply and there is only a small distance between the digested food and the blood for diffusion to take place.

The thin-walled **large intestine** receives the contents of the small intestine, by which stage all nutrients have been removed. What is left is a watery mixture containing indigestible food with bacteria, dead cells sloughed off from the gut itself, mucus, bile and a large amount of water.

The large intestine re-absorbs much of the water and the rest of the unwanted material is removed through the rectum and anus as faeces.

▼ **Figure 7A28** *The enzymes of the digestive system.*

The chemical digestion of the complex foods which we eat is brought about by the action of a whole range of enzymes (Figure 7A28). Some of them act on broad categories of food – proteins, carbohydrates or fats – whilst others are very specific and act only on particular types of bond with a particular type of molecule.

Organ	Digestive juice	Fats enzyme and action	Carbohydrates enzyme and action	Protein enzyme and action
Mouth	Saliva	No action	Amylase converts cooked starches to *disaccharide*	No action
Stomach	Gastric juice	No action	Hydrochloric acid stops the action of salivary amylase	Hydrochloric acid converts pepsinogen to *pepsin*. Pepsin converts all proteins to smaller molecule *polypeptides*
Small intestine	Bile	Bile salts emulsify fats	No action	No action
Small intestine	Pancreatic juice	Lipase converts fats to *fatty acids* and *glycerol*	Amylase converts all starches to *disaccharides* (sugars)	Enteropeptidase of intestinal juice converts trypsinogen and chymotrypsinogen to *trypsin* and *chymotrypsin*, which convert all polypeptides to *di-* and *tripeptides*
Small intestine	In microvilli	Lipase completes the digestion of fats to *fatty acids* and *glycerol*	Sucrase Maltase Lactase Convert all sugars to *monosaccharides*, mainly *glucose*	Peptidases complete the conversion of peptides to *amino acids*

Pancreas and liver

The **pancreas** and **liver** are also important in digestion (Figure 7A29). The pancreas has a double function. The endocrine pancreas produces hormones which regulate the way our bodies use glucose (see page 376), while the exocrine pancreas aids digestion. It produces enzymes and an alkaline fluid.

The first part of the small intestine or **duodenum** does not produce enzymes of its own. It receives acidic chyme from the stomach with partially digested proteins and carbohydrates, but has no means of continuing digestion. When the food arrives in the duodenum, a sequence of hormonally-controlled events causes the pancreas to release this alkaline mixture of enzymes, which helps to neutralize the acid from the stomach. The enzymes become active in this neutral environment and continue digestion.

The liver produces **bile** which is useful in fat digestion. Bile contains sodium hydrogencarbonate which, like the alkaline pancreatic juice, helps to neutralize stomach acid. Also, as the liver breaks down red blood cells it produces **bile salts**. These are surfactants (see page 368) which help with the physical breakdown of large fat droplets, **emulsifying** them into much smaller droplets. This greatly increases the surface area for the fat digesting enzymes to act on aiding fat digestion. The **gall bladder** stores the bile made by the liver and releases it down the bile duct into the gut when needed.

The liver also performs a range of biochemical tasks in processing of food after it has been digested. Blood from the ileum is carried straight to the liver in the **hepatic portal vein**, and the products of digestion are processed before further distribution.

▼ **Figure 7A29** *The success of the first part of the small intestine in digesting food depends on the secretions of the pancreas and the release from the gall bladder of the bile made in the liver.*

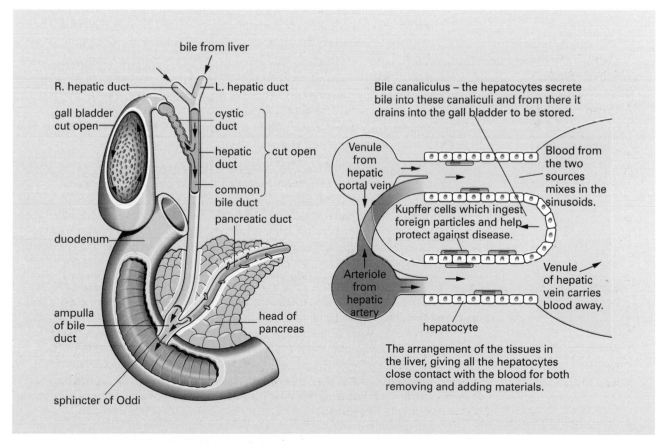

bile from liver

R. hepatic duct — L. hepatic duct

gall bladder cut open — cystic duct

hepatic duct — cut open

common bile duct

pancreatic duct

duodenum

ampulla of bile duct

head of pancreas

sphincter of Oddi

Bile canaliculus – the hepatocytes secrete bile into these canaliculi and from there it drains into the gall bladder to be stored.

Venule from hepatic portal vein

Blood from the two sources mixes in the sinusoids.

Kupffer cells which ingest foreign particles and help protect against disease.

Arteriole from hepatic artery

Venule of hepatic vein carries blood away.

hepatocyte

The arrangement of the tissues in the liver, giving all the hepatocytes close contact with the blood for both removing and adding materials.

Mammalian physiology

Physiology and health

A scientific understanding of how the human body works not only underpins improvements in the treatment of the sick but enables well people to organize their lives to stay healthy. Scientific knowledge and technical equipment which used to be confined to hospitals and laboratories is now available to the general public and used routinely in places such as health and fitness centres.

Fitter, leaner, healthier

'It isn't enough for people to realize that it is important for their health to be reasonably fit. They also need to enjoy getting and keeping fit or they simply won't bother. One of our aims here is to provide somewhere people can come and get fit in whichever way suits them – and go away feeling that they have had a good time.'

Rob Griffiths runs the Littledown Centre, a large leisure centre on the edge of Bournemouth that serves the surrounding area of Dorset. He took A levels in economics, psychology, history and maths and was all set to do a degree at Sheffield University when the opportunity arose to work as a professional squash coach in Germany for a few months. Rob never took up the university place. Four years later he returned to England and began working in a leisure centre. An accountancy qualification was added – 'I thought it might come in handy' grins Rob – and he now enjoys making sport, fitness and fun more accessible for everyone.

With 300 staff and a vast complex of wet and dry sports to supervise, Rob no longer gives squash lessons or washes out the changing rooms. But he has had lots of experience of what really goes on in every area of a leisure centre. Rob regards this as vital for understanding what ordinary members of the public want and need to get the best out of the facilities – and themselves.

One area which Rob and his staff have been particularly keen to develop are the cardiovascular and fitness rooms, where people can go to improve their overall fitness levels and to work specifically on the fitness of their heart and lungs. Sarah Lacey-Fisher is one of the team who work here. 'When people first come to us, they have very different aims' she explains. 'About 90% of the women want to lose weight but don't want to look too muscular, whilst the men are much more interested in building up lots of muscle than in getting thinner!'

When someone starts to use the fitness room, Sarah and her colleagues encourage them to fill in a questionnaire. This helps them to focus on what they want to gain from the sessions. 'To get the most out of the gym area, you need to use it properly', explains Sarah. 'It is important to warm up before you start to exercise hard, and to relax down again afterwards. Ideally you should be able to take your pulse at the end of the session and find that it is just the same as it was at the beginning – although of course it will have been raised during the exercise programme itself!'

▲ **Figure 7B1** *'The cardiovascular room is the place for really getting your heart and lungs fit – and the exercise you take can also help with weight loss' comments Sarah. 'By measuring your heart rate (taking your pulse) before, during and after exercise it is easy to monitor your fitness and make sure that the way you exercise is right for you.'*

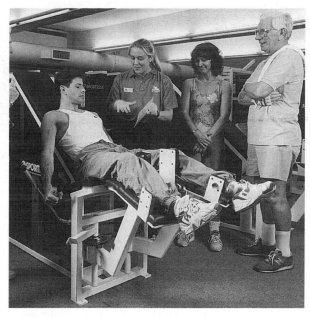

▲ **Figure 7B2** *At first sight the equipment in the fitness room of the gym can be very intimidating, but once you get used to what is going on it is easy to work on particular groups of muscles.*

Another member of the Littledown team is David Morrell. He is the GP referral scheme development officer – and his work reflects perhaps more than any other the close links there are between cardiovascular fitness and health. Along with Andrew Brewer, a local GP, David has developed a programme which doctors can use as a kind of 'prescription' for some of their patients.

Doctors recognize that a combination of being overweight and unfit, particularly if blood cholesterol is high as well, can spell heart trouble for the future. So GPs can refer their 'at risk' patients to David at the Littledown Centre, where they will be introduced to an exercise and fitness programme with lots of support and encouragement along the way. Doctors are also referring patients to David who already have problems such as high blood pressure, and some patients are coming along as part of their recovery programme from a heart attack. Dr Andrew Brewer keeps a particularly close eye on this group to make sure that they do themselves nothing but good, and the scheme is becoming increasingly popular.

'Most of the patients referred to us are in the 35–55 age range', explains David Morrell. 'We introduce them to preventative physical activity which they can enjoy.'

The initial referral period at the clinic is six weeks, and almost everyone shows some gains in fitness over that time. Some of the results have been spectacular! In young people an average blood pressure reading is said to be around 120/80 (see page 385). One overweight 30 year old was referred to David with a blood pressure of 145/98, heading for trouble fast. At the end of his six week course his blood pressure was down to 130/84 – an acceptable level for his age. As a way forward in preventative medicine, David's scheme has a lot to offer, giving people improved health and an enjoyable lifestyle. And perhaps in years to come, if more and more people take up and enjoy the facilities at centres like the Littledown, the need for GP referral schemes might be reduced or even disappear.

The heart of the matter

The heart is a muscular bag seated in the middle of the chest, protected by the bony ribs and sternum. Its job is to pump blood around the body. The special feature of heart muscle is that it does not fatigue – the cells can contract without long recovery periods – which means that the heart can beat throughout a lifetime without needing a rest.

The double pump

The human heart is a double pump. Blood is pumped to the lungs where the haemoglobin in the blood picks up oxygen. This blood returns to the heart and is then pumped around the body, carrying oxygen to the tissues. The deoxygenated blood returns to the heart to be pumped out to the lungs again. The structure of the heart reflects the way it works. There are two sides to the pump, and after birth the blood from one side never mixes with the blood from the other.

▼ **Figure 7B3** *The structure of the heart.*

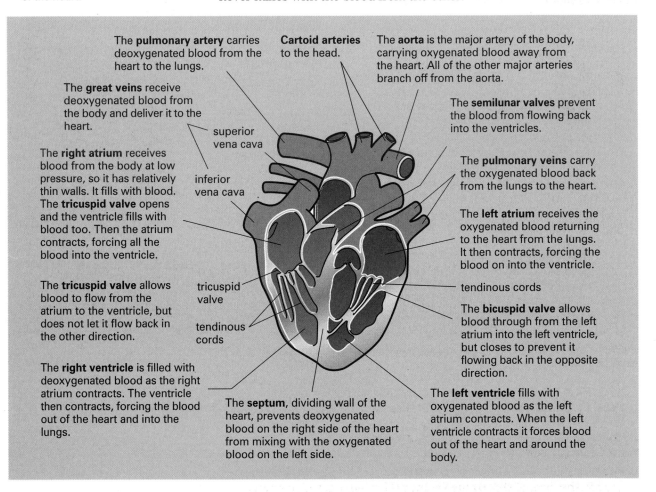

The **pulmonary artery** carries deoxygenated blood from the heart to the lungs.

Cartoid arteries to the head.

The **aorta** is the major artery of the body, carrying oxygenated blood away from the heart. All of the other major arteries branch off from the aorta.

The **great veins** receive deoxygenated blood from the body and deliver it to the heart.

The **semilunar valves** prevent the blood from flowing back into the ventricles.

superior vena cava

The **right atrium** receives blood from the body at low pressure, so it has relatively thin walls. It fills with blood. The **tricuspid valve** opens and the ventricle fills with blood too. Then the atrium contracts, forcing all the blood into the ventricle.

inferior vena cava

The **pulmonary veins** carry the oxygenated blood back from the lungs to the heart.

The **left atrium** receives the oxygenated blood returning to the heart from the lungs. It then contracts, forcing the blood on into the ventricle.

The **tricuspid valve** allows blood to flow from the atrium to the ventricle, but does not let it flow back in the other direction.

tricuspid valve

tendinous cords

The **bicuspid valve** allows blood through from the left atrium into the left ventricle, but closes to prevent it flowing back in the opposite direction.

tendinous cords

The **right ventricle** is filled with deoxygenated blood as the right atrium contracts. The ventricle then contracts, forcing the blood out of the heart and into the lungs.

The **septum**, dividing wall of the heart, prevents deoxygenated blood on the right side of the heart from mixing with the oxygenated blood on the left side.

The **left ventricle** fills with oxygenated blood as the left atrium contracts. When the left ventricle contracts it forces blood out of the heart and around the body.

How the heart works

The beating of the heart has two phases. In **systole** (contraction) first the atria and then the ventricles contract, forcing the blood out of the heart into the lungs and around the body. At this point in the **cardiac cycle** the blood pressure in the arteries is at its highest. In **diastole** (relaxation) the heart muscle is relaxed and the heart fills with blood. The blood pressure in the arteries is at its lowest.

How the heart is controlled

In an adult the average heart rate is around 70 beats in a minute. If a heart is removed from the body, disconnected from any nerve supply and kept in a warm solution similar to body fluids, it will continue to beat at about 60 beats per minute. This is known as its **intrinsic rhythm**. It is the natural contraction rate of the heart. It is brought about by a wave of excitation rather like a nerve impulse which travels through special tissue in the heart itself.

Hearts do not all beat at this intrinsic rate all the time. The heart supplies the body with oxygen and nutrients from the blood, so when tissues need more oxygen and nutrients the heart beats faster and more strongly to send the blood round the body more rapidly. Not only does this supply the extra materials needed, it also removes the waste products which result from muscular exertion. When asleep or relaxed, oxygen demand drops, and the heart rate slows. How does the heart respond to the different demands of the body?

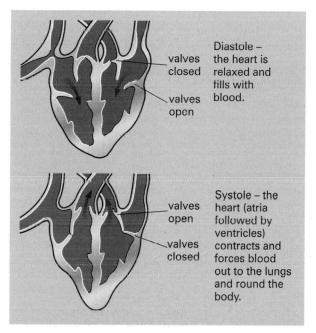

valves closed
valves open

Diastole – the heart is relaxed and fills with blood.

valves open
valves closed

Systole – the heart (atria followed by ventricles) contracts and forces blood out to the lungs and round the body.

▲ **Figure 7B4** *The heart in contraction (systole) and relaxation (diastole).*

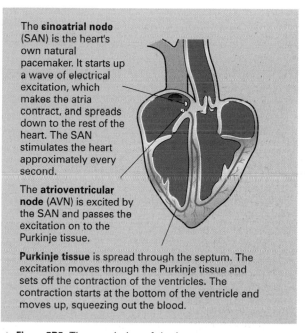

The **sinoatrial node** (SAN) is the heart's own natural pacemaker. It starts up a wave of electrical excitation, which makes the atria contract, and spreads down to the rest of the heart. The SAN stimulates the heart approximately every second.

The **atrioventricular node** (AVN) is excited by the SAN and passes the excitation on to the Purkinje tissue.

Purkinje tissue is spread through the septum. The excitation moves through the Purkinje tissue and sets off the contraction of the ventricles. The contraction starts at the bottom of the ventricle and moves up, squeezing out the blood.

▲ **Figure 7B5** *The regulation of the heart rate.*

- There is nervous regulation of the intrinsic heart rhythm – a **sympathetic nerve** (see page 398) speeds up the heart rate and a **parasympathetic nerve** (see page 399) (the **vagus**) slows it down. These nerves affect the **sinoatrial node** (SAN).
- Hormones (see page 396) affect the heart rate. **Adrenaline** will increase the heart rate as part of the response to fear or stress. A drop in the level of **thyroxine** (a thyroid hormone which controls the overall metabolic rate of the body) will lower the heart rate.
- **pH** changes and changes in the **body temperature** can also affect the heart rate. For example, at high temperature heart rate increases, but when the temperature is lowered heart rate slows down.

The heart responds in two ways to increased demand. The rate of the heart beat increases, and so does the amount of blood pumped at each heart beat. This is known as the **cardiac volume**. Therefore the **cardiac output (dm³ min⁻¹) = cardiac volume (dm³) × heart rate (min⁻¹)**.

Monitoring heart function

A fit, healthy heart pumping steadily is something everyone wants. But how can the heart be monitored, since it is hidden behind skin, muscle and the bony rib cage? There are two approaches to monitoring the performance of the heart.

Direct measurement

Heart sounds lub-dup, lub-dup...

The beating heart produces a sound: the **heartbeat**. This has two sounds – **lub-dup** – which are made by blood hitting the heart valves. The **lub** sound is made when blood is forced back against the bi- and tricuspid valves as the ventricles contract. The **dup** comes when a backflow of blood hits the semilunar valves of the pulmonary artery and aorta as the ventricles relax. The heart sounds can be heard simply by placing your ear onto someone's chest, but an instrument called a **stethoscope** is usually used. This magnifies and isolates the heart sounds. A stethoscope also picks up any unusual sounds or murmurs in the heart which may indicate that blood is leaking through a valve or that the chambers are not working together.

The electrocardiograph (ECG)

The wave of excitation through the Purkinje tissue (see page 383) can be picked up and measured using an **electrocardiograph** which produces a record of the electrical activity of the heart called an **electrocardiogram** or **ECG**. To make the recording a series of sensitive electrodes are positioned on the skin of the chest region.

▼ **Figure 7B6** *The ECG.*

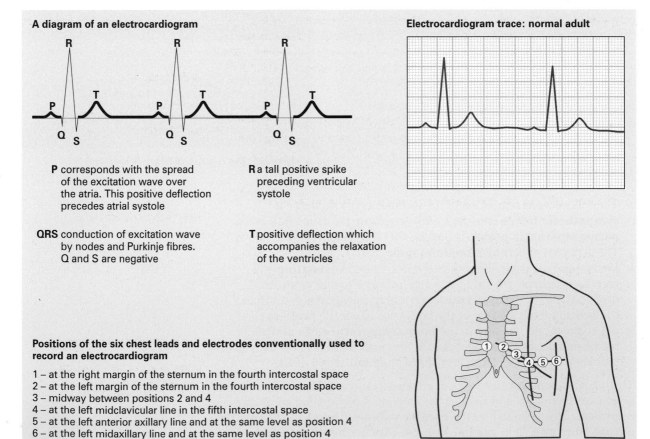

A diagram of an electrocardiogram

Electrocardiogram trace: normal adult

P corresponds with the spread of the excitation wave over the atria. This positive deflection precedes atrial systole

R a tall positive spike preceding ventricular systole

QRS conduction of excitation wave by nodes and Purkinje fibres. Q and S are negative

T positive deflection which accompanies the relaxation of the ventricles

Positions of the six chest leads and electrodes conventionally used to record an electrocardiogram

1 – at the right margin of the sternum in the fourth intercostal space
2 – at the left margin of the sternum in the fourth intercostal space
3 – midway between positions 2 and 4
4 – at the left midclavicular line in the fifth intercostal space
5 – at the left anterior axillary line and at the same level as position 4
6 – at the left midaxillary line and at the same level as position 4

Each part of the ECG curve represents particular electrical events in the heart:

- the P wave is caused by the excitation spreading from the sinoatrial node (SAN) to the atrioventricular node (AVN) causing atrial systole
- the QRS complex is the spread of excitation through the Purkinje tissue causing ventricular systole
- the T wave reflects the recovery or depolarization of the ventricles after contraction
- the flat area of the trace is caused by diastole, when there is no excitation of the heart.

Electrocardiography is an important tool in the diagnosis of heart problems. Medical staff quickly become very good at interpreting the ECGs from their patients and using them to help plan the best treatment for a rapid return to health.

Indirect measurements

A finger on the pulse

Each time the ventricles contract, blood is forced out into the aorta under high pressure, and then on into the other arteries. This pressure surge can be felt as a **pulse**, and one of the simplest ways to measure the heart rate is to feel this arterial pulse where the arteries run close to the surface of the skin in the wrist and in the neck. The pulse should be counted for fifteen seconds and then multiplied by four to give the number of heart beats per minute.

The pressure of life

The blood travels through the arteries at pressures which vary as the heart beats. The pressure at which the blood flows through the arteries is a measure of the health of the heart and of the arteries themselves. A weak heart will give a low blood pressure, whereas blood vessels which are closing up or less elastic give a raised pressure.

Scientists and clinicians measure blood pressure with a **sphygmomanometer**. In the traditional form of this instrument, a cuff is connected to a mercury manometer, a device for measuring pressure using a column of mercury. The cuff is put round the upper arm and inflated until the blood supply to the lower arm is completely cut off. By placing a stethoscope over the blood vessels at the elbow and slowly letting air out of the cuff, the pressure at which blood sounds first reappear can be recorded.

The first blood to get under the cuff is the blood at the highest pressure – in other words when the heart is contracting most strongly. This is the **systolic blood pressure**. The blood sounds return to normal at the point when the blood at the lowest pressure can get through the cuff. This is also recorded – it is the **diastolic blood pressure**. A systolic reading of around 120 mm Hg and a diastolic reading of 80 mm Hg are regarded as 'normal' and this is usually written as 120/80.

Increasing the amount of exercise causes the resting heart rate and blood pressure to fall, showing that the heart muscle is becoming fitter and stronger, and is doing its job more effectively.

▼ **Figure 7B7** *The ECG in patient diagnosis.*

Normal contraction

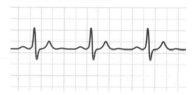

Tachycardia

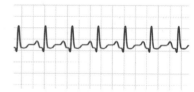

Ventricular extra-systole

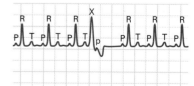

The first ECG shows a normal heartbeat, the second ECG shows a patient with a fast heartbeat, tachycardia. The third ECG shows a ventricular extra-systole.

A common cause of lung disease

Breathing problems, especially among children, are becoming more common. Some people are talking about an 'epidemic' of asthma and other respiratory diseases resulting from lungs not working properly. Epidemiologists (see page 406) are trying to discover what is the most likely reason for this increase. Air pollution may prove to be the main cause.

▶ **Figure 7B8** *Eamon Staunton teaching a young patient how to use a peak flow meter.*

Coughs and wheezes

Eamon Staunton is a busy GP at the Fordingbridge practice in Hampshire. He has about 2000 patients on his lists, and like any doctor one relatively frequent problem in his surgery is **asthma**. 'Asthma isn't one simple condition', comments Eamon. 'It can range from a very mild situation to a life-threatening inability to breathe. The problem is brought about when the bronchioles constrict, making it difficult to get air into and out of the lungs. This causes the breathlessness and "wheezing" sounds we think of as typical in asthma. But not all wheezes are due to asthma – and asthmatics do not always wheeze!'

'Very young children often wheeze when they have a cold, but this doesn't necessarily mean they will be asthmatic when they get older', comments Eamon. Older children, from two to five years, may develop asthma but fail to wheeze, so the diagnosis comes as something of a shock to their parents. A persistent cough which is worse at night, particularly if there is lots of sticky sputum, can be a symptom of asthma just as clearly as wheezing. Exercise can cause problems and colds tend to go on longer in these children. 'As children get older I start to try and get peak flow measurements (see Figure 7B9) which show how well their lungs are working, and I can also introduce more effective treatment', explains Eamon. 'And of course, children aren't the only people who get asthma. Lots of adults manage to live normal lives by careful management of their asthma.'

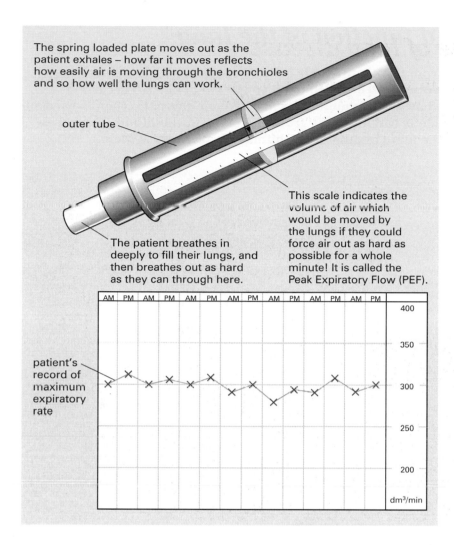

The spring loaded plate moves out as the patient exhales – how far it moves reflects how easily air is moving through the bronchioles and so how well the lungs can work.

outer tube

This scale indicates the volume of air which would be moved by the lungs if they could force air out as hard as possible for a whole minute! It is called the Peak Expiratory Flow (PEF).

The patient breathes in deeply to fill their lungs, and then breathes out as hard as they can through here.

patient's record of maximum expiratory rate

Figure 7B9 *When people have difficulty breathing, they and their doctors need information on how well the lungs are working. This can be obtained simply using a peak flow meter. If the peak expiratory flow is lower than it should be, asthma is one of the possible causes. People living with asthma use these meters regularly to monitor how their lungs are coping and record the results twice a day. The morning reading is usually lower than the evening one even in people who don't have asthma.*

Asthma – and how to live with it

Asthma may be an inherited tendency in a family, or it may occur as an allergic reaction, often to dust, or house dust mites and their faeces, or to animals such as cats and dogs. Everyone is capable of developing asthma – the respiratory tracts of the people who do are simply extra-sensitive to things which don't bother the rest of us. The **mast cells** (similar to blood **basophils**) in the lining of the respiratory tract produce extra histamine which causes swelling of the lining and contraction of the smooth muscle present, narrowing the tubes and making breathing difficult. Treatment is often very effective. It might include:

- **Beta agonists** – these are a mainstay of treatment for many asthma patients. They rapidly relax the smooth muscle of the respiratory tract, opening the tubes and so making breathing easier. Beta agonists are usually taken using an inhaler which delivers a set dose. They may be used regularly, or before exercise, or simply at the beginning of the asthma attack, depending on how badly an individual is affected.
- **Sodium cromoglycate** is a very useful preventative drug which was developed in Scandinavia for their Olympic athletes. It is particularly useful for allergy induced asthma and for asthma which is triggered by exercise. It works by stabilizing the mast cells so less histamine is produced.

The structure and function of the lung

Human beings need oxygen from the air for their cells to respire, providing the energy for movement, growth and synthesis. They also need to get rid of the toxic carbon dioxide gas which is produced as glucose molecules are broken down. Oxygen is carried to the cells, and carbon dioxide is carried away from the cells, in the blood. The gases are exchanged in the lungs, the main organs of the human respiratory system.

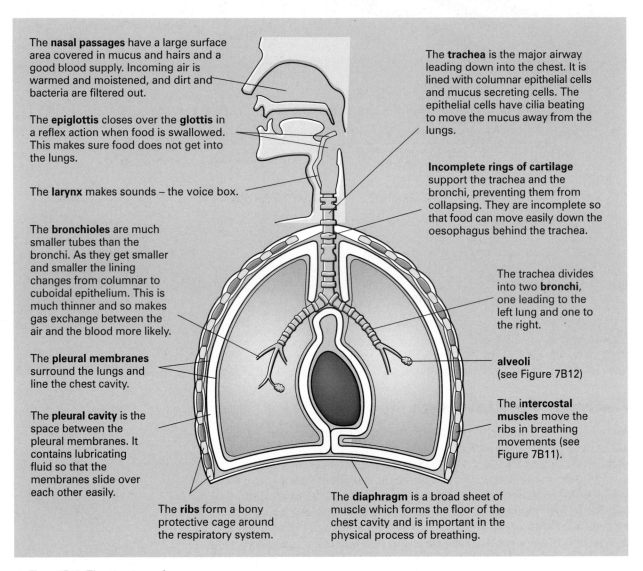

The **nasal passages** have a large surface area covered in mucus and hairs and a good blood supply. Incoming air is warmed and moistened, and dirt and bacteria are filtered out.

The **epiglottis** closes over the **glottis** in a reflex action when food is swallowed. This makes sure food does not get into the lungs.

The **larynx** makes sounds – the voice box.

The **bronchioles** are much smaller tubes than the bronchi. As they get smaller and smaller the lining changes from columnar to cuboidal epithelium. This is much thinner and so makes gas exchange between the air and the blood more likely.

The **pleural membranes** surround the lungs and line the chest cavity.

The **pleural cavity** is the space between the pleural membranes. It contains lubricating fluid so that the membranes slide over each other easily.

The **trachea** is the major airway leading down into the chest. It is lined with columnar epithelial cells and mucus secreting cells. The epithelial cells have cilia beating to move the mucus away from the lungs.

Incomplete rings of cartilage support the trachea and the bronchi, preventing them from collapsing. They are incomplete so that food can move easily down the oesophagus behind the trachea.

The trachea divides into two **bronchi**, one leading to the left lung and one to the right.

alveoli (see Figure 7B12)

The **intercostal muscles** move the ribs in breathing movements (see Figure 7B11).

The **ribs** form a bony protective cage around the respiratory system.

The **diaphragm** is a broad sheet of muscle which forms the floor of the chest cavity and is important in the physical process of breathing.

▲ **Figure 7B10** *The structure of the external respiratory system.*

How does air get into the lungs?

The respiratory system allows oxygen to be taken in and carbon dioxide to be removed. This exchange of gases takes place in the lungs. The air gets into the lungs as the result of **breathing**, although the lungs themselves are only passively involved. Simple observation shows us that this is a two part process – **inhalation** or breathing in and **exhalation** or breathing out.

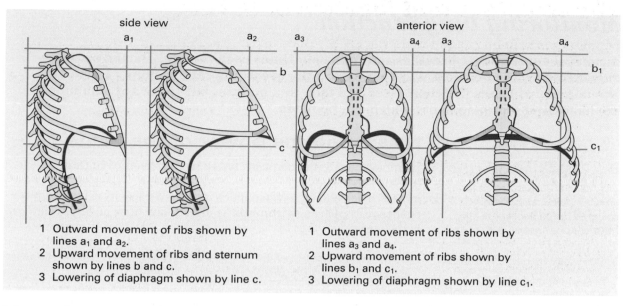

side view

anterior view

1 Outward movement of ribs shown by lines a_1 and a_2.
2 Upward movement of ribs and sternum shown by lines b and c.
3 Lowering of diaphragm shown by line c.

1 Outward movement of ribs shown by lines a_3 and a_4.
2 Upward movement of ribs shown by lines b_1 and c_1.
3 Lowering of diaphragm shown by line c_1.

How does gaseous exchange take place?

The alveoli are the main site of gaseous exchange in the body. An adult lung contains about 300 million alveoli which provide an enormous surface area for gaseous exchange – the total surface area of the lungs of an average adult is 60–$80\,m^2$. Alveoli also have very thin walls – a single layer of squamous epithelium – as well as moist surfaces for the gases to dissolve in and a very rich blood supply to exchange with.

Gaseous exchange takes place by diffusion between the blood in the capillaries and the gases of the alveolar air. The oxygen which moves into the blood is picked up by haemoglobin in the red blood cells and carried around the body. The carbon dioxide from the blood is exhaled.

Control of respiration

The levels of oxygen and carbon dioxide in the blood need to be very carefully controlled. The level of oxygen must be matched to the demands of the body tissues. There is a basic stimulus to inhale and exhale which is given by an area of the hindbrain called the **respiratory centre**. This gives a slow, deep breathing rhythm. Added to this are inputs from the higher centres of the brain, from stretch receptors in the bronchi and from receptors that are sensitive to the levels of carbon dioxide in the blood. These combine to give a finely tuned response, changing both the volume of air breathed with each inhalation and the frequency of breathing to match the oxygen demands of the body.

▲ **Figure 7B11** *The breathing mechanism.*
Left diagrams: Exhalation (relaxed diaphragm and intercostal muscles).
Right diagrams: Inhalation (contracted diaphragm and intercostal muscles).

▼ **Figure 7B12** *The fine structure of the lung.*

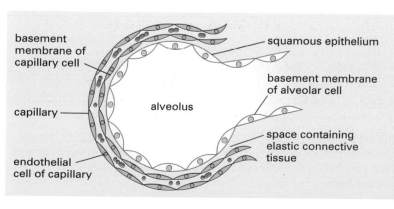

basement membrane of capillary cell

squamous epithelium

capillary

alveolus

basement membrane of alveolar cell

space containing elastic connective tissue

endothelial cell of capillary

The alveoli are the main respiratory surfaces of the lungs where most of the gaseous exchange takes place. Alveoli are made up of **squamous epithelial cells**. The capillaries which run close to the alveoli also have a wall which is only one cell thick. Between the capillary and the alveolus is a layer of elastic connective tissue which holds them together. The elastic elements in this tissue help to force air out of the stretched lungs. This is known as the **elastic recoil** of the lungs.

Monitoring lung function

A normal adult at rest breathes ten to fifteen times each minute. During exercise this increases. The easiest way to measure the breathing rate is simply to count the number of times the chest rises and falls in a minute, but there are also more sophisticated measurements which can be made.

Measuring the power of the lungs

▼ **Figure 7B13** *Spirometers come in all sorts of shapes and sizes – some of which can be carried round by the person whose lung function is being analysed.*

Breathing quietly and normally, only a small amount of air (around $500 \, cm^3$) enters and leaves the respiratory system. Taking hard exercise increases demand for oxygen; much more lung capacity is used. A piece of apparatus called a **spirometer** is used to find more about the air flow in the lungs.

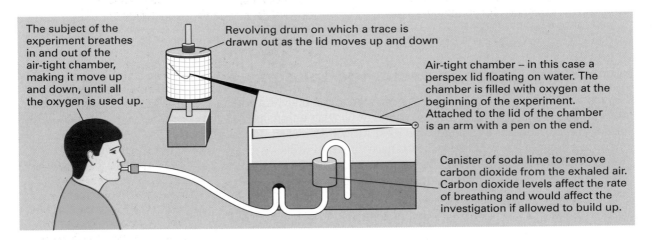

The subject of the experiment breathes in and out of the air-tight chamber, making it move up and down, until all the oxygen is used up.

Revolving drum on which a trace is drawn out as the lid moves up and down

Air-tight chamber – in this case a perspex lid floating on water. The chamber is filled with oxygen at the beginning of the experiment. Attached to the lid of the chamber is an arm with a pen on the end.

Canister of soda lime to remove carbon dioxide from the exhaled air. Carbon dioxide levels affect the rate of breathing and would affect the investigation if allowed to build up.

Components of lung volume

▶ **Figure 7B14** *Components of lung volume.*

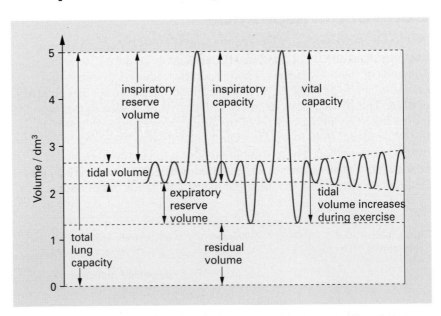

There is always some air in the respiratory system, just filling up space. Apart from this residual volume, the amount of air which is taken in and out of the respiratory system can be very variable, depending on the needs of the body.

- The **tidal volume (V_T)** is the volume of air which enters and leaves the lungs at each natural resting breath.
- The **inspiratory reserve volume (IRV)** is the extra air taken in when breathing in as deeply as possible.
- The **expiratory reserve volume (ERV)** is the extra air breathed out when air is forced out of the lungs as powerfully as possible.
- The **vital capacity (VC)** is the amount of air that can be breathed out by the hardest expiratory effort following the deepest possible inspiration.
- The **residual volume (RV)** is the volume of air left in the lungs after the strongest possible exhalation. It can only be measured indirectly.
- The **total lung capacity (TLC)** is the sum of the vital capacity and the residual volume.
- The **inspiratory capacity (IC)** is the volume that can be inspired from the end of a normal exhalation.

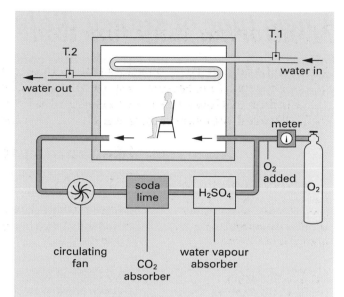

The Atwater–Benedict chamber for the determination of metabolism in man by direct calorimetry. The heat given off by the subject raises the temperature of the water in the cooling tubes and the heat evolved is calculated from this temperature rise (T.2 – T.1) and the rate of water flow.

▲ **Figure 7B15** *The human calorimeter. Using calorimeters such as this one it has been shown that an 'average' man needs to take in about 7500 kJ each day just to exist, and the 'average' woman needs to take in around 5850 kJ. Age, sex and the amount of activity undertaken all affect the amount of energy needed over and above the basal rate.*

Ventilation rate

A good way of expressing the breathing rate is to use **ventilation rate**. This is a useful measurement because it takes into account both the number of breaths per minute and the tidal volume of air taken in with each breath.

$$\text{ventilation rate (dm}^3\text{ min}^{-1}) = \text{tidal volume (dm}^3) \times \text{frequency of inspiration (min}^{-1})$$

Basal metabolic rate (BMR) and respiratory quotient (RQ)

How much energy do humans need? There is a basic level of food intake needed by every individual which will keep metabolism 'ticking over'. The minimum rate of energy expenditure on which a body can survive is known as the **basal metabolic rate**. The potential energy available from food is measured in **kilojoules (kJ)**.

The amount of oxygen used and carbon dioxide produced during cellular respiration depends on activity and the type of food being used in respiration. Comparing the volume of carbon dioxide produced with the volume of oxygen taken up (using a spirometer or similar piece of apparatus and adjusting the values obtained to standard temperature and pressure) produces a value known as the **respiratory quotient**:

$$\text{respiratory quotient (RQ)} = \frac{\text{volume of carbon dioxide produced}}{\text{volume of oxygen taken up}}$$

In theory, carbohydrates have an RQ of 1, fats 0.7 and protein 0.9. Measuring the RQ of a subject provides an estimate of the balance of foods being respired, and suggests whether the food is being respired aerobically or anaerobically. High RQ values suggest carbon dioxide is being given out but not much oxygen taken up.

A new type of kidney dialysis

Failure of an organ system can have dire consequences. However, modern medical technology can often provide an alternative method for doing the organ's job. Bernard Everard's kidneys began to fail ten years ago. Coping with the effects has demanded more and more technical intervention.

Healthy kidneys do two important jobs – they filter poisonous waste materials (mainly urea from protein breakdown) and remove excess water from the blood. If someone's kidneys stop working, urea builds up, the water balance of the cells is destroyed and they may burst.

Bernard Everard was a fit and active man in his fifties, when his kidneys started to fail. For nine and a half years Bernard managed his failing kidneys by a very careful choice of diet. 'I had to be very careful about the amount of protein I ate' says Bernard, 'and the levels of salt and liquid I took in mattered too. The doctors monitored my blood regularly to check on what my kidneys were up to. We tried hard to carry on as normal, and my kidneys worked for longer than the doctors expected, but last year I gradually became more and more tired and felt really unwell.'

Last year the results of Bernard's regular blood tests began to look increasingly poor. His kidneys were failing fast – to survive he needed their job done for them. Until about ten years ago there would have been only one option – **haemodialysis** (using a kidney machine). These machines are very good – but they involve several long sessions each week while the blood leaves the body and passes through a machine to be cleaned. Some people have a machine at home, but many have to go to hospital each time. Because the blood is only cleaned every few days, a very restricted diet is needed all the time. But Bernard feels he has been very fortunate. He was offered the chance of **continuous ambulatory peritoneal dialysis** (CAPD) see Figure 7B17.

'For me CAPD has so many advantages' comments Bernard. 'It means I can eat and drink fairly normally as my blood is being cleaned all the time. I feel so much better now. I can enjoy Thomas, our son's little boy, and I can travel to visit our daughter in London or to go on holiday.'

Both haemodialysis and CAPD allow many people who would otherwise die to live relatively normal lives. But only by receiving a new kidney can anyone whose own kidneys have failed become truly independent again. As Bernard continues to stabilize and improve on CAPD, he is already looking forward to the next step – a transplant.

Measuring progress

The kidneys clean the blood, removing toxic urea. They also balance the amount of water and salt (sodium chloride) in the body fluids. The balance between sodium ions (Na^+) and potassium ions (K^+) is very important for cells to work properly. When someone is ill, as Bernard was, and the symptoms suggest that the kidneys are not working well, blood samples are analysed. The blood is tested to check on the levels of urea, Na^+, K^+ and creatinine. Creatinine, like urea, is formed by the breakdown of proteins and removed by the kidney.

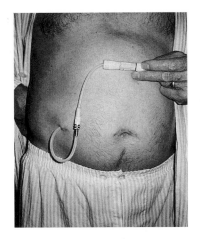

▲ **Figure 7B16** *Bernard Everard's abdomen, showing catheter insertion for CAPD. The external part is invisible under clothes. People can even go swimming as long as they cover the tube with a special waterproof plaster.*

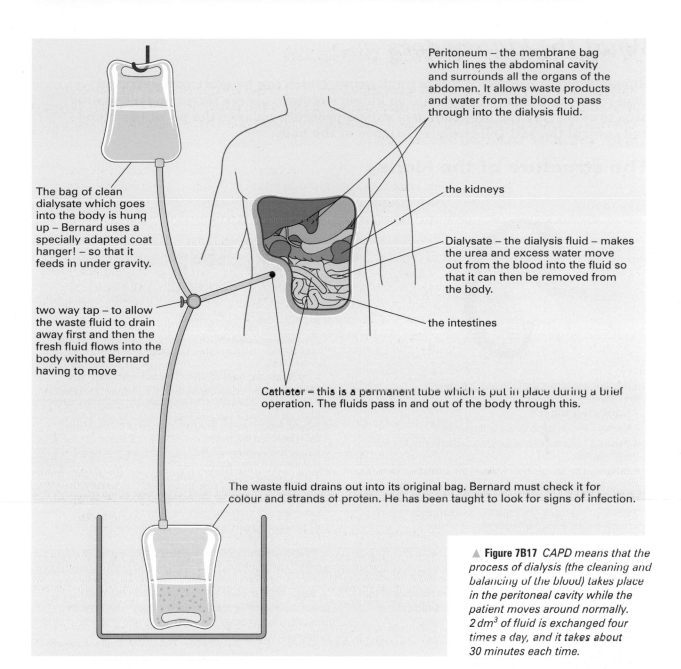

The bag of clean dialysate which goes into the body is hung up – Bernard uses a specially adapted coat hanger! – so that it feeds in under gravity.

two way tap – to allow the waste fluid to drain away first and then the fresh fluid flows into the body without Bernard having to move

Peritoneum – the membrane bag which lines the abdominal cavity and surrounds all the organs of the abdomen. It allows waste products and water from the blood to pass through into the dialysis fluid.

the kidneys

Dialysate – the dialysis fluid – makes the urea and excess water move out from the blood into the fluid so that it can then be removed from the body.

the intestines

Catheter – this is a permanent tube which is put in place during a brief operation. The fluids pass in and out of the body through this.

The waste fluid drains out into its original bag. Bernard must check it for colour and strands of protein. He has been taught to look for signs of infection.

▲ **Figure 7B17** *CAPD means that the process of dialysis (the cleaning and balancing of the blood) takes place in the peritoneal cavity while the patient moves around normally. 2 dm³ of fluid is exchanged four times a day, and it takes about 30 minutes each time.*

The results of some of the blood tests carried out on Bernard Everard before he began dialysis (January) and for the months after the treatment got under way (April onwards) are shown in Figure 7B18. Normal levels of substances have been shown for comparison.

▼ **Figure 7B18** *Table of Bernard's blood test results.*

Date of test	Na⁺	K⁺	Urea	Creatinine
Normal range	133–143	3.3–5.0	2.5–8.0	50–150
January	137	3.8	29.9	979
April	140	2.8	16.0	640
June	138	3.5	13.4	646
August	141	3.7	17	633
September	140	3.5	14.8	652

What the kidney does

Human kidneys produce a waste fluid, urine, which can be more concentrated than the body fluids themselves. The kidneys remove excess water and poisonous urea produced by the breakdown of excess proteins, balance the pH of the blood and control the salt (electrolyte) balance of the body.

The structure of the kidney

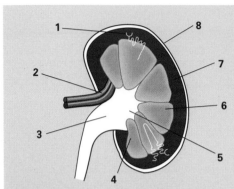

1 Cortical nephron – the loop only just enters the medulla

2 Renal artery and vein

3 Ureter – carries urine down to the bladder

4 Pyramid – a collection of tubules, collecting ducts and blood vessels

5 Pelvis – urine arrives here from all the collecting ducts

6 Medulla – this contains the loops of Henle from the nephrons

7 Cortex – this has a rich capillary blood supply and contains the Malpighian bodies of all the nephrons (kidney tubules)

8 Fibrous capsule

▲ **Figure 7B19** *The kidneys are attached to the back of the abdomen and are surrounded by fat for protection. They are the main organs in the excretory and osmoregulatory systems.*

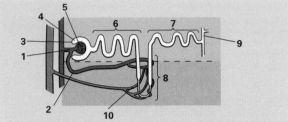

1 The **afferent vessel** brings blood into the nephron.

2 The **efferent vessel** takes blood away from the nephron. It is narrower than the incoming vessel; blood in the glomerulus is under pressure.

3 The **Malpighian body** consists of the Bowman's capsule and the glomerulus.

4 The **Bowman's capsule** is the site of ultrafiltration of the blood.

5 The **glomerulus** is a tangled knot of capillaries where the blood is under pressure. Fluid is forced out of the blood into the capsule and the nephron.

6 In the **first convoluted tubule** all of the sugar and much of the salt is reabsorbed into the blood.

7 In the **second convoluted tubule** water is taken back into the blood as the body needs it.

8 The **loop of Henle** is where urine is concentrated and water is conserved.

9 The **collecting duct** is where water can be taken back into the blood by osmosis.

10 Capillaries surround the tubules and loop so glucose, salts and water can be reabsorbed into the blood.

▲ **Figure 7B20** *It is in the nephrons – and there are about 1.5 million of them in each kidney – that waste products are removed from the blood and water is conserved for the body.*

How the kidney works

Put simply, the kidney filters the blood. It removes substances like urea which are harmful to the body, and saves everything that is needed. As the blood is forced under pressure into the glomerulus, some of the fluid from the blood is squeezed out into the Bowman's capsule to pass along the kidney tubule. This is known as **ultrafiltration**. The blood cells, some of the fluid and larger solute molecules are left behind in the blood capillaries.

As the fluid passes along the tubule, everything that the body needs is taken back into the blood, while toxic wastes such as urea and excess water and salts which the body doesn't need are left in the tubule. Eventually this liquid reaches the collecting ducts and leaves the kidney as urine. The blood which leaves the kidney has had all urea removed and the salt and water balance returned to the ideal levels for cells to function.

Getting rid of urea and saving the good bits

Urea is forced out of the blood in the capsule. The rest of the kidney tubule is not permeable to urea – it cannot pass back through the tube lining into the blood. It simply moves along the tubule with the rest of the liquid and is removed from the body in urine.

But the filtrate which is forced out of the blood into the capsule contains lots of things that the body needs; glucose is particularly important. As the filtrate travels along the first convoluted tubule all the glucose is transported back into the blood. This movement requires the expenditure of energy, since the concentration of glucose in the filtrate is reduced to much less than that in blood. The glucose has to be pumped back into the blood against a concentration gradient – a process known as **active transport**.

Balancing salt and water – osmoregulation

Hot summer days sunbathing on the beach reduce body water content sharply. Going to the pub and drinking several pints of beer overload the body with water. In both cases the kidneys prevent tissue cells from suffering damage. When the body is short of water, the kidneys produce a little, very concentrated urine. When the body is loaded with water the kidneys produce lots of very dilute urine.

When the body is short of water the concentration of solutes in the blood increases. This means that blood becomes a more concentrated solution than the inside of the cells it supplies. (Since cell membranes are **semi-permeable**, water will flow into blood from the cells by **osmosis**, causing cell damage.) Any rise in solute concentration in blood is detected by **osmoreceptors**, specialized nerve endings in the **hypothalamus** region at the base of the brain. The hypothalamus sends messages to the **pituitary gland**, which releases a hormone (see page 396) called ADH – **anti-diuretic hormone**. ADH makes the second convoluted tubule and the collecting duct much more permeable to water. This means water leaves the kidney tubule and goes back into the blood, diluting the solution to the correct level again and giving very concentrated urine.

When the body has too much water the detectors in the brain send messages to the pituitary gland making sure that very little ADH is produced. This means that the second convoluted tubule and the collecting duct are impermeable to water – very little passes back into the blood and large quantities of very dilute urine are formed.

Are they working?

There are two ways of investigating whether kidneys are working properly.

- **Testing the urine**. If the kidneys are working urine is a clear yellow liquid containing urea, water, some salt and a few impurities. Simple tests on the urine show if glucose or protein are present. If glucose is in the urine this is a symptom of diabetes – the kidney cannot cope with the amount of sugar in the blood. If protein is present in the urine this can be a sign that the kidneys themselves are not working properly.
- **Testing the blood**. If the kidneys are not doing their job the levels of urea, creatinine, Na^+ and K^+ in the blood will vary from their normal range. Repeating the measurements over a period of time will show whether kidney function is stable, improving or deteriorating.

The endocrine system – chemical co-ordination

A large organism is made up of millions of cells, arranged into organs which carry out particular jobs. It is important that there are communications between various parts of the body, so that the entire organism acts as a co-ordinated whole. One method of achieving co-ordination is the system of chemical messages known as *hormones* produced in *endocrine glands*.

The range of hormones

Hormones (usually either proteins, parts of proteins or steroids) are released directly into the bloodstream, which then transports them to their target cells. These may be all over the body or only in certain specialized places. The target cells have receptors which are sensitive to the hormone molecules. When the hormone arrives it sets up a response in the target cell.

▼ **Figure 7B21** *The main endocrine glands of the human body. Where they are and what they do.*

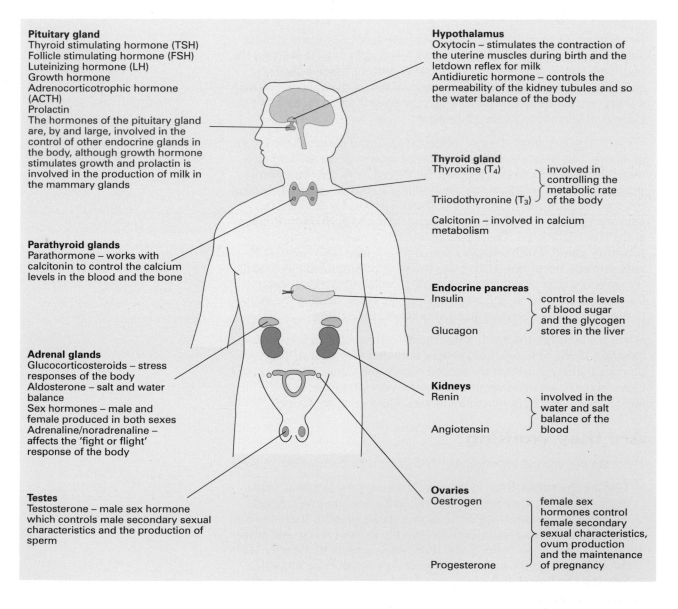

Pituitary gland
Thyroid stimulating hormone (TSH)
Follicle stimulating hormone (FSH)
Luteinizing hormone (LH)
Growth hormone
Adrenocorticotrophic hormone (ACTH)
Prolactin
The hormones of the pituitary gland are, by and large, involved in the control of other endocrine glands in the body, although growth hormone stimulates growth and prolactin is involved in the production of milk in the mammary glands

Parathyroid glands
Parathormone – works with calcitonin to control the calcium levels in the blood and the bone

Adrenal glands
Glucocorticosteroids – stress responses of the body
Aldosterone – salt and water balance
Sex hormones – male and female produced in both sexes
Adrenaline/noradrenaline – affects the 'fight or flight' response of the body

Testes
Testosterone – male sex hormone which controls male secondary sexual characteristics and the production of sperm

Hypothalamus
Oxytocin – stimulates the contraction of the uterine muscles during birth and the letdown reflex for milk
Antidiuretic hormone – controls the permeability of the kidney tubules and so the water balance of the body

Thyroid gland
Thyroxine (T_4)
Triiodothyronine (T_3) } involved in controlling the metabolic rate of the body

Calcitonin – involved in calcium metabolism

Endocrine pancreas
Insulin
Glucagon } control the levels of blood sugar and the glycogen stores in the liver

Kidneys
Renin
Angiotensin } involved in the water and salt balance of the blood

Ovaries
Oestrogen
Progesterone } female sex hormones control female secondary sexual characteristics, ovum production and the maintenance of pregnancy

Feedback loops – fine control for sensitive systems

Adrenaline is released from the adrenal glands when they are stimulated by the sympathetic nervous system (see page 398). Adrenaline works with the sympathetic system to prepare the body for emergency action, increasing the heart beat and dilating the bronchi to make deep, rapid breathing easier. The control of adrenaline levels in the blood is quite simple. When the gland is stimulated by the nerve, adrenaline is released. When the gland is not stimulated, no hormone is released.

For many other hormones the situation is not so simple. The activity of one gland is controlled by the secretions of another, which in turn is sensitive to blood levels of the first. If a rise or fall in the end product of a hormonal control system is counteracted and the system remains stable, it is known as a **negative feedback loop**.

▼ **Figure 7B22** *A summary of a negative feedback loop.*

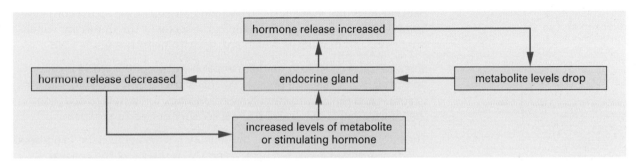

The thyroid gland and its hormones

A closer look at the thyroid gland demonstrates the far-reaching effects of hormones. The thyroid gland is found at the base of the neck and its main hormone is **thyroxine**. Thyroxine controls the rate of the metabolism – the reactions going on in all the cells. It affects the heart rate, the body temperature, the body mass and the rate of energy transfer in the individual. The production of thyroxine by the thyroid gland is in turn controlled by **thyroid stimulating hormone** (TSH) from the pituitary gland in the brain. If a thyroid gland becomes under- or overactive, the symptoms and signs of illness demonstrate the many roles of the hormone.

▼ **Figure 7B23** *Table of thyroid diseases their symptoms and treatment.*

Hyperthyroidism – too much thyroxine	Treatment	Hypothyroidism – too little thyroxine	Treatment
cannot cope with heat		cannot cope with cold	
excessive sweating		lack of energy	
good appetite but loss of weight		constipation	
tachycardia – a very rapid heart beat	carbimazole is a drug which blocks the release of thyroxine and is very effective	weight gain with no increase in appetite – causes obesity	thyroxine taken by mouth clears up all the symptoms and restores normal body function
swelling of the neck due to swollen thyroid	surgery or radioactive iodine may be used to remove part of the thyroid gland	bradycardia – slowing of the heart rate	
staring eyes		hoarse voice and dry skin	

The nervous system – electrical communication

Chemical communication in the form of hormones is one way of achieving co-ordination between the different parts of large animals, but it is a rather slow and non-specific system. The nervous system provides a rapid and direct route for getting information from one part of the body to another.

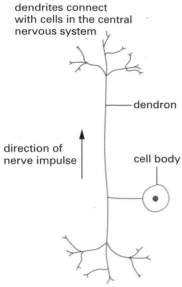

dendrites connect with cells in the central nervous system

dendron

direction of nerve impulse

cell body

nerve endings which may act as receptors themselves or may connect with other receptor cells or sense organs

▲ **Figure 7B25** *The structure of a motor neurone. Neurones are often surrounded by associated* **Schwann cells***. In such cells, electrical disturbances in the nerve (impulses) travel from Node of Ranvier to Node of Ranvier at very high speed.*

In – pending – out

To work successfully the body needs **information** about both the external environment (what is going on in the world around it) and the internal environment (what is going on inside it). This information is provided by the **sensory nervous system**.

The basic unit of a sensory nerve is a **sensory neurone** (see Figure 7B24), a cell specialized for connecting sensory nerve endings with the **central nervous system** (CNS), which consists of the spinal cord and brain. Electrical impulses travel along the **axon** to the **dendron**, which fragments into **dendrites** which link up with neurones in the CNS.

Much of the sensory information people have about the world is picked up through special sense organs. The eyes are sensitive to light, the ears to sound and the skin to stimuli such as touch, temperature and pain; the information is then carried along sensory nerves to the brain.

The information coming in from the sensory system needs to be **processed** – sorted, analysed and acted upon – and this is the job of the **central nervous system** (CNS), particularly the brain. The brain is complicated and not properly understood. The conscious parts of the brain deal with emotion, memory, awareness and thought – but there are also unconscious areas of the brain controlling basic metabolism, coordination and balance.

To enable the body to act on the information it has received, messages must go to the muscles and glands. These outgoing messages are carried in the **motor nervous system**.

Motor neurones (see Figure 7B25) have terminal cell bodies connected by dendrites to spinal cord and brain neurones. Long axons conduct messages (as electrical nerve impulses) to target organs which respond when they receive these impulses from terminal dendrites.

The motor nervous system – carrying the orders

The motor nervous system carries the instructions from the CNS to the muscles. The **voluntary nervous system** is under the direct control of the conscious areas of the brain – reaching out for a chocolate is a deliberate decision sending instructions through the voluntary motor nerves to the muscles in the arm.

The **autonomic nervous system** is involuntary – it doesn't have to be thought about. It controls bodily functions like sweating, breathing and the heart rate. When the body temperature starts to go up, instructions are sent through the autonomic motor nerves to produce more sweat. There are two sub-systems which work in opposition to one another – what one speeds up, the other slows down! **Sympathetic** nerves are usually excitatory – they speed up the heart and breathing rates and open the bronchi. **Parasympathetic** nerves are inhibitory – they slow the heart beat and breathing rate and constrict the bronchial tubes.

Reflexes

If all body functions were under voluntary control life would be very difficult. Imagine trying to walk, breathe, keep your heart beating at the same rate, and squeeze food along the gut, all at the same time. To release the brain for more complex thought processes, many routine bodily processes are under **reflex control**. Reflexes are also useful because they avoid the involvement of the conscious areas of the brain. This means they can take place very rapidly and are important in escaping from danger, for example, pulling a hand away from a hot plate or a foot from a pin.

A **reflex arc** is a nerve connection pattern which links a sensory area directly with a response organ. In a **knee-jerk reflex**, for instance, a blow to the knee-bone (patella) is detected by **stretch receptors** in the attached muscles. The information is conducted to the spinal cord by a sensory neurone. One of the connections made by that neurone in the CNS is directly with the motor neurone connected straight back to the same muscle block in the knee. The muscle responds by contracting, producing the knee-jerk.

When the brain stops working

In **Alzheimer's disease**, brain cells slowly shrivel up and disintegrate, leaving sticky clumps of damaged cells and tangled fibres that were once functioning brain tissue. Normal brain function is lost, leaving the victims as human shells – a living body without the mind which once filled it with purpose and humanity.

Ten years ago Alan Watts was a healthy man – he enjoyed his job, he had a wife and two teenage children and was a skilled artist and craftsman in his spare time with an enthusiasm for cricket and cars which he shared with his son. Then, as his wife Sheila recalls, things gradually began to fall apart. 'The changes were so small that we didn't really notice them at first', she explains. 'Alan got quieter, and would fall asleep more often in the evenings – but we just thought he was tired from his work.'

But at work it became increasingly apparent that Alan could no longer cope. 'At first even the doctors thought that Alan was suffering from stress and would soon be back to his normal self,' explains Sheila, 'but as the months passed it became clear that he would never work again and Alzheimer's disease was diagnosed.' To begin with Alan coped better at home, but soon he began to lose his memory of simple tasks – he couldn't lay the table, or dress himself properly. 'His behaviour became more and more child-like – he had violent temper tantrums if he couldn't have his own way.'

Eventually the disease reduced Alan to a shadow of his former self. He no longer knew his son and daughter, he was incontinent, almost unable to feed himself or speak, and he hardly slept at night. For eight years Sheila, with the support of Ian and Tracey, managed to look after Alan at home but finally the decision was made for Alan to go in to long term care. 'I visit him every day, and help to care for him, but Alzheimer's has robbed our family of so much – we've lost Alan, yet we can't even mourn properly because we have this hollow shell which still – just – looks like him.'

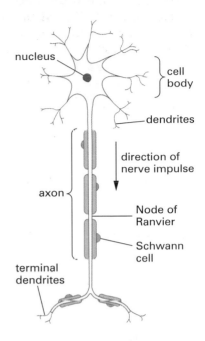

▼ **Figure 7B24** *Bundles of nerve cells or* **neurones** *form* **nerves**. *The structure of a sensory neurone is shown above.*

nucleus

cell body

dendrites

direction of nerve impulse

axon

Node of Ranvier

Schwann cell

terminal dendrites

▶ **Figure 7B26** *Alan Watts, then and now.*

Keeping people healthy

One man and his heart

This chapter is about organizing health care for individuals and groups. We begin with a case study of a patient who underwent open heart surgery to correct problems with his circulation system. Why did he need this serious operation and how was he diagnosed and cared for during surgery and convalescence?

▲ **Figure 7C1** *Peter walking.*

Coronary arteries

aorta — left coronary artery

left circumflex

right coronary artery

left anterior descending artery

▲ **Figure 7C2** *The heart, showing the position of the coronary arteries.*

Peter's story

Peter (who was 62 when he was operated on in 1993) has had a history of minor gastric problems but otherwise has been healthy. His main hobby is mountain walking with his wife Florence. On one of their hikes in 1988 Peter felt what he thought was heartburn (a chest pain associated with gastric upset) and had to rest before he could go on. Because the pain struck when he was exercising, Peter's doctor suspected a heart problem and referred him to the hospital cardiology department.

The heart specialist (cardiologist) tested Peter's heart function; starting with his pulse rate, blood pressure and electrocardiogram (ECG). Biochemical measurements were also made on his blood and he exercised on a treadmill while his stress ECG was measured (see page 384). The tests allowed the cardiologist to see if Peter's heart was short of oxygen during exercise.

The cardiologist suspected that there was something wrong with the arteries supplying blood to Peter's heart (**coronary arteries**). The heart pumps blood back to itself, via the coronary arteries, to supply it with nutrients and oxygen. People whose coronary arteries become constricted suffer pains in their chest when they exercise, known as **angina pectoris**. If the coronary arteries eventually become blocked then the heart can be permanently damaged – causing a heart attack.

The cardiologist decided to carry out an **angiogram** – to take pictures of the coronary arteries. He injected a local anaesthetic into Peter's groin and put a plastic tube into his femoral artery (at the top of his leg), into which he fed a series of fine tubes (**catheters**) that passed along Peter's arteries into the heart. He squirted a liquid into the heart through the coronary arteries. The liquid (called **contrast**) is a clear fluid containing iodine, which shows up white on X-ray photographs.

The cardiologist filmed the heart as this was going on, watching a VDU to see the speed at which the blood vessels filled, and where they narrowed. He could see from the angiogram that one of the three main branches of Peter's coronary arteries was severely constricted – Peter was suffering from **coronary heart disease** (CHD).

Peter's two open coronary branches supplied enough blood to his heart under normal conditions. But when the heart was working hard, the supply of blood from two branches was not enough. The muscle tired, producing the pain which Peter thought was heartburn but which was in fact angina. The cardiologist thought the situation would gradually get worse. The only permanent solution would be **coronary artery bypass graft surgery** – an operation to replace the blocked sections of coronary artery with short pieces of blood vessels taken from elsewhere in the body. One reason for conducting such open heart surgery is to improve the quality of patient life by increasing tolerance to exercise and relieving angina pectoris and breathlessness.

The cardiologist put Peter on a drug treatment regime. He prescribed a beta-blocker to slow the heart beat (to match the supply of blood to heart demand), vasodilators to relax arterial walls (widening the passages to allow greater blood flow), and aspirin to reduce the chance of blood clotting as it flowed through the coronary arteries (because such clots can lead to heart attacks). Taking the pills relieved Peter's angina pains and he felt fine for a couple of years.

▼ **Figure 7C3** *Peter's drug prescription.*

Drug	Action	Main side effects
Atenolol	Beta-blocker – reduces heart rate and force of contraction. A standard treatment for angina	Heartbeat may over-slow, some gastric and respiratory disturbance
Isosorbide mononitrate	Vasodilator – prevents angina	Headache, flushing, dizziness; tachycardia (abnormally rapid heart action)
Diltiazem	Vasodilator and calcium antagonist – prevents angina	Slows heart rate, hypotension (low blood pressure)
Aspirin	Analgesic, anti-inflammatory and anti-coagulant	Oedema (swelling) in ankles

Why do the coronary arteries block?

Coronary arteries can become clogged with fatty deposits. Many factors increase people's likelihood of developing CHD. Some risk factors, like age and a family history of heart disease, cannot be changed. People can modify other risk factors by changing their behaviour. These risk factors include high blood pressure, high blood cholesterol levels, high fat diet, lack of exercise and being overweight. But by far the most important risk factor is cigarette smoking.

Peter does not smoke, he is slim and fit and eats a healthy diet. He probably developed CHD because of his genetic make up.

Cholesterol

Cholesterol is an essential fat. However, if there is too much cholesterol in blood, it is deposited as an insoluble layer on blood vessel walls, narrowing arteries and leading to CHD. All fats, including cholesterol, must be attached to soluble blood **lipoproteins** to be moved about. There are two classes of lipoprotein. Low Density Lipoproteins (LDLs) are the main transporters of cholesterol. Too much cholesterol in the diet leads to higher LDL levels, more cholesterol in the blood and more deposits on the vessel walls. However, low cholesterol levels encourage High Density Lipoproteins (HDLs). These actively remove cholesterol stuck on blood vessel walls.

Peter feels he needs heart surgery

Peter continued on his regime of drugs, with regular visits to the cardiology department to check on his progress, for five years. In 1993, angina pains became more frequent and he felt tired all the time. Another angiogram showed that all three branches of Peter's coronary arteries were severely constricted. The cardiologist referred Peter to a consultant cardio-thoracic surgeon.

Before the operation

The surgeon met Peter and Florence in the out-patient clinic. He explained the nature of the problem and the need for bypass surgery. He outlined the size and scale of the operation and the risks and benefits. One per cent of the patients do not survive the operation but 95% are cured of their angina and can stop taking drugs.

Ten days before his operation Peter spent a day in hospital undergoing a battery of tests. He had an X-ray, a full blood count and blood chemical analysis, and measurements of his liver enzymes and kidney function. During the operation the kidneys and liver are put under tremendous strain, and doctors need to know the state of these organs.

The operation

Peter was prepared for surgery and anaesthetized. His body had to be carefully monitored during the operation and he was hooked up to a mass of equipment. The surgical team monitored his pulse, ECG, urine output, blood pressure, brain temperature, and the amount of oxygen in the blood.

The consultant set to work on the chest while his senior registrar started to open up the leg along the course of a blood vessel known as the saphenous vein. With the chest opened the surgeon carefully dissected out an artery, the internal mammary artery, leading directly off the aorta. He used this blood vessel for the main graft in the heart. He used pieces of veins from the legs for the other grafts. Before Peter was put on the heart-lung bypass machine the anaesthetist gave Peter heparin, which stopped his blood from clotting.

The feelings of an anaesthetist about her work.

'Anaesthesia is a balance of three components, (1) loss of awareness (sleep), (2) muscle relaxation and depression of reflex activity, and (3) analgesia (pain relief). We try to avoid sudden or large reflex changes in blood pressure and heart rate during surgery, so we use a combination of anaesthetic drugs to control the underlying reflexes.'

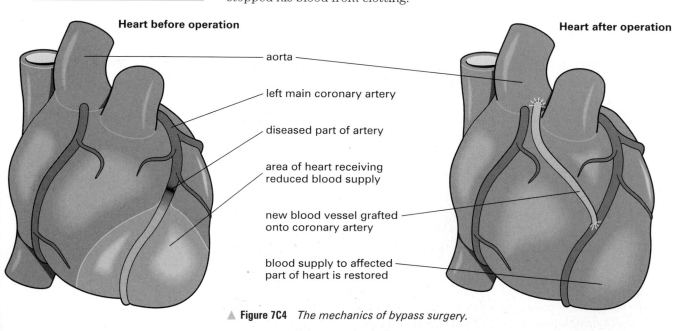

Heart before operation

Heart after operation

aorta

left main coronary artery

diseased part of artery

area of heart receiving reduced blood supply

new blood vessel grafted onto coronary artery

blood supply to affected part of heart is restored

▲ **Figure 7C4** *The mechanics of bypass surgery.*

Peter spent an hour on the heart-lung machine. This allowed the surgeon to stop Peter's heart intermittently so that he could perform the delicate graft surgery on a comparatively still organ.

The heart-lung machine is operated by the perfusionist team. It does the job of the heart (pumping blood around the body) and the lungs (oxygenating the blood). It is an expensive and highly controllable pump, with an oxygenator as a means of transferring oxygen to the blood. The oxygenator works in the same way as the lungs – with oxygen on one side of the membrane and blood on the other. There is also a heat exchanger, so that the patient can be cooled down and warmed up under controlled conditions.

A perfusionist describes his role, 'When he is ready, the surgeon says, "On bypass" and on you go. It is a bit like starting a car on a hill. You ease off on one (what the patient is doing) and increase what the machine is doing. Once the patient is on bypass you control the blood pressure and the oxygen levels. The blood pressure is controlled by a combination of vasoconstrictor and vasodilator drugs and the pump rate. You need to keep up the chemical balance – if you get a lot of urine output it affects the potassium levels, so you need to keep up the potassium. We are watching about ten different parameters, so every few seconds the eyes flicker around the monitors. We make recordings on a chart every ten minutes. Once the surgery is finished, the reverse procedure for coming off bypass is performed.'

While Peter was on the heart-lung machine his blood was cooled to 32 °C, slowing down all his chemical reactions. There are times during the operation when the heart itself gets a reduced blood supply. The cooler it is, the better it will survive; the brain and the kidneys also suffer less.

While the surgeon sewed the final graft, the heart-lung machine warmed Peter up to 37 °C. Then it was time to bring Peter off the heart-lung machine. The anaesthetist gave a drug, protamine, to reverse the effects of heparin and make the blood clot again. When everything was ready, the surgeon sewed up the breastbone, using strong wire. The bones will not heal unless they are tightly knitted together. The surgeon then stitched up the skin of the chest and leg.

After the operation, Peter was taken to the intensive care unit, where he recovered over the next 24 hours.

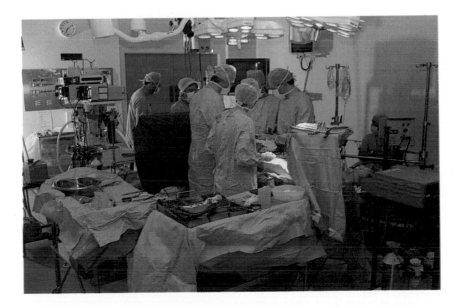

◀ **Figure 7C5** *The operation in progress.*

Peter's recovery and rehabilitation programme

'On the first night without morphine I woke up and thought, "What is this? I feel a totally different person." OK, I was sore in all sorts of places and very weak, but deep down I felt that my illness had gone absolutely and without trace.'

This is how Peter remembers feeling just two days after going through his bypass surgery. All the fatigue that he had never really associated with his heart condition, but which had been making life miserable for him, had been lifted. When Peter woke up after the operation he had several drips and drains in his body; these were for giving fluids and drugs and taking measurements (see Figure 7C6). He claims he looked like the outworks of a chemical plant.

▶ **Figure 7C6** *Patient after heart surgery.*

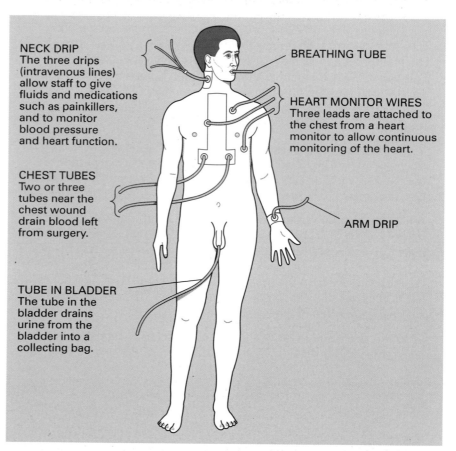

NECK DRIP
The three drips (intravenous lines) allow staff to give fluids and medications such as painkillers, and to monitor blood pressure and heart function.

BREATHING TUBE

HEART MONITOR WIRES
Three leads are attached to the chest from a heart monitor to allow continuous monitoring of the heart.

CHEST TUBES
Two or three tubes near the chest wound drain blood left from surgery.

ARM DRIP

TUBE IN BLADDER
The tube in the bladder drains urine from the bladder into a collecting bag.

The drips and drains were removed after a few days. Peter spent a week recovering from his operation in hospital. The staff in the cardiac unit encourage patients to build their confidence, with a positive, robust attitude towards their own recovery. A cardiac counsellor is available to talk to patients and their families about any concerns they might have.

When Peter left hospital the staff were relaxed about how he should look after himself. He was invited to attend a series of cardiac rehabilitation sessions, but there was no pressure and, in the event, Peter found that it was not convenient to attend. The 'don'ts' were all to do with bone healing; he was to avoid tension in his arms and shoulders – to allow the bones in his chest to knit together. He was advised to do everything he felt he could, especially to walk every day.

Immediately afterwards

On the first day after leaving hospital Peter walked up and down outside his home. Within ten days he was walking around the block. The hospital told him that he should aim to be walking three to five miles a day within eight weeks, they meant walking briskly; good aerobic exercise.

After eight weeks he went for his first hospital check up. He was given an ECG, blood and urine tests, and his chest was X-rayed to see how the bones were healing.

Benefits of exercise

In the year before his operation Peter became much less active and his muscle tone was poor. After two months of building up to the 3–5 miles of brisk walking every day this tone improved greatly. Once fully recovered he will fit exercise into his everyday life by walking to the shops and so on. He uses the car much less than he used to.

Peter talked to a thoracic physiotherapist who gave him some surprisingly gentle exercises; 75% were for stretching and flexing and 25% for strength. He did these regularly for three months, and will continue to do them from time to time. The physiotherapist recommended swimming as good exercise. Peter went swimming twice a week; doing nonstop breast stroke for twenty minutes each time.

Diet

The hospital advised that he could eat what he liked, but they recommended low fat foods and plenty of green vegetables and fruit.

Medication

Peter no longer takes drugs prescribed for angina. He takes aspirin (150 mg per day, when he remembers). Aspirin has been shown to prevent platelets from sticking to arterial walls and causing blockages.

Short- and long-term benefits

Peter always felt encouraged by the support he received from the hospital staff who built up a very positive attitude towards recovery among their patients. Peter thinks that he was able to sustain this attitude because he did not suffer any serious complications which would have set back his recovery.

Peter still tires more than he did five years ago, but this is acceptable, not as he felt before the operation when he was crushed by fatigue. He has never felt any heart pain (angina) since the operation, whatever he has done. Peter still feels pain in the breast bone area if he pushes against it, but he doesn't really find this a problem.

There was lots of information about exercise and diet to encourage participation. He says, 'They do a "road test" on you and send you off with the feeling that it's up to you. Now I feel great and look forward to plenty of hill walking.'

How lifestyle affects health

Many aspects of lifestyle – what people eat, where they live, where they work, the air they breathe, whether they smoke or drink or take exercise – affect health. Scientists study how lifestyles influence health so that they can make health care recommendations to prevent disease.

The science of epidemiology

Is it known what aspects of people's lifestyles affect their health? Many diseases, including cancers and heart disease, do not have simple causes. Diseases like these are **multifactorial**. There does not seem to be a single cause. Several agents, including dietary, environmental and genetic factors, are involved. **Epidemiology** is the branch of medical research which unravels the causes of disease in populations by studying patterns of disease and aspects of lifestyle, including exposure to infection and to toxic substances.

Retrospective studies

These look back at the past lifestyle of a group of people with the same disease and search for a common factor that might have caused it. One problem with retrospective studies is that people sometimes cannot remember details of their diets or lifestyle before they became ill.

Prospective studies

One way around this problem is an approach that looks forward – **prospective** studies. Here, researchers recruit a number of healthy people and ask them to report certain aspects of their lifestyle (their dietary, smoking and drinking habits for example), to give samples of their blood and other specimens and to report any illnesses they suffer during the study period. They follow-up the participants for a number of years, and compare the diet and biological condition of those who develop diseases such as cancer, heart disease or stroke, with those who stay healthy. Such studies are expensive because large numbers of healthy people need to be recruited and monitored over long periods so that numbers contracting disease are statistically significant.

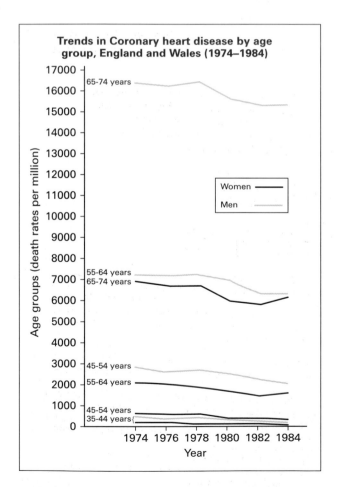

◀ **Figure 7C7** *The incidence of coronary heart disease.*

Risk factors

The results of epidemiological studies make it possible for doctors to identify **risk factors** for specific diseases. A risk factor for a disease is associated with a greater than average probability of developing that disease. Scientists are careful to distinguish between a 'risk factor' and the 'cause' of a disease. A risk factor for a disease is not necessarily the cause of the disease, although it may be. To investigate the causes of disease, scientists need to experiment at the molecular level. Epidemiological studies often provide the first clue in the hunt for the causes of disease.

Simply identifying the risk factors for a disease is useful. Epidemiologists can then advise people on the kinds of diets or lifestyle they should adopt to minimize their risks of that particular disease.

The findings of epidemiological studies are sometimes controversial. One study may show that eating too much of a particular nutrient is a risk factor for a disease, or that something we eat helps to prevent a disease, while another study might lead to different conclusions. Such variation between individual studies is not surprising; there are so many variables at work. The national press often report the findings of epidemiological studies – they are usually of great interest to us all.

The Government makes health recommendations to the public only when a series of epidemiological studies provides enough evidence to support them. One disease which epidemiologists have shown to be directly linked to lifestyle is lung cancer. Retrospective studies in the 1950s showed that over 90% of patients with lung cancer were tobacco smokers. Epidemiological studies have also shown that smokers are more likely than nonsmokers to die of other respiratory diseases and heart diseases.

▼ **Figure 7C8** *Epidemiological studies often make the news.*

Sir Richard Doll, the eminent Oxford scientist who first linked smoking with lung cancer, celebrates his 80th birthday today surrounded by his peers. His studies – covering a vast number of subjects from the effects of radon and asbestos on the body to the importance of diet and hormonal factors – have revolutionised our understanding about the disease. JO REVILL highlights important new findings discussed today at the Imperial Cancer Research Fund's meeting at the Royal Society

Smokers at risk of dying in middle-age

THE HAZARDS of long-term smoking are far greater than first believed, new results show.

The 40-year follow-up of a study instituted by Sir Richard Doll in 1951 has found that smokers are three times as likely as non-smokers to die in middle age.

Sir Richard, a consultant at the Imperial Cancer Research Fund's cancer studies unit in Oxford, spoke today at a conference at the Royal Society in London, held to celebrate his 80th birthday.

"These new results are much more extreme than had been suggested by the 20-year follow-up, where premature death was only twice as common in smokers as in non-smokers," he said.

"This is because the study can now assess the effects of really prolonged smoking.

"Our findings mean that those who start to smoke in their teenage years will be at particularly high risk of death from tobacco in later life."

But the study has also revealed good news. Stopping smoking works, and smokers who have managed to kick the habit avoid most of their risk of death from tobacco.

The first large study ever undertaken of the overall hazards of smoking began in 1951 when Sir Richard asked doctors in Britain what they smoked and then began to monitor the causes of death of those doctors. Four decades on, more than half the 34,000 doctors have died and the fates of the smokers and non-smokers can be compared.

There are about three million deaths a year from tobacco worldwide, but on the current smoking patterns, that looks likely to shoot up to 10 million when today's children reach middle age.

Sir Richard fuelled the debate currently raging over the ethics of allowing cigarette advertising. "Whether the promotion of tobacco, as opposed to the provision of opportunity for its sale, should be regarded as ethical behaviour in the modern world is a matter for personal judgement.

"In mine, it is not, especially in view of the extent to which the attitudes of children and teenagers can be manipulated by modern marketing techniques."

Evening Standard, 15 February 1994

Health promotion

Scientific research and the collective experience of physicians and surgeons in the clinical treatment of their patients produces new knowledge. The benefits of new knowledge then inform the training and practice of doctors. But new knowledge can also benefit the public directly, because sound advice can be given which will help people remain healthy. Health promotion is the process of giving such advice, monitoring whether people have followed it, and how they may have benefitted.

Can people look after their own health?

Life in modern Britain is different from life in the past in virtually every possible way. One very striking difference for young people is that today the majority survive their childhood. Most people now die in old age. In Victorian Britain half the deaths each year were among children under 14 years old. In 1860 the total population was under 20 million but 101 000 children died before they were one year old and another 60 000 before they were four. In 1992 the population of England was nearly 48 million but the number of under-ones who died was 4000 with another 700 dying before they were four.

In 1860 most of these children were dying from a combination of infectious diseases and being badly fed and housed. A disease like measles, which a properly fed child gets over fairly easily, may well kill an undernourished one. This is still commonly the case in parts of Africa for instance.

Today in Britain poor health is still associated with poverty. In the early 1990s Britain was in the grip of a long economic recession. Many people became poorer during the recession. A report in 1994 showed that death rates in young men rose in parts of Northern England for the first time in 60 years. This has led the government to set up an inter-departmental working group to look at how health and disease may depend on economic and social factors. It also seems that the poor, including unskilled and manual workers, do not seem to be able to take advantage of advice about health. They seem to get less explanation of their ill health from doctors and so understand it less well.

Can people look after their own health and prevent themselves becoming ill by adopting a sensible lifestyle? The idea certainly appeals to governments because they think it will save money – people's health would be improved, reducing the need for an expensive professional health service.

As a result there are a constant barrage of health messages – from the government's Chief Medical Officer; from newspapers, television, magazines; medical research charities. They tell people not to smoke; to be careful what they eat – plenty of fibre, not much sugar or fat; not to get too much sun; to be careful about casual sex; to take plenty of exercise. Health promotion is one of the major activities of the later 20th century.

But does health promotion actually work? Do people take any notice of all this well-meant advice? In any case how reliable is the information on which the 'good' advice is based? Finally, even if people are taking the advice, is it leading to the improvement in health that is intended? Some answers to these questions may emerge from looking at the effects of a successful health promotion campaign.

The cot deaths campaign

About a quarter of all deaths in babies under a year old are called cot deaths. Cot death means the unexplained death of a baby while it is sleeping. Typically, the dead baby was perfectly well the day before, was put to bed normally and found to be dead the next morning. The death of a baby in this way is particularly distressing for the baby's family because the baby was perfectly well and also because the police may have to be informed in case there are suspicious circumstances.

Television leads the way

In 1991 the Foundation for the Study of Infant Death (FSID) approached the English Department of Health who agreed that it was worth giving advice to the public on how to avoid cot death. In the summer of that year the young baby of television broadcaster Anne Diamond was the victim of cot death. Anne Diamond agreed to appear in the television programme *This week*, in October 1991, to launch a campaign by the FSID 'Reduce the Risks of Cot Death'.

The programme attracted an audience of 8 million and the television studio provided 20 live telephone help-lines to answer questions from viewers. It was thought as a result of the programme that practically every woman in the country of child-bearing age knew about the campaign. FSID kept up the pressure with leaflets and a short video which was shown in GPs' waiting rooms.

REDUCE THE RISK OF COT DEATH

- Place your baby on the back or side to sleep
- Don't smoke and avoid smoky atmospheres
- Do not let your baby get too hot
- If you think your baby is unwell, contact your doctor

The Foundation for the Study of Infant Deaths
35 Belgrave Square, London SW1X 8QB
Telephone: 071-235 0965
Cot Death Helpline: 071-235 1721

The printing of this leaflet has been made possible through a generous donation by

ORACLE®
Getting information to the people who need it

▶ **Figure 7C9** *The FSID campaign.*

Two months later the Department of Health started its own campaign 'Back to Sleep' with leaflets and an Anne Diamond video. The major advice given in both campaigns was the same; four key points of which every parent should take note (see Figure 7C9).

In 1991, 1134 babies under one died as cot deaths. In 1992, following the campaign, the number fell to 613, a drop of 45%. This seems to provide strong evidence that the campaigns were successful and this still seems to be true even though the number of cot deaths had been falling steadily since 1989.

The background to cot deaths

Research into cot death followed many different ideas over many years. Gradually it narrowed down to one main idea, overheating and the connection between the baby's sleeping position and his or her temperature. Babies are safest sleeping on their backs and unless there are very good reasons should not be put to sleep lying on their tummies. A second idea which is also important is smoking by the baby's parents, particularly the mother. The risk to the babies of smokers is at least twice that to non-smokers. It was believed that as many as 365 cot deaths in England and Wales each year, one a day, could be avoided if all mothers of newly born babies stopped smoking.

In most countries the traditional way for babies to sleep is on their backs. This was true in the UK until the 1960s but in the early 1970s babies in special care units were put to sleep on their fronts. This was thought to improve their breathing and stop them choking if they were sick. Within a few years the habit had become widespread for all babies.

The idea that there might be a link between sleeping position and cot death was looked at in the mid-1960s but what information was available did not support the idea. However, as more information was collected attitudes started to change. In many countries including the UK, Hong Kong and New Zealand there were consistent reports that the number of cot deaths were higher among babies sleeping on their fronts than their backs. In the late 1980s the idea received publicity in both the Netherlands and Australia and as a result it was reported that more babies were being put to sleep on their backs and that the number of cot deaths had fallen.

In the UK, numbers of cot deaths began to fall, in 1989 by an average of 14% a year. By 1991 they were down from more than 1800 to 1134.

What features of promotion campaigns make them successful?

The cot deaths campaign was obviously successful, even though cot deaths had been falling steadily throughout the 1980s. What can be learned from it?

It reached the widest possible audience. It created enough awareness and anxiety to make parents do something. It made some parents very anxious indeed. Some were reported sitting up all night with their babies, actively preventing them from rolling over. It looks as though the power to make people anxious is an important feature of a successful campaign.

However, remember that parents were not supposed merely to ensure that their babies slept in the 'right' position but **if they were smokers, to stop smoking**. This was also an important part of the message. Information collected at the time showed that although mothers would actively change their babies' sleeping habits they were much more reluctant to give up smoking.

It looks as though a key part of any health promotion message is that **what has to be done must be easy to do**. Clearly it was no more effort for mothers whether they put their babies to sleep on their backs or fronts, but it made a big difference (too big) for them to give up a long standing habit.

Another lesson might be that it is a good thing **if television or some other part of the mass media can be used to get the message over**. This seems to be true. Messages through the media seem much more effective than messages from official bodies like governments. This is presumably because the media are run by professional communicators. They know what people will listen to and they think about their audiences. The government believes that most people received their information from the television programme rather than the rest of the campaign.

Does it help to have a very well-known celebrity to help put the message across? In this case Anne Diamond probably helped in getting television's interest in making the programme but whether her part was essential to the programme's success is not so clear. Sixteen different countries have now had similar campaigns and in every country the number of cot deaths has fallen by between 40% and 60%. But all the campaigns were different and none but the British one used a celebrity to get the message over.

Another important lesson that can be learned from all health promotion campaigns, including those about cot deaths, is that the **message has to go on being given**. And new ways of giving it may have to be found. There is some evidence that the numbers of cot deaths are beginning to rise again. Campaigns aimed at cutting the spread of human immunodeficiency virus (HIV) which causes AIDS were very successful in persuading the first generations of people experiencing the disease to practise 'safe sex'. But this lesson does not seem to have been learned by the next generation and the problem is beginning all over again. The same is true of cigarette smoking. Up to and after World War II, far more men than women smoked. Today in the United Kingdom the numbers are very similar. In the USA, more women smoke than men.
It is now a habit very popular with young women.

Smoking and health

'Among an average 1000 young adults who smoke cigarettes regularly, it has been estimated that about one will be murdered, about six will be killed on the roads and about 250 will be killed before their time by tobacco.' (*Smoke-Free for Health*, HMSO, 1994). Smoking is the main risk factor for lung cancer and it kills twice as many people from other diseases. It is a risk factor for cardiovascular disease, stroke and respiratory diseases. Reducing smoking is a major objective of public health campaigns.

What's in a cigarette?

Cigarette smoke contains a mixture of **tar, nicotine** and **carbon monoxide**. All three have damaging effects on health. **Tar** is a sticky, brown substance that accumulates in the lungs, containing some 4000 different chemicals. About 60 of these are suspected or known **carcinogens** (chemicals that cause cancer).

Nicotine is what makes smoking a habit that is hard to kick; it causes addiction. It is a powerful drug which acts as a stimulant to the nervous system, increasing heart rate and raising blood pressure. **Carbon monoxide** is one of the harmful gases present in cigarette smoke. Among other effects, it reduces the oxygen carrying capacity of the blood.

The Laboratory of the Government Chemist analyses cigarettes and produces tables listing their yields of tar, nicotine and carbon monoxide. Yields of all three substances from cigarettes are lower now than they were 20 years ago; the average tar yield per cigarette was 21 mg in 1972, falling to 13 mg in 1990. A European Union (EU) directive will impose a limit of 12 mg tar per cigarette from 1 January 1998.

Short-term effects of smoking

Jenny is 20; she smokes between 15 and 20 cigarettes a day. She started smoking at school when she was about 15 because her friends smoked and it made her feel grown up. She thinks she could easily give up if she wanted to. When Jenny smokes a cigarette many changes happen in her body. Her heart speeds up by 15 to 25 beats per minute and her blood pressure rises ten to twenty points. Her skin temperature drops, because the blood flow to her extremities is constricted. These physiological changes occur because nicotine mimics the hormone **adrenaline** and the neurotransmitter **acetylcholine** producing the same effects as the natural hormone and neurotransmitter.

Effects of giving up smoking

Tom is 43; married with two teenage children. He'd been a heavy smoker since he was 17, but gave up four years ago, partly because of pressure from his kids and partly because, he says, he was 'beginning to feel past his "sell by" date'. He'd tried to give up several times in the past, but hadn't lasted more than a few days before the craving for a cigarette became too much. On a friend's recommendation, he went along to a group hypnotherapy session. 'We all sat around smoking cigarettes and talking about why we smoked. Then the hypnotherapist told us that this was the last cigarette we'd ever smoke. And for me it was.'

Tom has felt much fitter since he gave up smoking. He's noticed that his smokers' cough has gone. He's taken up running and plans to run in a marathon next year – something he'd never dreamed of doing when he was a smoker. Furthermore, Tom's risk of death from smoking-related diseases will fall to the levels of people who have never smoked if he does not smoke for fifteen years.

▼ **Figure 7C10** *Long-term benefits of stopping smoking.*

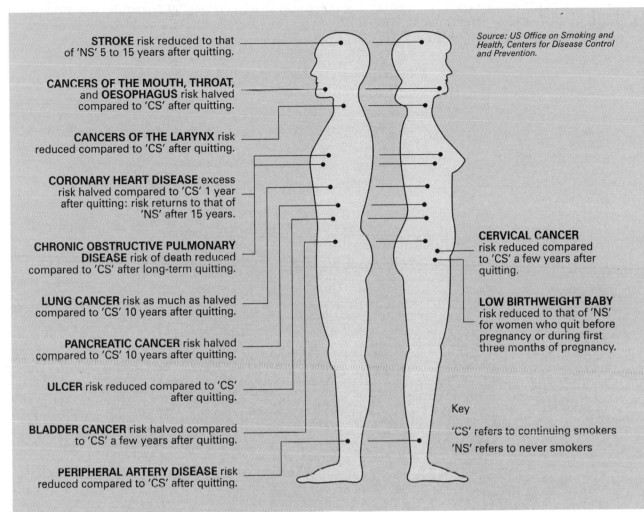

Source: US Office on Smoking and Health, Centers for Disease Control and Prevention.

STROKE risk reduced to that of 'NS' 5 to 15 years after quitting.

CANCERS OF THE MOUTH, THROAT, and **OESOPHAGUS** risk halved compared to 'CS' after quitting.

CANCERS OF THE LARYNX risk reduced compared to 'CS' after quitting.

CORONARY HEART DISEASE excess risk halved compared to 'CS' 1 year after quitting: risk returns to that of 'NS' after 15 years.

CHRONIC OBSTRUCTIVE PULMONARY DISEASE risk of death reduced compared to 'CS' after long-term quitting.

LUNG CANCER risk as much as halved compared to 'CS' 10 years after quitting.

PANCREATIC CANCER risk halved compared to 'CS' 10 years after quitting.

ULCER risk reduced compared to 'CS' after quitting.

BLADDER CANCER risk halved compared to 'CS' a few years after quitting.

PERIPHERAL ARTERY DISEASE risk reduced compared to 'CS' after quitting.

CERVICAL CANCER risk reduced compared to 'CS' a few years after quitting.

LOW BIRTHWEIGHT BABY risk reduced to that of 'NS' for women who quit before pregnancy or during first three months of pregnancy.

Key

'CS' refers to continuing smokers

'NS' refers to never smokers

▼ **Figure 7C11**

Passive smoking

Even breathing smoke-filled air from cigarette smokers (passive smoking) can damage people's health. Non-smokers exposed to environmental tobacco smoke (ETS) for most of their lives are at a greater risk of lung cancer than other non-smokers. Children exposed to ETS because their parents smoke are at a greater risk of respiratory diseases, 'glue ear' (middle ear disease that can cause deafness) and asthma. Even smokers' pets are at risk (see Figure 7C11).

Trends in smoking

People are taking notice of the health warnings about smoking. But the message needs to be constantly reinforced to discourage young people from taking it up. There has been a fall in the percentage of smokers in the UK population over the last two decades. The Government's target is for the percentage of the UK population who smoke to fall still further to 20% by the year 2000.

Budgie dies from passive smoking

EDWARD GORMAN

The death of a budgerigar has been blamed on passive smoking. Six-year-old Peter, whose owner smokes 40 cigarettes a day, fell off its perch two days after being diagnosed as suffering from lung cancer.

The Times, 27 January 1994

Exercise and health

Physical inactivity increases the risk of coronary artery disease by more than 30%. It is one of the reasons why people in the UK have a higher risk of developing coronary heart disease than people in many other countries. Only 29% of women and 40% of men in England take part in regular vigorous physical activity, according to a survey published in 1992. There is considerable scope for decreasing the risk of CHD in the population by increasing levels of participation in physical activity.

Physical activity and exercise

Physical activity is a term that describes all the bodily movements which involve energy transfer in our daily lives, at work, at home and during our leisure time, including exercise. **Exercise is one particular form of physical activity**. It is physical activity that is planned with the goal of improving or maintaining physical fitness (see Figure 7C12).

▼ **Figure 7C12** *Participation in different sports and exercise by age and sex.*

Type of sport or exercise	Men				Women			
	Age			All men	Age			All women
	16-44	45–64	65 and over		16–44	45–64	65 and over	
	Percentage participating in type of sport							
Exercises	26	10	10	18	18	10	7	14
Swimming	20	10	3	14	21	13	2	14
Cycling	24	15	7	18	14	12	3	11
Aerobics/keep fit	4	1	1	3	20	7	2	12
Running/jogging	19	6	1	12	6	1	–	3
Social dancing	8	6	5	7	14	11	4	11
Weight training	16	4	0	9	4	0	–	2
Football/rugby	17	2	0	9	0	1	–	0
Badminton/tennis	8	3	0	5	5	3	0	3
Squash	6	1	–	4	2	–	–	1

Short-term effects of exercise

Exercising muscles need more energy. This can be supplied aerobically – from glucose and oxygen, or anaerobically – from glycogen stored in the muscle.

During exercise the blood supply to active muscles needs to be increased. This is achieved by an increase in **cardiac output**, and an increase in the capillary circulation – the blood supply. Cardiac output is the volume of blood pumped out of the heart per minute. It is increased when the heart beats faster and when the volume of blood expelled by the ventricles at each contraction (**the stroke volume**) increases. Exercise activates the nervous system to increase the heart rate.

During exercise, capillary circulation is increased by dilation of arterioles in the active muscles, the lungs, the skin and the brain. Exercise also brings about an increase in the rate and depth of breathing.

Long-term effects of exercise

Regular vigorous exercise develops the capillary circulation and improves the blood supply to the muscles, including the heart. This improves the supply of oxygen to the muscles and to the heart itself, improving their functional capacity. Another important long-term effect of exercise is to develop the muscles themselves. Both these effects help people to improve their **physical fitness**.

Exercise helps to reduce the risk of heart disease. **But how much exercise?** There has been a great deal of research to find the precise amount of exercise that is needed to help prevent heart disease. Many studies have shown that increasing **physical fitness** needs regular vigorous exercise, at least three times a week for 20–30 minutes. But even moderate rather than vigorous exercise, such as brisk walking rather than running, when carried out consistently, can help to reduce the risk of coronary heart disease. Studies have shown that regular walking may increase levels of **HDL-cholesterol** (high density lipoprotein-cholesterol; the substance in blood which helps to ferry fats away from the coronary arteries).

How does exercise protect the heart?
- It lowers blood pressure
- improves the blood supply to the heart
- helps to control body weight
- raises high density lipoprotein (HDL) cholesterol levels
- lowers the risk of blood clot formation, and
- lowers the risk of developing diabetes.

What are the other benefits of exercise?
- It helps prevent heart disease
- helps people to remain **mobile in old age**
- helps to prevent **osteoporosis** (brittle bones)
- helps to prevent **obesity**
- helps prevent the onset of **adult diabetes**, and
- helps **reduce stress**.

Research shows that those who are the least physically active have the most to gain from increasing their level of physical activity. 'Couch potatoes' can reduce their risk of CHD by a relatively modest increase in physical activity.

'Brisk walking on the level, or hill walking, swimming and cycling and participation sports such as football are examples of the kinds of exercise you need to consider.'

Reducing the risk of a heart attack, British Heart Foundation

Physical fitness

Physical fitness is a measure of a person's ability to perform daily tasks without undue fatigue. A fit person's heart is more powerful than that of an unfit person. The resting pulse rate of a fit person is normally lower than for an unfit person and the fit pulse rate returns to normal faster after exercise than an unfit pulse rate.

A precise measure of physical fitness is given by VO_2 max. This is the fastest rate at which oxygen can be absorbed. It is measured on a person who is exercising up to maximum performance on a treadmill or exercise bike, while their expired air is collected for analysis.

Alcohol and health

There is nothing wrong with enjoying beer, wine or spirits, but remember that alcohol is a powerful drug. The alcohol content of beers, wines and spirits varies widely. Half a pint of beer has about the same alcohol content as a single measure of spirits, or a glass of wine (see Figure 7C13). The amount in all these drinks is about 10 cm³ of pure alcohol. This quantity is known as one unit of alcohol. Keeping an eye on the intake of alcohol units is a sensible health measure.

▶ **Figure 7C13** *Units of alcohol.*

Alcohol's effect on the body

Alcohol is a drug. It acts as a sedative interfering with the transmission of nerve impulses, slowing both mental and physical responses. In small amounts, alcohol helps people feel more relaxed but drinking even small quantities makes driving and operating machinery dangerous. Larger amounts make people lose control of their bodies; speech becomes slurred and movements become uncontrolled. Extremely large amounts of alcohol may depress the nervous system so much that unconsciousness and even death may occur.

Alcohol passes quickly through the lining of the stomach and intestines into the bloodstream. Because alcohol is readily soluble in water, it distributes evenly throughout the body fluids. It reaches every cell. The body removes about a tenth of the absorbed alcohol through breath, sweat and urine. The liver removes the rest from the bloodstream. The enzyme, **alcohol dehydrogenase** converts it into **acetylcholine**. Further enzymes convert acetylcholine to the final breakdown products – carbon dioxide and water.

Blood alcohol level

The liver of an individual removes alcohol from the blood at a constant rate, about 10 cm³ of pure alcohol (one unit of alcohol) per hour. The liver metabolizes a constant amount of alcohol regardless of the amount in the body. This is because the enzymes involved become saturated, (work flat out) at very low concentrations of alcohol. Beyond that point they work at a constant rate although there are differences between people in their rate of alcohol removal.

If alcohol is drunk faster than the liver can metabolize it, for example drinking more than half a pint of beer an hour, then the amount of alcohol in blood builds up. It takes approximately two hours to clear the blood of alcohol after drinking one pint of beer, or two glasses of wine.

The amount of alcohol in a person's blood at any particular time (the blood alcohol level – BAL) is expressed either as mg alcohol per 100 cm³ of blood, or as a percentage. The higher your BAL, the more pronounced the effects (see Figure 7C14). The factors which influence BAL include the amount drunk, the time spent drinking, the amount of food in the stomach and body weight. If the stomach is full, alcohol is absorbed more slowly than it is when drinking on an empty stomach. A light person will have a higher BAL than a heavy person after drinking the same amount of alcohol.

▼ **Figure 7C14** *Behavioural state and BAL.*

BAL/ mg 100 cm⁻³	Amount of alcohol		State
	double whiskies*	pints of beer**	
up to 50			Feelings of comfort and satisfaction
50	1	1.5	Beginning to be reckless, take liberties
100	2	3	Uncoordinated, speech begins to slur
200	4	6	Drunk but mobile
300	6	9	Drunk, in stupor
400	8	12	Dead drunk, anaesthetized and comatose

*1 English double whisky = 48 cm³ = 16 mg alcohol
**1 pint beer = 643 cm³ = 12–34 mg alcohol

NB People with the same BAL can show different states of drunkenness depending on their previous experience with alcohol.

People with more than 80 mg alcohol per 100 cm³ of blood are not legally permitted to drive. A man of average size (70 kg) reaches the legal limit for driving with alcohol in his blood after five units of alcohol. But lower amounts of alcohol in the blood can impair judgement and make driving dangerous.

Long-term effects of alcohol misuse

Some people can become addicted to alcohol. They develop tolerance, which means they need to drink more to experience the same effect. Alcoholics experience withdrawal symptoms if they go without a drink, or drink less than usual. These symptoms include nausea, cramps, tremors and shakes. In extreme cases withdrawal leads to **delirium tremens** (DTs), experiencing hallucinations, mental confusion and seizures.

Heavy drinking can begin to damage the body after only a few weeks. If people drink heavily over a number of years they risk damage to the liver, high blood pressure, anaemia, and even some kinds of cancer. Women who drink while pregnant risk the health of their babies who may be born with birth defects or mental disabilities. Doctors advise pregnant women to avoid drinking alcohol altogether.

Sensible drinking limits

Because of the dangers to health and the social costs of drinking excessive amounts of alcohol, doctors advise people to limit their drinking. The current recommended limits are 14 units of alcohol a week for women, and 21 units of alcohol a week for men. It is also advisable to abstain from drinking alcohol for 2–3 days each week.

Genetic screening

Promoting health through changes of lifestyle and economic development to give higher standards of living has helped reduce infections and other diseases which are caused by environmental factors. However, some diseases have a strong *genetic* component; individuals inherit a predisposition to succumb to particular disorders. At first sight it would seem that little can be done in health promotion terms for such individuals. However, that would be to reckon without genetic screening.

What is genetic screening?

Genetic screening involves testing groups in the population for the presence of genes which might cause health problems. In the UK every newborn baby is tested for phenylketonuria (PKU), an inherited disease which, if untreated, leads to severe mental retardation. It is caused by an inherited failure of an enzyme which should metabolize the amino acid, phenylalanine. The test for the disease looks for high concentrations of phenylalanine, an indirect measurement of a product. High circulating levels of phenylalanine cause brain damage in infants. The disease can be prevented by giving babies who screen positive for PKU a special diet in the first few weeks of life, to ensure that they receive only a minimum amount of phenylalanine.

New knowledge about human genetics means that the genes which are responsible for a range of inherited diseases can themselves be pinpointed. This has opened the way for direct tests for genes known to be important in certain disorders.

Some common diseases, such as certain kinds of cancer and heart disease, seem to run in families. In many cases the pattern of inheritance is complicated because a number of genes are involved. It is known that environmental factors, such as lifestyle, also play an important part in the development of these diseases. They occur as a result of environmental experience combined with **genetic predisposition**.

With the new knowledge comes new responsibilities and difficult decisions. Do people want to know if they have a strong possibility of developing heart disease or cancer? How would the knowledge affect their employment prospects and their ability to obtain life insurance? Would people want to know if they were carriers for genetic diseases, which might be passed on to their children? How might someone react if they found out that an unborn child would develop a crippling disease by the time it was sixteen? These are some of the questions faced by people now that more tests for inherited diseases are available.

Genetic counselling

People need information both before and after they take tests for a genetic disorder. Questions like those listed below need to be considered before people decide whether to be screened for a genetic disorder.

- How serious is the condition caused?
- What treatments are available?
- How reliable is the screening test?
- How is the disorder transmitted genetically and what does this mean for families?
- What does it mean to be a genetic carrier?
- What are the implications for present and future children if people are screened positive for an abnormal gene?

Cystic fibrosis

Cystic fibrosis (CF) is a serious inherited disease which affects the lungs and digestive system. Scientists in the UK were the first to develop screening methods for the gene which causes this disease.

About 1 in 2000 babies in the UK is born with CF. For a child to suffer from CF, both parents must be carriers of the gene for the condition. About 5% of the white population in the UK are carriers. Carriers of CF are themselves perfectly healthy and have no CF symptoms, but if their child inherits a CF gene from each parent then that child will suffer from the disease. For each pregnancy of a couple who are both carriers for CF, there is a 1 in 4 chance that the baby will inherit the CF gene from both parents and suffer from this disease.

Children with CF have sticky mucus in their lungs. They suffer from frequent chest infections and have difficulty digesting food. They need long-term treatment with antibiotics to treat infections, physiotherapy to clear the mucus from their lungs, and digestive enzymes to help them to digest their food.

In 1989 the CF gene was identified. This led to new understanding of the causes of the disease and opened the way to genetic testing in newborn babies and healthy adults to discover whether they are sufferers or carriers. Taking a test for CF simply involves rinsing the mouth with sterile saline solution and collecting the mouth wash.

Pre-natal screening

Babies can be tested for some potentially harmful genetic conditions before they are born. Most pregnant women in the UK have an ultrasound scan between the 18th and 20th week of their pregnancy as a way of checking on the development of the fetus. The technique allows doctors to detect fetal malformations, some of which may be genetic.

Women over 35 have an increased risk of having a baby with **Down's syndrome**, caused by the presence of an extra chromosome, and they are routinely offered screening by **amniocentesis**. Women have amniocentesis usually between the 15th and 18th week of pregnancy.

In amniocentesis, a small sample of the amniotic fluid (see page 367) is taken, using a needle guided by an ultrasound image. The amniotic fluid contains cells shed by the developing fetus. These cells are then grown in culture. Medical scientists examine the chromosomes to detect Down's syndrome, or analyse the DNA for mutations such as those that cause CF. The risks of amniocentesis to the pregnancy are low; between 0.5 and 1% of amniocenteses result in a miscarriage.

Chorionic villus sampling (CVS) involves taking a small sample of chorionic (placental) tissue. This has the same genetic makeup as cells in the fetus. As with amniocentesis, the fetal cells are analysed for genetic problems. Doctors use ultrasound scanning techniques to locate the placenta. Tests can give the parents genetic information about their fetus by the time it is 12 weeks old. CVS is more risky for the fetus than amniocentesis; between 2 and 4% of CVS procedures result in miscarriage.

Taking a CF test

'As I rinsed my mouth with the salt solution, a few cells from the inner lining of my cheeks got washed out and deposited in the specimen bottle. In less than four hours, the cells had been separated from the rest of the solution, the DNA teased out from the cells, copied many thousands of times, and my DNA matched against reference DNA samples containing mutations that cause CF.'

Perilous Knowledge, Tom Wilkie, 1993

Thoughts and actions

1 Distinguish between cytology and histopathology.

2 What is the resolving power of a microscope?

3 What is dialysis? How does it remove waste substances from blood:
   a during CAPD and
   b in a kidney machine?

4 Distinguish between amniocentesis and chorionic villus sampling. What are the advantages and drawbacks of the two procedures?

5 What are the physiological effects of the following substances on the human body?
   - steroids
   - antihistamines
   - prostaglandins
   - aspirin
   - nicotine
   - carbon monoxide
   - carbimazole
   - atenolol

6 Write a 350 word précis of the case study on the care of premature babies on pages 367–70, showing the interdependence of the physiology of the major organ systems.

7 The nutritional composition of milk varies from species to species. Why is cow's milk not satisfactory as a food for human infants?

8 Explain how the various subcellular components of epithelial cells operate in the protective and secretory functions of these tissues.

9 The normal resting heart rate of an adult male is 70 beats min^{-1}. Trained athletes often achieve resting heart rates of 40 beats min^{-1}. Explain the physiological mechanisms behind the control of heart rate and how training can produce reduced resting heart rates in athletes.

10 Explain how the histological structure of the walls of the different types of blood vessel suits them to their function.

11 Construct an annotated flow chart of the feedback mechanism involved when anti-diuretic hormone regulates loss of water from the human body.

12 The local leisure centre is producing a training manual for people who take their exercise seriously. They plan to include some basic physiology. Write a section of the manual for them using the following words:
   - blood plasma
   - ATP
   - intercostal muscles
   - voluntary muscle
   - BMR
   - physical exercise
   - CO_2
   - Krebs cycle
   - O_2
   - lung
   - heart rate
   - mitochondria
   - cardiac muscle
   - alveolus
   - RQ
   - diaphragm.

13 Compile a list of mammalian connective tissues. Why are these very different tissues classified in the same category?

14 Drug companies often need to measure the performance of healthy people before and after taking a new drug, to make sure it does not affect their vital functions. How would you set up an investigation to measure the performance of a volunteer in the following physiological parameters?
   - pulse rate
   - lung tidal volume
   - blood pressure
   - oxygen uptake
   - breathing rate

15 Explain how analysis of blood components would help in the diagnosis and analysis of cases of
   a kidney failure and
   b hyperthyroidism.

16 Describe a health screening programme in which X-ray photography of subjects plays a part. Evaluate the risks of using X-rays in the programme you have chosen.

17 What causes angina pectoris?

18 Draw up a table of the similarities and differences between respiration and photosynthesis.

19 Explain why anaerobic respiration occurs during short, sharp bursts of exercise, while sustaining exercise for a long time needs aerobic respiration.

20 Write and illustrate a hand-out advising visitors to clinics that less than 35% of their human body fuel energy should be in the form of fat.

21 Describe what happens when the casein component of a glass of skimmed milk is digested in the alimentary canal.

22 Look at Figure 7B18, the table of Bernard Everard's blood test results. Make graphs of Bernard's results, making clear the normal levels of each substance. What do these results tell you about the effectiveness of dialysis and the way the body tolerates different substances?

23 Jenny has just found out that she is expecting a baby. Jenny is a smoker. How would you try to convince her to give up smoking during her pregnancy?

24 Look at the data in the Reference section for smoking prevalence for men and women in different age groups (Figures R38.1 and R38.2). What are the smoking trends among teenagers? Place in rank order the factors which you think influence young people to take up smoking.

25 What percentage of the total circulating blood would be removed if 0.75 cm^3 of blood was taken from a premature baby with a mass of 1.8 kg?

26 A premature baby with a mass of 2.2 kg had a nappy put on at 20.00. This was removed at 02.00. The nappy was wet but otherwise unsoiled. What approximate difference in mass would be expected if the nappy had been weighed at these two times and the baby had normal kidney function?

27 Using the table of energy values for a range of foods in the Reference section, Figure R37.1, plan out two days of an appropriate diet for the following people:
a a kidney patient who must have a very limited protein intake yet needs to build up strength for a transplant
b an athlete in training for 2000 metre rowing races
c a recovering cancer patient who has lost a considerable amount of weight and needs to regain body tissue – but not just get fat.
In each case consider all needs. Explain your suggestions.

28 Devise and carry out a survey to assess the smoking habits of your year group. Compare smoking habits between males and females. Does your data follow the national trends?

29 The yields per cigarette of nicotine, tar and carbon monoxide have gone down over the past twenty years. Survey data up to 1992 shows that while the percentage of smokers in the population has gone down, the average weekly cigarette consumption of men who smoke has not changed much over the same period, while that of women who smoke has increased slightly. What implications do you think these data have for future trends in smoking-related disease?

30 In 1991 and 1992, the British Government published papers setting the agenda for improving the overall health of all the people in England. Their first targets were mental illness, cancer, heart disease, HIV/AIDS and trauma (injury). Do you agree that these targets are the right ones? What targets would you choose?

31 In the early part of the twentieth century tuberculosis (TB) killed 75 000 people each year in the UK. There was no effective treatment. In the 1940s a drug, streptomycin, was discovered in the USA which promised to be an effective treatment. The British government bought 50 kg of the drug, enough to treat 200 patients at a total cost of £150,000 (a great deal of money in those days).

Because not many patients could be treated and there was a need to find out just how effective streptomycin was, it was decided to carry out a 'randomized clinical trial'. Sir Austin Bradford Hill, the best statistician of his day, designed the trial. One hundred and seven patients were monitored in hospitals in London, Wales, Scotland and Yorkshire. Streptomycin was given to 55 patients and the other 52 received the only other available treatment, bed rest. A particular patient's treatment was decided at random, by the equivalent of tossing a coin. At the end of 6 months, 14 patients given bed rest had died and 4 had shown a considerable improvement. Of those given streptomycin, only four had died and 28 were much better.

What features of the trial allow you to be confident that streptomycin is an effective treatment for TB?

32 Read the case history about cot death on pages 408–11. Do you think there is good evidence that the campaign to reduce cot deaths worked? Is the evidence the same sort as that collected by Bradford Hill? (See question 31.) In what way would you describe these procedures as scientific?

33 On 17 November 1994, ITV broadcast an edition of *The Cook Report*, in which the investigative reporter, Roger Cook, commissioned research which appeared to show that one cause of cot death is the fire retardant found in cot mattresses. In 1989 Barry Richardson proposed that under damp conditions, such as those caused by urine soaking into the mattress, species of fungi could grow in the mattress and release potentially poisonous gases from the antimony and arsenic in the retardant chemicals. At the time, this hypothesis was regarded as unproven. *The Cook Report* spent £3000 on analytical chemistry in independent laboratories, which showed that mattress samples from homes where cot deaths had occurred and the preserved tissues of babies who had died of cot death had high levels of antimony, compared with tissues preserved from babies who had died of other causes. The programme recommended wrapping cot mattresses in polythene sheeting to prevent the leakage of potentially lethal gases.

The effects of the programme were rapid. Many manufacturers withdrew their cot mattresses with fire retardants from sale and the TV company switchboard was jammed with calls. In the next few days the Government Chief Medical Officer and other scientists poured scorn on the programme, saying its results and conclusions were unscientific and invalid.

Do you agree with the Chief Medical Officer that needless alarm had been raised among parents? Can you suggest the reasons why he claimed the programme was unscientific? What are the potential benefits and dangers of journalists carrying out supposedly scientific investigations?

On 30 November 1994, the government announced that it was starting a fresh inquiry into whether toxic gases were the cause of cot deaths. Why do you think the government's attitude changed within two weeks?

UNIT 8

Communicating information

Dealing with data

Setting standards

A police officer flags down an erratic motorist. Back at the police station, the motorist blows into a breathalyser. There is a positive result. But how can the motorist, the police officer – and the court – be sure that the breathalyser gave a correct reading of the alcohol content of the driver's breath? The accuracy of the breathalyser can be traced back to the National Physical Laboratory, the UK agency responsible for developing and maintaining many of the standards used in industry.

Back at the station

The breathalysers used by police to test the breath of suspected drink-drivers must be checked before and after each use. At the police station, air is bubbled through a mixture of ethanol and water maintained at a constant temperature. This produces a known concentration of ethanol vapour in air, which is then used to check the breathalyser.

The National Physical Laboratory (NPL) has now devised an improved method for checking this **calibration**. They have developed a technique to produce stable gas mixtures of ethanol and air. These standard mixtures have been shown to have an **accuracy** of ± 0.5%, and are stable for at least two years. Police stations will be supplied with cylinders of standard gas mixtures. These are a much more convenient and accurate method of calibration than the old way.

NPL has also developed a 'dynamic breath-simulator', which can emulate the breath-flow and alcohol concentration of a drink-driver. It will be used to measure the accuracy of new types of breathalyser to ensure that they conform to the latest **standards**.

The standard alcohol gas mixtures, which will be produced by commercial firms, can be traced back to the work of NPL. The validity of new designs for breathalysers can also be traced back to NPL, because they will have been tested with the breath-simulator. This 'traceability' means that drivers, police and the courts can have an increasingly high degree of **confidence** in the results of breathalyser tests.

Primary standards

Reliable measurements are vital in an industrial society – in manufacture and commerce, in health and safety. NPL has the task of maintaining a National Measurement System allowing calibrations and tests to be made which are traceable to national standards. The National Measurement System must also be co-ordinated with those of overseas trading partners.

Amongst the many different standards provided by NPL are highly reliable standard mixtures of gases. Individual components might have concentrations of 10% or more, or as low as a few parts per billion. The lab produces primary standard mixtures, which are tested to ensure that they give consistently accurate results. The primary standards are used to establish the concentrations of secondary standard mixtures, which are supplied to industry and to government and other research labs. Some of the uses of standard gas mixtures are shown in Figure 8A1.

Use	Mixture
Measuring gas pollutants from vehicle and aircraft engines	CO, CO_2, NO, hexane and propane in N_2
Flammability measurements	Methane in air
Measuring air pollution	Volatile organic compounds in nitrogen
The quality of urban air	SO_2, NO and NO_2 in air

◀ **Figure 8A1** *Standard gas mixtures and their uses.*

100 percent accurate?

Because of its skill in producing precisely-controlled mixtures of gases, NPL provides gases used in comparing the measurements of other labs around the world. The gases are used in 'round-robin' exercises, in which samples of a standard gas mixture are sent out to about twenty labs around the world. These labs analyse the mixtures and send in their results, to be collated by NPL. This gives a picture of the reliability of the measurements in these other labs – and it is not always a happy picture! Figure 8A2 shows the results from one round robin exercise. One lab found more than seven times the amount of propane than was actually present. This sort of result is likely to arise where the equipment of a lab has become contaminated. This happens especially in labs where a particular gas is regularly being tested in the equipment.

▼ **Figure 8A2** *Results of gas analysis tests from eighteen labs. Each analysed the same mixture of gases. A figure of +100% means that the lab found twice as much of that gas as was actually present. It is noticeable that some labs (e.g. L, N and T) gave results consistently close to actual concentrations of the NPL's standard mixture. Others varied very widely.*

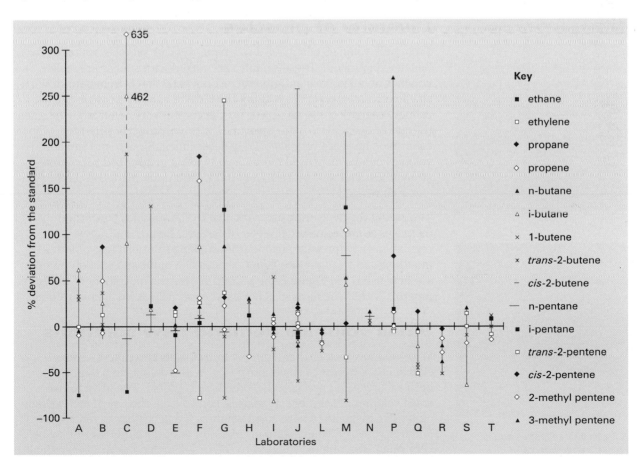

Smaller volumes, higher costs

Scales and balances for measuring mass are found in every laboratory; many of them are complex and expensive devices which can determine very small masses with great accuracy. Chemists and biologists also need to measure out volumes of solution consistently and accurately. Their labs are always well equipped with glassware for measuring volumes, such as measuring cylinders, volumetric flasks, burettes and, above all, pipettes – tubes of various shapes, sizes and types for dispensing pre-determined volumes of solution.

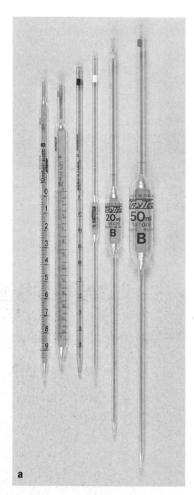

a

b

▲ **Figure 8A3** *a Pipettes and b pipette attachments.*

Mass and volume

Until recently there was a considerable difference in the cost of mass-determining analytical balances compared to volume-measuring glassware. Analysis in chemistry, biochemistry and physiology depends on making up **primary standards** (see page 24) by accurately weighing quantities of pure chemical and dissolving them in a known volume of solvent. These standards are often made up in relatively large volumes ($100 \, cm^3$ or $1 \, dm^3$, for instance), although the mass of chemical dissolved is often small, perhaps only g, mg or even μg quantities. Accurate measurement of these very small masses, within a small degree of error (see pages 428–9), needs sophisticated pieces of machinery.

Accurate determination of volumes greater than $100 \, cm^3$ can be done with relatively cheap glassware. The difficulty in seeing precisely where the meniscus of a fluid volume lines up with a calibration mark produces only small errors in relatively large volumes.

Diversity of pipettes

From bulk volumes of standard solutions, smaller samples are taken for bench experiments. These samples are mixed with similar or smaller volumes of unknown solutions whose concentration is to be found. With smaller volumes, errors in reading the level of a fluid meniscus against a calibration mark are greater. For very accurate work, even large volumes ($20 \, cm^3$ or even $50 \, cm^3$) are measured with **volumetric pipettes**, whose calibration lines are very accurately determined. Similar and smaller volumes can be dispensed more cheaply using **graduated pipettes**, straight glass tubes with relatively thick calibration marks on them (see Figure 8A3a).

The size of the measuring error relative to the volumes concerned increases as the volume delivered decreases. Health and safety regulations now prevent anyone from sucking solutions into pipettes by mouth. A variety of pipette filling devices like bulbs and suction pumps are now used (see Figure 8A3b). Control over the movement of fluids in pipettes with these devices is not easy, especially at small fluid volumes.

Small volumes demand new solutions

With volumes greater than $1 \, cm^3$, standard laboratory pipettes are sufficiently accurate for most purposes. With volumes less than this, both accuracy and precision become unacceptable. The drive to use small volumes of solutions in analysis comes from the use of increasingly expensive reagents (where small volumes are necessary to reduce costs) and from biology, where volumes of blood or other fluids taken may be very small. The original solution to the problem of measuring very small blood volumes used expensively calibrated, thick-walled bulb pipettes with attached suction tubes. These were not easy to use. Accurate and consistent sample dispensing is difficult.

Drawing fluids directly into narrower and narrower glass tubes has not proved the best solution to the problem of measuring small volumes. Modern biomedical and analytical chemical work often involves large numbers of small-volume fluid samples, accurately and consistently dispensed. Pipette design and cost have changed radically to allow this to take place.

Pipettes for small volumes, micropipettes, have been replaced by **pipettors**, which are large and expensive devices (see Figure 8A4). The barrel of the dispenser contains complex apparatus for providing a wide, and continuously varying, range of small volumes at great accuracy. These barrel and piston chambers never contain fluid. Pipettors have disposable plastic **pipette tips** fitted to their working ends. Piston suction draws a known fluid volume into the tip. The piston is then used to dispense the fluid from the tip. The tips are disposable and discarded when fresh solutions are used. The pipettors never get wet and therefore never need washing. Nowadays, a single pipettor can be used with multiple tips, to measure accurate micro-volumes of fluid into several tubes at once (a process which can now be automated for large scale and fast working micro-analysis).

Measuring small volumes accurately has changed the type of equipment used, increased its complexity and pushed up the price. Measuring small volumes is still cheaper than measuring small masses, but the cost difference between them is decreasing all the time.

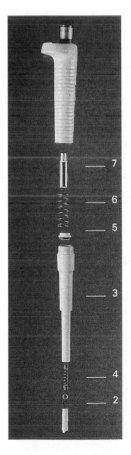

▼ **Figure 8A4** *A pipettor, pipette tips and a multichannel pipettor.*

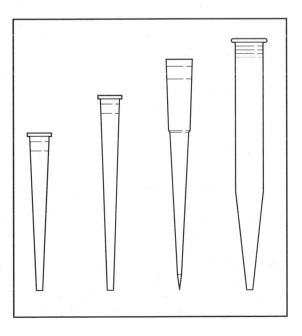

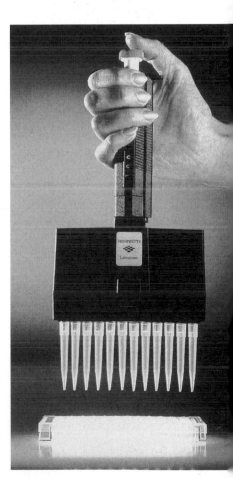

Cutting down on errors

Almost every measurement has some degree of error or uncertainty in it. This comes from the technique used to make the measurement. Understanding how errors arise can help scientists to develop strategies for reducing them.

Making judgments

Which instrument to use? The choice of a suitable measuring instrument is a matter of judgment. The length of a piece of wire must be measured when determining resistivity. An appropriate choice for this might be a metre rule. The wire shown in Figure 8A5 is about 256 mm long. It would be wrong to say that its length is precisely 256 mm; no measuring instrument could give such perfect precision. However, if the result is quoted with an indication of the **error**, then this will give anyone looking at the result an idea of the degree of precision to which the measurement was made.

▶ **Figure 8A5** *How long is a piece of wire?*

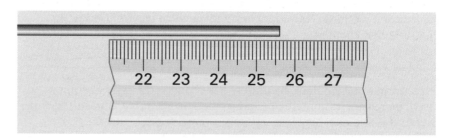

The metre rule in Figure 8A5 can be read to the nearest 1 mm (or possibly 0.5 mm). Hence the result can be given as:

length of wire = (256 ± 1) mm

To improve on this, a different measuring instrument would have to be used. A travelling microscope can measure lengths; the end of the wire being measured can be seen magnified by the microscope, and this improves the precision of the measurement. The scale incorporates a vernier device (see R6 in the Reference section), and the length can be measured to within 0.1 mm.

To measure the thickness of the wire, a metre rule would be inappropriate. A micrometer screw gauge can measure to within 0.01 mm, because this is the size of the finest scale divisions (see R6 in the Reference section).

There are many other measuring instruments for which the error can be judged in this way, for example, **analogue** ammeters and voltmeters, in which a needle moves across a scale. The reading can usually be made to the nearest whole or half scale-division.

For a **digital** meter, the error is usually assumed to be ± 1 (or ± 0.5) in the final digit of the display. So when a digital voltmeter, which shows readings to two decimal places, displays a reading of 1.49 V, this should be quoted as:

voltage = (1.49 ± 0.01) V

Sometimes, the measurement will be slightly too high, and sometimes slightly too low. That is why the error is quoted as ±, indicating that there is a range of uncertainty on either side of the quoted result. The true result is believed to lie within this range.

Repeat measurements

In finding the rate of flow of water in a channel, repeat measurements are needed. This is because the flow may vary, and because the method of measurement itself may be imprecise. Some results are shown in Figure 8A6.

These results are scattered randomly about their mean value, $182\,m^3min^{-1}$. The greatest differences are +5 and –8. The average of these is 6.5; usually the error would be quoted as about two-thirds of this, that is ± 4.

Measurements /m³	184	180	186	181	174	187
Mean value /m³	182 ± 4					

◀ **Figure 8A6** *Six measurements of the volume of water flowing in a channel in 1 minute.*

Random and systematic

Scientists always hope that their results will be **reproducible**. If they, or someone else, repeats the experiment, the results should be the same. However, it is very unlikely that exactly the same results will be found. The equipment and other conditions will not be precisely the same, so the results will vary slightly.

This means that there is a degree of **random error** in the results. Sometimes a reading is a little higher, sometimes a little lower. For example, when measuring lengths using a metre rule, sometimes the nearest scale division will be above the actual length, and sometimes below. If the experimenter is making unbiased judgments, roughly half of the measurements would be expected to be too high, and half too low.

The experimenter in Figure 8A7 is introducing error into the results in a different way. Because he is looking at the reading on the burette from an angle above the horizontal, the value he records is too high. If he always works like this, his results will be consistently too high. This is an example of a **systematic error**. It can be corrected by taking the reading while looking horizontally at the meniscus.

> Note that errors are usually only quoted to one or two significant figures. They are not precise quantities; they are an indication of the appropriate degree of confidence in the results, based on an evaluation of the precision of the techniques and equipment used.

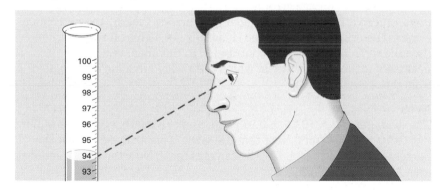

◀ **Figure 8A7** *Introducing a systematic error into a measurement of volume.*

A voltmeter which is incorrectly zeroed (so that all readings are too high or too low) will introduce a systematic error into voltage measurements. So will a voltmeter which has been incorrectly calibrated. It may be possible to overcome this by applying a correction factor to the results. In general:

- random errors can be **reduced** by using an instrument which gives measurements to a higher degree of precision, or by making multiple measurements;

- systematic errors can reduced or **eliminated** by using better equipment or improved techniques.

Errors and more errors

In many situations, several different quantities are measured and their values contribute to the value of a final quantity – the Young modulus of a metal, for example. The error in each quantity contributes to the overall error in the Young modulus. But how can the final error be found?

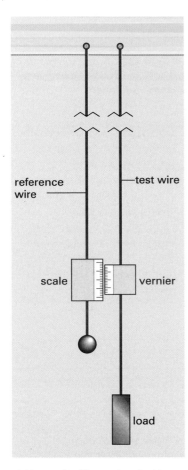

▲ **Figure 8A8** *Measuring the Young modulus of a metal wire.*

Percentage error

The Young modulus of a material is a measure of its stiffness (see page 70). One way to find the Young modulus of steel involves hanging a load on the end of a steel wire and measuring the extension (see Figure 8A8). Figure 8A9 shows some typical results, where only one value of load has been used.

Quantity	Measured by ...	Value ± error	Percentage error
Original length	Metre rule	(2.051 ± 0.001) m	± 0.05
Diameter	Micrometer	(0.20 ± 0.01) mm	± 5.0
Extension	Vernier scale	(15.1 ± 0.1) mm	± 0.7
Load	Balance	(49 ± 1) N	± 2.0

▲ **Figure 8A9** *Results and errors in determining the Young modulus of steel.*

In the table, the third column includes the **absolute error** in each quantity. In order to compare the errors in the different quantities, the **percentage error** in each has been calculated and is shown in the last column:

$$\text{percentage error} = \frac{\text{absolute error}}{\text{value of quantity}} \times 100\%$$

Because the percentage error is a ratio of similar quantities, it has no units, and so it is possible to compare the errors. Clearly, the percentage error in the original (unstretched) length is not significant compared to the others. To find how each contributes to the final result, it is necessary to look at the way in which the Young modulus is calculated from these figures.

Area

The diameter is $d = (0.20 \pm 0.01)$ mm, and halving this gives the radius $r = (0.10 \pm 0.005)$ mm. Note that the error is also halved, so that the percentage error in r is ± 5%, the same as for d. Now the cross-sectional area A is calculated using πr^2:

$$A = \pi r^2 = 3.142 \times (0.10\,\text{mm})^2 = 3.14 \times 10^{-8}\,\text{m}^2$$

Because the radius is squared, it contributes twice to the error in A. Therefore the percentage error in A is ± 10%.

Young modulus

Now the Young modulus Y can be calculated:

$$\text{Young modulus} = \frac{\text{original length} \times \text{load}}{\text{area} \times \text{extension}}$$

$$= \frac{2.051\,\text{m} \times 49\,\text{N}}{3.14 \times 10^{-8}\,\text{m}^2 \times 15.1 \times 10^{-3}\,\text{m}} = 212 \times 10^9\,\text{N}\,\text{m}^{-2}$$

The error in each of the four quantities contributes to the error in Y. The percentage errors must be added together.

Percentage error in $Y = \pm (10\% + 2\% + 0.7\% + 0.05\%) = \pm 12.75\%$

Significant figures

Considering these results, it makes no sense to quote the final result to three significant figures and the error to four. A percentage error is usually quoted to one or at most two significant figures; in this case, the value should be rounded off to $\pm 13\%$. The value of Y should be correspondingly rounded off:

Young modulus of steel $Y = 210 \times 10^9\,\text{N}\,\text{m}^{-2} \pm 13\%$

Reducing errors

It is worth examining the contributions of individual errors to the final result. The dominant error in this experiment is in the measurement of the diameter of the wire ($\pm 5\%$) and because this is squared it contributes 10% to the overall error. The error in the measurement of the load is the only other important contribution. (At first sight, it might have seemed that the use of a metre rule to measure the length of the wire was a poor choice; in fact, analysis of the errors shows that this is the smallest contribution to the overall error. A metre rule is entirely appropriate in the circumstances.)

This gives an idea of how the precision of the experiment might be improved. A better way of measuring the diameter of the wire should be found, to reduce the overall error.

Rules for combining errors

To find the **compound error**, when several errors contribute to the error in a quantity:

- quantities <u>added or</u> subtracted: take the absolute errors a and b and calculate $\sqrt{a^2 + b^2}$
- quantities multiplied or divided: take the percentage errors and add them
- a quantity squared (or to another power): take the percentage error and double it (multiply by the power).

Over and over again

An important technique for improving the precision of data is simply to make multiple repeat measurements. This is particularly valuable for reducing the effect of random errors in data. A simple statistical analysis then allows the mean and standard deviation to be calculated, so that anyone reading the results can appreciate the degree of variation in the data.

Variability

Most measurements have a degree of variability in them – if repeat measurements are made, the answers will be slightly different. There are a variety of reasons why this may be so.

▶ **Figure 8A10** *Some factors producing random variability in data.*

Quantity	Reason for variability
Volume of acid used in titration	End-point of titration may be a matter of judgment
Strength of polymer fibres	Composition and conditions of manufacture may vary
Yield of alcohol from fermentation	Starting materials and conditions of fermentation may vary
Crop yield from wheat	Genetic variability in wheat, and variation in growing conditions
Resistance of wire	Calibration of meters may vary

The effect of this is to produce a degree of uncertainty (an error) in the final result, and this needs to be reported in some way to anyone who is likely to make use of the data. To find out the degree of variability in the data, it is necessary to make repeat measurements; the more, the better.

Repeat measurements

Figure 8A11 shows the results of a titration; the volume of acid required to neutralize a solution has been found 21 times. There are slight variations in the results; these may be because of variability in the experimenter's judgment of the end-point, or in the volume of alkali used, or some other condition.

▶ **Figure 8A11** *Results from a titration.*

Trial	Volume /cm^3	Trial	Volume /cm^3	Trial	Volume /cm^3
1	8.61	8	8.60	15	8.75
2	8.63	9	8.61	16	8.62
3	8.62	10	8.65	17	8.62
4	8.64	11	8.59	18	8.63
5	8.62	12	8.66	19	8.64
6	8.63	13	8.62	20	8.60
7	8.62	14	8.61	21	8.63

At this point, it is sensible to eliminate **anomalous results**. Twenty of the results fall in the range $8.59\,cm^3$ to $8.66\,cm^3$; trial 15 gave a result which is well outside this range, and this result should therefore be discarded.

One way to show the variation in this data is to construct a frequency chart of the results (Figure 8A12) and use it to plot a **frequency histogram** (Figure 8A13). These show that the most frequent result (the **mode**) is $8.62\,cm^3$. The histogram gives a good visual indication of the variability in the results. However, a statistical analysis is needed in order to produce a numerical value for the average volume and its error.

Mean and standard deviation

A calculator or computer program can be used to calculate the mean value $\bar{x}$ and the standard deviation σ of the data. With the calculator in statistics mode, the twenty values of volume are input using the x key. The values of $\bar{x}$ and σ can then be read out (both rounded off to three decimal places):

$$\bar{x} = 8.623\,cm^3 \qquad \sigma = 0.017\,cm^3$$

The **mean value** is simply the arithmetic average, found by adding the 20 results and dividing by 20. The **standard deviation** gives an indication of the extent to which the results are spread around the mean. In this case, most of the results fall within $\pm 0.017\,cm^3$ of the mean value. If the results had been more scattered, σ would have been greater.

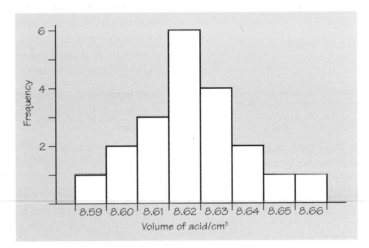

Volume/cm³	Counts	Frequency
8.59	I	1
8.60	I I	2
8.61	I I I	3
8.62	◁⃦⃦I	6
8.63	I I I I	4
8.64	I I	2
8.65	I	1
8.66	I	1

▲ **Figure 8A12** *Frequency chart for the data in Figure 8A11.*

▲ **Figure 8A13** *Frequency histogram for the data in Figure 8A11.*

Confidence intervals

The standard deviation can be used to give a value for the error in the value of volume. The graph (Figure 8A14) shows the sort of distribution of results which would have been expected if a very large number of repeat measurements had been made. The frequency histogram (Figure 8A13) is an approximation to this. It is not possible to be sure that the true mean value for the volume of acid is precisely $8.623\,cm^3$; however, it can be said that the true value is probably within *two* standard deviations of this value.

A full analysis shows that, in a situation like this, the true value has a 95% probability of lying within $\pm 1.96\sigma$ of $\bar{x}$. There is a small chance (5%) that it lies above or below this range, but this range or **confidence interval** can be used to give a figure for the error in the volume.

Volume of acid = $(8.623 \pm 0.033)\,cm^3$

Note that, although the individual values of volume were measured to two decimal places, the final result is deduced from twenty values, and it is reasonable to give both the value and the error to three decimal places.

To obtain a more precise answer, more measurements would be needed. The mean value would then be closer to the true value and the standard deviation would be smaller, so the error would be smaller. In principle, if four times as many results are collected, the error is halved.

▼ **Figure 8A14** *Distribution graph for a large number of results spread randomly about the mean value; this curve is known as a **normal distribution**.*

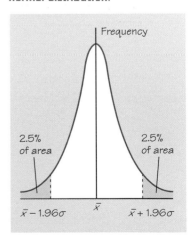

Electronic data

In many laboratories, where research and testing are carried out, as well as on production lines, computers have replaced people as the collectors, recorders and processors of data. Sensors are available which can detect many different varying quantities, and which can provide the necessary voltages for the computer.

Sensors

Any **sensor** must produce a voltage which changes as its input changes. The input may be any one of a great number of different factors: temperature, light, position, pressure, oxygen concentration, humidity, pH, voltage, current, radiation, sound ....

In addition, an on–off output may be provided by a variety of switches – push, magnetic, electromagnetic relay and so on.

A sensor provides a voltage which may be supplied to a **datalogger**, or direct to a computer. A datalogger is itself a small computer, designed to capture and store data from sensors. It may process the data itself, or pass it on to a computer which is likely to have more capacity for manipulating the data.

Software is the program which determines how the data is collected, processed and displayed.

▶ **Figure 8A15** *The general 'architecture' of a data collecting system. Sensors are interchangeable, as they all give a voltage output in an appropriate range, usually up to 1 V.*

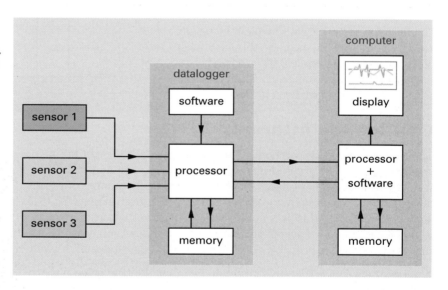

More and better data

A computer-based data collection system can be an improvement on the traditional human recorder – see Figure 8A16. There are some disadvantages, though. A human observer may notice features that are not being recorded by the computer system – perhaps a solution changes colour, when only its pH and temperature are being recorded. And care is necessary to ensure that any automatic system is correctly set up. All components must be correctly calibrated and operating within their correct ranges.

Feature	Comment
Speed of collection	Computers can collect thousands of pieces of data each second, far faster than any person.
Memory	Large quantities of data can be stored, either in the computer's memory or on disc.
Precision	Electronic sensors can be calibrated accurately to reduce errors in data.
Sensitivity	Electronic sensors can detect very small changes which are then amplified.
Multiple inputs	Several different quantities can be monitored simultaneously.
Endurance	A computer system can operate over long periods of time, day and night.
Fieldwork	A computer system can work in many different environments, including places where people cannot go, e.g. space.
Data handling	Large amounts of data can be manipulated by the system, with complex statistical calculations possible.
Speed of display	The data can be manipulated and displayed as the experiment proceeds (in 'real time').

▼ Figure 8A17 *In a sports physiology lab like this one where French Olympic athletes train, several different specialized sensors are at work, monitoring an athlete in training. They supply data on heart and breathing rates, oxygen uptake, rate of working and so on.*

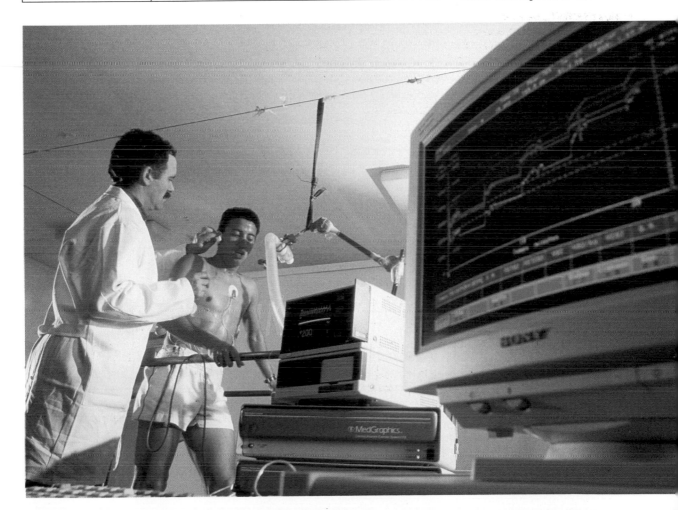

Data display

Scientists make measurements with a purpose. The message of their work is in the data. To show up the meaning contained in their data, they need to choose the best way in which to display it. Tables, graphs and charts can all help to convey the significance of the data.

Salt and seedlings

Where salt is used for de-icing wintry roads, a ribbon of salty soil develops by the roadside. Most plants cannot tolerate the high levels of salinity which develop, but some specialized plants (halophytes) have spread inland from the sea along these corridors.

This is an example of a more general problem. Significant areas of farmland throughout the world are affected by salinity, either because of tidal inundation, or because of excessive extraction of fresh water from groundwater supplies. Sea water floods in underground and contaminates the soil.

Elizabeth Whitaker, a student at Long Road Sixth Form College in Cambridge, chose to study the effect of salt on ryegrass. She knew that this grass, *Lolium perenne*, was salt tolerant, but she wanted to know just how much salt would affect the germination and growth of ryegrass seedlings. She looked at the effect of different concentrations of salt on the germination of seeds (Figure 8A18), and the effect of salt in the nutrient solution on the growth of the roots of seedlings (Figure 8A19).

Elizabeth chose to show her results in the form of **histograms**. These show clearly the pattern of the effect of increasing salt concentrations. Histograms are appropriate here because there was no expectation that the results would show a clear mathematical relationship between the variables.

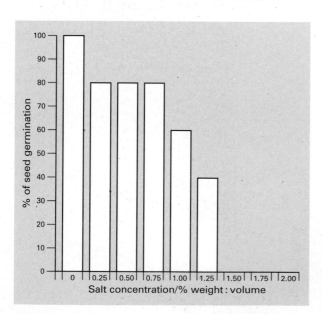

▲ **Figure 8A18** *Ryegrass germination in different salt concentrations. The histogram suggests that any salt concentration may inhibit successful germination; concentrations of 1.5% w/v or higher prevent all germination.*

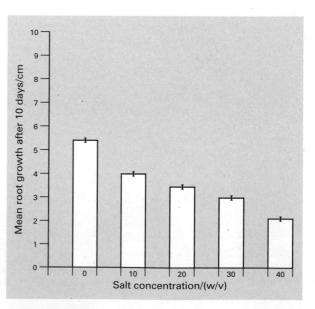

▲ **Figure 8A19** *Ryegrass root growth with different salt concentrations. The error bars show the error in the mean root growth, found by measuring the roots of seedlings.*

Into the darkness

Students at a college in Barcelona investigated some fascinating beetles. Larvae of the *Tenebrio* beetle respond to light; they tend to move away from it. In their study, they placed a larva at the centre of a circle, with two lights nearby. The larva tended to move away from the light, and the students recorded which sector of the circle the larva moved out along.

The results of this experiment were published in three forms: as a table (Figure 8A20a), as a histogram (Figure 8A20b) and as a **circular histogram** (Figure 8A20c). The table is important to show the precise data which the students obtained. In the circular histogram, the length of the bar represents the number of larvae leaving the circle in that sector. This shows in a very dramatic way how the larvae tended to move directly away from the source of light. It also gives an indication of the spread of the data; on average, the larvae moved directly away from the light, but some moved slightly to the left, others slightly to the right.

Sector	Test 1	Test 2
1	2	2
2	0	0
3	0	0
4	0	0
5	0	0
6	0	1
7	0	0
8	0	1
9	1	0
10	0	1
11	1	3
12	0	2
13	3	3
14	2	4
15	1	6
16	7	5
17	7	14
18	12	28
19	14	25
20	20	33
21	18	30
22	25	31
23	35	31
24	32	20
25	29	13
26	25	9
27	24	1
28	19	1
29	10	0
30	7	4
31	7	1
32	1	3
33	3	2
34	1	1
35	0	4
36	0	0
Total	306	279

▲ **Figure 8A20 a** *Data from the study of the response of* Tenebrio *beetle larvae to light. In Test 1, a single 100 W lamp was positioned at sector 5; in Test 2, an additional 40 W lamp was positioned at sector 32.*

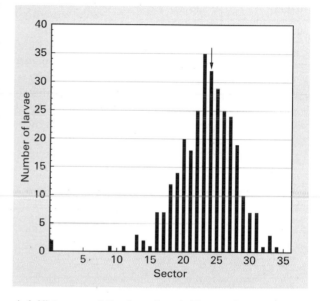

▲ *b Histogram of the data given in Figure 8A20a for Test 1.*

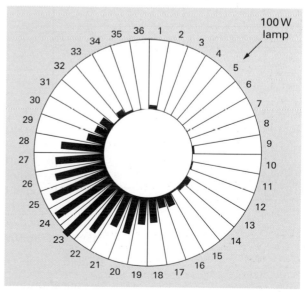

▶ *c Circular histogram for the same data. The larva is positioned heading 'north' towards sector 1.*

Going for graphs

Graphs can show the pattern in data. They can be used to deduce values of quantities by interpolation or extrapolation. And they can be used to deduce the mathematical relationship between quantities, so that the final result of an investigation can be presented as an equation.

Calibration curve

Rachel Hunt is a pharmacy student. She has been learning how to find the concentration of the hormone adrenaline by colorimetry. Adrenaline is colourless, but it forms a coloured complex with iron(II) ions in the presence of citrate ions. Here are her instructions for carrying out the determination.

- Dilute sample by taking $1\,cm^3$ and making it up to $200\,cm^3$ with water.
- Make up a set of standards as follows: mix $10\,cm^3$ of each standard solution with $0.25\,cm^3$ of a solution containing iron(II) ions and citrate ions.
- Treat the diluted test sample in the same way.
- Set the spectrophotometer to $540\,nm$ – a wavelength which is strongly absorbed by the coloured complex.
- Use a blank containing water to zero the instrument.
- Measure the absorbance for each standard and for the test sample (the unknown).

Concentration /% w/v	Absorbance (arbitrary units)	
blank (0.000)	0.000	0.000
0.002	0.105	0.110
0.004	0.192	0.187
0.006	0.395	0.305
0.010	0.490	0.480
unknown	0.269	0.265

▲ **Figure 8A21** *Rachel's results for the adrenaline determination. Notice that she made repeat measurements of each reading.*

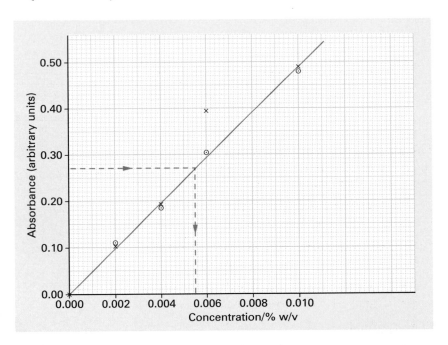

▶ **Figure 8A22** *Graph of Rachel's results.*

The graph (Figure 8A22) shows that one point is anomalous, and this was ignored when the line was drawn. Rachel was able to read off the concentration of the diluted sample; finding the value at an intermediate point between the data points is called **interpolation**. (If the graph had to be extended beyond the experimental data, the process would be called **extrapolation**.)

Diluted sample concentration = 0.00545% w/v

So concentration of undiluted solution = $200 \times 0.00545 = 1.09\%$

Degrading drugs

Rachel has also been studying the way in which pharmaceutical products tend to degrade while they are stored. To find the 'shelf life' of a product, it has to be stored for a period of months, and the concentration of its active ingredient determined at regular intervals. Its shelf life is the time for which it can be stored until the concentration of the active ingredient has dropped by 10%.

Figure 8A23 shows how the concentration C of a particular drug declined over a period of several months. The graph is a straight line, showing that degradation is a zero order process (see page 327).

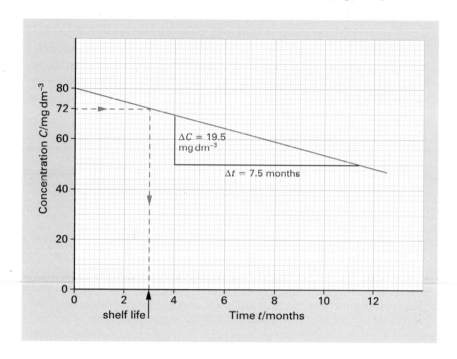

◀ **Figure 8A23** *A graph showing the degradation of a pharmaceutical drug over time.*

A zero order process can be represented by an equation relating concentration C to time t. This equation can be compared with the equation of a straight line.

$C - C_0 - kt$ (equation of degradation process)
$y = c + mx$ (equation of straight line)

Comparing these equations shows that, by plotting concentration C on the y-axis and time t on the x-axis, we can find:

c = intercept on y-axis = C_0 = initial concentration (when time $t = 0$)
$-m$ = $-$gradient = k = zero order rate constant

From the graph:

Initial concentration $C_0 = 80\,\text{mg}\,\text{dm}^{-3}$

Rate constant = $k = \dfrac{\Delta C}{\Delta t} = \dfrac{19.5\,\text{mg}\,\text{dm}^{-3}}{7.5\,\text{months}} = 2.6\,\text{mg}\,\text{dm}^{-3}\,\text{month}^{-1}$

Interpolation also allows the shelf life to be determined; its value is 3.0 months.

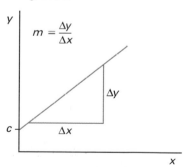

▼ **Figure 8A24** *Graph of a straight line.*

In the equation of a straight line (Figure 8A24):
$y = mx + c$
m is the gradient, and c is the intercept on the y-axis.

Straight lines are best

When a graph is plotted to show the relationship between two quantities, it is often curved. This shows that they are not related in a linear (straight line) way. By choosing the appropriate quantities to plot on the graph axes, a straight line can often be achieved, and this allows an equation relating the quantities to be deduced. Because experimental data has errors, it is often necessary to draw a best straight line; there are mathematical techniques to help with this.

Impact graph

In a laboratory version of an impact test (such as that shown on page 252), a model car is crashed at different speeds into a barrier. A cardboard tube mounted on the front of the car acts as a crumple zone. The length of cardboard which is crushed in the impact is measured for different impact speeds. The results from a series of test-runs are shown in the table, Figure 8A25.

▶ **Figure 8A25** *Crumple zone test results; the first two columns show the experimental data; the third and fourth columns are calculated from the first two.*

Speed v /ms^{-1}	Length l /cm	v^2 /m^{2}s^{-2}	v^2/l /m^{2}s^{-2}cm^{-1}
1.0	2.9	1.0	0.69
2.0	6.1	4.0	0.66
3.0	13.7	9.0	0.66
4.0	22.0	16.0	0.73
5.0	35.8	25.0	0.70

These results are shown as graphs in Figure 8A26. The first graph is simply a graph of length l of cardboard crumpled against speed of impact v. This graph is clearly curved, indicating that l is not proportional to v.

The second graph, of l against v^2, has been drawn to achieve a straight line. Since the data gives a good straight line which passes through the origin, it follows that l is proportional to v^2, and so

$$l = \text{const} \times v^2 \qquad \text{or } l = kv^2$$

In this case, the graph has allowed the relationship between the variables to be deduced. Now the experimenters might go on to try to explain why the relationship has this form. Alternatively, they might have predicted the relationship. Since the kinetic energy of the car is $\frac{1}{2}mv^2$, the experimenters might have predicted that the amount of damage would be proportional to v^2. The graph is then a test of their prediction.

Table calculations

It was possible to guess the relationship between l and v from the shape of the curved graph Figure 8A26a. It often helps to test this using the data in the form of a table. In Figure 8A25, values of v^2 have been calculated in column 3, and v^2/l in column 4. Since the figures in column 4 are virtually constant, it follows that v^2/l is constant.

Choosing axes

Where a relationship between two quantities is known or suspected, the relationship can be used to decide which quantities should be plotted on the x- and y-axes of a graph. This is done by comparing the relationship

▼ **Figure 8A26** *Two graphs representing the data in Figure 8A25.*

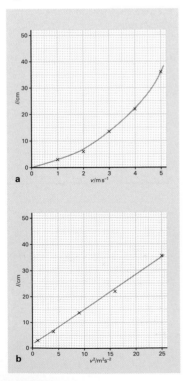

with the equation of a straight line. For example, if the resistance R of a length of wire is thought to be inversely proportional to the square of its diameter d:

$$R = k \times \frac{1}{d^2} \quad \text{(where k is a constant)}$$

$$y = m \times x + c$$

In this case, a graph of R (on the y-axis) against $1/d^2$ (on the x-axis) should be a straight line. Since the intercept $c = 0$, it should pass through the origin.

The best fit

If experimental data gives a very good straight line graph, it is easy to deduce the gradient and intercept. However, when there is scatter in the data, it is necessary to draw a best straight line. In Figure 8A27, the best straight line has been drawn with the help of a calculator. The data points are keyed into the calculator, and it uses a program (linear regression or least squares fit) to deduce the straight line which most closely fits the data.

With a **graphics calculator**, it is possible to display the graph on the screen. With simpler calculators, the values of m and c for the best straight line are given. The program also gives a value for r, a number which indicates how good a fit to the data has been achieved. The closer r is to 1, the better the fit.

Warning! Problems can arise when using a calculator to deduce the best fit to data. Figure 8A28 shows two examples.

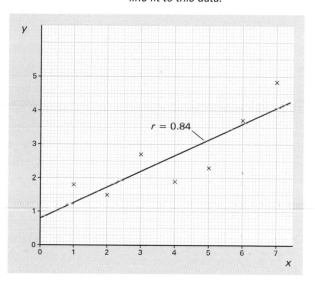

▼ **Figure 8A27** *A calculator has been used to find the best straight line fit to this data.*

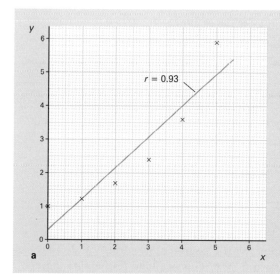

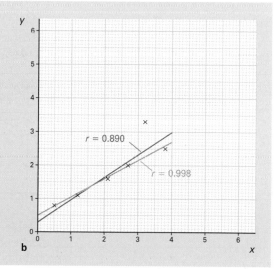

▲ **Figure 8A28 a** *This data does not fit a straight line well. A calculator has been used to draw the best straight line, but the data points clearly lie on a curve. **b** One data point is anomalous, but the calculator cannot be expected to know that (red line). The line changes significantly when the anomalous point is omitted (green line).*

Significant findings

Sometimes the results of an experiment are unambiguous. At other times, the experimenter may be uncertain just what conclusion can be safely drawn from a set of results. Caution is well-advised – jumping to conclusions on the basis of limited data can be a trap for the unwary. Statistical tests can be applied to data to see whether it is possible to have confidence in one's conclusions.

Testing a hypothesis

Some students investigated the effect of sulphur dioxide (SO_2) gas on the germination and growth of cress seedlings. They suspected that SO_2, which is found in acid rain, would affect both the germination and the growth of the cress. They tested 500 cress seeds, half in an atmosphere of SO_2 and half in uncontaminated air, as a control. Here are their results:

> number germinating in presence of SO_2 = 180
> number germinating in absence of SO_2 = 202
> (total number germinating = 382).

It seemed that there was clear evidence of better germination without the SO_2. But could they be sure that the gas was really having an effect? Could the difference in results be simply a chance variation?

To investigate this question in an unambiguous way, it is appropriate to use the **chi-squared statistical test**. It is simplest to start by establishing a hypothesis which is to be tested. In this case, the hypothesis is:

> The presence of SO_2 has no effect on the germination rate.

This is called a **null hypothesis**, since it suggests no effect. The students hoped to find that the hypothesis was wrong. If this hypothesis was correct, the students might have expected to find the following results:

> number germinating in presence of SO_2 = 191
> number germinating in absence of SO_2 = 191
> (total number germinating = 382, as before).

The statistic χ^2 (chi-squared) is calculated from the observed (O) and expected (E) values as shown in Figure 8A29.

▶ **Figure 8A29** *Calculating* χ^2.

O	E	$(O - E)^2$	$(O - E)^2 / E$
180	191	$11^2 = 121$	0.63
202	191	$11^2 = 121$	0.63
			total = χ^2 = 1.26

Now a table of values of χ^2 has to be read to find out whether this is significant or not. From tables (with 1 degree of freedom), $\chi^2 = 1.26$ has a probability p between 50% and 20%. This is a high probability, and so the null hypothesis is probably true. In other words, the experimental results do not show that the SO_2 had any significant effect on the germination of the seedlings.

A second test

The students went on to investigate the effect of SO_2 on the growth of their seedlings. They grew 200 seedlings in an atmosphere of SO_2 and a control of 200 in uncontaminated air. After seven days, they compared the lengths of pairs of seedlings, one from each batch, to see which one was the longer. Here are their results:

number of cases with longer seedlings grown in presence of SO_2 = 38
number of cases with longer seedlings grown in absence of SO_2 = 162
(total number of pairs of seedlings = 200).

The new null hypothesis to be tested is:

The presence of SO_2 has no effect on the growth of cress seedlings.

Figure 8A30 shows the calculation of χ^2.

O	E	$(O - E)^2$	$(O - E)^2 / E$
38	100	$62^2 = 3844$	38.4
162	100	$62^2 = 3844$	38.4
			total = χ^2 = 76.8

◄ **Figure 8A30** *Calculating χ^2 for the second hypothesis.*

In this case, the value of χ^2 has a probability p which is very low (much lower than 1%) and so the hypothesis is almost certainly false. Hence the students' results show that SO_2 does indeed have an effect on the growth of cress seedlings.

Using the chi-squared test

1 Establish the hypothesis which is to be tested.
2 Use the hypothesis to determine the expected results (E).
3 Compare the expected results with the observed results (O) by calculating χ^2:

   χ^2 = sum of values of $(O - E)^2 / E$

4 Use tables of χ^2 values to deduce probability p.
5 Interpret probability p.

Where have all the stoneworts gone?

Katie Hargreaves, a seventeen-year-old GNVQ Science student, spent a month of her summer vacation working in the Botany Department of The Natural History Museum in London, funded by the Nuffield Science Bursary Scheme. Her project was to assess data on plant specimens and to put information on to a computer database. Here she describes what she did, and why.

Stonewort specimens

'The specimens I was working on were dried and pressed specimens of stoneworts, stored in files in the Herbarium. Some were collected by 19th century European botanists and others were collected more recently. Stoneworts are a family of green algae that grow in fresh water. Some species of stonewort are threatened because of increasing water pollution, especially from nitrates and phosphates in sewage and fertilizers. Others are more resistant to pollution. Mapping the changing patterns of distribution of stonewort species is an important step in the conservation of these plants.

'All the specimens stored at The Natural History Museum have labels, giving information such as the genus and species of plant, the collector's name, the place where the plant was found and the date collected (see Figure 8A32). Not all the labels give all the data, and part of my task was to track down information not given on the labels.'

▼ **Figure 8A31** *Katie Hargreaves at work on the stonewort database in The Natural History Museum, London.*

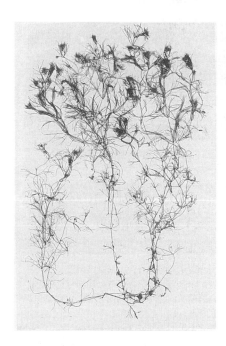

① Name of plant
② Population centre
③ Date of collection
④ Habitat data (not entered on screen)
⑤ Collector

◀ **Figure 8A32** *Specimen of a stonewort from the Herbarium collection, together with its label. This information had to be entered into the computer database.*

1 Name of plant
2 Population centre
3 Date of collection
4 Habitat data (not entered on screen)
5 Collector

Into the database

'My first challenge was to decipher the handwriting on the labels. Then I put an exact copy of the information on the label into the database (see Figure 8A33). This means that if somebody using the database questions the entry, they can refer to the copy of the label, without having to look at the original specimen in the Museum.

'Once the copy of the label was in the database, I had to interpret the information on that label and input data that I'd found from it. For instance, the scientific name of the plant might have changed since the label was written, so I would check the up-to-date name in a source reference book. I would also enter information about where the plant was found. Finding many of the locations was like playing a guessing game, especially when the letters of mis-spelt place names on the plant label were barely readable.

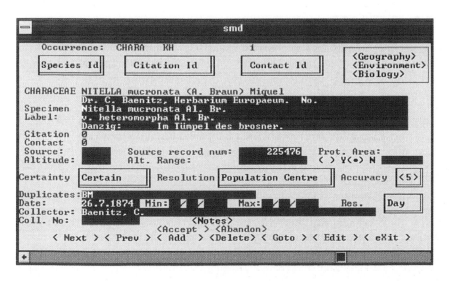

◀ **Figure 8A33** *Inside the database: the main screen for a specimen record.*

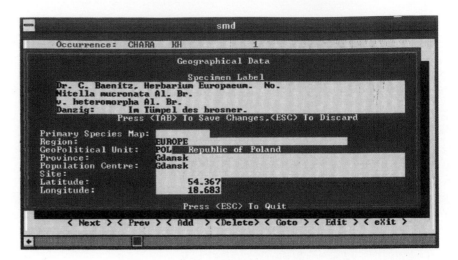

▶ **Figure 8A34** *The geography sub-screen for the specimen shown in Figure 8A32.*

'Sifting through the atlases and gazetteers in the Museum Library Map Room felt like detective work. I would look in an atlas and find the place on the map where the plant was found, for example, a tiny stream in the Jura mountains or a fountain in the palace of Salem. I would make a note of the exact grid reference, and enter the longitude and latitude co-ordinates into the database. Then I would look up the nearest population centre and enter that.

'I also entered information about how certain I was that the location co-ordinates I had found were correct; this estimate of certainty ranges from certain, through probable and possible, to long shot.

'I entered information about "resolution", or how specific the information is about the location, for example, whether the label gives information about the region, the country, the population centre or the exact centre where the specimen was found.

'Then I estimated how accurate the latitude and longitude co-ordinates were – within 20 km, within 5 km, and so on. The information I put in had to be internally consistent; I had to check that I hadn't put in contradictory information. The result was a complete geographical record for each specimen (see Figure 8A34).'

Map-making

'Entering the data on the computer was fairly straightforward, and by the third week it was time to move on to distribution mapping. All the records of a single species can be put on a distribution map using a Geographic Information System (GIS).

'Using the GIS was a bit like playing God – zooming in and out of areas of Europe, changing the border colours and wiping out countries was only the beginning. You can bring up anything on the database that might help to explain the distribution patterns of plants. For example, you can map how climate change or a change in land use affects the distribution of a plant species.

'Having produced my maps, the final stage of my work involved reading about the species which I had mapped so that I could write a brief summary about each one, including a description, its habitat, and any threat to it (see Figure 8A35).'

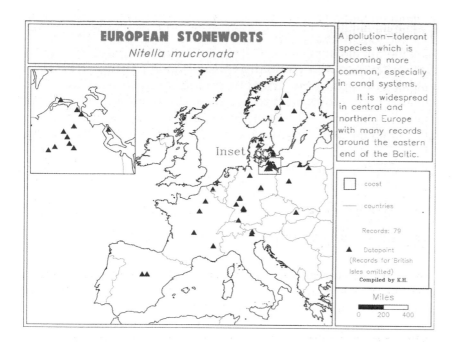

'While I was at the Museum, I prepared 184 records covering three widespread species of stonewort. I left feeling satisfied that I had fully covered an area of work, understood something about the species, and the importance of mapping their distribution – particularly with increasing contamination in many of their habitats. The Museum provides information used by conservationists to protect certain species and their habitats. I felt that I had contributed to an important area of the Museum's work that most of the public are unaware of as they wander around the exhibits.'

What's in a database?

A computer **database** is a very powerful tool for handling information. In Katie's work, she prepared a **record** for each stonewort specimen in the Museum's collection. (One such record is shown in Figure 8A33.) A database consists of a **file** of records.

A record consists of a number of **fields** – for example, the scientific name of the species, or the date on which the specimen was collected. A field may contain words, numbers, or yes/no answers.

The power of a database is in the way the information can be handled once someone like Katie has put it into the computer. The computer's software allows the user to select, for example, all the records on a particular species. They can be arranged geographically to make a map, or by altitude, to find out at what heights the plant will grow. The changing distribution of the plant can be related to environmental changes, by combining information from more than one database.

A database can be rapidly up-dated whenever new information comes to hand. The Natural History Museum publishes printed versions of some of the information, but active researchers in the field are more likely to make use of the database, which can be supplied in up-to-date form simply by sending a disc through the post or by transferring the information along a telephone line.

Data from clinical trials

Theresa White works for a Plymouth research company called Phase I Clinical Trials. Much of the work involves testing potential new drugs by giving them to healthy volunteers. The volunteers are carefully monitored to see how the drug behaves in the body and how the body responds to the drug. This generates enormous amounts of data and it is part of Theresa's job to co-ordinate the handling and transfer of the data.

▲ **Figure 8A36** *Theresa White (on the right) working with a colleague.*

'I started working for Phase I four and a half years ago as a secretary. It was only meant to be a temporary job but I soon discovered that they really needed someone to do much more than secretarial work and I set about proving that I could do it. After that, my job expanded and so did my salary. My job is always changing as we get new software, upgrades of old software and new methods of handling data. I don't have any medical or scientific training but when I arrived I had more experience with computers than a lot of the older people and I wasn't afraid to play about with new programs in order to make them work.

'To fit into an organization like ours you have to have the right attitude towards data. Our clients are companies in the business of developing and selling drugs. They pay us to find out information about their drug, so we're selling information just as a car manufacturer sells cars. And just as the car buyer wants a reliable car, our clients want reliable data. One of the studies we're doing now is on a new anti-inflammatory drug. Anti-inflammatories are the sorts of drugs given to people with arthritis and conditions like "tennis elbow". This new drug seems to work in a different way to the ones already available, so it may work better for some people. For the last few years the company that synthesized the new compound has studied it with biochemical and *in vitro* tests. They've given the drug to animals and now they judge it is time to try it on humans for the first time.

'The basic plan of the trial is to start by giving twelve volunteers a minute dose of the drug and then give them increasingly large doses over a series of days until they are getting the amount of drug that the company believes will be beneficial to patients. Obviously great care must be taken and the doctors must be sure every volunteer is all right before anyone is given a higher dose. The volunteers are monitored at very close intervals, starting from the day before they actually take the first dose. The nurses take their pulse, blood pressure, ECG, a blood sample, a urine sample and ask them how they feel. For some studies they also have to do things like measure the size of their pupils or stick a ball of cotton wool in their mouths and weigh it to find out how much saliva it has soaked up in a given amount of time.

In vitro *tests*

An *in vitro* test is one done outside a living organism – literally a test carried out 'in glass'.

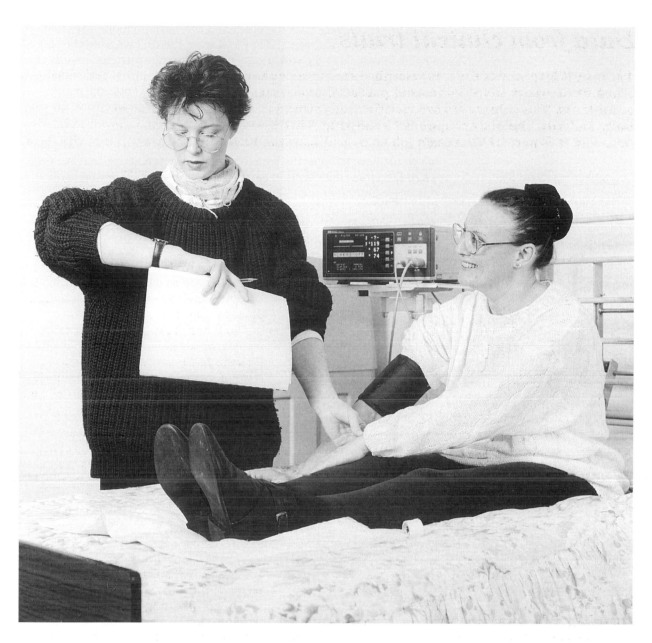

▲ **Figure 8A37** *A nurse recording data after examining a volunteer.*

'All these measurements and samples have to be taken according to a set schedule and the nurses have to be extremely efficient to do everything in the time available. To make it easier for them, we use special forms called CRFs. This is pronounced "crefs" and means **Clinical Research Forms**. The CRFs have boxes where the nurse writes the time, the results of each reading they take, and a tick to say they have taken a blood sample or whatever. Each study has its own set of CRFs which are specially designed, usually by me, using a desk-top publishing program.

'We can do some blood and urine tests ourselves but samples are also sent by courier to laboratories which specialize in more complex tests and often to the client company's own labs where they test for levels of their drug. During some trials, we have couriers leaving here every hour with a batch of samples. Usually it's essential that we have the results of the laboratory tests back immediately. For example, the doctors have to know the results of the tests on volunteers given the lower dose of a new drug before they agree to give them a higher dose.

'We agree in advance with the client and the various laboratories how the data will be presented and at the start of the trial we send the labs a blank spreadsheet file which has been set up to receive the results of the blood and urine tests. We do this by file transfer from our computer network to theirs via a modem (see page 468). They enter the results from each batch of samples as they get them and then electronically transfer the completed spreadsheet back to us.

'When I first started working here, the labs would fax us the results and we would have to enter the data into our computers ourselves (see page 470). Electronic data transfer saves us the boring job of keying in data but, more important than that, it increases the accuracy of the data. Every time data is keyed in or written down there's a chance a mistake will be made. The lab data is keyed in only once, so there is only one chance for a mistake to occur.'

▶ **Figure 8A38** *Sample CRF.*

SPONSOR - STUDY NO.

SCREENING VISIT

SUBJECT ID: ⬚⬚⬚⬚⬚⬚⬚   **SUBJECT NO:** ⬚⬚⬚⬚

PREVIOUS STUDY PARTICIPATION

HAS SUBJECT PARTICIPATED IN A CLINICAL STUDY IN THE LAST 3 MONTHS?

YES: ⬚   NO: ⬚   *If The Answer Is 'Yes' - Do Not Proceed To Screen This Subject*

DATE, IF ANY, OF LAST STUDY PARTICIPATION: ⬚⬚⬚⬚⬚⬚

LOCATION: _____

DATE OF SCREENING VISIT FOR THIS STUDY (NO. XXXXXX): ⬚⬚⬚⬚⬚⬚

DATE OF BIRTH: ⬚⬚⬚⬚⬚⬚   **AGE AT SCREENING:** ⬚⬚

WRITTEN INFORMED CONSENT SIGNED: TIME ⬚:⬚ DATE ⬚⬚⬚⬚⬚⬚

SEX: MALE ⬚ FEMALE ⬚

RACE: CAUCASIAN ⬚   ORIENTAL ⬚
NEGROID ⬚   ASIAN ⬚
OTHER ⬚ _____
Specify

HEIGHT: ⬚:⬚ cm   **ELBOW WIDTH:** ⬚:⬚ cm

WEIGHT: ⬚:⬚ kg   **FRAME SIZE:** SMALL ⬚ MEDIUM ⬚ LARGE ⬚

ALCOHOL CLASSIFICATION One (1) Unit=One half pint beer, one glass wine, one measure spirits

CONSUMPTION PER WEEK: ⬚⬚ Units   (If none - enter 0)

CAFFEINE CLASSIFICATION

COFFEE: ⬚⬚ Cups Per Day   TEA: ⬚⬚ Cups Per Day

SMOKING CLASSIFICATION

NEVER SMOKED: ⬚
EX SMOKER: ⬚
Has not smoked for: ⬚⬚ ⬚⬚ ⬚⬚
Days Months Years

SMOKER: ⬚
Daily Consumption   Cigarettes ⬚
Cigars ⬚
Pipe Tobacco ⬚

COMPLETED BY: ⬚⬚⬚⬚⬚⬚   DATE: ⬚⬚⬚⬚⬚⬚

A spreadsheet is a type of computer software. Data is entered into cells which make up the rows and columns of a grid. The computer can then process the data according to instructions in the software.

'I think the next big technological change we will introduce is electronic CRFs. Right now the nurses write their results onto the paper CRF and then someone has to sit down with a pile of CRFs keying the data onto the spreadsheet. It actually has to be done twice because we use double data entry to increase accuracy. The data are entered onto two different spreadsheets by two different people. We have a program that compares the two spreadsheets and points out where they differ. We then go back to the CRF and find the true value. It's unlikely that both people will have keyed in exactly the same wrong number so this finds virtually all the errors and ensures that the data is keyed in accurately. The problem is, of course, that it takes a lot of time and it's boring work.

▲ **Figure 8A39** *Entering data into a spreadsheet.*

'It would be far better for the nurses to carry around a portable computer rather than a clipboard full of CRFs. As they take their measurements they could enter the data straight onto the computer rather than write it down on a piece of paper. The computer would automatically record the time the data was entered so the nurse wouldn't have to bother to note the time. The volunteer's ECG could also be recorded right onto the computer rather than onto a strip of paper which the nurses have to stick onto the CRF.

'We could introduce electronic CRFs now but our clients and the drug licensing authorities are holding it up. The CRF is actually a legal document signed by the nurse who took the measurements and the doctor who checked them. The data we collect are used by the drug company in their application to governments around the world for a licence to sell their drug and our CRFs are proof that we collected that data. If fraud is ever suspected, the signatures on the CRF reveal who was responsible for collecting and verifying the data so they can be asked to defend the work they did. Our clients fear that an electronic document won't stand up in a court of law as well as a signed piece of paper. It'll be interesting to see if software and hardware can be developed which will convince people that electronically stored data is as trustworthy as data stored with a pen on a piece of paper.'

Data gathering in the field

Scientific investigation can produce reliable knowledge about nature because it often imposes carefully controlled conditions and strict procedures on experimental observations and measurements in the laboratory. Reproducible and accurate data can be gathered. Outside the laboratory, because there are far more variables and less control over what is going on, collecting reliable data is more difficult. The classic example is the collection of field data for ecological investigations.

Ainsdale sand dunes

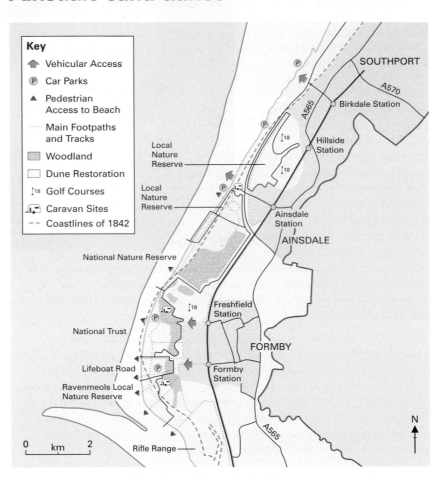

► **Figure 8A40** *Ainsdale Sand Dunes National Nature Reserve.*

The Ainsdale dunes are among the finest examples of natural dune systems in Britain. A National Nature Reserve was set up in these dunes on Merseyside in 1965. The reserve is managed by English Nature as part of the Sefton Coast Management Scheme. The overall objective is to retain all the semi-natural habitats with their associated species, preferably through natural processes but, where necessary, by human intervention.

Sand dunes are a sensitive and fragile habitat. Overuse of the dunes in the past for grazing livestock and cutting marram grass for thatching caused devastating sand drift. The problem was only brought under control by strict laws to prevent the use of the dunes, backed up by many years of hard work replanting grasses to stabilize the sand. Coastal pinewoods were also planted later to 'fix' the wandering dunes which lie further from the coast.

During this century, overuse by visitors, lack of steady management and natural erosion have created, and continue to create, problems for those who are trying to preserve this landscape.

Fieldwork and its problems

In 1994, a group of GNVQ students at Blackpool and the Fylde College set out to study the plant biology of the reserve in relation to the physical and chemical properties of the site and its soils. The National Nature Reserve occupies quite a large area of land between various local nature reserves, coastline owned by the National Trust and various golf courses (see Figure 8A40). Within the reserve, topography, soil type, exposure and proximity to the sea are all highly variable, creating a complex network of variations in the local flora. Before any analysis of the variables at work here can be attempted, this complex pattern had first to be **described in summary**. How can this be done?

The vegetation and soil types of the reserve must be **sampled**. This sampling must allow a reasonable picture of the general plant cover and soils to be described from careful measurements of very limited parts of it. The samples must be **representative**. There are several ways in which this could be achieved, each with different levels of effort needed on the part of data-gatherers and producing different **degrees of confidence** about how reasonable the picture of the reserve drawn from the samples is.

The students were not expert field-workers; they did not have a great deal of time at their disposal and a fairly rough and ready description of the reserve was good enough for them to move onto the next stage of their exercise, a consideration of problems of reserve management. They decided to take soil, topography and vegetation measurements along a **transect**, an imaginary line drawn across the reserve.

The dominant controls over the behaviour of the dunes and their plant cover are exposure to wind and sea. The reserve clearly changes character from the sea's edge to the mature woodland on its inland side, which is fairly well sheltered from full exposure to the weather. The transect was therefore drawn on the map at right angles to the coastline and passed through six reasonably distinct **communities** (see Figure 8A41). Going from the coast inland, ignoring the beach and the embryo dunes immediately behind it, these were:

- mobile dunes (dunes still moving under the impact of coastal winds, although covered with long-rooted marram grass)
- dune slacks (flat areas behind the mobile dunes, often covered in standing water)
- fixed dunes (stabilized dunes, sufficiently sheltered and covered in grasses not to be moved by the wind)
- dune scrub (fixed dunes covered in sparse woody vegetation)
- dune heath (dune landscape dominated by heather, maintained by grazing of domestic animals)
- woodland (pine woodland, the trees able to grow because the ground is stable and wind exposure is not too severe). At Ainsdale trees have been planted to help stabilize the dunes. They are, however, in the correct place in the succession sequence.

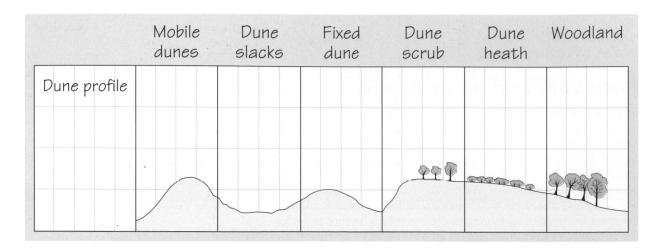

| | Mobile dunes | Dune slacks | Fixed dune | Dune scrub | Dune heath | Woodland |

▲ **Figure 8A41** *The profile of the six main communities along the transect.*

Using standard techniques, the students measured a variety of environmental and soil properties at specific points along the transect in the middle of the six communities. They also counted the total number of **herbaceous** plant species they could observe in the 'typical' community around the sites at which they measured the soil and exposure factors. The results they obtained are summarized in Figure 8A42.

	Mobile dunes	Dune slacks	Fixed dune	Dune scrub	Dune heath	Woodland
Distance from high water /m	15	65	180	320	570	920
Wind speed /m s^{-1}	11	7	0.5	2	8	1
Humidity /%	94	88	82	86	74	86
Drainage rate – time taken to collect 10 cm^3 /s	20	29	40	80	100	135
Percentage bare ground /%	80	10	2	5	2	100
Number of plant species	22	40	42	16	20	0
Temperature /°C	6.5	8	8	8.5	9	8.5
Soil conductivity /S m^{-1} × 10^{-5}	7.9	8.0	7.4	6.2	4.5	4.5
Organic content of the soil /%	0.94	4.4	3.4	2.2	16.55	4.98
Water content of the soil /%	8.6	24.8	8.3	7.8	8.1	6.5
pH of the soil	8.0	8.0	7.0	4.0	4.5	4.5

▲ **Figure 8A42** *Summary of physical and soil characteristics along the transect.*

The students also undertook another type of **vegetation sampling**, to determine the frequency with which certain characteristic and common plant species occurred in each community. This analysis involved throwing **quadrats**. A quadrat is simply a square of certain area, formed of wire. Within a reasonably uniform section of each community, these are simply thrown **at random** onto the ground, and the presence of the chosen indicator species is checked. A total of ten quadrat determinations were made at each location in this exercise. A summary of results obtained, with an estimate of how much of the ground was covered with vegetation in each case, is given in Figure 8A43.

Herbaceous species	Mobile dunes	Dune slacks	Fixed dune	Dune scrub	Dune heath	Woodland
Marram	10	2	6	0	0	0
Thistle	2	2	2	0	0	0
Creeping willow	2	10	8	2	0	0
Yellow iris	0	8	0	0	0	0
Plantain	0	2	4	0	0	0
Sheep's fescue	0	6	10	2	0	0
Rush	0	8	0	0	0	0
Moss	0	8	6	2	4	0
Bent grass	0	2	6	2	6	0
Rose-bay willow herb	0	0	0	8	0	0
Heather	0	0	0	0	10	0
% Bare earth	80%	10%	2%	5%	2%	100%
Dominant vegetation	Marram	Willow	Sheep's fescue	Rose-bay willow herb	Heather	Pine trees

These data can be re-expressed in the form of a **kite diagram**, showing graphically how the relative density of the marker species varies across the six community types along the transect.

▲ **Figure 8A43** *Vegetation analysis from quadrat estimations.*

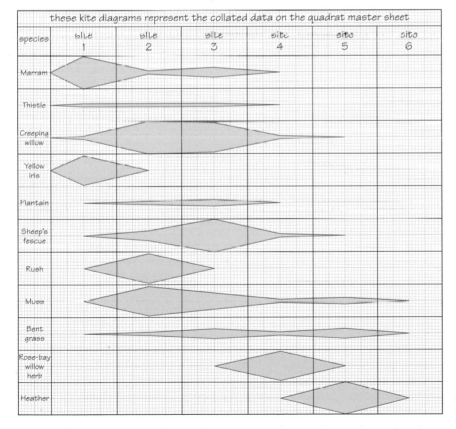

◀ **Figure 8A44** *Graphic representation of the abundance of marker species.*

Data and discovery

Data analysis is often carried out to solve a clearly defined problem. For instance, an industrial process must be monitored if it is to be improved, or the extent of pollution must be determined before appropriate regulations can be drawn up. At other times, data analysis is part of a process of discovery or invention, both of which can be intensely rewarding. Those lucky enough to join inventive research teams when they are young, as technicians or junior researchers, can share in this pleasure.

Research on sleeping sickness

More than twenty years ago, soon after she left school, Janet King started work as a technician in a medical research institute. The small team that she joined were working on African sleeping sickness, a disease caused by the *Trypanosoma* parasite (see Figure 8A45). Their tasks were to improve the methods of diagnosis of people who might be suffering from the disease and to test whether certain assumptions which doctors had made about sleeping sickness were true.

▶ **Figure 8A45** *The* Trypanosoma *parasite.*

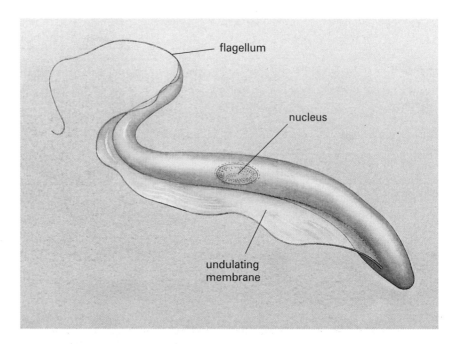

Sleeping sickness is one of the most dangerous tropical diseases. The microscopic trypanosome parasites are common in the blood of wild animals living in the African jungles and savannas. They do not cause these animals any harm, but if the parasites find their way into the blood of humans or their farm animals, a serious disease occurs. The parasites are transmitted among animals and humans by the blood-sucking **tsetse fly**, an insect widely distributed across the whole of central Africa.

The fly makes a small wound in the skin of its victim and injects saliva which prevents blood from clotting, so that it can suck the blood. An insect infected with trypanosomes carries the parasites in its saliva and they are injected into the blood of the human or animal which has been bitten. The fly then sucks up the blood which, if it is from an infected host, passes trypanosomes into the stomach of the fly. From here the fly's salivary glands become infected and thus the parasites are transferred to the next victim it bites (see Figure 8A46).

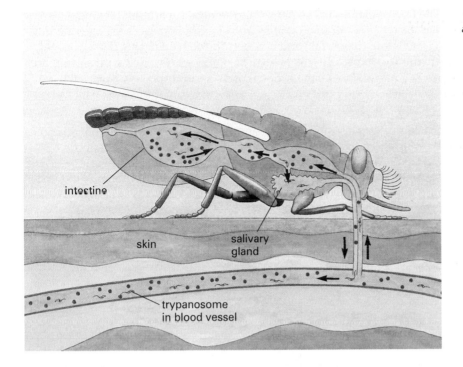

intestine

skin

salivary gland

trypanosome in blood vessel

If a human is bitten by an infected tsetse fly, the trypanosomes enter the blood. They multiply rapidly. For several weeks the patient shows no symptoms but then begins to have fevers and becomes weak and anaemic. These symptoms are caused by toxins given off by the parasites which destroy blood cells.

In the last stages, the parasites invade the cerebrospinal fluids which surround the brain. The patient loses consciousness and goes to 'sleep'. The patient may then die from the damage done to the brain. Until effective drugs were found which killed trypanosomes in the blood and schemes were set up to remove tsetse flies, large areas of central Africa were uninhabitable by humans or their livestock.

A technical breakthrough

One major problem in studying sleeping sickness was separating parasites from blood. To study the properties of the parasites in detail it is necessary to remove all traces of blood from them. A scientist in Janet's team hit on a method of separating trypanosomes quickly and cleanly from infected blood. Once the technique was perfected it was possible to work on pure samples of the parasite for the first time. The new technique made getting and interpreting data about sleeping sickness much easier.

The breakthrough in technique happened like this. The great advances in the rather different disciplines of biochemistry and molecular biology which have occurred in the last 30 years have been made possible partly because a range of new techniques have been invented. A key problem in biochemical investigations is the separation of different molecules, especially when they are very similar to each other in size and chemical behaviour and are easily destroyed by heat, pressure or chemical attack. Traditional separation methods devised for chemical analysis and production in the 19th and early 20th centuries are not good enough; they destroy delicate biological molecules.

The largest classes of the newer biochemical separation techniques are various types of chromatography and electrophoresis (see pages 28 and 34). One very powerful variant widely introduced in the 1960s was **gel chromatography**. In this procedure, gel beads swollen with solvent are packed into a glass column. The properties of these beads are such that molecules below a certain size are absorbed into the beads, while larger ones cannot enter and move only in the spaces between them.

Smaller molecules thus take longer to move through the column because they have to move through the beads, while large ones move more quickly through the shorter solvent-filled spaces. Molecules are separated by size, larger ones coming off the bottom of the column first (see Figure 8A47). By carefully selecting gels with different properties, sets of molecules of similar size can be separated from each other.

▼ **Figure 8A47** *The principles of gel chromatography.*

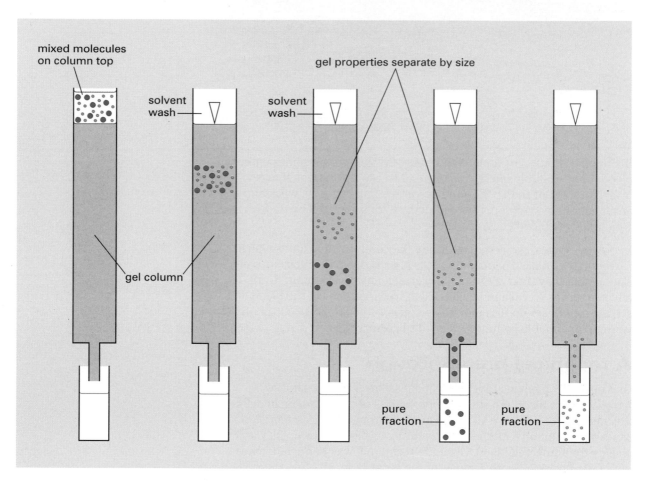

A medical scientist in the team that Janet joined had a clever idea. Could this biochemical technique for the separation of large molecules of reasonably similar size be used to separate blood cells from *Trypanosoma* parasites? These particles were much bigger than the protein and nucleic acid molecules which the biochemists were separating. There was no reason to suppose it would work since the sizes and proportions involved were so different. But the parallels in the objectives of separating particles of reasonably similar size to purify them, led the scientist to try it out anyway. She was excited to discover that it worked; using gels suitable for the largest of the biochemists' molecules, *Trypanosoma* parasites could be separated directly from red and white blood cells and from blood platelets.

Janet describes the result as being like magic! Her job was to repeat and refine the method by consistently changing the detailed conditions under which it was carried out and carefully recording and evaluating the results, until it worked every time.

She then had the daunting task of demonstrating the technique to many other scientists at a meeting of the Royal Society, one of the most important scientific organizations in the UK. She was also responsible for teaching the method to other *Trypanosoma* researchers who came to her team's laboratory to learn how to obtain pure samples of parasites for themselves.

From this technical breakthrough, members of Janet's team and others were able to make significant advances in the investigation of sleeping sickness.

- A mini-version of the technique was developed for use with patients in the bush in Nigeria. This showed that many more people were infected with low doses of *Trypanosoma* than had previously been suspected. They did not suffer from sleeping sickness. The discovery was important because it demonstrated that the parasite did not always cause serious disease when present in humans. Some people probably have natural resistance to it. In others, detecting the presence of trypanosomes before they begin to cause serious damage, allows drug treatment to begin early and to be more effective against the low parasite numbers.
- Once pure samples of parasites could be obtained, different strains and species of *Trypanosoma* were found to have different electrical charges on their surfaces. This confirmed earlier assumptions about the classification of different strains and allowed the separation of the strains from patients who were infected with two or more different types of *Trypanosoma* at the same time, by using techniques which separate particles by electrical charge rather than by particle size.
- Study of the chemical composition of the parasite was now far simpler, and highly magnified photographs of the parasite, taken with an electron microscope, gave much better pictures of the parasite than had ever been seen before.

This new application of the gel chromatography technique originally invented and developed in biochemistry thus had important consequences in the study of parasite disease. Parasitologists applied the new technique to learn a great deal more about sleeping sickness. New techniques and new ideas are hard to invent but the widespread application of new ideas in fresh places has proved extraordinarily fruitful in scientific investigation.

Electronic data transfer

Communicating around the global village

Developments in electronics over the last forty years have changed the way people communicate beyond all recognition. Today it is as easy to telephone relatives, friends or work colleagues on the other side of the world as it was for earlier generations to speak to people just down the road. And with equipment not much more complicated than a telephone it is possible to send text, pictures or scientific data – coded as a series of electronic pulses – around the world too.

Scientific communication

▼ **Figure 8B1** *Scientists may communicate by talking directly to each other, by using computer networks to send electronic mail ('e-mail' for short), by fax machine and in many other ways. Electronic communication means that a large amount of complicated information can be communicated quickly and easily.*

Scientists need to communicate with other scientists around the world for several reasons. Sometimes they may need to find out information, for example, the exact conditions for making a new chemical compound. Often one group of scientists wants to tell other groups about the work they have done. They may want to share their results so that the two groups can work together. Collaboration often means that a solution to a problem which the two groups face may be found more quickly. Alternatively one group may wish to have their results checked by another to be sure that their data are reliable. A scientist proposing a new theory needs to persuade other scientists to accept the new ideas. And because science can be big business, it may be very important to let other scientists know about new ideas as quickly as possible.

Communicating electronically

Sometimes the easiest way to explain something to someone is to talk to them. If they are not close by they can always be contacted by telephone. After all, there are over a billion telephone subscribers in the world. However, if the other person is on the opposite side of the world this is often inconvenient because of time differences – 11.30 am in the UK is 9 pm in Central Australia!

However, scientific information is usually communicated using ways other than speech. This is not just because of time differences, but because a spoken communication can be easily misunderstood, and readily forgotten. More importantly, it is usually much better to communicate scientific information so that the person receiving the communication can see the message on paper (or on a computer screen). They can then read and understand it in their own time.

One scientist might need to tell another in a different continent how to prepare a piece of scientific equipment for use in an experiment. The information to be sent might include:

- text
- numbers
- drawings or photographs.

Most scientific information falls into one of these three types, although in certain circumstances scientists may need to send sounds and moving pictures too.

Before information can be sent electronically it needs to be converted into a series of electronic signals. Once this has been done, these signals can be processed and then transmitted in a number of ways, as Figure 8B2 shows.

▼ Figure 8B2

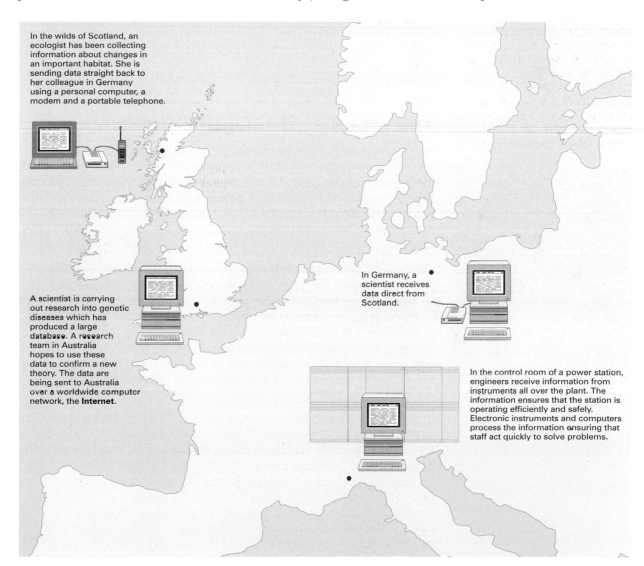

In the wilds of Scotland, an ecologist has been collecting information about changes in an important habitat. She is sending data straight back to her colleague in Germany using a personal computer, a modem and a portable telephone.

A scientist is carrying out research into genetic diseases which has produced a large database. A research team in Australia hopes to use these data to confirm a new theory. The data are being sent to Australia over a worldwide computer network, the **Internet**.

In Germany, a scientist receives data direct from Scotland.

In the control room of a power station, engineers receive information from instruments all over the plant. The information ensures that the station is operating efficiently and safely. Electronic instruments and computers process the information ensuring that staff act quickly to solve problems.

Electronic publishing

Scientists thrive on information. They learn what other people are doing by reading scientific journals and they tell others about their own work by publishing results in the same journals. The mass of scientific journal literature is now enormous. Some journal publishers are moving into publishing electronically. They believe this is both more efficient and more effective than traditional publication of print on paper.

Testing the water

'When we started to publish an electronic version of one of our physics journals, we knew that it would provide physicists with quicker and easier access to information. What we didn't know was how it would improve the access that scientists in the developing world have to the wider scientific community,' says Giles Colborne, Electronic Products Analyst at Institute of Physics Publishing.

Institute of Physics Publishing is a company owned by the Institute of Physics, the learned society in the UK concerned with the study of physics. The company publishes over 30 research journals in many different areas of physics. The journal that they have now made available in electronic form is *Classical and Quantum Gravity*, published twelve times each year. The reason for choosing this journal was quite simple. 'The physicists who work in this area were already communicating with each other using electronic methods, and using computer networks to swap files. As a highly computer literate group, they were a natural choice as the first target audience for an electronic journal,' says Giles.

The process of scientific publishing

Before the results of a piece of scientific research become accepted as scientific knowledge they must be approved by other scientists who work in the same field, in a process called **peer review**. An important part of peer review involves publishing a **paper** describing the research and its results in a **journal** which is read by scientists with similar interests. A scientist who wishes to publish a paper sends it to the journal's editor, who decides if it is likely to be of interest to the journal's readers.

The paper is then sent to **referees**, who are not told the name of the person who wrote the paper. The referees (expert scientists in the area the research is concerned with) read the paper and write comments about it. They advise the editor about whether the paper should be accepted, and if it needs to be changed in any way. The editor then writes to the author of the paper. The paper may be rejected for publication, or the editor may ask for some amendments to be made before it is accepted. Sometimes the paper may be accepted without any changes at all.

'Electronic publishing has advantages for everyone concerned,' says Giles. 'It helps us to manage the peer review process on a computerized database so that we can select the best referees to advise the journal's editor. We use e-mail to get their comments as quickly as possible. This speeds up the whole process – receiving a paper for publication, getting it reviewed, and then asking for changes before publication. By using global computer networks to send files containing the text of the paper to subscribers and communicating by electronic mail, we can achieve significant gains over traditional paper-based methods of publishing. Journal subscribers still receive a paper copy of each edition of the journal, but they can get access to the electronic version as much as three weeks before they receive the paper copy. This is significant in competitive research fields.'

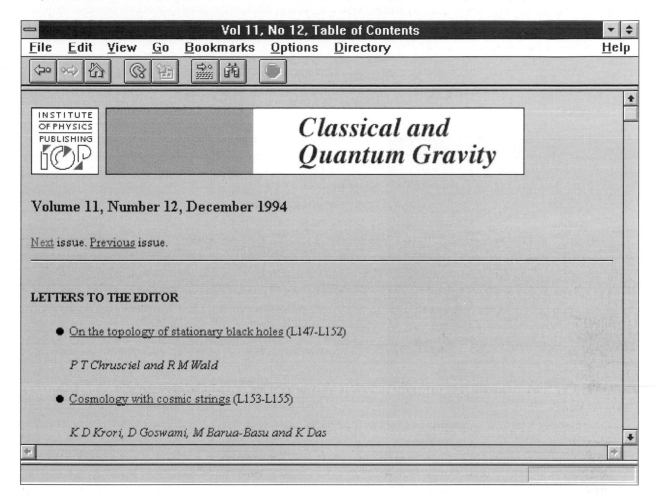

▼ **Figure 8B3** *The contents page of* Classical and Quantum Gravity. *By simply pointing and clicking a mouse, a physicist looking at this contents page can choose to read the text of an article on screen. An electronic copy of the article can be downloaded. This can then be printed out using a printer attached to the user's computer, or can be saved on disk.*

Access to information is very important in the academic world, since without the opportunity to read and comment on the work of other people, the process of peer review cannot work properly. Institute of Physics Publishing gave a lot of thought to the way in which the electronic version of *Classical and Quantum Gravity* is published, so that readers do not need sophisticated equipment.

Giles explains: 'Although access to *Classical and Quantum Gravity* needs a computer which is connected to the worldwide network known as the **Internet** (see page 468), the computer doesn't need to be very sophisticated. We have made sure that the text of the journal can be accessed using quite simple software which is available free and which does not require powerful or expensive computers. The success of this approach is shown by the way in which scientists in the developing world have taken up the electronic version of this journal. Using computers to access and discuss current developments with scientists in other parts of the world really enables researchers in South America, for example, to be part of the mainstream science community. That's something that traditional communication and publishing techniques just can't produce.'

Electronic publishing in the future

Electronic publishing is still in its infancy, and the future will certainly bring many interesting developments. What does Giles think these may be? 'Electronic journals will certainly develop so that they will give more information,' he says. 'When a scientific paper mentions another article or book, the details of it are given in a list of **references** at the end of the paper. At present both the electronic and traditional versions of journals simply give a list of references at the end of each paper. In future, however, electronic journals will let readers see information about the articles mentioned in the reference list, probably by linking each reference to its **abstract**, a sort of summary included at the beginning of every paper.'

There are likely to be other developments too. 'One reason computers are so useful in publishing is the power that they have to store and manipulate information,' continues Giles. 'In future it's likely that a computer, which a scientist accesses regularly to read electronic journals, will keep a record of the journals that scientist uses. It will also carry details of the scientist's research work obtained on the basis of the articles he or she has read.

'This system will then offer scientists information that fits most closely with their interests, alert them to papers they may have missed, and keep them informed about papers that are in the process of being submitted. In this way, the computer will make finding and reading the latest research much easier, leaving scientists with more time to carry out their own work.'

◄ **Figure 8B4** *a Journals of the past, printed on paper and stored on miles and miles of library shelves, with indexes held on paper.* *b Journals of the future, stored as information on disks, available almost instantly via computer from wherever the scientist is working, and with indexes tailored to the interests of each individual scientist reading them.*

Data protection

Computers are powerful tools for processing and manipulating information. When they are used for storing information about people's personal lives, particular care must be taken to ensure that the information is not misused, and that there can be no unauthorized access to it. The Data Protection Act is an important piece of legislation which covers the way that personal information is held on computer, and how it can be used.

The Data Protection Act

Many people take out life insurance at some point in their lives. This ensures that their debts are paid off if they are unable to repay them through illness, unemployment or death, for instance. Taking out such insurance is sensible if buying a house or entering some other large financial commitment. Before agreeing to insure anyone, an insurance company will need certain details of their medical history, and perhaps other information too, such as details of their bank account – all of which will be held on computer.

One insurance company which has made extensive use of computers to store and process policy holders' personal information is Friends Provident, based in Dorking, Surrey. Ian Codd, Data Analyst with Friends Provident, says 'The Data Protection Act covers the treatment of personal information, which is held on computer, and provides a set of legal requirements which govern the way that such information is obtained, stored and used. The Act includes eight Data Protection Principles (see Figure 8B5) with which anyone holding information on computer must comply. The Act does not apply to information held on paper.'

Ian explains, 'The first seven Data Protection Principles deal with the way that a company obtains, processes and uses personal information about people. The Act makes it possible for a company to keep a computer database of (for example) customer names and addresses. But the company cannot give this information to anyone else unless the customers have been told that their names and addresses may be given to other people, and the company has registered with the Data Protection Registrar to say that this is what they intend to do with the information. The names and addresses must be kept up-to-date and accurate, and people must be able to correct their name and address in the database if this information is incorrect.'

'Any responsible company would be likely to manage information in accordance with the Data Protection Principles,' says Ian, 'but the Principles provide valuable legal protection to ensure that all companies behave responsibly. The Act applies to a company's employees too, so that they can be sure that their employer holds accurate information about them. New technology such as document imaging – holding electronic images of documents on file rather than as bits of paper – present new implications for data protection, which Friends Provident are considering very seriously.'

Data Protection Principles	
1	'The information to be contained in personal data shall be obtained, and personal data shall be processed, fairly and lawfully.'
2	'Personal data shall be held only for one or more specified purposes.'
3	'Personal data held for any purpose or purposes shall not be used or disclosed in any manner incompatible with that purpose or those purposes.'
4	'Personal data held for any purpose or purposes shall be adequate, relevant and not excessive in relation to that purpose or those purposes.'
5	'Personal data shall be accurate and, where necessary, kept up to date.'
6	'Personal data held for any purpose or purposes shall not be kept for longer than is necessary for that purpose or those purposes.'
7	'An individual shall be entitled: (a) at reasonable intervals and without undue delay or expense: 　(i) to be informed by any Data User whether he holds personal data of which that individual is the Subject, and 　(ii) to access any such data held by a Data User; and (b) where appropriate, to have such data corrected or erased.'
8	'Appropriate security measures shall be taken against unauthorized access to, or alteration, disclosure or destruction of, personal data and against accidental loss or destruction of personal data.'

▲ Figure 8B5

Data security at Friends Provident

The eighth Data Protection Principle is concerned with computer security, and loss of data. Employees must have access to information that they need to do their job, but must not have access to any other information. 'At Friends Provident, we design information systems so that information is grouped in different databases,' Ian says. 'This means that it is relatively easy to give employees access to information for their work, and to prevent them having access to information they do not need.'

'Using separate databases like this is important. For example, an insurance company might hold information on policy holders' medical histories in one database and customer names in another database. An employee who needed to know the medical history of any particular customer would be given access to this information by enabling them to use the computer system to cross reference the database containing customer names with the database containing customer medical histories. Another employee who did not need this specific information could still obtain information about policy holders' medical histories in general. This could be done by giving them access to the database containing customer medical histories. But this employee would not be allowed to use the computer to cross-reference this database with the customer name database – so they would be unable to use the computer system to work out a particular customer's medical history.'

'Loss of and damage to information is something that we take great pains to avoid,' explains Ian. 'Access to all computers within Friends Provident is very strictly controlled by a system of identification used when people log on to a computer. Each person employed by the company has their own **logonid** which is unique to them. This logonid sets their 'access privileges', which determine what information they may see and use. Each employee has their own computer password in addition to their logonid. This password is known only to the individual employee, and must be changed regularly. In addition, we use a whole range of back-up techniques to ensure that if any information does get damaged, for example by a computer failure, it can be replaced relatively easily.'

▲ **Figure 8B6** *When you complete a life insurance application form the information is stored in a database. You are providing some very personal information about yourself. The Data Protection Act helps to ensure that the information you provide remains accurate, and is not used in ways that you have not been told about.*

Getting it together – computer communications

In principle, sending information between two computers is simple. Computers can be connected using telephone lines, or by permanent connections. A group of computers which are interconnected is known as a network. By using telephone connections and networks, we can connect together computers at opposite ends of the Earth – for the cost of a local telephone call.

Computers communicating

To send messages between computers some way of connecting them to each other is needed. This can be done using an ordinary telephone line, with a piece of equipment called a **modem** at each end of the line. The modem at the transmitting end of the telephone line combines the digital signals produced by the computer with a **carrier wave**. This combined signal can then be sent down a telephone line. At the receiving end of the line, the other modem removes the carrier wave to recover the digital signals, which the computer can process.

Computers in a small area (at the headquarters of a company, for example) can be connected together permanently by a series of cables. This type of network is known as a **LAN** (Local Area Network). Computers and LANs which are some distance apart may be connected together to form a **WAN** (Wide Area Network). The computers in the WAN may be hundreds of miles apart. They can be connected using cables, but optical fibres, microwave beams or even satellite links may also be used. WANs can be linked together to form even larger networks. For example, Southampton University has its own computer network called **SIGNET**. SIGNET links individual computers and small networks in different parts of the University by means of cables and optical fibres. SIGNET is then linked to **JANET**, a large network which links the networks in virtually all of the universities in the UK. Finally, JANET is connected to other computer networks across the world, in a network of networks called the **Internet** (see Figure 8B8).

▶ **Figure 8B7** *This student is sending a message to someone on the other side of the world – a service that will cost the student nothing!*

Probably the most common use of computers to communicate is **electronic mail** (or e-mail for short). E-mail is quick (it takes a matter of seconds to send a long message to the other side of the world) and it is cheap too – once a network of computers exists, it costs virtually nothing to use it to send a message. One disadvantage of e-mail is that it is difficult to use it to send graphic images (diagrams or photographs, for example). For this reason, e-mail messages are normally restricted to text.

▼ **Figure 8B8**

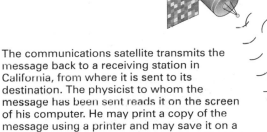

to satellite

A physicist in Gloucester has just written a research paper. She wants to send a copy of it to a colleague in California. She types an e-mail message on her computer, combines this with the text of the paper she wishes to send, and saves the two as a text file on a floppy disk.

She does not have direct access to a computer network, so she uses communications software to send the file from her computer to a modem connected to it via a cable (the modem is the small box on the left hand side of her computer).

The modem transmits the file by telephone to a computer network in London. This file is then sent from London to a satellite broadcasting station. Here it is combined with another carrier wave, and sent to a communications satellite in orbit 35 000 km above the Earth's equator.

The communications satellite transmits the message back to a receiving station in California, from where it is sent to its destination. The physicist to whom the message has been sent reads it on the screen of his computer. He may print a copy of the message using a printer and may save it on a disk if he wants to keep a copy to be edited later.

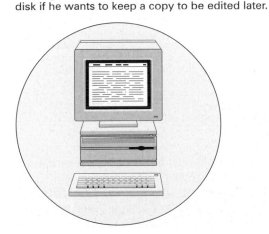

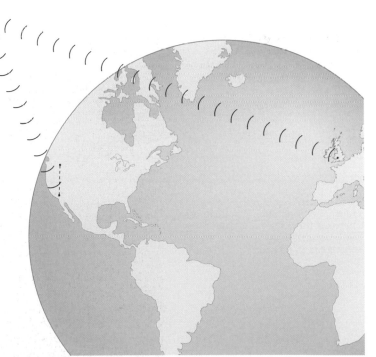

Getting it together – FAX communications

Computer communication is quick and easy if information is already in electronic format. However, it is not so convenient for sending paper documents quickly from one place to another. This is where facsimile machines (or 'fax machines' for short) really come into their own, since they make it possible to transmit a copy of a paper document along a telephone line.

Fax transmission

The way in which a fax machine operates is simple. The transmitting machine takes the document to be sent and converts the image on the paper into a series of electronic pulses. These are then passed to a modem. The modem combines the pulses with a carrier wave and transmits the combined signal through the telephone system to the receiving fax machine. At the receiving end another modem removes the carrier wave from the signal and recovers the electronic pulses. These pulses are then processed and used to print a copy of the transmitted document onto a piece of paper.

▼ Figure 8B9

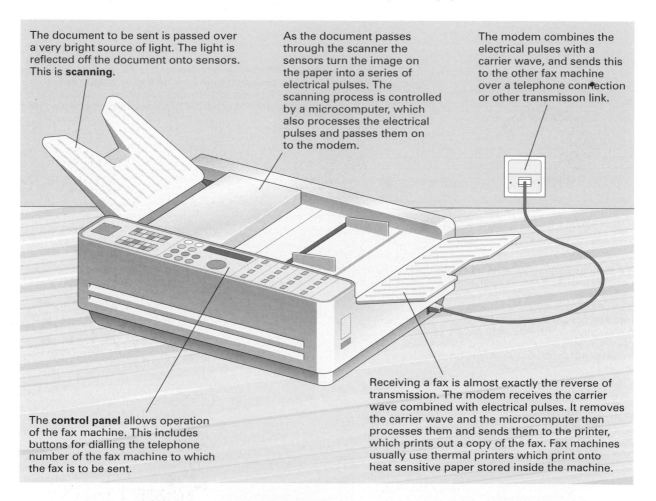

The document to be sent is passed over a very bright source of light. The light is reflected off the document onto sensors. This is **scanning**.

As the document passes through the scanner the sensors turn the image on the paper into a series of electrical pulses. The scanning process is controlled by a microcomputer, which also processes the electrical pulses and passes them on to the modem.

The modem combines the electrical pulses with a carrier wave, and sends this to the other fax machine over a telephone connection or other transmisson link.

The **control panel** allows operation of the fax machine. This includes buttons for dialling the telephone number of the fax machine to which the fax is to be sent.

Receiving a fax is almost exactly the reverse of transmission. The modem receives the carrier wave combined with electrical pulses. It removes the carrier wave and the microcomputer then processes them and sends them to the printer, which prints out a copy of the fax. Fax machines usually use thermal printers which print onto heat sensitive paper stored inside the machine.

Scanning is done by feeding the document past a row of **light-emitting diodes** (LEDs). Light from these LEDs is focused by a lens and is reflected from the document. It passes through another lens and falls on a row of sensors. Each sensor produces an electric charge when light hits it – the size of this charge depends on the amount of light.

The scanning process divides the document up into a series of squares or **pixels**. An A4 document is broken down into 1728 pixels across its width, and the document is scanned as 1145 lines. This means that the page is represented by nearly 2 million pixels:

1728 lines × 1145 pixels = 1978560 pixels

Using a special modem called a **faxmodem**, it is possible to send and receive fax messages using computers. This method of sending faxes has the advantage that documents do not have to be printed on paper – instead they can be sent directly from the computer itself. Using this method, text and diagrams produced from word-processing, graphics or desktop publishing programs can be stored on disk and sent as a fax. Computers equipped with a faxmodem can also receive faxes. These may then be printed or stored on disk. If **optical character recognition** (OCR) software is available, a fax that contains text may be converted into a document that can be edited using a word processor.

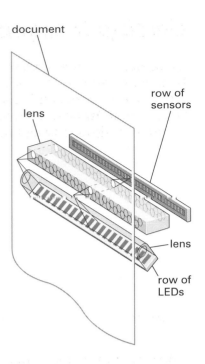

▶ **Figure 8B10** *The distance from the LED array to the sensors is only a few centimetres. This keeps the fax machine very compact.*

▼ **Figure 8B11**

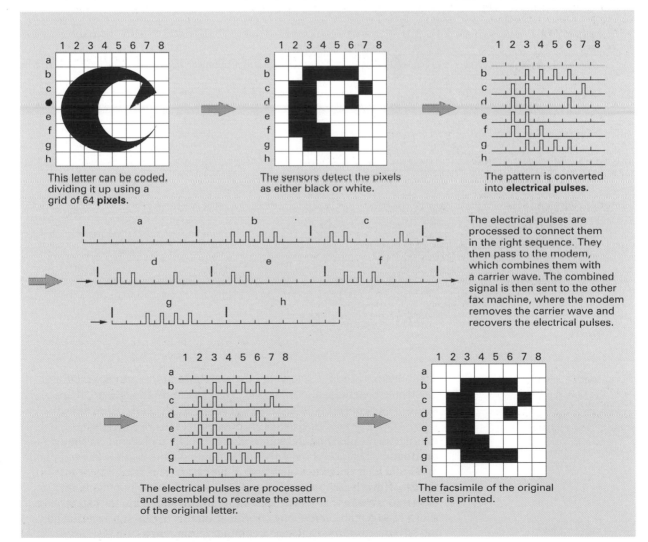

This letter can be coded, dividing it up using a grid of 64 **pixels**.

The sensors detect the pixels as either black or white.

The pattern is converted into **electrical pulses**.

The electrical pulses are processed to connect them in the right sequence. They then pass to the modem, which combines them with a carrier wave. The combined signal is then sent to the other fax machine, where the modem removes the carrier wave and recovers the electrical pulses.

The electrical pulses are processed and assembled to recreate the pattern of the original letter.

The facsimile of the original letter is printed.

Communication basics

Humans have always tried to improve long distance communication. Simple methods include sound waves (for example, elaborate systems of whistling which can be heard several miles away through dense jungle), light (for example, semaphore signalling) and the use of animals such as carrier pigeons. The telecommunications revolution began in the early 19th century. Steady electric currents could be produced which meant that messages could be sent quickly. This proved essential on the rapidly developing railways.

Telegraphs

The earliest telecommunications systems were telegraphs. Messages were transmitted as a series of electrical pulses along a cable, using a series of dots and dashes known as Morse code after its inventor, Samuel Morse. The first telegraph system in the UK was installed in 1830, on the railway between Euston and Camden in London. In 1876 the invention of the telephone by Alexander Graham Bell made possible the transmission of speech as electric currents. Figure 8B12 compares the telegraph with the telephone.

▼ Figure 8B12

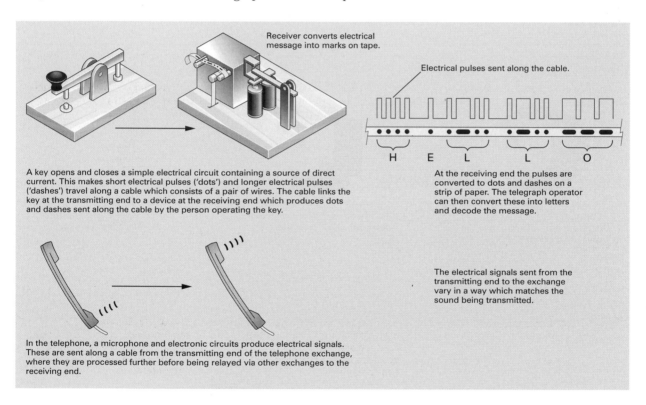

Receiver converts electrical message into marks on tape.

Electrical pulses sent along the cable.

H E L L O

A key opens and closes a simple electrical circuit containing a source of direct current. This makes short electrical pulses ('dots') and longer electrical pulses ('dashes') travel along a cable which consists of a pair of wires. The cable links the key at the transmitting end to a device at the receiving end which produces dots and dashes sent along the cable by the person operating the key.

At the receiving end the pulses are converted to dots and dashes on a strip of paper. The telegraph operator can then convert these into letters and decode the message.

The electrical signals sent from the transmitting end to the exchange vary in a way which matches the sound being transmitted.

In the telephone, a microphone and electronic circuits produce electrical signals. These are sent along a cable from the transmitting end of the telephone exchange, where they are processed further before being relayed via other exchanges to the receiving end.

The telegraph and the telephone illustrate two of the principles behind electronic communication. The electrical signals in the telegraph are sequences of on–off pulses. This kind of signal is called a **digital** signal. In contrast, the electrical signals produced by the telephone vary continuously, following the sound input. This kind of signal is called an **analogue** signal. Until recently telecommunication systems like telephone and radio have made use of analogue signals, transmitting electrical signals which match the sound to be transmitted. Developments in electronics mean that it is now possible to transmit complex signals, like those used to carry telephone conversations, as digital signals. This has big advantages, especially when communicating over long distances.

A signal travelling along a transmission link slowly becomes smaller and smaller as the energy in the signal is absorbed – this is called **attenuation**. As well as being attenuated, the signal becomes contaminated by **noise** as it travels. Noise is caused by a number of factors, depending on the transmission link. Random electrical energy from the electronic circuits is found in all links, while cables produce noise caused by the motion of electrons in the metal conductors. Radio transmission links introduce noise due to simple things like rain and clouds.

When a signal is transmitted over a long distance the signal strength needs to be increased (**amplified**) at regular intervals, to overcome the problem of attenuation. This is where digital signals have a big advantage over analogue signals, since a digital signal can be **regenerated** as Figure 8B13 shows.

▼ Figure 8B13

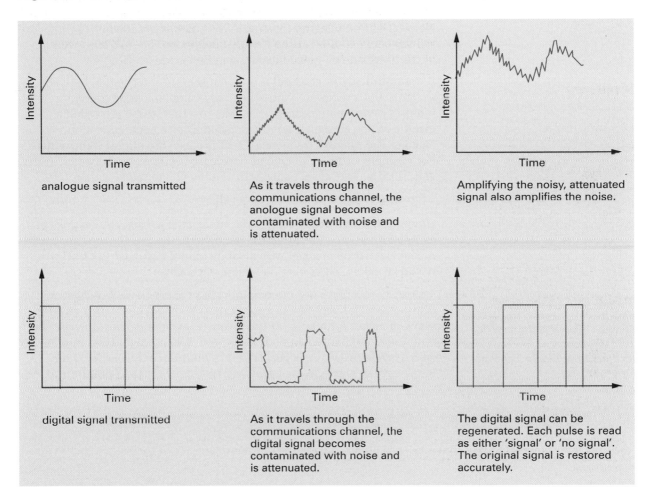

analogue signal transmitted

As it travels through the communications channel, the anologue signal becomes contaminated with noise and is attenuated.

Amplifying the noisy, attenuated signal also amplifies the noise.

digital signal transmitted

As it travels through the communications channel, the digital signal becomes contaminated with noise and is attenuated.

The digital signal can be regenerated. Each pulse is read as either 'signal' or 'no signal'. The original signal is restored accurately.

A long cable must have amplifiers/regeneration units (called **repeaters**) spaced regularly along it to boost the signal. The space between the repeaters depends on the attenuation of the signal and the gain of the repeaters. The signal must be amplified/regenerated before the signal is attenuated to a level too close to that of noise. The amount it can be amplified is limited, since amplifying the signal too much can lead to **distortion**. (This is what happens to the signal in a radio receiver when the volume is turned up too high.) The level of a signal in a transmission link compared to the noise level in the link is measured by the **signal-to-noise ratio**. Signal-to-noise ratio, amplification and attenuation are all measured in **decibels** (**dB**) (see R9 in the Reference section).

Communicating information

Sending information along a transmission link involves encoding it, whether as a series of short and long electrical pulses (the first telegraph systems), as an electrical signal which varies with a sound wave (the telephone) or in some other way. Some basic decisions have to be made about the link, depending on how we wish to go about sending information along it.

Diversity of transmission systems

Sending information using a simple **direct current** (dc) electrical circuit like that used in the telegraph system is slow, and only one message can be transmitted at a time. Transmission links which make use of **alternating current** (ac) allow information to be transmitted faster and also allow more than one signal to be sent along the link at the same time. In addition, the use of ac enables several different ways of encoding the signal to be used.

A **communication channel** is a way of sending information between a source and a receiver. Normal two way communication therefore requires two communication channels; together, these are called a **circuit**. When ac signals are transmitted along a communication channel, the range of frequencies sent is called the **signal bandwidth**. For example, ordinary telephone lines carry frequencies between 300 Hz and 3400 Hz. The signal bandwidth of a telephone signal is therefore

$$3400\,\text{Hz} - 300\,\text{Hz} = 3100\,\text{Hz, or } 3.1\,\text{kHz}.$$

Channel bandwidth describes the capacity of a transmission link to carry information – the larger the bandwidth, the greater the capacity. A communication channel with a bandwidth of 1 MHz (= 1000 kHz) would be able to carry over 300 telephone calls.

A signal containing voice or computer data cannot be sent along a transmission link directly. Instead, it must be combined with a **carrier wave** of higher frequency. At the receiving end the carrier wave is removed and the information is recovered. When a signal is combined with a carrier wave, the signal is said to **modulate** the carrier wave. Removing the carrier wave to recover the signal is called **demodulation**.

▼ **Figure 8B14** *Ordinary radio broadcasts use carrier frequencies between about 200 kHz and 100 MHz. Carrier wave frequencies for other links may be higher or lower than this.*

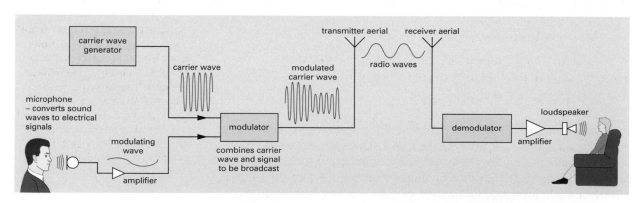

A carrier wave may be modulated in several ways. **Amplitude modulation** (AM) uses a carrier wave that has a **constant frequency**. The amplitude of this carrier wave changes with the signal to be transmitted. In **frequency modulation** (FM) the carrier wave has a **constant amplitude**, and the frequency of the wave varies.

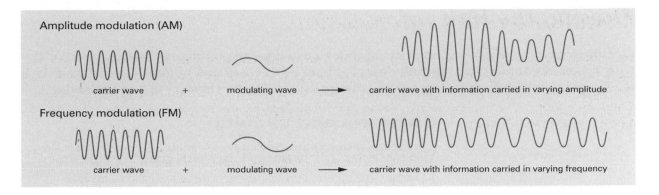

Amplitude modulation (AM)

carrier wave + modulating wave → carrier wave with information carried in varying amplitude

Frequency modulation (FM)

carrier wave + modulating wave → carrier wave with information carried in varying frequency

A third method of modulation produces a digital signal from an analogue signal, using **pulse code modulation** (PCM). The analogue signal to be transmitted is sampled at regular intervals. At each instant it is sampled, the analogue value of the signal is assigned to one of a number of values. Each of these values is expressed by a binary number. A single **bi**nary digit is known as a **bit**. (A bit may have a value of 0 or 1.) If we use an 8-bit number to represent the possible values of the signal, the signal may have any one of $2^8 = 256$ possible values, from 0000 0000 to 1111 1111.

The rate of sampling depends on the frequency of the signal to be sampled – as a general rule, an analogue signal of frequency f needs to be sampled at a minimum rate of $2f$ in order to produce a digital signal which accurately represents it. (This means that a sampling rate of around 8 kHz must be used for telephone signals.)

The result of pulse code modulation is a string of pulses which represent the analogue signal. At the receiving end the analogue signal is produced from the digital signal again.

The rate at which bits are sent to transmit the signal is called the **bit rate**. If the sampling frequency is 8000 Hz and each sample is represented by 8 bits, then

    bit rate = number of bits × sampling frequency
            = 8 bits × 8000 Hz
            = 64 000 bits per second

It is useful to be able to calculate the bandwidth of a PCM signal. The signal bandwidth is found from the relationship

    PCM signal bandwidth = 0.5 × bit rate

For the signal above, the bandwidth is 32 kHz.

A big advantage of using modulated carrier waves to send information is that it allows us to send more than one message at a time along a single transmission link. This is called **multiplexing**. For example, **frequency division multiplexing** may be used to send a number of AM or FM signals along a single transmission link. Each signal is sent with a carrier wave, which has a different frequency to the carrier waves of each of the other signals. At the receiving end, electronic circuits tuned to pick up only the required carrier frequency enable each carrier wave with its modulating signal to be detected. The modulated carriers can then be demodulated, and the signal processed.

▲ **Figure 8B15** *Amplitude modulation is used for short, medium and long wave radio transmissions and the picture signal in TV broadcasts. Frequency modulation is used for vhf radio broadcasts and to transmit TV sound. It is also the method of modulation used in computer and facsimile communication.*

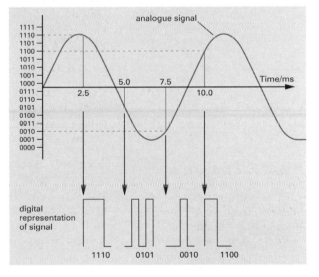

▲ **Figure 8B16** *A simple sinusoidal analogue signal, showing how sampling produces a digital signal. For clarity, the analogue value of the signal has been assigned to one of 16 levels rather than to one of 256 levels. This produces a 4-bit number representing the signal, rather than an 8-bit number. The sampling rate here is 400 Hz.*

Making the link

Deciding what type of communication link to use depends on many factors. Each of the four types of communication link described here has costs and benefits associated with it. Choosing which technology to use involves weighing up these costs and benefits.

Channels and circuits

A **communication channel** is a way of sending information between a source and a receiver. Normal two way communication therefore requires two communication channels; together, these are called a **circuit**.

Coaxial cables

Coaxial cables are a well proven means of communication. A typical coaxial cable contains steel wires (for strength) and two copper conductors arranged coaxially, one inside the other. The conductors are separated by an insulating layer, usually polythene. The whole cable is insulated, and may then have a protective coating around it, depending on where it is to be used.

▶ **Figure 8B17** *A cross section through a typical coaxial cable.*

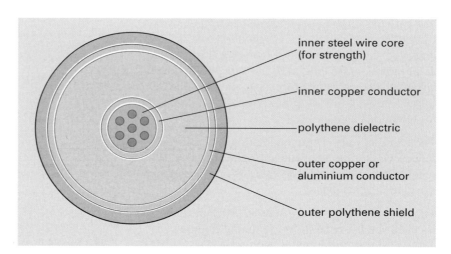

inner steel wire core (for strength)

inner copper conductor

polythene dielectric

outer copper or aluminium conductor

outer polythene shield

▼ **Figure 8B18**

Coaxial cables	
Advantages	**Disadvantages**
A tried and tested technology – coaxial cables have been used for years, and are well understood.	Coaxial cables have a relatively low bandwidth compared with optical fibres and microwave links.
Reliable – cables and repeaters are designed to last 25 years.	Prone to electromagnetic interference (for example, from cables carrying electric currents).
	Leakage of electromagnetic waves from the cable leads to **crosstalk** between channels. (The signal from one channel can be heard on another channel.)
	It is possible to tap the information travelling through a cable by connecting a circuit from outside the cable into the communication circuit.
	Repairing faulty cables or repeaters can be expensive where the cable is underground or where it runs on the seabed.

Optical fibres

Optical fibres are made of glass. A fine glass fibre, which can be thinner than a human hair, is coated with another type of glass in such a way that light travelling through the fibre is reflected off the walls of the fibre and stays inside it. It is effectively a 'pipe' for light to travel through.

Like coaxial cables, the signal becomes attenuated as it travels through the optical fibre, and so repeaters are needed at intervals. **Dispersion** is the other main problem with optical fibres. This arises in two ways (see Figure 8B19). Both of these distort the signal and limit the rate at which data can be transmitted.

Dispersion is minimized by using light from a laser, which is very nearly monochromatic. In addition, the fibres used are designed so that the effect of different path lengths on the light travelling through them is very small.

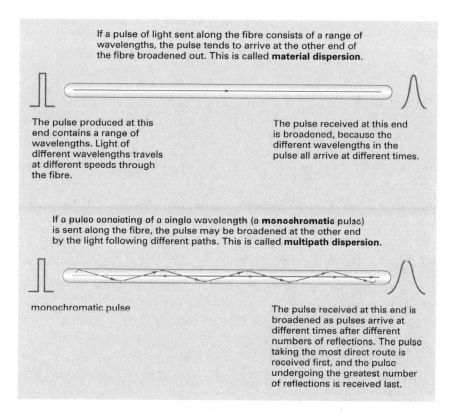

◀ Figure 8B19

If a pulse of light sent along the fibre consists of a range of wavelengths, the pulse tends to arrive at the other end of the fibre broadened out. This is called **material dispersion**.

The pulse produced at this end contains a range of wavelengths. Light of different wavelengths travels at different speeds through the fibre.

The pulse received at this end is broadened, because the different wavelengths in the pulse all arrive at different times.

If a pulse consisting of a single wavelength (a **monochromatic** pulse) is sent along the fibre, the pulse may be broadened at the other end by the light following different paths. This is called **multipath dispersion**.

monochromatic pulse

The pulse received at this end is broadened as pulses arrive at different times after different numbers of reflections. The pulse taking the most direct route is received first, and the pulse undergoing the greatest number of reflections is received last.

▼ Figure 8B20

Optical fibres	
Advantages	**Disadvantages**
Optical fibres are very thin. This means that the cables are small and easy to handle.	Optical fibre technology is relatively new, and its reliability is uncertain.
There is almost no crosstalk between fibres.	Optical fibre cables are difficult to repair if they break.
Repeaters can be spaced very far apart.	Repairing faulty cables or repeaters can be expensive where the cable is underground or where it runs on the seabed.
The signals travelling along an optical fibre are completely immune to electromagnetic interference.	
Optical fibres are almost impossible to tap.	

Terrestrial microwave links

Terrestrial (Earth-based) microwave links have been used to carry information in the UK since 1950. Microwaves are electromagnetic waves with a wavelength longer than infra-red radiation. The microwaves used in telecommunication work have a frequency of around 11 000 MHz (= 11 GHz). Microwaves travel in approximately straight lines, so the distance between a microwave transmitter and receiver is limited by the curvature of the Earth's surface.

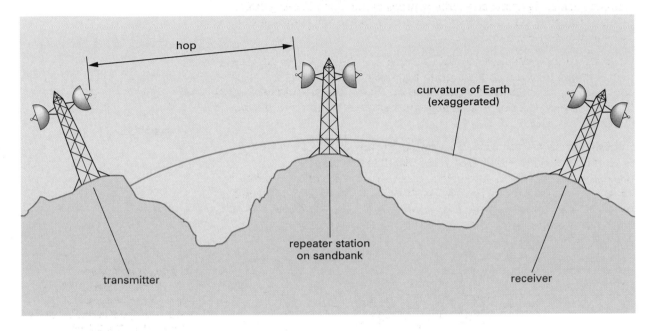

hop

curvature of Earth (exaggerated)

repeater station on sandbank

transmitter

receiver

▲ **Figure 8B21** *Because of the Earth's curvature, a microwave link may need to include a number of 'hops'.*

The transmitting aerials for microwave links use a dish to concentrate the signals in the required direction. At the receiving end a dish is also used – this helps to gather signals over a wider area than if a simple rod or wire aerial were used. The signal at the receiver has a much lower signal-to-noise ratio than the transmitted signal because:

1 the signal spreads out as it travels (like the beam of light from a torch), so only part of the beam falls on the receiving aerial. This is called **free space loss**

2 the signal is attenuated as it travels through the atmosphere, just like the signal in a coaxial cable or optical fibre

3 noise is introduced into the signal. This noise is mainly due to the atmosphere. The electronic systems in the transmitter and receiver contribute some noise too.

▼ **Figure 8B22**

Terrestrial microwave links	
Advantages	**Disadvantages**
A tried and tested technology – terrestrial microwave links have been used for years, and are well understood.	The towers needed to support microwave transmitters/receivers can be expensive, especially when they need to be sited in cities or in stretches of water.
A microwave communication channel has a very large bandwidth so it can carry many signals.	The microwave signal is much more easily tapped than a signal in a cable.
Maintaining microwave links is inexpensive.	

Satellite microwave links

Satellite microwave links are similar to terrestrial microwave links. Satellite microwave links use frequencies ranging from 3 GHz up to 30 GHz. Signals are affected by factors similar to those that affect terrestrial links. Free space loss is much more of a problem in satellite links than it is in terrestrial links, as the signal has to travel about 35 000 km from the transmitting station to the satellite. Noise is also introduced from a much wider range of sources, including terrestrial sources such as lightning and radio sources in and outside our galaxy. Satellite transmitting and receiving stations make use of dishes in the same way as terrestrial links.

Communications satellites (including those used for broadcasting television programmes) are placed in a **geostationary orbit**, 35 000 km above the equator. At this height above the Earth, the satellite orbits the Earth once every 24 hours, so it appears stationary when viewed from the Earth's surface.

Satellites are very expensive to design, build and launch. They have a limited lifetime of around seven years. Satellites use solar cells to produce electricity for their electronic circuits. Failure of the satellite is usually due to failure of these solar cells, together with exhaustion of the fuel for the attitude jets, used to keep the satellite lined up with the transmitting and receiving stations on Earth. Once launched, satellites are generally very reliable.

◀ **Figure 8B23** *When you telephone someone 10 000 km away via satellite link, the telephone signal makes a journey of more than 70 000 km!*

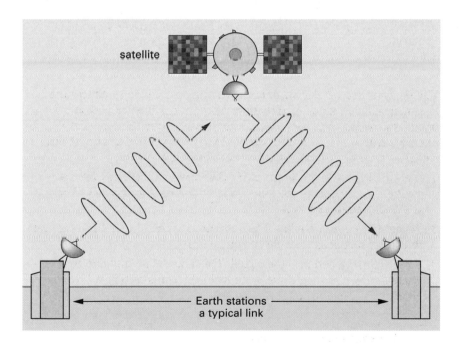

▼ **Figure 8B24**

Satellite microwave links	
Advantages	**Disadvantages**
Satellite technology has a history of great reliability.	It is very expensive to build a communications satellite and launch it into orbit.
Satellite microwave links may have even larger bandwidths than terrestrial microwave links.	Satellite signals are easily received, and so the signals can be readily tapped.
	Satellites have a limited lifetime.

Thoughts and actions

1 In measurements to find the Young modulus of a metal (using the technique shown on page 430), a student found the following results:

original length of wire = 2.370 ± 0.002 m
extension = 12 ± 1 mm
diameter = 1.03 ± 0.01 mm
load = 49 ± 0.5 N

Calculate:
a the percentage error in each quantity
b the value of the Young modulus
c the percentage error in the Young modulus. Which measurement contributes most to the error in the final answer?

2 It is often found that measurements of a quantity vary, and so it is necessary to make repeat measurements. For each of the following quantities give a reason why measurements might vary:
a the density of polyurethane foam
b the pH of soil samples from a field
c the milk yield from cows in a herd
d the useful life of a battery.

3 Graphs are a useful way of presenting information. Figure 8T1 shows how the consumption of fruit and vegetables has changed in the UK over a period of three decades.

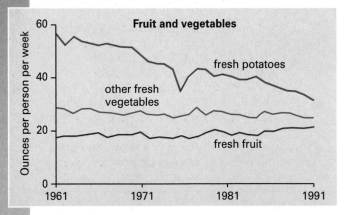

▲ **Figure 8T1**

a Write a paragraph to summarize the information contained in the graph.
b What reasons might there be for the changes you have identified?
c The graph itself does not allow you to decide the true causes of any change. How could you set about testing any theories you may have?

4 Figure 8T2 shows the numbers of new drug addicts notified over a period of twenty years. How might this information be best displayed to show the trends? What trends can you see in the data?

	1973	**1981**	**1986**	**1991**	**1992**
Heroin	508	1660	4855	6328	7658
Methadone	328	431	659	2180	2493
Cocaine	132	174	520	882	1131
Morphine	226	355	343	185	161
Opium	0	0	23	12	5

▲ **Figure 8T2** *New addicts notified: selected types of drug (UK).*

5 A correspondent of *The Independent* newspaper presented figures for the cumulative rainfall in his back garden over a period of 40 years, for different days of the week. He noticed that Thursdays seemed abnormally wet, and Sundays abnormally dry.

Day of week	**Rainfall** /inches
Sunday	125.17
Monday	132.78
Tuesday	136.43
Wednesday	134.85
Thursday	143.16
Friday	133.94
Saturday	132.57

▲ **Figure 8T3**

a Calculate the mean value of the rainfall figures, and their standard deviation.
b Comment on the variation of the data.
c Comment on the number of significant figures presented.
d Is it unwise to hang out washing on Thursdays?

6 Figure 8A22 on page 438 shows a graph with an anomalous point. Study the data and the graph, and suggest what went wrong.

7 What advantages and disadvantages might there be for a student if this book was published **a** on the Internet, or **b** on CD-ROM?

8 In the Ainsdale National Nature Reserve study (page 452) students identified a number of trends in the data.

   a Pick out the rows in Figure 8A42 on page 454 where you believe the data show a consistent trend. Briefly describe the trend in each case. Can you explain these trends?

   b In the rows where there are no consistent changes in the values of the parameters concerned, would you have expected any trends? If so, say what they are. Discuss the reasons why the measurements might not have produced the expected patterns.

9 In the Ainsdale Nature Reserve study, summaries of the changes in herbaceous vegetation in the different communities appear in Figures 8A42 and 8A43 (pages 454–5).

   a Explain the differences between the species present in the dune slacks and the fixed dunes.

   b What are the numbers of marker species present in each community? As far as you can, explain the differences between the numbers of herbaceous plant species in the communities.

10 In their study of the Ainsdale National Nature Reserve (page 452), the students of Blackpool and the Fylde College made measurements of several environmental factors – temperature, wind speed etc. They were only able to make measurements over a short space of time. Their study would have benefitted from long-term measurements, perhaps over twelve months.

Design an automatic datalogging system which they could have used to build up a picture of how environmental conditions vary at one point in the reserve.

What measurements would be difficult to carry out automatically?

11 Computer-based data collection systems have many advantages over human recorders. Nine advantages are shown in Figure 8A16 on page 435. For each of these, give a practical example where this feature would be of great benefit.

Suggest some situations in which a human recorder might be advantageous over a computer-based system.

12 A database is a useful way of storing information; it can be accessed and updated rapidly. Design a database for shoe sole materials – see page 75. What fields would an individual record include? Why would such a database be useful?

13 In an investigation of the breeding of guinea pigs, rough-haired pigs are crossed with smooth-haired. Sixty offspring were examined. The results obtained were:

rough-haired: 49
smooth-haired: 11

Genetic arguments suggested that rough and smooth should be produced in a 3:1 ratio.

   a How many rough and smooth would you predict in a sample of 60 offspring?

   b Use the χ^2 test to determine whether the observed number of rough-haired offspring was significantly greater than expected.

14 The data for Test 1 in Figure 8A20a on page 437 is shown as two types of histogram. Draw similar histograms for the data for Test 2.

Write a short conclusion, summarizing the results of the two tests.

15 To understand the term **bandwidth** (page 474), it is helpful to investigate a radio. Find a radio set which can be tuned by turning a dial. Start with the longwave band, and tune slowly right across the dial. You should hear several stations.

   a BBC Radio 4 uses a frequency of 198 kHz, but it can be picked up at a range of frequencies above and below this. Record the highest and lowest frequencies at which you can just detect the station. Find the frequencies of other stations broadcasting on this waveband. What is the spacing of their frequencies?

   b The stations using a waveband must be sufficiently separated that your radio set can tune to each one individually. The bandwidth of human speech is about 15 kHz – that is, the frequencies of our voices and which we can hear extend up to 15 kHz. Radio 4 occupies a frequency range between about 183 kHz and 213 kHz (i.e. 198 ± 15 kHz). Are the broadcast stations which you have found sufficiently far apart to allow the full range of audible frequencies to be broadcast?

   c Many music stations broadcast on the VHF (FM) band, between 88 MHz and 108 MHz. Use the idea of bandwidth to explain why this is a better waveband than longwave for broadcasting high quality sound. How many stations could be fitted into this waveband? Check your prediction by tuning across the VHF band.

16 Security can be important in international communication of information. Some communication systems are more easily tapped than others.
  a Compare the security of the following systems: coaxial cables, radio and microwave links, optical fibres.
  b Suggest a suitable communication system for an international network of spies. Who else might require a high-security data transmission network?
  c What other security measures might be taken to ensure the confidentiality of data?

17 The physicist shown in Figure 8B8 (page 469) is sending a message from Gloucester to a colleague in California. Her message follows a complicated path as it crosses the world.

Draw a block diagram to show the various transformations of the message. At each stage, say whether the message is being transmitted as an optical, electrical or electromagnetic signal.

18 Communications satellites orbit at a height of 35 000 km above the equator. Draw a scale diagram to show the path of a signal sent by a scientist in Newcastle (55 °N) to a colleague in Sydney (34 °S) via a satellite. Estimate the time taken for the signal to follow this path. Would such a time delay be noticeable during a telephone conversation?
(Radius of Earth = 6400 km)

19 Medical records are increasingly stored on computers. Such records might be of interest to doctors, nurses, administrators, researchers, drug companies and, of course, the patient. Suggest reasons why this computerization is useful. Are there any disadvantages?

How could a patient's interests be harmed if the requirements of the Data Protection Act are not followed?

20 In measurements to find the resistance of a lamp, a digital voltmeter and a digital ammeter were used. The results shown in the table (Figure 8T4) were obtained. These were analysed using a calculator to deduce a best-straight-line fit, with the gradient being the resistance R.

a Comment on the precision with which the data are presented in the table.
b Using a calculator, deduce values for R, and for the correlation coefficient r.
c Draw a graph of V against I.
d Comment on the use of a calculator to analyse the data.
e What would you conclude from the data?
f Design a circuit incorporating a datalogger which would provide more satisfactory results. Why would this be better than the simple circuit described above?

Voltage V/V	Current I/A
1.01	0.03
2.00	0.05
3.04	0.08
3.98	0.12
5.00	0.13
6.04	0.15
6.98	0.17
8.01	0.19
9.10	0.21
10.02	0.22
11.03	0.24

▲ **Figure 8T4**

21 In the course of your GNVQ Science studies, you will have made many laboratory measurements.
  a Identify at least one set of measurements which included a random error. Explain the origin of this error, and say how it could have been reduced.
  b Identify at least one set of measurements which included a systematic error. Explain the origin of this error, and say how it could have been reduced or eliminated.

22 The data shown in Figure 8A11 on page 432 were analysed using a calculator capable of calculating simple statistical quantities.
  a Use such a calculator to check the results shown on page 433 for the mean and standard deviation.
  b If the anomalous result (trial 15) is included, does this change the results significantly?

Reference section

R1 SI units

There are standard international units for all the things people measure in science.

Some basic SI units

◀ Figure R1.1

Quantity	Symbol	Unit	Unit symbol
Length	l	metre	m
Mass	m	kilogram	kg
Time	t	second	s
Electric current	I	ampere	A
Temperature	T	kelvin	K
Amount of substance		mole	mol

Some more SI units

◀ Figure R1.2

Quantity	Symbol	Unit	Unit symbol
Area	A	square metre	m^2
Volume	V	cubic metre*	m^3
Distance	s	metre	m
Speed	v	metre per second	$m\,s^{-1}$
Acceleration	a	metre per second per second	$m\,s^{-2}$
Density	ρ	kilogram per cubic metre	$kg\,m^{-3}$
Force	F	newton	N
Pressure and stress	p	pascal	Pa
Work and energy	W	joule	J
Power	P	watt	W
Electric potential difference (voltage)	V	volt	V
Electrical resistance	R	ohm	Ω
Electrical resistivity	ρ	ohm metre	$\Omega\,m$
Electrical conductivity	σ	siemen per metre	$S\,m^{-1}$

*You will also see volume measured in centimetre cubed (cm^3), decimetre cubed (dm^3) and litre (l). $1\,dm^3 = 1\,l = 10^{-3}\,m^3$.

Some SI prefixes for large and small numbers

Number	Sub-multiple	Prefix	Symbol		Number	Multiple	Prefix	Symbol
1/100	10^{-2}	centi	c		1000	10^3	kilo	k
1/1000	10^{-3}	milli	m		1000000	10^6	mega	M
1/1000000	10^{-6}	micro	μ		1000000000	10^9	giga	G
1/1000000000	10^{-9}	nano	n					

For example, a millimetre is one thousandth of a metre, or $10^{-3}\,m$. A kilogram is a thousand grams.

▲ Figure R1.3

R2 Definitions

Density: the mass per unit volume

Tensile strength: the stretching force needed to break a sample of the material divided by its cross-sectional area

Compressive strength: the compressing force needed to break a sample of the material divided by its cross-sectional area

Young modulus: the ratio of the tensile stress to the resulting strain on a sample of material

Refractive index of a transparent material: the ratio of the speed of light in vacuum to the speed of light in the material

Electrical conductivity: the current through a cross section of $1\,m^2$ when the potential difference is $1\,V$ for every metre of length

Thermal conductivity: the rate of energy transfer through a cross section $1\,m^2$ when the temperature change is $1\,K$ for every metre of length

Specific latent heat of fusion: the energy needed to change $1\,kg$ of a substance at its melting point in its solid state to $1\,kg$ of the material in its liquid state, and the energy released when $1\,kg$ of the liquid changes to $1\,kg$ of the solid

Specific heat capacity: the energy needed to raise the temperature of $1\,kg$ of a substance by $1\,K$

Thermal linear expansivity: the fractional increase in length of a material for a temperature change of $1\,K$

Temperature scales

The **thermodynamic temperature scale** is used for scientific measurement. It is measured in the unit **kelvin (K)**. The scale is defined by the triple point of water – the temperature at which water vapour, pure water and ice are in equilibrium. This temperature is defined as $273.16\,K$. $0\,K$ is the point where all molecular motion has effectively ceased. The symbol for the Kelvin temperature is T.

The Celsius temperature scale is defined by $\theta = T - 273.16$. The unit of the Celsius scale is °C.

A $1\,K$ change in temperature is the same as a 1°C change.

R3 Properties of materials

Substance	Density	Tensile strength	Compressive strength	Young modulus	Type
Units	$kg\,m^{-3}$	pascals (or $N\,m^{-2}$)	pascals (or $N\,m^{-2}$)	pascals (or $N\,m^{-2}$)	
Aluminium	2700	6 to 40×10^7	6 to 40×10^7	7.0×10^{10}	polycrystalline
Copper	8940	2.2 to 4.3×10^8		13×10^{10}	polycrystalline
Iron	7860	2.1×10^8		21.1×10^{10}	polycrystalline
Lead	11350	1.5×10^7		1.6×10^{10}	polycrystalline
Mild steel	7700	2.5×10^8	2.5×10^8	2.0×10^{11}	polycrystalline
Stainless steel	7800	7 to 15×10^8	7 to 15×10^8		polycrystalline
Oak timber	720	2.1×10^7	4.4 to 15×10^6	5 to 14×10^9	fibrous composite
Plasterboard	700 to 1300	2 to 5×10^6			amorphous
Common brick	1500 to 1800	depends on joints	7 to 70×10^6	7×10^9	amorphous
Breeze block	1300 to 1500		4 to 6×10^6	2 to 4×10^{10}	composite
Concrete	2200 to 2400	cracks unless reinforced	6 to 70×10^6	1.5 to 4.0×10^{10}	composite
Sheet glass	2460	3 to 9×10^7		7.0×10^{10}	amorphous
Earthenware	2500	5.0×10^7 (bending test)		5.0×10^{10}	amorphous, ceramic
Electrical porcelain	2500	1.05×10^8 (bending test)		7.0×10^{10}	amorphous, ceramic
Acrylic (e.g. Perspex)	1170 to 1200	5.5 to 7×10^7	8.3 to 12×10^7	2.5 to 3.5×10^9	polymer
Nylon 6	1120 to 1140	4.5 to 9.0×10^7		7.0×10^8	polymer
Polythene (low density)	920	1.5×10^7		1.5×10^8	polymer
Polythene (high density)	960	2.9×10^7		1.0×10^9	polymer
Polyvinylchloride (PVC)	125 to 139	2 to 6×10^7	0.9 to 5.5×10^7	2.4 to 4.1×10^9	polymer
Glass-reinforced polyester	1500 to 2000	7.0 to 50×10^7	1.0 to 4.0×10^8	5 to 7×10^9	composite
Dental enamel	2960	8.3 to 10.3×10^6	3.6 to 9.7×10^8	46.2 to 47.6×10^9	
Dentine	2110	3.7 to 5.2×10^7	2.3 to 3.5×10^8	8.3 to 9.0×10^9	

▲ **Figure R3.1** *Mechanical properties of some solids.*

Substance	Refractive index	Electrical resistivity	Thermal conductivity	Specific latent heat of fusion	Specific heat capacity	Thermal linear expansivity
Units		$\Omega\,m$	$W\,m^{-1}K^{-1}$	$J\,kg^{-1}$	$J\,kg^{-1}\,K^{-1}$	K^{-1}
Aluminium	opaque	2.4×10^{-8}	200	4.12×10^5	8.99×10^2	2.30×10^{-5}
Copper	opaque	1.6×10^{-8}	385	2.05×10^5	3.87×10^2	1.67×10^{-5}
Iron	opaque	8.9×10^{-8}	80	2.69×10^5	4.50×10^2	1.17×10^{-5}
Lead	opaque	1.9×10^{-7}	38	2.5×10^4	1.28×10^2	2.89×10^{-5}
Mild steel	opaque	1.7×10^{-7}	60			1.20×10^{-5}
Stainless steel	opaque	5.5×10^{-7}	25			1.15×10^{-5}
Oak timber	opaque		0.16			3×10^{-6}
Plasterboard	opaque		0.18			
Common brick	opaque		1.0			6×10^{-6}
Breeze block	opaque		0.4			1.2×10^{-5}
Concrete	opaque		1.45			1.2×10^{-5}
Sheet glass	1.51	3×10^6				8.5×10^{-6}
Earthenware	opaque		1.6			7.0×10^{-6}
Electrical porcelain	opaque	10^{10} to 10^{12}	1.6			7.0×10^{-6}
Acrylic (e.g. Perspex)	1.49	10^{13}	0.04 to 0.14		1500	9.0×10^{-6}
Nylon 6	opaque	10^9 to 10^{11}	0.25		1600	8.0×10^{-6}
Polythene (low density)	1.51	10^{14}	0.33		2300	1.5 to 2.0×10^{-4}
Polythene (high density)	1.54	10^{14}	0.45 to 0.52		2300	1.0×10^{-4}
Polyvinylchloride (PVC)	1.52	10^9 to 10^{14}	0.12 to 0.17		900 to 2000	5.0 to 24×10^{-5}
Glass-reinforced polyester	opaque	10^{13}				2.0 to 3.0×10^{-4}

▲ **Figure R3.2** *Physical properties of some solids.*

R4 Some useful physical quantities

Quantity	Symbol	Value	Units
Speed of light in a vacuum	c	3.0×10^8	$m\,s^{-1}$
Faraday constant	F	9.6×10^4	$C\,mol^{-1}$
Avogadro constant	L, N_A	6.0×10^{23}	mol^{-1}
Speed of sound in air		3.3×10^2	$m\,s^{-1}$
Acceleration caused by gravity	g	9.8	$m\,s^{-2}$

◀ **Figure R4.1**

R5 Some other approximate values

Lengths

10^{-10} m	diameter of a hydrogen atom
2×10^{-6} m	diameter of a *Staphylococcus* bacterium
10^{-4} m	thickness of paper
10^{-1} m	the width of an adult hand
10^{2} m	the distance that a top level athlete can sprint in 10 seconds
10^{4} m	maximum depth of the ocean
1.2×10^{7} m	the diameter of the Earth
1.5×10^{11} m	the distance from the Earth to the Sun

Masses

10^{-7} kg	grain of sand
1.5×10^{-2} kg	house mouse
4 kg	house brick
6.5×10^{2} kg	small car
10^{5} kg	blue whale
3×10^{8} kg	laden super tanker

Times

10^{-8} s	light to cross a room
10^{-1} s	human reaction time
10 s	time for athlete to sprint 100 m
5×10^{2} s	time for light to travel from Sun to Earth
10^{5} s	1 day
2×10^{9} s	human life span

R6 Small measurements

There are two devices which can measure thicknesses to a much more precise level than a rule.

Vernier callipers

Vernier callipers measure to the nearest 0.1 mm and can be used to measure thicknesses up to several centimetres.

The position of the vernier zero against the main scale gives the approximate distance between the jaws. The next level of precision is given by the mark on the vernier scale that exactly coincides with a mark on the main scale.

Vernier scales are also found on travelling microscopes.

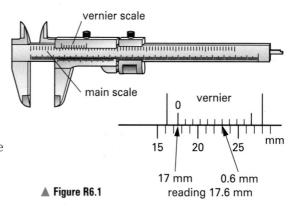

▲ Figure R6.1

Micrometer screw gauge

The micrometer measures distances of a few millimetres to the nearest 0.01 mm.

The accurately threaded screw is attached to the drum so that when the drum rotates the jaw opening changes by a known distance. Normally a complete rotation of the drum gives a jaw movement of 0.5 mm. The drum is graduated into 50 divisions so each division represents 0.01 mm.

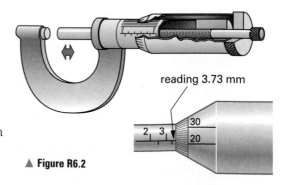

reading 3.73 mm

▲ Figure R6.2

R7 Electrical and electronic circuit symbols

Labelling resistors

There is an international code for the labelling of resistors.

1st letter (shows position of the decimal point):   R ohms   K kilohms   M megohms

2nd letter shows tolerance: F ±1%   G ±2%   J ±5%   K ±10%   M ±20%

So: 1R0M denotes $1.0\,\Omega \pm 20\,\%$ 100K0K denotes $100\,k\Omega \pm 10\%$ 6K8G denotes $6.8\,k\Omega \pm 2\%$

Circuit symbols

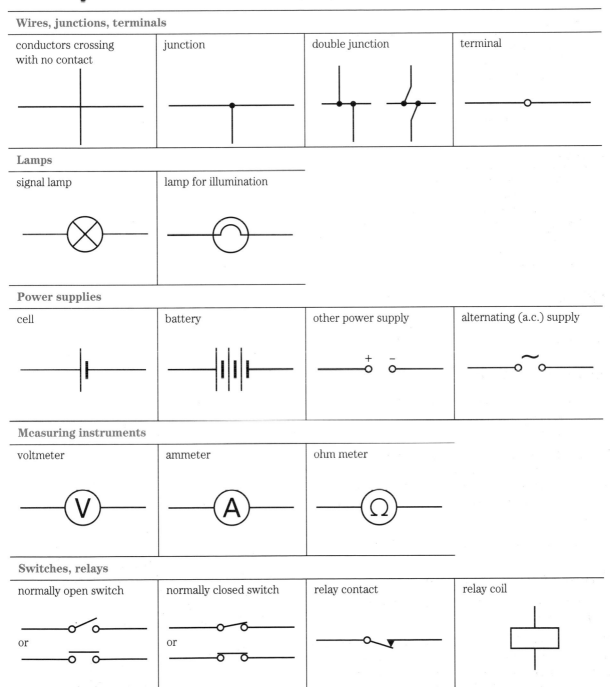

▲ **Figure R7.1** *(continued overleaf)*

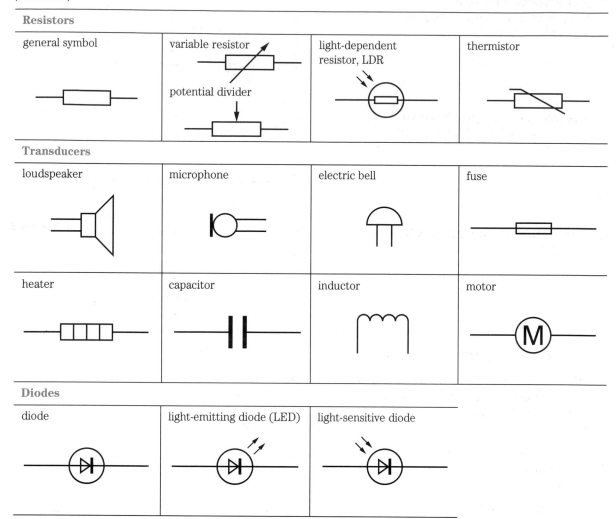

Resistors

general symbol	variable resistor / potential divider	light-dependent resistor, LDR	thermistor

Transducers

loudspeaker	microphone	electric bell	fuse
heater	capacitor	inductor	motor

Diodes

diode	light-emitting diode (LED)	light-sensitive diode

R8 Graphs

It is useful to be able to recognize certain shapes of graph. Where appropriate, the examples below show how to change the quantities on the axes to produce a straight line graph.

1 *y* is directly proportional to *x*
m = gradient
$y = mx$

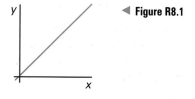

◀ **Figure R8.1**

2 linear relationship between *y* and *x*
m = gradient
c = intercept on y-axis
$y = mx + c$

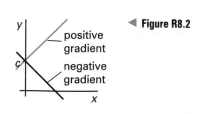

◀ **Figure R8.2**

positive gradient

negative gradient

3 y is proportional to x^2
k = gradient of straight line graph
$y = kx^2$

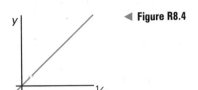
◄ **Figure R8.3**

4 y is inversely proportional to x
k = gradient of straight line graph
$y = k/x$

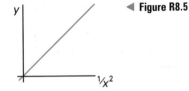
◄ **Figure R8.4**

5 y is inversely proportional to x^2
$y = k/x^2$

◄ **Figure R8.5**

Errors on graphs

On this graph of voltage V against current I, the data points have been drawn with error bars, to show the error in the experimental values of V. The resistance R is found by determining the gradient of the graph. To deduce R and the error in R, proceed as follows.

1 Draw the best fit straight line through the data points.

2 The gradient of this line is R.

3 Draw a second straight line which lies more-or-less within the limits of the error bars, or within the scatter of the data. This is the error line.

4 Find the gradient of the error line. This is the upper (or lower) limit on the value of R.

5 Write down the value of R with its error.

From best fit line: $R = 10.0\,\Omega$

From error line: $R = 11.5\,\Omega$

Hence $R = (10.0 \pm 1.5)\,\Omega$

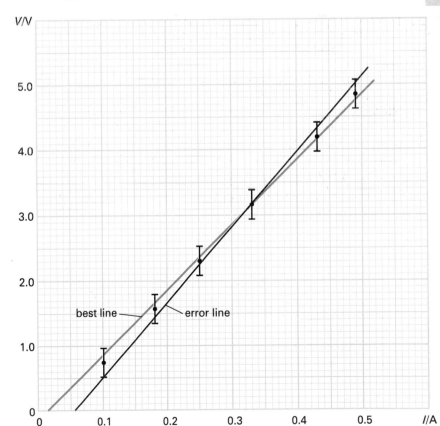

► **Figure R8.6**

R9 Comparing power levels using decibels

The **decibel** is a unit for measuring loudness of sounds. In fact, decibels are used to compare power levels, something that is often done in telecommunications work. Decibels (dB) measure ratios, using logarithms. Using decibels helps because,

1 a wide range of powers is used in telecommunications, and,

2 the effect of a series of increases and decreases in power level in a transmission link can be found by simply adding together all the changes expressed in decibels.

The basic unit for comparing power levels is the **bel**, named after Alexander Graham Bell. This is a rather large unit, so in practice the decibel (dB) is used:

$$1 \text{ bel} = 10 \text{ dB}$$

The ratio of two power levels P_1 and P_2 in dB is given by:

$$\text{ratio in dB} = 10 \log_{10} \frac{P_1}{P_2}$$

The units used to measure P_1 and P_2 must be the same in each case. As they are power levels, they will normally be measured in **watts** (W).

Signal-to-noise ratio is calculated in a similar way:

$$\text{signal-to-noise ratio in dB} = 10 \log_{10} \frac{\text{signal power}}{\text{noise power}}$$

Example 1

The input to a repeater unit in a cable is 20 mW, and the output from it is 300 mW.

$$\text{ratio} = 10 \log_{10} \frac{300 \,\text{mW}}{20 \,\text{mW}}$$

$$= 10 \log_{10} 15$$

$$= 10 \times 1.176$$

$$= 11.76 \,\text{dB}$$

The repeater has a **gain** (i.e. the output is greater than the input power) of 11.76 dB.

Example 2

The power input to a transmission link is 800 mW. The signal is attenuated to 200 mW after 10 km.

$$\text{ratio} = 10 \log_{10} \frac{200 \, \text{mW}}{800 \, \text{mW}}$$

$$= 10 \log_{10} 0.25$$

$$= 10 \times -0.602 \, \text{dB}$$

$$= -6.02 \, \text{dB}$$

The **loss** over 10 km of the link is 6.02 dB, so the rate of power loss along the link is $0.602 \, \text{dB km}^{-1}$. (The word loss shows that the output power is less than the input power.)

Example 3

If a signal is amplified by the repeater in Example 1 above, and then travels along 10 km of line as in 2 above, the overall change is given by

$$+11.76 \, \text{dB} - 6.02 \, \text{dB} = +5.74 \, \text{dB}$$

i.e. a total gain of 5.74 dB.

Example 4

The signal power in a telephone line should be at least 100 times the noise power if the telephone signal is to be of a reasonable quality. What signal-to-noise ratio is this?

$$\text{signal-to-noise ratio} = 10 \log_{10} \frac{100}{1}$$

$$= 10 \times 2$$

$$= 20 \, \text{dB}$$

R10 Chemical formulas

The formulas of compounds listed in Figure R20.1 have all been determined by experiment. Consider for example, iron(II) chloride, $FeCl_2$. The chemical formula records:

- the elements present   iron, Fe and chlorine, Cl
- the number of atoms of each element   1Fe and 2Cl.

The proportion of one iron atom to two chlorine atoms is fixed.

When a solid contains **water of crystallization**, in a fixed proportion, the number of molecules of water may be recorded after the formula of the salt using a dot as in hydrated iron(II) chloride, $FeCl_2.4H_2O$, compared to anhydrous iron(II) chloride, $FeCl_2$.

The general rule about writing the formulas of ionic compounds is that the numbers of each ion have to be chosen so that the positive and negative charges balance. In iron(II) chloride there are two choride ions, Cl^-, to each iron(II) ion, Fe^{2+}.

In chemical equations follow the guidelines in Figure R10.1.

◀ **Figure R10.1**

Type of substance	Examples
If the element or compound is molecular, write the formula for the molecule.	Most non-metals, and most compounds of non-metals with non-metals, including: chlorine, Cl_2; oxygen O_2; water, H_2O; ethane, C_2H_6; ammonia, NH_3.
If the substance is an element with a giant structure of atoms, write the symbol for a single atom.	All metals, including: magnesium, Mg; calcium, Ca; iron, Fe; sodium, Na. A few non-metals, especially: carbon, C; silicon, Si.
If the substance is a compound with a giant structure, write the simplest formula for the compound.	All ionic compounds (metals with non-metals), such as: sodium chloride, NaCl; magnesium oxide, MgO; zinc sulphate, $ZnSO_4$; potassium carbonate, K_2CO_3; copper nitrate, $Cu(NO_3)_2$. A few compounds of non-metals with non-metals – in particular: silicon dioxide, SiO_2.

R11 Balancing equations

There is no change in the total number of atoms of each element as reactants turn into products. Follow four steps to write a balanced equation. Consider the reaction of iron with dilute hydrochloric acid.

Step 1 Identify the reactants and products by name: iron and hydrochloric acid react to form iron(II) chloride and hydrogen

Step 2 Write down their correct formulas:

$$Fe + HCl \longrightarrow FeCl_2 + H_2$$

Step 3 Balance the numbers of atoms of each element by adjusting the number of entities of each substance:

$$Fe + 2HCl \longrightarrow FeCl_2 + H_2$$

Step 4 Arrive at a complete balanced equation by adding information about the physical state of the compounds:

$$Fe(s) + 2HCl(aq) \longrightarrow FeCl_2(aq) + H_2(g)$$

Balancing redox equations

Oxidation numbers (see pages 10–11) can help to balance the equation for a redox reaction. Consider the oxidation of iron(II) ions by chlorate(V) ions.

$$ClO_3^- + H^+ + Fe^{2+} \longrightarrow Cl^- + Fe^{3+} + H_2O$$

First identify the elements which actually change in oxidation number. The chlorine changes from +5 in $ClO_3^-(aq)$ to −1 in $Cl^-(aq)$, a change of 6 units. The iron changes from +2 in $Fe^{2+}(aq)$ to +3 in $Fe^{3+}(aq)$, a change of 1 unit.

The total change in oxidation number must be the same in both directions, so there must be six $Fe^{2+}(aq)$ ions reacting with every $ClO_3^-(aq)$ ion. The first stage of balancing thus gives:

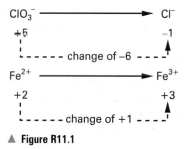

▲ **Figure R11.1**

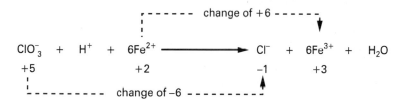

◀ **Figure R11.2**

The remaining balancing numbers may now be inserted, so that the balanced equation is

$$ClO_3^-(aq) + 6H^+(aq) + Fe^{2+}(aq) \longrightarrow Cl^-(aq) + Fe^{3+}(aq) + H_2O(l)$$

To balance a redox equation:

1 write down oxidation numbers

2 calculate changes in oxidation numbers which occur

3 balance to give a total oxidation number change of zero

4 balance for oxygen, hydrogen and water

5 check that the + and − charges balance.

R12 Chemical amounts

Amounts in moles

One *mole* of any substance is the amount of substance which contains as many elementary entities as there are carbon atoms in 12 grams (exactly of pure carbon–12).

The unit is the **mole** and its symbol is **mol**. Note that the unit 'mole', the symbol 'mol', and the adjective 'molar' are *not* connected to the terms 'molecule' or 'molecular'.

The **molar mass** of a substance is defined as the mass of one mole of the substance; the entities must be specified.

The symbol for the molar mass of an element is A, and for a molecule is M; the unit is g mol^{-1}. Molar masses of the elements are given in Figure R19.1: the specified entitities for tables of elements are **single atoms**.

To work out the molar masses of compounds you add up the molar masses of the elements in the compound.

Molar mass of ethanol $2C = 24$
C_2H_5OH $\qquad\qquad$ $6H = 6$
$\qquad\qquad\qquad$ $1O = \underline{16}$
$\qquad\qquad\qquad\qquad$ 46 g mol^{-1}

The formula of the entity must be specified.

◀ **Figure R12.1**

Substance	Entity	Molar mass /g mol^{-1}
Iron(II) sulphate	$FeSO_4$	152
Iron(III) sulphate	$Fe_2(SO_4)_3$	400
Hydrated iron(III) sulphate	$Fe_2(SO_4)_3.9H_2O$	562

When an organic compound is liquid it is often convenient to measure it by volume rather than mass, using the relationship

$\qquad$ mass = density $\times$ volume

- Amount of substance /mol $= \dfrac{\text{mass of substance /g}}{\text{molar mass /g mol}^{-1}}$

- Mass of substance /g = amount of substance /mol $\times$ molar mass /g mol^{-1}

Concentrations

For chemists the most useful information about a solution is how many moles of a compound there are per cubic decimetre of solution. For sodium chloride a concentration of 1 mole in 1 cubic decimetre of solution is written as:

$\qquad$ [NaCl] = 1 mol dm^{-3} or 1 M

Notice that square brackets, [ ], are used to identify the entity whose concentration is being recorded. When measuring the sodium chloride very accurately as 58.44 g, dissolving the crystals in water and then adding water to give 1.000 dm^3 of solution the concentration can be written

$\qquad$ [NaCl] = 1.000 mol dm^{-3} or 1.000 M

To prepare solutions of other concentrations, work out the amounts in proportion:

For $\quad$ 1 dm^3 of solution of $\;$ 1 mol dm^{-3} NaCl $\quad$ use 1 mol (1×58.5)g
for $\quad$ 5 dm^3 $\qquad\qquad\qquad\quad$ 1 mol dm^{-3} $\qquad\qquad$ use 5 mol (5×58.5)g
for $\quad$ 100 cm^3 $\qquad\qquad\qquad$ 1 mol dm^{-3} $\qquad\qquad$ use $\dfrac{1}{10}$ mol ($\dfrac{1}{10} \times 58.5$)g

The general expression is:

■ amount of substance /mol = volume /dm^3 × concentration /mol dm^{-3}

where, volume /dm^3 = $\dfrac{\text{volume /cm}^3}{1000 \,\text{cm}^3/\text{dm}^3}$

Because sodium chloride consists of the entities Na$^+$ and Cl$^-$, when [NaCl] = 1 mol dm^{-3} it is also correct to write [Na$^+$] = [Cl$^-$] = 1 mol dm^{-3}.

For sulphuric acid, when [H$_2$SO$_4$] = 1 mol dm^{-3} the concentrations of the ions in solution are

[H$^+$] = 2 mol dm^{-3} and [SO$_4{}^{2-}$] = 1 mol dm^{-3}.

Laboratory reagents

◀ Figure R12.2

Reagent	Concentration
Concentrated sulphuric acid	[H$_2$SO$_4$] = 18 mol dm^{-3}
Concentrated nitric acid	[HNO$_3$] = 16 mol dm^{-3}
Concentrated hydrochloric acid	[HCl] = 10 mol dm^{-3}
Dilute acids, e.g. hydrochloric acid	[HCl] = 2 mol dm^{-3} usually
Dilute alkali, e.g. sodium hydroxide	[NaOH] = 2 mol dm^{-3} usually
Metal salts, e.g. copper sulphate	[CuSO$_4$] = 0.1 mol dm^{-3} typically

Titration calculations

Substance A reacts with substance B according to the equation:

$n_A A + n_B$ ⟩ products

This means that n_A moles of A reacts with n_B moles of B.

Figure R12.3 shows the apparatus that could be used for a titration involving this reaction. The concentration of the solution of A in the flask is c_A mol dm^{-3} and its volume is V_A cm^3. The concentration of the solution of B in the burette is c_B mol dm^{-3}. V_B cm^3 of the solution of B is added from the burette until an indicator shows that the reaction is complete. These quantities are related by this equation:

$$\frac{V_A \times c_A}{V_B \times c_B} = \frac{n_A}{n_B}$$

Amounts of gases

If the pressure and temperature are fixed, then the volume of gas depends on the number of gas molecules present. The type of gas does not matter. The volume of a gas, V, is proportional to the amount of gas, n, if the pressure and temperature are kept constant where amounts are measured in moles.

Two sets of conditions are often used to compare one gas with another.

■ Standard temperature and pressure, stp.
  The standard conditions for gases are 273 K (0 °C) and one atmosphere pressure. Under these conditions, one mole of any gas has a volume of 22.4 dm^3 (22 400 cm^3).
■ Room temperature (20 °C) and pressure (one atmosphere).

a c_B mol dm^{-3} solution of substance B

burette

V_A cm^3 of a c_A mol dm^{-3} solution of substance A

white tile

▲ Figure R12.3

Many experiments in educational laboratories are done under these conditions. The volume of one mole of gas is larger at room temperature than at stp. At room temperature and pressure, the volume of one mole of any gas is approximately $24\,dm^3$ ($24\,000\,cm^3$).

The following formulas can be used in calculations involving gases:

- amount of gas $/mol = \dfrac{\text{volume of gas } /cm^3}{\text{volume of one mole of gas } /cm^3\,mol^{-1}}$

- volume of $=$ amount of $\times$ volume of
  gas $/cm^3$ gas $/mol$ one mole $/cm^3 mol^{-1}$

R13 Naming inorganic compounds

The ending **–ide** shows that a compound contains just the two elements mentioned in the name. Sodium chloride is a compound of sodium and chlorine. Sulphur dioxide is a compound of sulphur and oxygen.

The Roman numerals in the names of compounds are the oxidation numbers of elements (see pages 10–11). For example, in CuO the oxidation number of copper is $+2$ and the compound is copper(II) oxide. In the oxide Cu_2O the oxidation number of copper is $+1$ and the compound is copper(I) oxide.

Simple compounds of non–metals such as NO and NO_2 are often called nitrogen monoxide (or nitric oxide) and nitrogen dioxide, rather than the alternative names nitrogen(II) oxide and nitrogen(IV) oxide.

When naming oxoacids, the oxidation number of the central atom in the acid is written after the rest of the name, which always ends in '**–ic**'. For example, H_3PO_4 is phosphoric(V) acid.

The salts and ions of oxoacids are named by writing the oxidation number of the central atom after the rest of the name, which ends in **–ate**. For example, in Na_2SO_4 (anion SO_4^{2-}), sulphur has an oxidation number of $+6$ and the compound is called sodium sulphate(VI). In Na_2SO_3 (anion SO_3^{2-}), sulphur has an oxidation number of $+4$ and the compound is called sodium sulphate(IV). It is still common to call these two compounds simply sodium sulphate and sodium sulphite.

The salts of the common acids are usually named without including the appropriate oxidation number: Na_2SO_4 is sodium sulphate, rather than sodium sulphate(VI) and $NaNO_3$, sodium nitrate, rather than sodium nitrate(V).

R14 Naming organic compounds

The rules for naming compounds are settled by international agreement through the International Union of Pure and Applied Chemistry (IUPAC).

Names for alkanes with unbranched carbon atom chains

These are hydrocarbons in which the molecules are made up of straight chains of carbon atoms. The general name for these is alkanes. Names for individual compounds all have the ending **–ane**. For example,

$$CH_3—CH_2—CH_2—CH_2—CH_3 \quad \text{pentane}$$

◀ **Figure R14.1**

Number of carbon atoms	Molecular formula	Name
1	CH_4	methane
2	C_2H_6	ethane
3	C_3H_8	propane
4	C_4H_{10}	butane
5	C_5H_{12}	pentane
6	C_6H_{14}	hexane
7	C_7H_{16}	heptane
8	C_8H_{18}	octane
9	C_9H_{20}	nonane
10	$C_{10}H_{22}$	decane
11	$C_{11}H_{24}$	undecane
12	$C_{12}H_{26}$	dodecane
20	$C_{20}H_{42}$	eicosane

Names for alkanes with branched chains

Saturated hydrocarbons with branched chains of carbon atoms are also alkanes, but the rules for the individual names are more complicated. An example is 2-methylbutane (Figure R14.2).

$$CH_3—CH_2—CH_2—CH_3$$
$$|$$
$$CH_3$$

▲ **Figure R14.2**

Chemists name these compounds by referring to groups of atoms called alkyl groups. These are derived from hydrocarbons with unbranched carbon chains by removing one hydrogen atom from the end carbon atom of the chain. For example, $CH_3—CH_2—CH_3$ (propane) becomes $CH_3—CH_2—CH_2—$ with one bond unoccupied. Alkyl groups are named from the parent hydrocarbon by substituting the ending **–yl** for the ending **–ane**. Thus, $CH_3CH_2CH_2—$ is the **propyl** group. A list of alkyl groups is given in Figure R14.3.

◀ **Figure R14.3**

Hydrocarbon	Alkyl group	Formula for alkyl group
Methane	methyl	$CH_3—$
Ethane	ethyl	$C_2H_5—$
Propane	propyl	$C_3H_7—$
Butane	butyl	$C_4H_9—$
Pentane	pentyl	$C_5H_{11}—$
Hexane	hexyl	$C_6H_{13}—$
and so on		

Branched chain hydrocarbons are named by combining names of alkyl groups with the name of an unbranched chain hydrocarbon. The simplest is methylpropane, Figure R14.4.

$$CH_3—CH—CH_3$$
$$|$$
$$CH_3$$

▲ **Figure R14.4**

The hydrocarbon name is always derived from the longest continuous chain of carbon atoms in the molecule. The position of the side chain is found by numbering the carbon atoms in the chain. The numbering is done so that the lowest number(s) possible is used to indicate the side chain (or chains). Thus the structure in Figure R14.5 is 2–methylpentane, *not* 4–methylpentane.

$$CH_3—CH—CH_2—CH_2—CH_3$$
$$|$$
$$CH_3$$

▲ **Figure R14.5**

When there is more than one side chain of the same kind, the figures indicating the positions of the groups are separated by commas. This is shown in Figure R14.6.

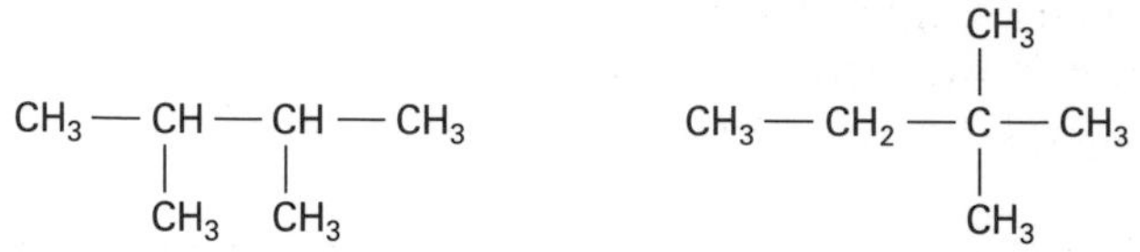

◀ Figure R14.6

$$CH_3 - CH - CH - CH_3$$

with CH_3 and CH_3 below

is 2,3-dimethylbutane, and

$$CH_3 - CH_2 - C - CH_3$$

with CH_3 above and CH_3 below

is 2,2-dimethylbutane.

Names for alkanes with a ring of carbon atoms

Hydrocarbons with rings of carbon atoms are called cycloalkanes. For example, cyclohexane is shown in Figure R14.7.

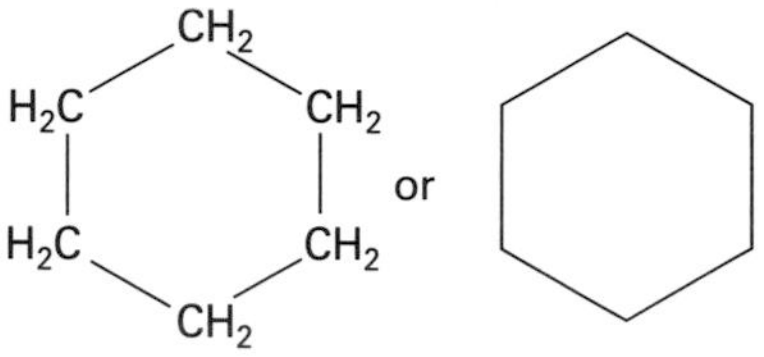

They are named from the corresponding unbranched hydrocarbon by adding the prefix **cyclo–**.

▲ Figure R14.7

All the carbon atoms in an unsubstituted cycloakane ring are equivalent, so far as substitution is concerned, so that if only one alkyl group is added as a substituent there is no need to number the carbon atoms. Thus methyl-cyclohexane is shown in Figure R14.8.

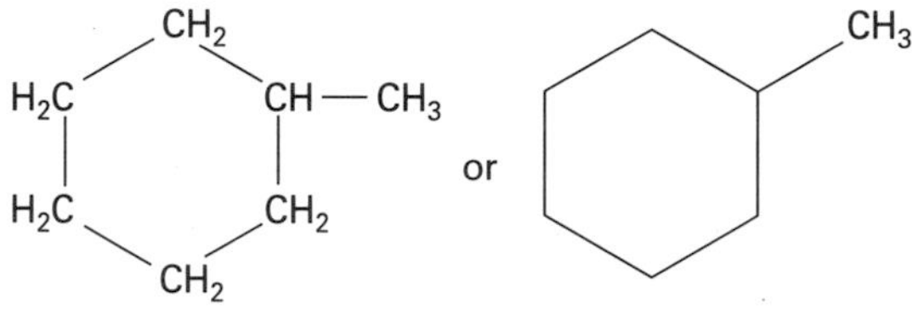

▲ Figure R14.8

Names for alcohols

Alcohols have a hydroxyl group, —OH, attached to a carbon atom. The —OH group is an example of a **functional group**. The first three members of the alcohol series are methanol, ethanol and propanol. Name them by changing the end of the name of the corresponding alkane to **–ol**.

CH_4	methane	$CH_3 - OH$	methanol
$CH_3 - CH_3$	ethane	$CH_3 - CH_2 - OH$	ethanol
$CH_3 - CH_2 - CH_3$	propane	$CH_3 - CH_2 - CH_2 - OH$	propan-l-ol

◀ Figure R14.9

When the —OH group of an alcohol is attached to a carbon atom which is attached directly to only one other carbon atom, the compound is known as a **primary alcohol**.

When the —OH group is attached to a carbon atom which is attached directly to two other carbon atoms, the compound is a **secondary alcohol**, and when attached to three other carbon atoms, it is a **tertiary alcohol**.

The structural formulas in Figure R14.10 are all isomers of $C_4H_{10}O$.

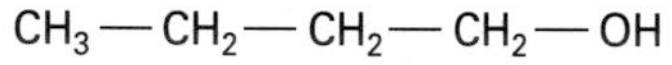

$$CH_3 - CH_2 - CH_2 - CH_2 - OH$$ butan-1-ol, a primary alcohol

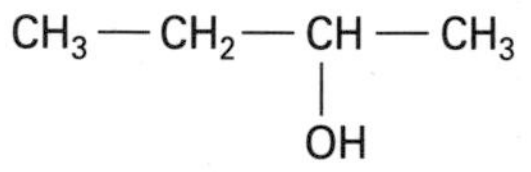

◀ Figure R14.10

$$CH_3 - CH_2 - CH - CH_3$$ with OH below butan-2-ol, a secondary alcohol

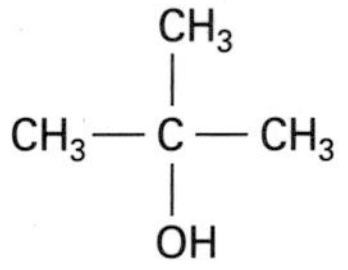

$$CH_3 - C - CH_3$$ with CH_3 above and OH below 2-methylpropan-2-ol, a tertiary alcohol

$$CH_2 - CH_2$$ with OH and OH below ethane-1,2-diol (glycol)

$$CH_2 - CH - CH_2$$ with OH, OH and OH below propane-1,2,3-triol (glycerol)

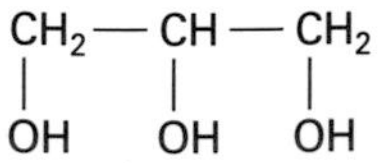

▲ Figure R14.11

When alcohols contain more than one hydroxyl group they are known as diols or triols, and so on (Figure R14.11).

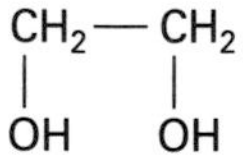

R15 Names and structures of some functional groups

In this table the structures of the functional groups are printed out in the second column so as to show the atomic linkages. When these structures are repeated in the examples given in the fourth column they are printed on one line only, so as to show this abbreviated method of writing them.

Class of compound	Sample of the functional group	Example of a compound name	Formula
Alkene	$\diagdown C = C \diagup$	propene	$CH_2 = CH - CH_3$
Arene	(benzene ring structure)	benzene	C_6H_6 or ⬡
Alcohol	$-OH$	propan-1-ol	$CH_3 - CH_2 - CH_2 - OH$
Amine	$-NH_2$	propylamine	$CH_3 - CH_2 - CH_2 - NH_2$
Nitrile	$-C \equiv N$	propanenitrile	$CH_3 - CH_2 - CN$
Halogenoalkane	$-Cl$ etc	1-chloropropane	$CH_3 - CH_2 - CH_2 - Cl$
Aldehyde	$-C{\diagup H \atop \diagdown O}$	propanal	$CH_3 - CH_2 - CHO$
Ketone	$\diagdown C = O$	propanone	$CH_3 - CO - CH_3$
Carboxylic acid	$-C{\diagup O-H \atop \diagdown O}$	propanoic acid	$CH_3 - CH_2 - CO_2H$
Carboxylate ion	$-C{\diagup O^- \atop \diagdown O}$	sodium propanoate	$CH_3 - CH_2 - CO_2^-Na^+$
Acyl chloride	$-C{\diagup Cl \atop \diagdown O}$	propanoyl chloride	$CH_3 - CH_2 - COCl$
Acid anhydride	$-C{\diagup O \atop \diagdown O} -C{\diagup O}$	propanoic anhydride	$(CH_3 - CH_2 - CO)_2O$
Amide	$-C{\diagup NH_2 \atop \diagdown O}$	propanamide	$CH_3 - CH_2 - CONH_2$
Nitro compound	$-N{\diagup O \atop \diagdown O}$	nitrobenzene	$C_6H_5NO_2$ or NO_2⬡
Sulphonic acid	$-{O \atop \| \atop \underset{\|}{\overset{}{S}} \atop O} - O - H$	benzenesulphonic acid	$C_6H_5SO_2OH$ or SO_2OH⬡
Ether	$-C-O-C-$	ethoxyethane	$CH_3 - CH_2 - O - CH_2 - CH_3$

▲ Figure R15.1

R16 Tests for selected functional groups

Functional group	Test	Results
$>C=C<$ in **alkenes**	■ Investigate solubility in water and organic solvents	■ Alkenes do not mix with water but they do mix with other hydrocarbon solvents
	■ Test flammability	■ Alkenes burn readily with a yellow, smoky flame
	■ Shake with a dilute solution of bromine	■ Alkenes decolorize the orange solution of bromine
	■ Shake with a very dilute, acidic solution of potassium manganate(VII)	■ Alkenes decolorize the purple solution of manganate(VII) ions
—CH_2OH in **primary alcohols**	■ Investigate solubility in water and measure the pH of the solution with a test paper	■ Alcohols with relatively few carbon atoms in the molecules mix with water giving neutral solutions
	■ Add a solution of sodium carbonate	■ Alcohols do not react with sodium carbonate solution
	■ Add phosphorus pentachloride to the **anhydrous** compounds	■ Alcohols react with phosphorus pentachloride giving off fuming hydrogen chloride gas
	■ Add a very small piece of sodium to the **anhydrous** compound	■ Alcohols react with sodium giving off hydrogen gas
	■ Warm with an acidic solution of sodium dichromate(VI)	■ Primary alcohols are oxidized and the solution turns from orange to green. (Alcohols are not oxidized by Fehling's solution.)
$>C=O$ in **aldehydes and ketones**	■ Investigate solubility in water and measure the pH of the solution with a test paper	■ Aldehydes and ketones with relatively few carbon atoms in the molecules mix with water giving neutral solutions
	■ Mix with a solution of 2,4-dinitrophenylhydrazine	■ Aldehydes and ketones produce yellow, orange or red precipitates
	■ Warm with Fehling's solution – an alkaline solution of complexed copper(II) ions	■ Aldehydes reduce the copper(II) ions forming an orange-red precipitate of copper(I) oxide
—CO_2H in **carboxylic acids**	■ Investigate solubility in water and measure the pH of the solution with a test paper	■ Carboxylic acids with relatively few carbon atoms in the molecules dissolve in water forming an acidic solution. Benzoic acid is much more soluble in hot water than cold water. Acids which are insoluble in water are more soluble in sodium hydroxide solution
	■ Add a solution of sodium carbonate	■ Carboxylic acids react with carbonates producing carbon dioxide gas
	■ Add phosphorus pentachloride to the anhydrous compounds	■ Carboxylic acids react with phosphorus pentachloride giving off fuming hydrogen chloride gas
	■ Add a very small piece of sodium to the **anhydrous** compound	■ Carboxylic acids react with sodium giving off hydrogen gas
	■ Warm with an acidic solution of sodium dichromate(VI)	■ Most carboxylic acids are not oxidized by this reagent – exceptions are methanoic (formic) acid and ethanedioic (oxalic) acid
	■ Add neutral iron(III) chloride solution to a solution of the compound	■ Methanoic and ethanoic acids (and their salts) give a red colour

▲ **Figure R16.1** *(continued opposite)*

—NH$_2$ in amines	■ Investigate solubility in water and measure the pH of the solution with a test paper	■ Amines such as ethylamine dissolve in water and the solution is alkaline. Aryl amines such as phenylamine are insoluble in water but soluble in hydrochloric acid
	■ Hold a drop of concentrated hydrochloric acid in the vapour of the compound	■ The vapour of an amine forms a white smoke with hydrogen chloride
	■ Add a solution of the amine to a few drops of a dilute solution of copper(II) sulphate	■ Most amines form deep blue complex ion with copper(II) ions. Phenylamine gives a green precipitate

R17 Charges on some common ions

	Positive ions (cations)				Negative ions (anions)	
Charge	Cation	Symbol		Charge	Anion	Symbol
1+	copper(I)	Cu$^+$		1–	bromide	Br$^-$
	hydrogen	H$^+$			chloride	Cl$^-$
	lithium	Li$^+$			hydrogencarbonate	HCO$_3^-$
	potassium	K$^+$			hydroxide	OH$^-$
	silver	Ag$^+$			iodide	I$^-$
	sodium	Na$^+$			nitrate	NO$_3^-$
					nitrite	NO$_2^-$
2+	calcium	Ca^{2+}		2–	carbonate	CO$_3^{2-}$
	copper(II)	Cu^{2+}			oxide	O^{2-}
	iron(II)	Fe^{2+}			sulphate	SO$_4^{2-}$
	lead(II)	Pb^{2+}			sulphide	S^2
	magnesium	Mg^{2+}			sulphite	SO$_3^{2-}$
	nickel	Ni^{2+}				
	zinc	Zn^{2+}				
3+	aluminium	Al^{3+}		3–	nitride	N^{3-}
	iron(III)	Fe^{3+}			phosphate	P^{3-}

▲ Figure R17.1

R18 Qualitative analysis to identify simple salts

Effect of heat on the solid salt

Observations on heating	Inference
Water vapour/steam evolved turning cobalt chloride paper pink	Crystals contain water of crystallization, or the solid is a hydroxide which decomposes
Colourless gas evolved which relights a glowing splint	Oxygen from a nitrate of potassium or sodium
Brown gas evolved and a glowing splint relights	Nitrogen dioxide and oxygen from the decomposition of a nitrate
Gas given off which turns limewater cloudy	Carbon dioxide from the decomposition of a carbonate
Pungent gas evolved which turns acid dichromate paper from orange to green	Sulphur dioxide from the decomposition of a sulphate
Sublimate forms on a cool part of the tube	Likely to be an ammonium salt. (Ammonia may also be detected with moist red litmus: it turns it blue.)
Residue turns yellow when hot and then white again when cold	Zinc oxide, which may have been formed by the decomposition of another zinc compound

▲ Figure R18.1

Tests to identify positive ions (cations)

Metal ion	Sodium hydroxide solution added to solution of metal ion	Ammonia solution added to solution of metal ion	Flame test (on solid salt)
Aluminium	White precipitate which dissolves in excess to give colourless solution	White precipitate insoluble in excess	No characteristic colour
Barium	No precipitate	No precipitate	Green
Calcium	White precipitate insoluble in excess	No precipitate	Red
Copper(II)	Blue precipitate insoluble in excess	Blue precipitate which dissolves in excess to give dark blue solution	Blue–green
Iron(II)	Green precipitate insoluble in excess	Green precipitate insoluble in excess	No characteristic colour
Iron(III)	Brown precipitate insoluble in excess	Brown precipitate insoluble in excess	No characteristic colour
Potassium	No precipitate	No precipitate	Violet
Sodium	No precipitate	No precipitate	Yellow
Zinc	White precipitate which dissolves in excess to give colourless solution	White precipitate which dissolves in excess to give colourless solution	No characteristic colour

▲ Figure R18.2

Tests to identify negative ions (anions)

Test	Observation	Inference
1 Add dilute hydrochloric acid to the solid salt. Warm gently if there is no reaction in the cold	Gas which turns limewater cloudy	Carbon dioxide from a carbonate
	Gas which is acidic, has a pungent smell and turns acid dichromate paper from orange to green	Sulphur dioxide from a sulphite
2 Test for halide ions Make a solution of the salt. Acidify with nitric acid, then add silver nitrate solution. Test the solubility of the precipitate in ammonia solution	White precipitate soluble in dilute ammonia solution	Chloride
	Cream precipitate soluble in concentrated ammonia solution	Bromide
	Yellow precipitate insoluble in excess ammonia	Iodide
3 Test for sulphate ions Take a fresh solution of the salt. Acidify with nitric acid then add a solution of barium nitrate or barium chloride	White precipitate	Sulphate
4 Test for nitrate ions Take a fresh solution. Add an equal volume of iron(II) sulphate solution. Then pour concentrated sulphuric acid down the side of the tube	Brown gas appears where the two layers meet	Nitrate

▲ Figure R18.3

Tests to identify oxidizing agents

Test	Results	Explanation
Add a solution of potassium iodide	Solution turns brown and grey specks may be seen	I^- oxidized to I_2, which is sparingly soluble
or Test with starch–iodide paper	Paper turn blue–black	I^- oxidized to I_2, which then reacts with starch
Add a fresh solution of iron(II) sulphate	Changes from very pale green to yellow–brown	Fe^{2+} oxidized to Fe^{3+} – the formation of Fe^{3+} may be confirmed by adding $NaOH(aq)$

▲ Figure R18.4

Tests to identify reducing agents

Test	Results	Explanation
Add a solution of potassium manganate(VII) acidified with dilute H_2SO_4	Purple solution is decolorized	Purple MnO_4^- ions are reduced to very pale pink Mn^{2+} ions
Add potassium dichromate(VI) solution acidified with dilute H_2SO_4	Orange solution turns green	Orange $Cr_2O_4^{2-}$ ions are reduced to green Cr^{3+} ions
Add aqueous bromine	Orange-red solution is decolorized	Br_2 is reduced to colourless Br^- ions

▲ Figure R18.5

R19 Physical properties of elements

Atomic number	Element	Molar mass /g mol^{-1}	Melting point /°C	Boiling point /°C	Density /g cm^{-3}	Symbol
1	hydrogen	1.0	−259	−253	0.07 $^{253°C}$	H
2	helium	4.0	−272$^{26\ atm}$	−269	0.15 $^{-270°C}$	He
3	lithium	6.9	181	1342	0.53	Li
4	beryllium	9.0	1278	2970	1.85	Be
5	boron	10.8	2300	2550^{sub}	2.34	B
6	carbon – diamond – graphite	12.0	>3550 3697^{sub}	4827	3.51 2.25	C
7	nitrogen	14.0	−210	−196	0.81$^{-196°C}$	N
8	oxygen	16.0	−218	−183	1.15$^{-183°C}$	O
9	fluorine	19.0	−220	−188	1.15$^{-188°C}$	F
10	neon	20.2	−248	−246	1.20$^{-246°C}$	Ne
11	sodium	23.0	98	883	0.97	Na
12	magnesium	24.3	649	1107	1.74	Mg
13	aluminium	27.0	660	2467	2.70	Al

▲ Figure R19.1 *(continued overleaf)*

(continued)

Atomic number	Element	Molar mass /g mol⁻¹	Melting point /°C	Boiling point /°C	Density /g cm⁻³	Symbol
16	sulphur – monoclinic – rhombic	32.1	 119 113	445	1.96 2.07	S
17	chlorine	35.5	−101	−35	$1.56^{-35\,°C}$	Cl
18	argon	39.9	−189	−186	$1.40^{-186\,°C}$	Ar
19	potassium	39.1	63	760	0.86	K
20	calcium	40.1	839	1484	1.54	Ca
21	scandium	45.0	1541	2831	2.99	Sc
22	titanium	47.9	1660	3287	4.50	Ti
23	vanadium	50.9	1890	3380	5.96	V
24	chromium	52.0	1857	2670	7.20	Cr
25	manganese	54.9	1244	1962	7.20	Mn
26	iron	55.9	1535	2750	7.86	Fe
27	cobalt	58.9	1495	2870	8.90	Co
28	nickel	58.7	1455	2730	8.90	Ni
29	copper	63.5	1083	2567	8.92	Cu
30	zinc	65.4	420	907	7.14	Zn
31	gallium	69.7	30	2403	5.90	Ga
32	germanium	72.6	937	2830	5.35	Ge
33	arsenic	74.9	817^{sub}		5.73	As
34	selenium	79.0	217	685	4.81	Se
35	bromine	79.9	−7	59	3.12	Br
36	krypton	83.8	−157	−152	$2.15^{-152\,°C}$	Kr
47	silver	107.9	962	2212	10.5	Ag
50	tin	118.7	323	2270	7.28	Sn
53	iodine	126.9	114	184	4.93	I
55	caesium	132.9	29	669	1.88	Cs
56	barium	137.3	725	1640	3.51	Ba
78	platinum	195.1	1772	3827	21.45	Pt
79	gold	197.0	1064	3080	18.88	Au
80	mercury	200.6	−39	357	13.59	Hg
82	lead	207.2	328	1740	11.34	Pb

R20 Physical properties of inorganic compounds

The following abbreviations are used in Figure R20.1.

dec – which means that the compound decomposes before it melts or boils
h – which mean that the crystals are often hydrated so that they give off water on heating before they melt

The solubility is indicated approximately using these abbreviations.

i – insoluble
sl.s – slightly soluble
s – soluble
vs – very soluble
r – means that the compound reacts with water

All the compounds are white or colourless unless otherwise stated.

Compound	Formula	Structure	Melting point /°C	Boiling point /°C	Solubility	Notes
Aluminium chloride	$AlCl_3$	giant (ions)	sub		r	
Aluminium hydroxide	$Al(OH)_3$	giant (ions)	300	dec	i	
Aluminium oxide	Al_2O_3	giant (ions)	2015	2980	i	
Ammonia	NH_3	molecular	−78	−34	vs	
Ammonium chloride	NH_4Cl	giant (ions)	sub		s	
Ammonium nitrate	NH_4NO_3	giant (ions)	170	dec	vs	
Ammonium sulphate	$(NH_4)_2SO_4$	giant (ions)	dec		s	
Barium chloride	$BaCl_2$	giant (ions)	963	1500	s	h
Barium sulphate	$BaSO_4$	giant (ions)	1580		i	
Calcium carbonate	$CaCO_3$	giant (ions)	dec		i	
Calcium chloride	$CaCl_2$	giant (ions)	782	2000	s	h
Calcium hydroxide	$Ca(OH)_2$	giant (ions)	dec		sl.s	
Calcium nitrate	$Ca(NO_3)_2$	giant (ions)	561	dec	vs	h
Calcium oxide	CaO	giant (ions)	2600	3000	r	
Carbon monoxide	CO	molecular	−250	−191	i	
Carbon dioxide	CO_2	molecular	sub		sl.s	
Copper(II) chloride	$CuCl_2$	giant (ions)	620	dec	s	h, green
Copper(II) nitrate	$Cu(NO_3)_2$	giant (ions)	114	dec	vs	h, blue
Copper(I) oxide	Cu_2O	giant (ions)	1235		i	red
Copper(II) oxide	CuO	giant (ions)	1326		i	black
Copper(II) sulphate	$CuSO_4$	giant (ions)	dec		s	h, blue
Hydrogen bromide	HBr	molecular	−87	−67	vs, r	
Hydrogen chloride	HCl	molecular	−114	−85	vs, r	forms hydro–chloric acid in water
Hydrogen iodide	HI	molecular	−51	−35	vs, r	
Hydrogen peroxide	H_2O_2	molecular	0	150	vs	

▲ Figure R20.1 *(continued overleaf)*

(continued)

Compound	Formula	Structure	Melting point /°C	Boiling point /°C	Solubility	Notes
Hydrogen sulphide	H_2S	molecular	−85	−60	sl.s	
Iron(II) chloride	$FeCl_2$	giant (ions)	667	sub	s	yellow–green
Iron(III) chloride	$FeCl_3$	giant (ions)	307	dec	s	h, orange
Iron(III) oxide	Fe_2O_3	giant (ions)	1565		i	red
Iron(II) sulphate	$FeSO_4$	giant (ions)	dec		s	pale green
Lead(II) chloride	$PbCl_2$	giant (ions)	501	950	sl.s	
Lead(II) nitrate	$Pb(NO_3)_2$	giant (ions)	dec		s	
Lead(II) oxide	PbO	giant (ions)	886	1427	i	yellow
Lead(IV) oxide	PbO_2	giant (ions)	dec		i	brown
Lead(II) sulphate	$PbSO_4$	giant (ions)	1170			
Magnesium carbonate	$MgCO_3$	giant (ions)	dec		i	
Magnesium chloride	$MgCl_2$	giant (ions)	714	1418	s	h
Magnesium nitrate	$Mg(NO_3)_2$	giant (ions)	dec		vs	h
Manganese(IV) oxide	MnO_2	giant (ions)	dec		i	black
Manganese(II) sulphate	$MnSO_4$	giant (ions)	700	dec	s	h, pink
Concentrated nitric acid	HNO_3	molecular	−42	83	vs, r	
Nitrous oxide	N_2O	molecular	−91	−88	sl.s	
Nitric oxide	NO	molecular	−163	−151	sl.s	
Nitrogen dioxide	NO_2	molecular	−11	21	s	brown
Potassium bromide	KBr	giant (ions)	730	1435	s	
Potassium chloride	KCl	giant (ions)	776	1500	s	
Potassium hydroxide	KOH	giant (ions)	360	1322	vs	
Potassium iodide	KI	giant (ions)	686	1330	vs	
Potassium manganate(VII)	$KMnO_4$	giant (ions)	dec		s	purple
Potassium nitrate	KNO_3	giant (ions)	334	dec	vs	
Silicon dioxide	SiO_2	giant (ions)	1610	2230	i	
Silver bromide	$AgBr$	giant (ions)	432	dec	i	pale yellow
Silver chloride	$AgCl$	giant (ions)	455	1550	i	
Silver iodide	AgI	giant (ions)	558	1506	i	yellow
Silver nitrate	$AgNO_3$	giant (ions)	212	dec	vs	
Sodium bromide	$NaBr$	giant (ions)	755	1390	s	
Sodium carbonate	Na_2CO_3	giant (ions)	851	dec	s	h
Sodium chloride	$NaCl$	giant (ions)	808	1465	s	

(continued opposite)

Compound	Formula	Structure	Melting point /°C	Boiling point /°C	Solubility	Notes
Sodium hydrogencarbonate	$NaHCO_3$	giant (ions)	dec		s	
Sodium hydroxide	NaOH	giant (ions)	318	1390	s	
Sodium nitrate	$NaNO_3$	giant (ions)	307	dec	vs	
Sodium sulphate	$NaSO_4$	giant (ions)	890	dec	s	
Sulphur dioxide	SO_2	molecular	−75	−10	vs, r	
Sulphur trioxide	SO_3	molecular	17	43	r	
Concentrated sulphuric acid	H_2SO_4	molecular	10	330	vs, r	
Titanium(IV) oxide	TiO_2	giant (ions)	1830		i	
Zinc oxide	ZnO	giant (ions)	1975		i	yellow when hot
Zinc sulphate	$ZnSO_4$	giant (ions)	740	dec	s	
Water	H_2O	molecular	0	100		

R21 Physical properties of selected organic compounds

Compound	Formula	Melting point /°C	Boiling point /°C	Density /g mol^{-1}
Alkanes				
Methane	CH_4	−182	−161	0.466^{liq}
Ethane	CH_3CH_3	−183	−88	0.572^{liq}
Propane	$CH_3CH_2CH_3$	−188	−42	0.585^{liq}
Butane	$CH_3(CH_2)_2CH_3$	−138	−0.5	0.601^{liq}
Pentane	$CH_3(CH_2)_3CH_3$	−130	36	0.626
Hexane	$CH_3(CH_2)_4CH_3$	−95	69	0.660
Decane	$CH_3(CH_2)_8CH_3$	−30	174	0.730
Eicosane	$CH_3(CH_2)_{18}CH_3$	37	344	0.789
Cycloalkanes				
Cyclopentane		−94	49	1.407
Cyclohexane		7	81	1.426
Alkenes				
Ethene	$CH_2{=}CH_2$	−169	−104	0.610^{liq}
Propene	$CH_2{=}CH{-}CH_3$	−185	−48	0.514^{liq}
Cyclohexene		−103	83	0.811^{liq}
Arenes				
Benzene		6	80	0.879
Methylbenzene (toluene)		81	218	0.867

▲ **Figure R21.1** *(continued overleaf)*

Compound	Formula	Melting point /°C	Boiling point /°C	Density /g mol^{-1}
Alcohols				
Methanol	CH_3OH	−98	65	0.793
Ethanol	CH_3CH_2OH	−114	78	0.789
Propan-1-ol	$CH_3CH_2CH_2OH$	−126	97	0.804
Butan-1-ol	$CH_3CH_2CH_2CH_2OH$	−89	118	0.810
2-methylpropan-2-ol	$(CH_3)_3COH$	−26	82	0.789
Cyclohexanol	⬡—OH	25	161	0.962
Aldehydes				
Methanal	HCHO	−92	−21	0.815
Ethanal	CH_3CHO	−121	20	0.778
Propanal	CH_3CH_2CHO	−81	49	0.797
Ketones				
Propanone	CH_3COCH_3	−95	56	0.789
Butanone	$CH_3CH_2COCH_3$	−86	80	0.805
Carboxylic acids				
Methanoic (formic) acid	HCO_2H	9	101	1.220
Ethanoic (acetic) acid	CH_3CO_2H	17	118	1.049
Propanoic acid	$CH_3CH_2CO_2H$	−21	141	0.993
Esters				
Ethyl ethanoate (acetate)	$CH_3CO_2CH_2CH_3$	−84	77	0.900
Ethyl propanoate	$CH_3CH_2CO_2CH_2CH_3$	−74	99	0.890
Methyl ethanoate	$CH_3CO_2CH_3$	−98	57	0.972
Methyl propanoate	$CH_3CH_2CO_2CH_3$	−87	80	0.915
Hydrogen-containing compounds				
Bromoethane	CH_3CH_2Br	−118	39	1.461
1,2-dibromoethane	CH_2BrCH_2Br	10	131	2.179
1,1,1-trichloroethane	CH_3CCl_3	−30	74	1.339
1-bromopropane	$CH_3CH_2CH_2Br$	−110	71	1.354
1-iodopropane	$CH_3CH_2CH_2I$	−101	103	1.748
1-chlorobutane	$CH_3CH_2CH_2CH_2Cl$	−123	79	0.886
1-bromobutane	$CH_3CH_2CH_2CH_2Br$	−112	102	1.276
1-iodobutane	$CH_3CH_2CH_2CH_2I$	−103	131	1.615

R22 Electronegativity values for some elements

The electronegativity of an element is a measure of its ability to attract the electron pair in a covalent bond, relative to that of other elements. The figures in this table are on a scale devised by Linus Pauling.

◀ **Figure R22.1**

			H 2.1			
Li 1.0	**Be** 1.5	**B** 2.0	**C** 2.5	**N** 3.0	**O** 3.5	**F** 4.0
Na 0.9	**Mg** 1.2	**Al** 1.5	**Si** 1.8	**P** 2.1	**S** 2.5	**Cl** 3.0
K 0.8	**Ca** 1.0					**Br** 2.8
Rb 0.8	**Sr** 1.0					**I** 2.5

R23 The electromagnetic spectrum

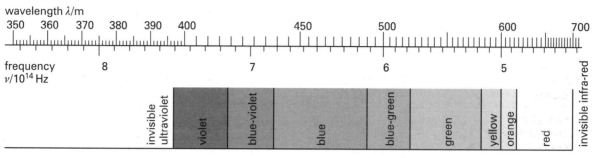

| | radiofrequency | | microwave | infra-red | visible | ultraviolet | X-rays | γ-rays |

frequency ν/Hz 10^5 10^6 10^7 10^8 10^9 10^{10} 10^{11} 10^{12} 10^{13} 10^{14} 10^{15} 10^{16} 10^{17} 10^{18} 10^{19} 10^{20}

wavelength λ/m 10^3 1 10^{-3} 10^{-6} 10^{-9}

Enlargement of visible region

wavelength λ/m
350 360 370 380 390 400 450 500 600 700

frequency ν/10^{14} Hz 8 7 6 5

invisible ultraviolet | violet | blue-violet | blue | blue-green | green | yellow | orange | red | invisible infra-red

Converting frequencies to wavelengths

$$\lambda = \frac{c}{\nu} = \frac{2.99 \times 10^8 \text{ m s}^{-1}}{\nu}$$

for λ measured in nm and ν in s^{-1}(Hz)

$$\lambda = \frac{2.99 \times 10^{17} \text{ nm s}^{-1}}{\nu}$$

ultraviolet

uv (A): 400 nm–320 nm
uv (B): 320 nm–280 nm
uv (C): < 280 nm

▲ Figure R23.1

R24 Characteristic infra-red absorptions in organic molecules

M   Medium
S   Strong

Bond	Location	Wavenumber /cm^{-1}	Intensity
C—H	alkanes, alkenes, arenes	2850–2950	M-S
	alkenes, arenes	3000–3100	M-S
	alkynes	3300	S
C=C	alkenes	1610–1680	M
⬡	arenes	several peaks in range 1450–1650	variable
C≡C	alkynes	2070–2250	M
C=O	aldehydes, ketones, acids, esters	1680–1750	S
C—O	alcohols, ethers, esters	1000–1300	S
	aromatic ethers and esters	1300–1400	S
C≡N	nitriles	2200–2280	M
C—Cl		700–800	S
O—H	free	3580–3670	S
	hydrogen-bonded in alcohols, phenols	3230–3550	S (broad)
	hydrogen-bonded in carboxylic acids	2500–3300	M (broad)
N—H	primary amines	3100–3500	S

▲ Figure R24.1

R25 Nuclear magnetic resonance spectroscopy

Chemical shifts for hydrogen relative to TMS (tetramethylsilane) and calculated from the relationship:

$$\delta/\text{ppm from TMS} = \frac{B_{\text{TMS}} - B_{\text{sample}}}{B_{\text{TMS}}} \times 10^6$$

B is a measure of the magnetic field strength.

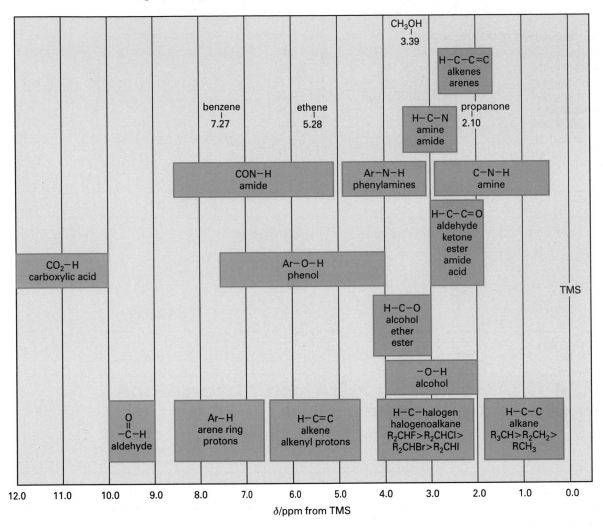

▲ **Figure R25.1** *In the partial structures in the table: R represents any alkyl group, Ar represents a benzene ring.*

R26 K_a values for some weak acids

For a weak acid HA, the ionization constant K_a is given by:

$$K_a = \frac{[H^+(aq)]\,[A^-(aq)]}{[HA(aq)]}$$

The values given are at 25°C.

Acid	Formula	K_a /mol dm^{-3}
Phosphoric(V) acid	H_3PO_4	7.9×10^{-3}
Nitrous [nitric(III)] acid	HNO_2	4.7×10^{-4}
Methanoic acid	HCO_2H	1.6×10^{-4}
Ethanoic acid	CH_3CO_2H	1.7×10^{-5}
Propanoic acid	$CH_3CH_2CO_2H$	1.3×10^{-5}
Butanoic acid	$CH_3CH_2CH_2CO_2H$	1.5×10^{-5}
Benzoic acid	$C_6H_5CO_2H$	6.3×10^{-5}
Chloric(I) acid	$HClO$	3.7×10^{-8}
Boric acid	H_3BO_3	5.8×10^{-10}
Hydrogencarbonate ion	HCO_3^-	4.8×10^{-11}

◄ Figure R26.1

R27 K_b values for some weak bases

For a weak base B, the ionization constant K_b is given by:

$$K_b = \frac{[BH^+(aq)]\,[OH^-(aq)]}{[B(aq)]}$$

The values given are at 25°C.

Base	Formula	K_b /mol dm^{-3}
Ethylamine	$CH_3CH_2NH_2$	5.6×10^{-4}
Ammonia	NH_3	1.7×10^{-5}
Phenylamine	$C_6H_5NH_2$	3.8×10^{-10}

◄ Figuro R27.1

R28 Indicators

Indicator	Acid	pH range	Alkaline
Methyl violet	yellow	0.0–1.6	blue
Thymol blue (acid)	red	1.2–2.8	ycllow
Methyl orange (screened)	purple	3.2–4.4	green
Methyl orange	red	3.2–4.4	yellow
Bromophenol blue	yellow	2.8–4.6	blue
Bromocresol green	yellow	3.8–5.4	blue
Methyl red	red	4.2–6.3	yellow
Azolitmin (litmus)	red	5.0–8.0	blue
Bromothymol blue	yellow	6.0–7.6	blue
Phenol red	yellow	6.8–8.4	red
Thymol blue (base)	yellow	8.0–9.6	blue
Phenolphthalein (in ethanol)	colourless	8.2–10.00	red

Warning Certain indicators are poisonous and should be handled carefully, particularly when concentrated.

▲ Figure R28.1 *Most indicators are 0.1% solutions in water unless stated otherwise.*

R29 Buffer solutions

The following mixtures give the indicated pH at 298 K.

pH	x	Composition of solutions	pH	x	Composition of solutions
1.0 1.5 2.0	67.0 20.7 6.5	2 cm³ of 0.2 mol dm⁻³ KCl + x cm³ of 0.2 mol dm⁻³ HCl	8.5 9.0	15.2 4.6	50 cm³ of 0.025 mol dm⁻³ borax (Na₂B₄O₇.10H₂O) + x cm³ of 0.1 mol dm⁻³ HCl
2.5 3.0 3.5 4.5	38.8 22.3 8.2 0.1	50 cm³ of 0.1 mol dm⁻³ potassium hydrogenphthalate (KHC₈O₄H₄) + x cm³ of 0.1 mol dm⁻³ NaOH	9.5 10.0 10.5	8.8 18.3 22.7	50 cm³ of 0.025 mol dm⁻³ borax (Na₂B₄O₇.10H₂O) + x cm³ of 0.1 mol dm⁻³ NaOH
4.5 5.0 5.5	8.7 22.6 36.6	50 cm³ of 0.1 mol dm⁻³ potassium hydrogenphthalate (KHC₈O₄H₄) + x cm³ of 0.1 mol dm⁻³ NaOH	11.0 11.5 12.0	4.1 11.1 26.9	50 cm³ of 0.05 mol dm⁻³ disodium hydrogenphosphate (Na₂HPO₄) + x cm³ of 0.1 mol dm⁻³ NaOH
6.0 6.5 7.0 7.5 8.0	5.6 13.9 29.1 41.1 46.7	50 cm³ of 0.1 mol dm⁻³ potassium dihydrogenphosphate (KH₂PO₄) + x cm³ of 0.1 mol dm⁻³ NaOH	12.5 13.0	20.4 66.0	25 cm³ of 0.2 mol dm⁻³ KCl + x cm³ of 0.2 mol dm⁻³ NaOH

▲ Figure R29.1

R30 Relative sizes of atoms and ions

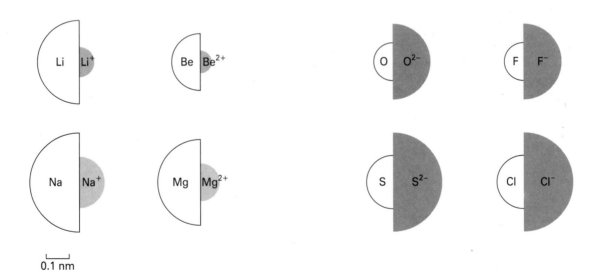

0.1 nm

▲ Figure R30.1

R31 Covalent bond lengths and bond energies

Bond	Substance(s)	Bond length /nm	Bond energy /kJ mol^{-1}
H—H	hydrogen	0.074	436
O=O	oxygen	0.121	498
O—H	water	0.096	464
N≡N	nitrogen	0.110	945
Cl—Cl	chlorine	0.199	243
Br—Br	bromine	0.228	193
I—I	iodine	0.267	151
H—Cl	hydrogen chloride	0.127	432
H—Br	hydrogen bromide	0.141	366
H—I	hydrogen iodide	0.161	298
C—H	average	0.109	413
C—C	alkanes	0.154	347
C=C	alkenes	0.134	612
C—N	amines	0.147	286
C=N	average	0.132	615
C≡N	nitriles	0.116	887
C—O	alcohols	0.143	336
C=O	ketones	0.122	749

▲ Figure R31.1

R32 Biotechnology

Traditional biotechnology

Industry	Sales /£m
Brewing	3190
Spirits	1860
Cheese	415
Cider, wine	190
Bread	150
Antibiotics	100
Yogurt	65
Yeast	25
Citric acid	20

◀ **Figure R32.1** *The sales of products from the UK fermentation industry in 1980.*

Metabolites

Primary metabolite	Producing organism	Commercial significance
Ethanol	*Saccharomyces cerevisiae*	'active ingredient' in alcoholic beverages
Citric acid	*Aspergillus niger*	various uses in the food industry
Acetone and butanol	*Clostridium acetobutyricum*	solvents
Glutamic acid	*Corynebacterium glutamicum*	flavour enhancer
Lysine	*Corynebacterium glutamicum*	feed additive
Polysaccharides	*Xanthomonas* spp.	applications in the food industry; enhanced oil recovery
Fe^{3+}	*Thiobacillus* and *Sulfolobus*	ore leaching

▲ **Figure R32.2** *Some examples of microbial primary metabolites and their commercial significance.*

Secondary metabolite	Commercial significance
Penicillin	antibiotic
Cephalosporin	antibiotic
Tetracyclines	antibiotic
Streptomycin	antibiotic
Griseofulvin	antibiotic (anti-fungal)
Actinomycin	anti-tumour
Pepstatin	treatment of ulcers
Cyclosporin A	immunosuppressant
Krestin	cancer treatment
Bestatin	cancer treatment
Gibberellin	plant growth regulator

◀ **Figure R32.3** *Some examples of microbial secondary metabolites and their commercial significance.*

R33 Crop growth

Crops in the UK

Common name	Scientific name	Family	Main part(s) harvested
*Wheat	*Triticum aestivum*	Gramineae	seed
*Barley	*Hordeum distichon*	Gramineae	seed
Oats	*Avena sativa*	Gramineae	seed
Rye	*Secale cereale*	Gramineae	seed
Maize	*Zea mays*	Gramineae	all aerial parts
*Ryegrass	*Lolium perenne*	Gramineae	leaves and stems
*All other grasses	*Various*	Gramineae	leaves and stems
*Sugar beet	*Beta vulgaris*	Chenopodiaceae	tap root
Mangold	*Beta vulgaris*	Chenopodiaceae	tap root
Beetroot	*Beta vulgaris*	Chenopodiaceae	tap root
Spinach	*Spinacea oleracea*	Chenopodiaceae	leaves
*Rape	*Brassica rapus*	Cruciferae	seed (oil) leaves (fodder)
*Kale	*Brassica oleracea*	Cruciferae	leaves and stem
*Cabbage	*Brassica oleracea*	Cruciferae	leaves
Brussels sprout	*Brassica oleracea*	Cruciferae	axillary leaf buds
Cauliflower	*Brassica oleracea*	Cruciferae	inflorescence
Broccoli	*Brassica oleracea*	Cruciferae	inflorescence
Kohl rabi	*Brassica oleracea*	Cruciferae	leaves and stem
*Turnip	*Brassica rapa*	Cruciferae	swollen stem/root
Swede	*Brassica rapus*	Cruciferae	swollen stem/root
Radish	*Raphanus sativus*	Cruciferae	swollen root
Runner bean	*Phaseolus coccineus*	Leguminosae	seeds or young pod
French bean	*Phaseolus vulgaris*	Leguminosae	young pod
*Broad bean	*Vicia faba*	Leguminosae	seeds or young pod
*Pea	*Pisum sativum*	Leguminosae	seeds
Lucerne	*Medicago sativa*	Leguminosae	leaves and stem
*Red clover	*Trifolium pratense*	Leguminosae	leaves and stem
*White clover	*Trifolium repens*	Leguminosae	leaves and stem
Flax and linseed	*Linum usitatissimum*	Linaceae	stem (linen):seed *(oil)
*Potato	*Solanum tuberosum*	Solanaceae	underground stem
Tomato	*Lycopersicon esculentum*	Solanaceae	fruit
Carrot	*Daucus carota*	Umbelliferae	swollen tap root
Parsnip	*Pastinaca sativa*	Umbelliferae	swollen tap root
Hop	*Humulus lupulus*	Moraceae	female cones
Lettuce	*Lactuca sativa*	Compositae	leaves

▲ **Figure R33.1** *Plants grown as farm and horticultural crops in the UK (continued overleaf).*

(continued)

Common name	Scientific name	Family	Main part(s) harvested
Jerusalem artichoke	*Helianthus tuberosus*	Compositae	flower bud
Onion	*Allium cepa*	Liliaceae	swollen leaf stalks
Leek	*Allium ampeloprasum*	Liliaceae	swollen leaf stalks
Asparagus	*Asparagus officinalis*	Liliaceae	stem sprout
Rhubarb	*Rheum rhaponticum*	Polygonaceae	leaf stalks
Apple	*Malus pumila*	Rosaceae	fruit
Pear	*Pyrus communis*	Rosaceae	fruit
Plum	*Prunus* spp	Rosaceae	fruit
Cherry	*Prunus avium*	Rosaceae	fruit
Strawberry	*Fragaria* spp	Rosaceae	fruit
Raspberry	*Rubus idaeus*	Rosaceae	fruit
Currant	*Ribes* spp	Grossulariaceae	fruit
Gooseberry	*Ribes grossularia*	Grossulariaceae	fruit
Grape	*Vitus* spp	Vitaceae	fruit
Cucumber	*Cumumis sativas*	Cucurbitaceae	fruit
Vegetable marrow	*Curcurbita pepo*	Cucurbitaceae	fruit

* Those of greatest economic importance.

The total area of agricultural land in the UK is 18 553 000 hectares, which is utilized as shown in Figure R33.2.

Crop	Area /ha
Wheat	1 870 000
Barley	1 943 000
Oats	132 000
Mixed corn	15 000
Rye	9 000
Maize	1 000
Potatoes	190 000
Sugar beet	200 000
Oilseed rape	292 000
Hops	6 000
Beans for stock feeding	39 000
Turnips, swedes and fodder beet	105 000
Mangels	7 000
Rape (for grazing)	65 000
Kale	60 000
Grass	7 100 000
Rough grazing	6 000 000
Horticultural crops	400 000
Other (roads, buildings, etc.)	500 000

◀ **Figure R33.2** *The use of agricultural land in the UK.*

Vegetable	Crop yield $/m^{-2}$
Beans, broad	1.2 kg
Beans, French	700 g
Beans, runner	12 kg
Beans, haricot*	200 g
Beetroot	2.5 kg
Broccoli	3.0 kg
Brussels sprouts	1.0 kg
Cabbage (spring)	2.0 kg
Cabbage (autumn and winter)	3.5 kg
Cauliflower	2.5 kg
Carrots (main)	3.0 kg
Carrots (early)	1.5 kg
Endive	10–12 heads
Kale	2.3 kg
Leek	2.3 kg
Lettuce	12–14 heads
Mushrooms	4–8 kg
Onions	2.5 kg
Parsnips	2.3 kg
Peas	700 g
Potatoes (main)	2.5 kg
Savoys	2.8 kg
Shallots	3.6 kg
Spinach (summer)	1.5 kg
Swedes	2.7 kg
Turnips (main)	2.7 kg
Tomatoes (under glass)	6.8 kg
Tomatoes (outdoor)	4.8 kg

◀ **Figure R33.3** *Approximate yield of vegetables grown in the UK.*

* Seeds only

Nutrients

Nutrients and their chemical symbols	Principal chemical form taken up by plants	Nutrient removal with wheat harvest (5t ha,$^{-1}$ 20% moisture) /kg ha^{-1}
Macronutrients		
Nitrogen (N)	NH_4^+, NO_3^-	105
Phosporus (P)	$H_2PO_4^-$	18
Potassium (K)	K^+	15
Sulphur (S)	SO_4^{2-}	8
Magnesium (Mg)	Mg^{2+}	6
Calcium (Ca)	Ca^{2+}	2
Micronutrients		
Chlorine (Cl)	Cl^-	3
Iron (Fe)	Fe^{2+}	0.2
Manganese (Mn)	Mn^{2+}	0.2
Zinc (Zn)	Zn^{2+}	0.2
Copper (Cu)	Cu^{2+}	0.03
Boron (B)	H_3BO_3	0.02
Molybdenum (Mo)	MoO_4^{2-}	–

Other elements required by some plants: sodium. cobalt, vanadium. silicon, nickel (Loue, 1986).

▲ **Figure R33.4** *Plant nutrients.*

Fertilizers

Crop	Area * /thousand ha	Average application rate /kg ha⁻¹ **		
		Nitrogen (N)	Phosphorus (P)	Potassium (K)
Wheat	1695	180	22	38
Barley	2143	122	20	41
Other cereals	122	88	20	38
Potatoes	195	188	86	208
Sugar beet	199	155	32	133
Oilseed rape	222	272	27	48
Other crops	450	66	24	53
Grass	6954	105	10	22
Total	11980	121	16	34

* Areas are for the UK as a whole.
** Application rates are for England and Wales.

▲ **Figure R33.5** *The use of fertilizers on crops in England and Wales, 1982/83.*

The proportion of applied nitrogen taken up by the crop is affected by many factors including crop species, climate and soil conditions.

	Per cent
Taken up by the crop (above ground parts)	40–60
Incorporated in the soil's organic matter	20–50
Mineral form in the soil's organic matter	5–20
Lost by denitrification and volatilization	2–30
Lost by leaching	2–10

◀ **Figure R33.6** *Fate of fertilizer nitrogen applied to a crop.*

	Fertilizer	No fertilizer
Grain yield /t ha⁻¹	6.29	3.14
Grain price /£ t⁻¹	112	112
Output /£ ha⁻¹	704	352
Costs per ha /£		
Seed	34	34
Fertilizer	70	0
Sprays	74	37*
Miscellaneous	6	6
Total variable costs	184	77
Fixed costs	347	347
Total costs	531	424

◀ **Figure R33.7** *Comparison of wheat crops grown with and without fertilizer 1981/2.*

* In the absence of fertilizers, it is ssumed that spray costs will be halved.

Diseases

The ten commonest fungal diseases of cereal crops are listed below.

Loose smut (*Ustilago nuda*)
Yellow rust (*Puccinia striiformis*)
Covered smut (*Tilletia caries*)
Brown rust (*Puccinia recondita*)
Take-all (*Gaumannomyces graminis*)

Eyespot (*Cercosporella herpotrichoides*)
Powdery mildew (*Erysiphe graminis*)
Leaf stripe (*Pyrenophora graminea*)
Ergot (*Claviceps purpurea*)
Leaf blotch (*Rhynchosporium scalis*)

R34 Safety issues

Pesticide	*Content /parts billion^{-1}	**Intake /μg kg^{-1} body mass day^{-1}
BHC (benzene hexachloride)	<1	0.011
DDT	<1	0.034
DDE (major metabolite of DDT)	4.8	0.031
Dieldrin	3.3	0.022
Methoxychlor	<1	0.007
Lindane (BHC)	<1	0.003
Hexachlorobenzene	<1	0.007
2 chloroethyl linoleate	14.5	0.197
Diazinon	<1	0.004
2-ethylhexyl diphenyl phosphate	98.5	1.85
Malathion	<1	0.203
Nonachlor	<1	<0.001
Pentachloroanisole	<1	<0.002
Pentachlorophenol	8.4	0.04
Polychlorinated biphenyls	2	0.008

* Figures given are average values for all samples of meat, fish and poultry.
** Figures given are the estimated sum total intake from all dietary sources.

▲ **Figure R34.1** *Pesticide residues in food.*

Chemical compound	Acute oral LD50 to rats /mg kg^{-1}
Herbicides	
Chlorotoluron	>10000
Asulam	>5000
Imazapyr	>5000
Sulfometuron – methyl	>5000
Glyphosate	4320
Other chemicals	
Table salt (NaCl)	3000
Aspirin	1750
Caffeine	200
Nicotine	50

▲ **Figure R34.2** *Toxicity of some herbicides and common chemicals. Acute toxicity or LD50 is the dose required to kill 50% of a population of laboratory rats.*

The safety of food and medicines

The Food Safety Act 1990

This constantly reviews the law on food safety and consumer protection in the food sector throughout Great Britain. The Act does not contain rules or regulations; it merely gives the Government powers to formulate regulations on specific areas of food production as and when necessary.

The aims of the Act are;

- to ensure that all food produced for sale is safe to eat and not misleadingly presented,
- to strengthen legal powers and penalties,
- to enable the UK to fulfil its role in the European Union and the Single Market,
- to keep pace with technological change.

The law requires that all food businesses register with the **Local Authority Environmental Health Department**.

Regulations require food businesses to instruct, train and supervise their staff in food hygiene appropriate to the job they perform. Furthermore there must be a thorough system of managing hygiene throughout a food business. Potential hazards must be identified, with written procedures to show that they are under control. For complex businesses, there is a formal **Hazard Analysis Critical Control Point** (**HACCP**, pronounced 'ha-sup') system.

The key provisions in food law are contained in regulations, such as;

- the Food labelling Regulations 1984,
- the Imported Food Regulations 1984,
- the Food Hygiene (General) Regulations 1970,
- the Food Premises (Registration) Regulations 1991.

The Act is enforced at the county level by the **Trading Standards Service** and on the district level by the **Environmental Health Department**. Central Government may sometimes become involved in certain emergency situations. Members of the **State Veterinary Service** may be involved in enforcement on farms and in slaughterhouses.

The Medicines Control Agency (MCA)

This is part of the Department of Health and is responsible for safeguarding public health by ensuring that all medicines on the UK market meet acceptable standards.

Before a medicine can be prescribed or sold it must obtain a **Product Licence** from the MCA. The MCA examines all the research carried out on the product and the test results. It seeks expert advice from the **Medicines Committee**, the **Committee on Safety of Medicines** and the **Committee on Dental and Surgical Materials**.

Only when experts are satisfied that the medicine meets the standards of the Medicines Act or the relevant EU legislation is a licence granted. The licence will stipulate the appropriate dosages and times to take the medicine, the **format** (tablets, liquid, syrup, lotion, cream etc.), the **specific diseases** to be treated by the medicine and the **type of person** for whom it is suitable or unsuitable (for example; children).

Gene technology and Health and Safety

In April 1990 the European Union issued a pair of directives on the use of genetically engineered organisms in controlled (contained) situations and when released into the environment. Each country was asked to approve national legislation quickly but only Denmark did so by early 1992. In this country, existing legislation on gene technology comes under the Health and Safety at Work and Environmental Protection Acts.

A Health and Safety Commission consultation paper issued in October 1991 proposed that there should be new regulations. It aimed at preserving a balance between the public right to impose safety, to be given information and debate ethical constraints, and the right of industry to develop commercial products without too much red tape, restriction, extra cost and legal disputes.

▲ **Figure 34.3** *Summaries of the main regulations governing the safety of foods and medicines.*

R35 Human organ systems

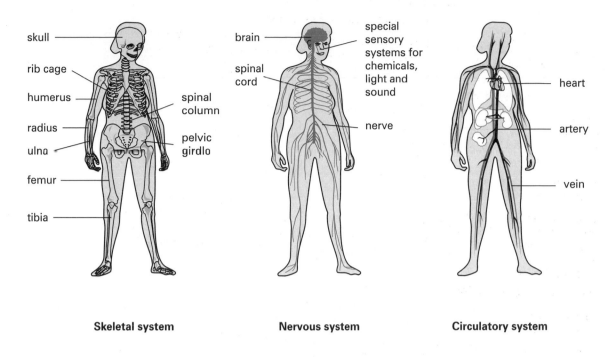

Skeletal system

skull
rib cage
humerus
radius
ulna
femur
tibia
spinal column
pelvic girdle

Nervous system

brain
spinal cord
special sensory systems for chemicals, light and sound
nerve

Circulatory system

heart
artery
vein

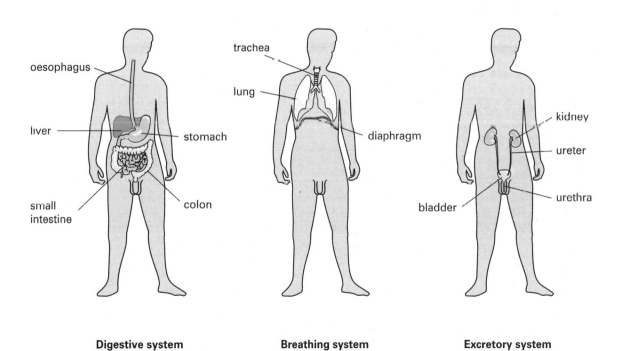

Digestive system

oesophagus
liver
small intestine
stomach
colon

Breathing system

trachea
lung
diaphragm

Excretory system

kidney
ureter
urethra
bladder

▲ **Figure R35.1** *The location of the major human organ systems.*

R36 Minerals and vitamins

Minerals

Mineral	What do they do?	Where to find them?	RDA
Calcium	Vital for building and maintaining bones and teeth. Essential for blood clotting and the normal functioning of muscles and nerves	Milk, cheese, yogurt, bread, fish eaten with bones, (e.g. canned sardines), green leafy vegetables	500 mg
Phosphorus	Required with calcium for bones and teeth. Essential for energy metabolism	Milk, cheese, yogurt, eggs, wholemeal bread and other cereals, meat and poultry	(800 mg USA)
Iron	Vital for formation of haemoglobin in the red blood cells	Liver, kidney, red meat, bread, fortified breakfast cereals, eggs	12 mg
Sodium	Essential for maintenance of fluid balance within the body (with potassium). Required for muscle and nerve activity	Salt (sodium chloride), cured meat (ham and bacon), cheese, smoked fish, processed food, bread, breakfast cereals	(1100–1133 mg USA)
Potassium	Required with sodium for maintenance of fluid balance within the body. Essential for muscle and nerve activity	Fruit and fruit juices, vegetables, meat, milk, wholemeal bread, whole grain cereals	(1875–5625 mg USA)

RDA = Recommended Daily Amount (i.e. the quantity of mineral recommended to be consumed by an adult each day to prevent deficiency symptoms).

▲ **Figure R36.1** *The what and where of minerals.*

Trace elements

Trace element	What do they do?	Where to find them?	RDA
Chromium	Helps with the normal control of blood sugar levels	Liver, wholemeal bread, yeast, yeast extract	(0.05–0.2 mg USA)
Copper	Essential for the function of many enzymes in body cells	Liver, shellfish, bread, wholegrain breakfast cereals, vegetables	(2–3 mg USA)
Fluorine	Very important for bones and teeth. Helps to prevent tooth decay	Fluoridated water, tea, seafood	(1.5–4.0 mg USA)
Iodine	Required by the thyroid gland for the production of hormones	Milk, seafood, iodised salt, vegetables, grains, meat, eggs	(150 µg USA)
Magnesium	Required for healthy bones and muscle tissue. Plays an important part in energy metabolism	Wholemeal bread, wholegrain cereals, nuts, crab, oysters	(350 mg USA)
Manganese	Required for the function of many enzymes in body cells	Wholegrain cereals, nuts, spices, leafy vegetables, tea	(2.5–5.0 mg USA)
Selenium	Acts as an antioxidant protecting body cells and tissue from damage	Seafood, wholegrain cereals, meat, egg yolk, liver, kidney	(70 µg USA)
Zinc	Essential for growth and normal development. Required for the function of many enzymes in body cells	Red meat, liver, cheese, wholemeal bread, wholegrain cereals, nuts	(15 mg USA)

RDA = Recommended Daily Amount (i.e. the quantity of mineral recommended to be consumed by an adult each day to prevent deficiency symptoms).

▲ **Figure R36.2** *The what and where of trace elements.*

Water-soluble vitamins

Vitamin	What do they do?	Where to find them?	RDA
B₁ (Thiamin)	Helps the body use carbohydrates in energy metabolism. Essential for healthy nerve and muscle tissue	Bread, breakfast cereals, vegetables (especially potatoes), milk, meat (particularly pork)	1.2 mg
B₂ (Riboflavin)	Helps the body use food in energy metabolism and build tissues. Important for healthy skin and eyes	Milk, cheese, fortified breakfast cereals, eggs, meat (particularly liver), green leafy vegetables	1.6 mg
B₃ (Niacin)	Helps the body use food in energy metabolism. Essential for healthy nerve tissue and the skin	Meat, poultry, fish, cheese, milk, bread, fortified breakfast cereals	18.0 mg
B₆ (Pyridoxine)	Necessary for red blood cell production. Helps the body use protein from the diet	Wholemeal bread, wholegrain/brain breakfast cereals, liver, fish, eggs, nuts	(2.0 mg USA)
B₁₂ (Cyanocobalamin)	Required for red blood cell formation and normal growth. Essential for a healthy nervous system	Meat (especially liver and kidney), fish, eggs, milk, cheese, fortified breakfast cereals	(2.0 µg USA)
Folic acid (Folate)	Essential for healthy formation of all body cells including red blood cells	Liver, kidney, green leafy vegetables, fortified breakfast cereals, wholemeal bread, oranges, bananas	(200 µg USA)
C (Ascorbic acid)	Essential for energy metabolism and growth. Important for resistance to infection and healing wounds. Required for healthy skin, bones, teeth, gums and blood vessels	Fruit (particularly oranges and orange juice, blackcurrants, and blackcurrant juice), fresh and frozen vegetables – including potatoes	30.0 mg

RDA = Recommended Daily Amount (i.e. the quantity of vitamin recommended to be consumed by an adult each day to prevent deficiency symptoms).

▲ **Figure R36.3** *The what and where of water-soluble vitamins.*

Fat-soluble vitamins

Vitamin	What do they do?	Where to find them?	RDA
A (Retinol)	Essential for vision, especially in dim light. Helps the body to resist infection and is required for healthy skin and bones	Liver, kidney, oily fish (e.g. herring, mackerel), egg yolk, green leafy vegetables, carrots, margarine, butter, whole milk	750 µg
D (Cholecalciferol)	Essential for the absorption of calcium from food. Required for the growth and maintenance of bones and teeth	Oily fish (including canned salmon, tuna, sardines). Eggs, margarine, fortified breakfast cereals. Major source is from the action of sunlight on the skin	2.5 µg
E (Tocopherol)	Acts as an antioxidant protecting the body cells and tissues from damage. Also protects nutrients such as Vitamins A and C and polyunsaturated fats from destruction	Vegetable oils, margarine, wholemeal bread, green leafy negetables, nuts	(10 mg USA)
K	Necessary for normal blood clotting	Vegetables (especially cauliflower, brussels sprouts, broccoli, lettuce, spinach), liver. Also produced by bacteria in the intestine	(80 µg USA)

RDA = Recommended Daily Amount (i.e. the quantity of vitamin recommended to be consumed by an adult each day to prevent deficiency symptoms).

▲ **Figure R36.4** *The what and where of fat-soluble vitamins.*

R37 Energy and nutrients

Food (1 helping)	Energy /kJ	Protein /g	Carbohydrate /g	Fat /g
Grapefruit (half)	92	1	5	0
Sugar (spoonful)	188	0	12	0
Breakfast cereals (with milk) **Corn Flakes**	1403	10	60	8
Weetabix	1274	12	49	9
Rice Krispies	1274	9	53	9
Porridge	728	7	18	9
Cooked breakfast **Bacon** (rasher)	1132	6	0	27
Kipper	922	19	0	16
Boiled egg	376	7	0	7
Fried egg	504	7	0	10
Buttered toast	393	2	16	3
Preserves (for one slice of bread or toast) **Honey**	172	0	11	0
Jam or marmalade	155	0	10	0
Golden syrup	176	0	11	0
Drinks (one cup or glass) **Tea with milk**	54	1	1	0
Coffee with milk	72	1	2	2
Drinking chocolate (made with milk)	636	7	15	8
Milk	539	6	10	8
Sugar (teaspoon)	94	0	6	0
Fruit juice (pure)	394	2	23	0
Snacks **1 slice of buttered bread**	393	2	16	3
Ham (slice)	250	2	0	6
Cheese (slice)	245	4	0	5
Fish finger	342	6	9	3
Sausage	439	3	3	9
Meat pattie	558	5	10	6
Beefburger	660	5	5	13
Fishcake	510	9	14	5
Meat samosa	512	5	16	6
Sardine	224	4	0	4
Tomato soup	400	2	14	5

▲ **Figure R37.1** *Fuel energy in food (continued opposite).*

Food (1 helping)	Energy /kJ	Protein /g	Carbohydrate /g	Fat /g
Meat				
Pork chop	3762	32	0	86
Lamb chop	1596	15	0	34
Fried liver	1156	30	4	16
Steak	1014	29	0	14
Beef curry	1250	26	1	22
Roast lamb	1190	25	0	20
Roast pork	1344	25	0	23
Roast beef	1050	27	0	15
Meat pie	2166	23	28	36
Chicken (quarter)	1542	59	0	15
Fish				
Fried cod	834	20	8	10
Poached fish	492	27	0	1
Tinned salmon	557	20	0	6
Vegetables (cooked)				
Chips	1405	6	53	13
Boiled potatoes	331	1	20	0
Roast potatoes	515	3	27	2
Baked beans	385	6	17	0
Garden peas	102	3	4	0
Mushy peas	201	4	9	0
Sprouts	67	2	2	0
Cabbage	34	1	1	0
Carrots	96	1	5	0
Cauliflower	101	3	3	0
Vegetable stir fry	500	5	20	10
Rice, pasta and dough				
Rice	854	4	49	1
Spaghetti	864	6	48	1
Chapatti	1500	19	20	0
Yoghurt				
Natural	335	5	8	4
Fruit	460	5	19	3
Fresh fruit				
Apple	220	0	14	0
Orange	252	1	14	0
Banana	540	2	33	0
Puddings, cakes and sweets				
Fresh raspberries	105	1	6	0

(continued overleaf)

Food (1 helping)	Energy /kJ	Protein /g	Carbohydrate /g	Fat /g
Fresh strawberries	109	1	6	0
Tinned apricots	444	1	28	0
Tinned peaches	369	0	23	0
Tinned pineapple	318	0	20	0
Apple pie	2462	6	81	29
Single cream	225	1	1	5
Custard	867	6	31	8
Ice cream	805	4	20	11
Currant bun	1374	8	59	9
Fruit cake	3084	9	110	32
Plain cake	2703	11	75	36
Jam tart	1638	3	68	14
Rice pudding	595	4	16	8
Chocolate bar (100 g)	2422	9	55	38

EAR /MJ day^{-1}			EAR /MJ day^{-1}		
Age	Males	Females	Age	Males	Females
0–3 mo	2.28	2.16	11–14 yr	9.27	7.92
4–6 mo	2.89	2.69	15–18 yr	11.51	8.83
7–9 mo	3.44	3.20	19–50 yr	10.60	8.10
10–12 mo	3.85	3.61	51–59 yr	10.60	8.00
1–3 yr	5.15	4.86	60–64 yr	9.93	7.99
4–6 yr	7.16	6.46	65–74 yr	9.71	7.96
7–10 yr	8.24	7.28	74+ yr	8.77	7.61

These figures were calculated by taking the BMR and multiplying it by a factor which takes account of the physical activity level (PAL).

▲ **Figure R37.2** *Estimated average requirements (EAR) for energy.*

Energy EAR = BMR × Physical Activity Level (PAL)

The Committee on Medical Aspects of Food Policy suggested that a factor of 1.4 reflected the lifestyle of most adults in the UK. This factor is suitable for people who do little physical activity at work or in leisure time. If people are more active, larger factors are used.

▼ **Figure R37.3** *Essential amino acid content of a number of food products compared with the amount found in human milk.*

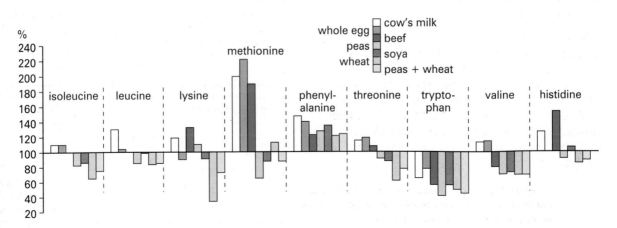

R38 Health issues

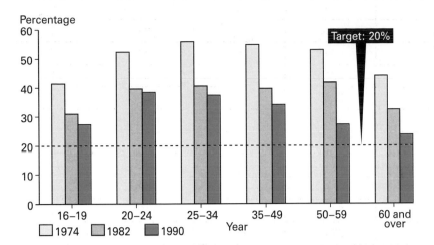

◀ **Figure R38.1** *Prevalance of smoking cigarettes among men aged 16 and over, for England, 1974, 1982, 1990.*

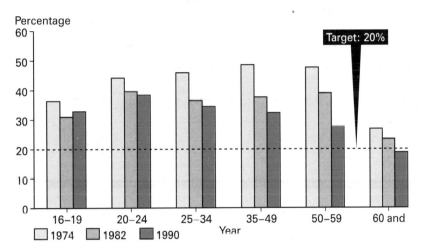

◀ **Figure R38.2** *Prevalance of smoking cigarettes among women aged 16 and over, for England, 1974, 1982, 1990.*

R39 The light microscope

How the light microscope works

A specimen or thin slice of biological material is placed on the stage and illuminated from underneath. The objective lens produces a magnified and inverted image, which the eyepiece lens focuses at the eye.

The amount of detail seen with the light microscope is limited by its **resolving power**. The limit of resolution for an unaided human eye is about 0.1 mm. Anything closer than this is seen as one object. The resolution of the light microscope is limited by the wavelength of light. The resolution which can be achieved is 0.2 μm. This allows a maximum magnification of about 1500 times life size with a clear image.

▶ **Figure R39.1** *Light passes through the specimen and on through the lens to give an image which is greatly magnified – and upside down.*

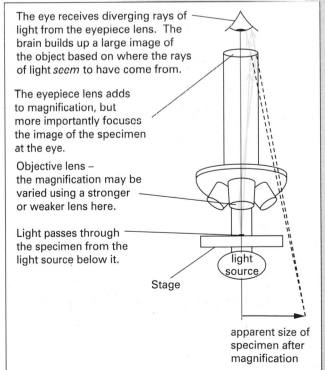

The eye receives diverging rays of light from the eyepiece lens. The brain builds up a large image of the object based on where the rays of light *seem* to have come from.

The eyepiece lens adds to magnification, but more importantly focuses the image of the specimen at the eye.

Objective lens – the magnification may be varied using a stronger or weaker lens here.

Light passes through the specimen from the light source below it.

Stage

light source

apparent size of specimen after magnification

Index

Heinemann Educational Publishers,
a division of Heinemann Publishers (Oxford) Ltd,
Halley Court, Jordan Hill, Oxford, OX2 8EJ

OXFORD LONDON EDINBURGH
MADRID ATHENS BOLOGNA PARIS
MELBOURNE SYDNEY AUCKLAND SINGAPORE TOKYO
IBADAN NAIROBI HARARE GABORONE
PORTSMOUTH NH (USA)

© The Nuffield Foundation 1995

First published 1995

99 98 97 96 95
10 9 8 7 6 5 4 3 2 1

ISBN 0 435 63253 1

Designed and typeset by Gecko Ltd, Bicester, Oxon

Illustrated by Harvey Collins, Chris Etheridge, Gecko Limited, David Poole
and Barry Rowe

Cover design by Threefold Design

Cover photo by Image Bank

Printed and bound in Spain by Mateu Cromo

Acknowledgements

The authors and publishers would like to thank the following for permission to use
photographs:

1A1: SPL/Adam Hart-Davis. 1A2: SPL/Peter Menzel. 1A3: Courtesy of Zeneca
Specialities. 1A4 and 1A5: Roger Scruton. 1A16: SPL/Roberto de Gugliemo. 1B1:
Roger Scruton. 1B2: SPL/Geoff Tomkinson. 1B5, 1B12, 1B18, 1B20 and 1B22:
Roger Scruton. 1C1: SPL/James Holmes. 1C2: SPL/Photo Library International.
1C3: Courtesy of Johnson Matthey. 1C10: Chubb Fire Ltd. 1C13: Geoffry
Richardson, Medical Illustrators. 1C16 and 1C17: Courtesy of Johnson Matthey.
1C20: George Wright Photography. 2A1: BSI Testing. 2A4 and 2A5: Courtesy of
Seymour Powell Design. 2A6: Crown copyright National Physical Laboratories.
2A9: Fairclough Engineering Ltd. 2A13: Meg Sullivan Photography. 2A16 and
2A17: Wolpert GmbH. 2A19: Mark Galer. 2A31: Courtesy of Shirley Products.
2A36: MPS Imaging. 2A39: SPL/Heine Schneebeli. 2A40: ZEFA. 2A42 and 2A50:
Meg Sullivan Photography. 2B1: Chris Honeywell Photography. 2B2 and 2B3:
Cranfield University/P Logan. 2B4: SPL/Graham J Hills. 2B5: SPL/G Muller,
Struers GmbH. 2B10: SPL/Manfred Kage. 2B22: Anthony Bourdillon, University of
New South Wales. 2B25: Dunlop Slazenger International Ltd. 2B26: SPL/Astrid &
Hans Friedler Michler. 3A1: Mary Evans Picture Library. 3A2: Quest
International/Countrywide Photographic. 3A3: Courtesy of Harvard University
Archives. 3A12: SPL/Geoff Tomkinson. 3A15: NHPA. 3A21 and 3A22: Norfolk
Lavender Ltd. 3A27: Meg Sullivan Photography. 3B13: Zeneca Agrochemicals.
3B16: Dave Maw. 3B17: Roger Philips, Pan Books. 3B19: Dave Maw. 3B21, 3B22,
3C14 and 3C16: Roger Scruton. 3C21: Photothèque Pêchiney Progil. 3C24, 3C25
and 3C27: Paul Felix. 4A1 and 4A2: NHPA. 4A3: SPL/James Holmes. 4A11:
Amgen. 4B1 and 4B2: NHPA/ 4B3: Holt Studios/Nigel Cattlin. 4B4: NHPA. 4C1
and 4C2: Paul Bryans Photography. 4C3 and 4C4: Meg Sullivan Photography. 4C6,
NHPA. 4C7 and 4C9: NHPA. 5A1: Press Association/John Giles. 5A10 and 5A12:
Courtesy of Cranfield Impact Centre. 5A22, 5A23, 5A24 and 5A25: Courtesy of
Rolls Royce. 5A27: British Engineerium. 5B1: Geoff Roberts. 5B4: Tony Stone.
5B6: ABB/Kent Taylor. 5B10: Roger Scruton. 5B24: Courtesy of British Gas. 5C2
and 5C7: Meg Sullivan Photography. 5C10: ICI Polyurethanes. 5C12: Data
Harvest. 5C24: West Bromwich Spring Company. 6A1: Kodak Research Division.
6A3: Geoff Roberts. 6A4: Roger Scruton. 6B1: Standard Fireworks. 6B26: Ballard
Power Systems Inc. 6C1: Meg Sullivan Photography. 6C2 and 6C3: Esso. 6C4:
Zeneca Agrochemicals/CTC Publicity. 6C5, 6C7, 6C8 and 6C9: Roger Scruton.
6C11: Roger Scruton. 6C15: Brunner Mond Co Ltd. 7A1 and 7A2: Paul Coward.
7A13, 7B1, 7B2 and 7B8: Meg Sullivan Photography. 7B16: Kind permission of
Bernard Everard. 7B26: Kind permission of Sheila Watts. 7C1: Dieter Pevsner.
7C5: Impact Photos/Ben Edwards. 7C13: Roger Scruton. 8A3: Courtesy of Philip
Harris Education. 8A4a: Courtesy of Eppendorf/supplied by Merck Ltd. 8A4b:
Fisons. 8A16: SPL/Philippe Plailly/Eurelios. 8A31 and 8A32: The Natural History
Museum. 8A36, 8A37 and 8A39: Meg Sullivan Photography. 8B4a and b Mark
Powell. 8B5: Meg Sullivan Photography. 8B8: Mark Powell.

We are grateful to the following for permission to reproduce their copyright
material:

1B11, 1B13, 1B27, 1B29 & 1B31 Royal Society of Chemistry; 1C4, 1C5, 1C7 &1C9
Health and Safety Executive; 1C15 School Science Service, Brunel University; 2A2
British Standards Institution; 2B8 & 2B9 British Steel plc; page 73 The New
Science of Strong Materials or Why You Don't Fall Through The Floor (p.43),
J E Gordon, Penguin Books 1976 copyright © J E Gordon 1976; 2A38 Bellingham
& Stanley Limited; 2A43 © Crown copyright is reproduced with permission of the
Controller of HMSO and the Building Research Establishment; 2A51 reproduced
with permission of the Institute of Materials; 2B18 ICI Chemicals and Polymers
Ltd; 2B34 reproduced with permission of the Institute of Materials; 3B1 based on
SATIS 16-19 Unit 39 Fig.3, ASE; 3C17 based on Heinemann Advanced
Chemistry, Heinemann 1994; 3C19 based on Salters Advanced Chemistry:
Activities, Heinemann 1994; 4A4, 4A5, 4A6, 4A7, 4A9 based on Heinemann
Advanced Biology, Heinemann 1994; 4A8 Cell Biology, Ambrose &
Easty,Thomas Nelson; 4B6, 4B11, 4B12 & 4B35 based on Heinemann Advanced
Biology, Heinemann, 1994; 4B10 Crown copyright is reproduced by permission of
the Controller of HMSO; 4C8 'Research on the Nitrogen Cycle' – A Sixth Form

Study Resource, by permission of Biotechnology and Biological Sciences Research
Council; 5A19 Extract from BS6863: 1989 is reproduced with permission of BSI.
BSI, 389 Chiswick High Road, London, W4 4AL; 5A20 Tyre Industry Council
(British Rubber Manufacturersí Assoc., The Imported Tyre Manufactures' Assoc.
and Retread Manufactures' Assoc.); 5A21 & 5A28 The Way Things Work,
D Macauley, © Dorling Kindersley and reproduced by permission; 5B2 & 5B3
Electronics Education (Spring 1994), reproduced by permission of Institution of
Electrical Engineers; 5B7, 5B8 & 5B9 BP Educational Service, British Petroleum
Co. plc; 5B13, 5B14 & 5B15 ITT Flygt Ltd; 5B16, 5B17 & 5B18 The Way Things
Work, D Macauley, © Dorling Kindersley and reproduced by permission; 5B20 &
5B23 BP Educational Service, British Petroleum Co. plc; 5B21 Education
Department, British Gas; 5C1 © Crown copyright, reproduced by permission of
BRECSU; 5C3, 5C4 & 5C5 National Energy Services Ltd; 5C6 Bristol City Council;
5C14 Energy, D Sang & R Hutchings, Thomas Nelson; 5C16 Education
Department, British Gas; 5C18 Open University; 5C22 Education Department,
British Gas; 6A2 based on Salters Advanced Chemistry: Storylines, Heinemann,
1994; 6A23 based on Heinemann Advanced Chemistry, Heinemann, 1994; 6A24
based on Salters Advanced Chemistry: Ideas, Heinemann, 1994; 6B2 Royal
Society of Chemistry; 6C6 & 6C10 Rhône Poulenc Chemicals Ltd; 6B18 based on
Salters Advanced Chemistry: Ideas, Heinemann, 1994; 7A3 The Living Cell by
Jean Brachet. Copyright © September 1961 by Scientific American, Inc. All rights
reserved; 7A4 Advanced Biology, C.J.Clegg and D.G.Mackean, reproduced by
permission of John Murray (Publishers) Ltd; 7A5, 7A6, 7A9, 7A10, 7A10, 7A11,
7A12, 7A14, 7A18, 7A20, 7A25, 7A26 & 7A27 based on Heinemann Advanced
Biology, Heinemann, 1994; 7A7 'Intracellular Digestion' p.68 9 by Bunji Tagawa,
from The Lysosome, Christian de Duve. Copyright © May 1963 by Scientific
American, Inc. All rights reserved; 7A8 Nuffield Foundation; 7A15, 7A16, 7A17 &
7A19 An atlas of histology, WH Freemann & B Bracegirdle, Heinemann, 1966;
7A21, 7A28 & 7A29 An anatomy and physiology in health and illness, K
Wilson, Churchill Livingstone, 1990; 7B3, 7B4, 7B5, 7B10, 7B12, 7B13, 7B14,
7B19, 7B20, 7B21, 7B22, 7B24 & 7B25 based on Heinemann Advanced Biology,
Heinemann, 1994; 7B6 & 7B25 Nuffield Foundation; 7B11 An anatomy and
physiology in health and illness, K Wilson, Churchill Livingstone, 1990; 7C2
Fighting Heart Disease by C Patel, © Dorling Kindersley and reproduced by
permission; 7C4 National Medical Slide Bank – Wellcome Centre (ref. 12548 &
12550); 7C7 reproduced with permission of the Kings Fund, Health Educational
Authority and London School of Hygiene & Tropical Medicine; 7C8 London
Evening Standard, reproduced by permission of Solo Syndications; 7C9
reproduced by courtesy of Foundation for the Study of Infant Deaths; page 412
Crown copyright is reproduced by permission of the Controller of HMSO; 7C10
Crown copyright is reproduced by permission of the Controller of HMSO; 7C11
'Budgie dies from passive smoking' by Edward Gorman 27/1/94, © Times
Newspaper Limited 1994; 7C12 from Health Survey for England 1991, © Crown
copyright is reproduced by permission of the Controller of HMSO and Office of
Population Censuses & Surveys; page 415 Health Education Authority; 7C14
Lewis's Pharmacology, Churchill Livingstone; page 419 Perilous Knowledge,
Tom Wilkie, reproduced by permission of the publishers Faber and Faber; 8A2
National Physical Laboratory; 8A18, 8A19 & 8A20 Journal of Biological
Educational, © 1994, Vol.28(1), p.13, p.14, pp.132–3, published and reproduced
by permission of Institute of Biology; 8A40 Metropolitan Borough of Sefton. Based
upon the Ordnance Survey mapping © Crown copyright is reproduced by
permission of the Controller of HMO ; 8A46 Animals Without Backbones (p.56),
Ralph Buchsbaum, Penguin Books, 1951 © Ralph Buchsbaum, 1951; 8B10, 8B11
& 8B12 Cannon (UK) Limited; 8B14, 8B15, 8B16 & 8B19 based on Heinemann
Advanced Physics, Heinemann, 1994; 8B17, 8B21 & 8B23 IEE/BT © 1991,
reproduced by permission of the Institution of Electrical Engineers and BT; 8T1
Crown copyright is reproduced by permission of the Controller of HMSO; R32.1,
R32.2, R32.3, R34.1 & R37.3 Royal Society of Chemistry; R34.3, R38.1 & R38.2
Crown copyright is reproduced by permission of the Controller of HMSO; R37.2
British Nutritional Foundation.

The publishers have made every effort to trace the copyright holders, but if they
have inadvertently overlooked any, they will be pleased to make the necessary
arrangements at the first opportunity.